Elements of Cytology

Second Edition

Elements of Cytology

SECOND EDITION

Norman S. Cohn

Ohio University

HARCOURT, BRACE & WORLD, INC.

New York / Chicago / San Francisco / Atlanta

574.87
C 678-1

TO MY WIFE, PEGGY

New drawings for the Second Edition by Julie Romoser

Preface

Knowledge of biomolecular organization and function, despite the microscopic size of a cell, appears to grow exponentially. This creates the problem of organizing the available information for ease of reference and, equally important, for ease of initial reading. Moreover, recent advances in cytology have shown that particular constituents of a cell have specialized biological roles, although these are truly meaningful only when related to the heredity, physiology, and development of the whole organism.

The second edition of this book thus continues to be divided into three parts—The Cytoplasm, The Nucleus, and Nucleocytoplasmic Relations—with individual chapters devoted to specific cell components. Within this framework, the text has grown in length from 368 to 495 pages, the latter painstakingly assessed, with both the student and the latest research journals in mind. Much of what has been added is newer research on the cell's ultrastructure and chemistry, as is apparent in many of the new electron micrographs and newly revised drawings. At the same time, more attention has been given to structural and functional interrelations among cell components.

Most of what has been added also reflects the current extension of cytology toward cell biology. In the context of modern biology the field of cytology is, by its own structure and function, cell biology. Major sections of the book, in fact, are devoted to the biochemistry of macromolecules, an important base for cell biology.

I am indebted to a number of colleagues, notably to Professors Norman H. Giles and Morris Foster, who read parts of the original manuscript; to Professors Carl R. Partanen and Earl H. Newcomer, who provided extensive and detailed suggestions for the revision; to Dr. Judith Reighard Graffius and Dr. Laurence A. Larson for valuable discussions; and to all the investigators who made their work and their photomicrographs available for this book.

Norman S. Cohn

Contents

Summary of Historical Events

We shall not cease from exploration
And the end of all our exploring
Will be to arrive where we started
And know the place for the first time.
——T. S. ELIOT, *Four Quartets*

1590 Z. JANSSEN and H. JANSSEN produced the first operational compound microscope.

1661 M. MALPIGHI (1628–1694) discovered capillaries; confused blood corpuscles with fat globules; suggested cells when referring to "utricles" and "saccules."

1665 R. HOOKE (1635–1703), first curator of the Royal Society of London, described cork and other cells; introduced the term *cell;* published *Micrographia.*

1674 A. VAN LEEUWENHOEK (1632–1723) improved microscope lens systems by grinding; observed sperm, bacteria, and protozoa; observed, but did not identify, nuclei in blood cells.

1682 N. GREW (1641–1712) described bladders and pores in wood and pith; published two illustrated volumes on the microscopic anatomy of plants.

1759 C. F. WOLFF (1738–1794), founder of embryology, made reference to "little globules which may be distinguished under a microscope."

1809 J. B. LAMARCK (1744–1829) stated the importance of the cell in the living organism.

1823   J. B. AMICI (1784–1860) observed the development of the pollen tube.

1824   R. J. H. DUTROCHET (1776–1847) separated cells of *Mimosa* by boiling in nitric acid; "All organic tissues are actually globular cells . . . united only by simple adhesive forces."

1825   F. V. RASPAIL (1794–1878) used iodine for the detection of starch; developed the frozen-section technique. Beginning of cytochemistry.

1828   R. BROWN (1773–1858) observed what is known as the Brownian movement.

1830   AMICI observed the entrance of the pollen tube into the ovary.

1830–
1837   J. E. PURKINJE (1787–1869) studied the anthers of flowering plants, the oocyte nucleus of the hen's egg, and ciliary movement; introduced the term *protoplasm;* used microscopes with a resolution of just under 1 micron.

1833   BROWN discovered the cell nucleus in the flowering plant *Tradescantia.*

1835   H. VON MOHL (1805–1872) described cell division and emphasized the importance of protoplasm.

1838   M. J. SCHLEIDEN (1804–1881) observed nucleoli; provided an explanation of the cellular derivation of plant tissues; formulated the cell concept, although with erroneous views.

1839   T. SCHWANN (1810–1882) applied the cell concept to animals.

1845   A. DONNÉ (1801–1878) studied spermatozoa, using photomicroscopy for the first time, with L. FOUCAULT.

1846   K. NÄGELI (1817–1891) showed that plant cells arise from the division of preexisting cells.
AMICI showed that the egg in the ovary is stimulated to develop into an embryo by the entrance of the pollen tube.

1849   W. HOFMEISTER (1824–1877) studied nuclear division in *Tradescantia* stamen hairs; observed fertilization.

1855   R. VIRCHOW (1821–1902) confirmed the principle that cells arise only from preexisting cells ("Omnis cellula e cellula").

1858   VIRCHOW published *Cellular Pathology,* showing the importance of the cell in disease and cancer.

1865   G. MENDEL (1822–1884) developed the fundamental principles of heredity (rediscovered independently by CORRENS, DE VRIES, and TSCHERMAK in 1900).

1870 W. His (1831–1904) invented the microtome.

1871 F. Miescher (1844–1895) isolated nuclei and nucleoprotein.

1873 H. Fol (1845–1892) described spindle and astral rays.

1874 Miescher isolated *protamine* from salmon sperm.

1876 O. Hertwig (1849–1922) studied reproduction in the sea urchin; concluded that fertilization involves the union of sperm and egg nuclei.

1877 E. Abbe (1840–1908) produced oil immersion objectives with a resolution of 0.25 micron.

1879 Fol showed that only one sperm enters the egg in fertilization.

1881 E. G. Balbiani (1825–1899) discovered larval salivary gland chromosomes in *Chironomus*.

1882 W. Fleming (1843–1915) proposed the term *mitosis;* showed that chromosomes split longitudinally during nuclear division and formation of daughter nuclei; refined techniques of fixation and staining; suggested a correlation between *chromatin* and nucleic acid.

1883 E. van Beneden (1845–1910) showed that in *Ascaris* the number of chromosomes in the gametes is half that in the body cells.
W. Roux (1850–1924) proposed that the chromosomes contain the units of heredity.

1884 E. Strasburger (1844–1912) described fertilization in angiosperms.
A. Kossel discovered *histone* in red blood cell nuclei.

1886 R. Altmann (1852–1901) stained the granular components of the cytoplasm (including the mitochondria) and suggested that they have a role in cellular respiration.
Abbe developed apochromatic lenses.
V. St. George described what were later called *mitochondria* by Benda.

1887 Van Beneden discovered the central body and indicated that it is the origin of the aster.

1888 T. Boveri (1862–1915) described the centriole.
W. Waldeyer (1836–1921) introduced the term *chromosome.*
Strasburger showed that when gametes are formed the chromosome number is halved in the cell divisions preceding pollen grain and embryo sac formation.

1892 A. WEISMANN (1834–1914) indicated the importance of the germ plasm as independent from the body cells and as the only carrier of inherited variations, in his theory of "continuity of the germ plasm"; stated that the chromosomes are the most important part of the nucleus.
BOVERI described meiosis in *Ascaris*.

1898 C. COLGI (1844–1926) described the Golgi apparatus in nerve cells.
C. BENDA introduced the term *mitochondrion;* studied this organelle in spermatozoa and other cells.

1899 ALTMANN introduced the term *nucleic acid.*

1900 C. GARNIER introduced the term *ergastoplasm.*
K. E. CORRENS, H. DE VRIES, and E. TSCHERMAK rediscovered the fundamental principles of heredity, first developed by MENDEL in 1865.

1901 DE VRIES (1848–1935) postulated the occurrence of mutations in hereditary material in his work with *Oenothera.*
STRASBURGER introduced the term *plasmodesmata.*

1902 C. E. McCLUNG (1870–1946) identified the sex chromosomes in *Hemiptera.*
W. S. SUTTON (1876–1916) showed the significance of reduction division; proposed the chromosome theory of heredity.

1903 E. BUCHNER received the Nobel Prize for discovery of the first enzyme.
BOVERI showed the importance of the chromosomes in development.

1904 F. MEVES demonstrated the presence of mitochondria in plant cells.

1905 J. B. FARMER coined the term *maiosis* (meiosis) with J. E. MOORE.

1907 R. G. HARRISON developed techniques for growing tissues in culture.

1909 F. A. JANSSENS indicated that chiasmata are produced by exchanges between chromatids of nonhomologous chromosomes.

1915 T. H. MORGAN (1866–1945) published *The Mechanism of Mendelian Heredity;* correlated genetic studies with cytological studies in *Drosophila.*

1920 A. F. BLAKESLEE discovered trisomics in *Datura.*

1921 C. B. BRIDGES observed triploid intersexes in *Drosophila.*

1923 BRIDGES discovered duplications, deficiencies, and translocations.

1924 R. FEULGEN and H. ROSSENBECK described a test for the presence of DNA.

1926 A. H. STURTEVANT discovered inversions.

1927   H. J. MULLER studied the production by X rays of mutations in animals.

1928   L. J. STADLER studied the production by X rays of mutations in plants.

1931   C. STERN presented cytological proof of crossing over in *Drosophila.*
H. B. CREIGHTON and B. McCLINTOCK presented cytological proof of crossing over in corn.

1932   M. KNOLL and E. RUSKA produced one of the first electron microscopes.

1935   F. ZERNICKE introduced the principle of phase-contrast microscopy.

1938   T. CASPERSSON began development of ultraviolet photomicrography for the study of nucleic acids.

1944   O. T. AVERY , C. M. McLEOD, and M. McCARTY showed the significance of DNA as the hereditary material by studies of transformation in bacteria.

1946   MULLER received the Nobel Prize for work in radiation genetics.

1948   A. BOIVIN, R. VENDRELY, and C. VENDRELY showed the quantitative constancy of DNA in different cells of the same organism.

1952   R. BRIGGS and T. J. KING made nuclear transplants in embryonic studies and showed the importance of nuclei in differentiation.

1953   J. D. WATSON and F. H. C. CRICK proposed a model for the DNA molecule.

1956   S. OCHOA succeeded in the in vitro synthesis of polyribonucleotides.
A. KORNBERG demonstrated the in vitro synthesis of polydeoxyribonucleotides.
P. I. MARCUS, S. J. CIECIURA, and T. T. PUCK developed methods for growing human cells in culture.

1958   G. W. BEADLE, E. L. TATUM, and J. LEDERBERG received the Nobel Prize for work in the field of genetics.

1959   F. SANGER received the Nobel Prize for determination of the amino acid sequence in insulin.
OCHOA received the Nobel Prize for the in vitro synthesis of polyribonucleotides.
KORNBERG received the Nobel Prize for the in vitro synthesis of polydeoxyribonucleotides.

1962   WATSON and CRICK, with M. H. F. WILKINS, received the Nobel Prize for their model of the DNA molecule.

1965   A. LWOFF, J. MONOD, and F. JACOB received the Nobel Prize for the demonstration of prophage, synthesis of inducible enzymes, the concepts of messenger RNA and the operon, and episomes.

1966   P. ROUS and C. HUGGINS received the Nobel Prize for their work on cancer.

1968   R. HOLLEY, H. KHORANA, and M. W. NIRENBERG received the Nobel Prize for the delineation of the genetic code and molecular mechanisms of protein synthesis.

REFERENCES

L. C. Dunn, *A Short History of Genetics,* McGraw-Hill, New York, 1965.
A. Hughes, *A History of Cytology,* Abelard-Schuman, New York, 1959.
A. E. Mirsky, "The Discovery of DNA," *Scientific American,* **218**(6), 78 (1968).

part one

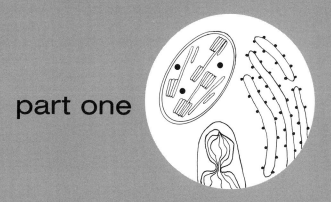

The Cytoplasm

1

Morphology
and Chemistry

The advent of the electron microscope in 1932, a relatively recent event in the history of the biological sciences, stimulated renewed interest in and more intensive and rewarding studies of the physical and chemical organization of the cell. Prior to the availability of this remarkable instrument, information about the structure of the cytoplasm was rather sparse and structural details were not clear. There was a need not only for an increase in magnification but also for techniques to permit observations under natural conditions of life and growth. After 1940 several types of instruments and new techniques were developed that removed many of the limitations on the study of cells; some of these instruments and techniques will be described in Chapter 2. However, the need for methods of studying cells under normal living conditions, rather than artificial laboratory conditions, has not yet been met fully.

Because of this continuing need, the understanding of cell function to be gained from a morphological approach is sometimes questioned. Yet it is necessary to determine the framework of the cell in which the various activities take place, and the use of the electron microscope and other optical instruments has contributed to greater clarification of cell function as well as cell structure. Admittedly, the information obtained is not always accurate in terms of the actual cellular condition; the handling of cells for observation often changes them in such a way as to increase the possibility that the observed material may be misinterpreted. In addition, there are sometimes as many interpretations of the collected data as there are observers. However, the questions raised by differing opinions about a specific observation or the doubt cast upon the validity of a reported phenomenon provides the impetus for continued investigation.

Morphology

Cell shapes are almost as numerous as cell types; there is no typical shape. Graphic evidence for this variety appears in Figure 1–1. The cells of unicellular forms, such as diatoms, *Acetabularia, Amoeba,* and bacteria, exhibit a number of shapes, and those of multicellular organisms exhibit still other shapes. A nerve cell as found in mammals and other animals is unique and may reach a length of over 3 feet owing to the extensions or processes that give it its peculiar shape.

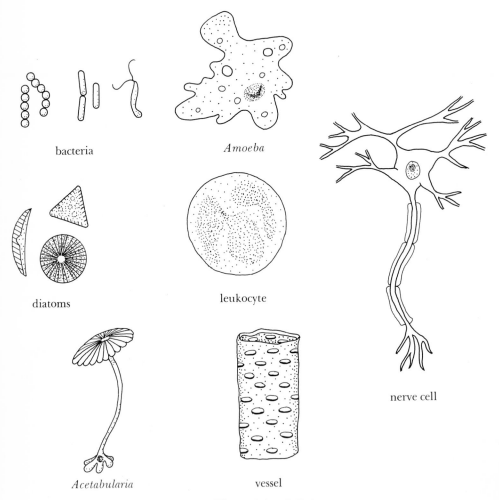

bacteria

Amoeba

diatoms

leukocyte

Acetabularia

vessel

nerve cell

Figure 1–1.   Cell shapes.

The long nerve cell is also an example of the extremes in cell sizes, the range of which is quite remarkable in the living world. The smallest cells so far observed are the pleuropneumonia-like organisms, such as *Mycoplasma gallisepticum,* which produces respiratory disease in poultry. These organisms are filterable like the viruses, but are capable of growing outside a living cell, whereas the viruses are not. The smallest *Mycoplasma* species are 0.1 micron (μ) in diameter (1 μ is 0.001 mm). This is approximately one-tenth the size of the average bacterium. In spite of its extremely small size, a *Mycóplasma* has all the necessary materials for conducting the activities of a living organism. In contrast, the egg cells of avian types, of which the ostrich egg is a striking case, are measured in inches rather than in microns. However, most cells are not visible to the naked eye and require the use of a microscope for observation.

The natural boundary of a cell is the *plasma membrane.* In plant cells, this membrane is ordinarily surrounded by a cellulose wall. Additional wall materials may include pectins and/or lignins. Certain animal cells, such as the protozoa of the class Ciliata and various arthropod bristles, have an exterior material composed of protein–carbohydrate complexes. This wall material may occur as a pellicle, as in the ciliates, or it may be composed of chitin or a mucoid substance. The organization of cell boundaries will be discussed at some length in Chapter 3.

The *cytoplasm* of the cell can be described as that portion of the protoplasm which is outside the nucleus and inside the plasma membrane, and it often comprises the main bulk of cell volume. In a living cell, the cytoplasm is a rather heterogeneous mass containing granules of different sizes and shapes. The mass of cytoplasm remaining after all the major particulate components, or *organelles,* are removed can be called the *hyaloplasm.* This portion of the cytoplasm is an aqueous substance in which many organic and inorganic particles are dissolved or suspended. The organelles are embedded in this matrix or hyaloplasm.

It is becoming increasingly evident that many of the cytoplasmic organelles have a membranous organization comparable to that of the plasma membrane (see Chapter 3). It has been suggested that these organelles exhibiting a membranous structure may have been derived in evolution from evaginations and invaginations of the plasma membrane. This derivation would be applicable to *mitochondria,* the *Golgi* structures, the *endoplasmic reticulum,* and the *nuclear envelope* (Figures 1–2, 1–3, and 1–4). The *plastids* in plant cells may be added to this list. In each of these organelles, the structure has been observed to incorporate at least some degree of a membrane system comparable to that of the plasma membrane. The hypothesis embodying these homologies implies that each membranous unit of a cell is derived from some preexisting membrane.

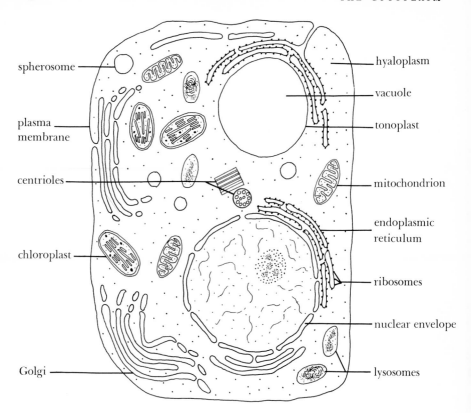

spherosome

plasma
membrane

centrioles

chloroplast

Golgi

hyaloplasm

vacuole

tonoplast

mitochondrion

endoplasmic
reticulum

ribosomes

nuclear envelope

lysosomes

Figure 1–2. A composite cell showing the
ultrastructural organization of the cytoplasm.

Additional evidence for the homology of cytoplasmic membranes is the observation of connections between the plasma membrane and the endoplasmic reticulum, between the endoplasmic reticulum and the nuclear
envelope, and possibly between the nuclear envelope and the plasma membrane. These connections indicate a continuous array of membranes
throughout the cytoplasm between the plasma membrane and the nuclear
envelope. A significant feature of these membranes is their similar chemical composition, which is based upon the presence of lipid and protein
arranged in a particular molecular pattern.

Figure 1–3. A meristematic cell from corn ($\times$10,660) showing the nucleus (N),
pores (NP) in the nuclear envelope (NE), endoplasmic reticulum (ER), mitochondria (M), Golgi structure (G), and the plasma membrane (PM). COURTESY
W. G. Whaley, The Cell Research Institute, The University of Texas.

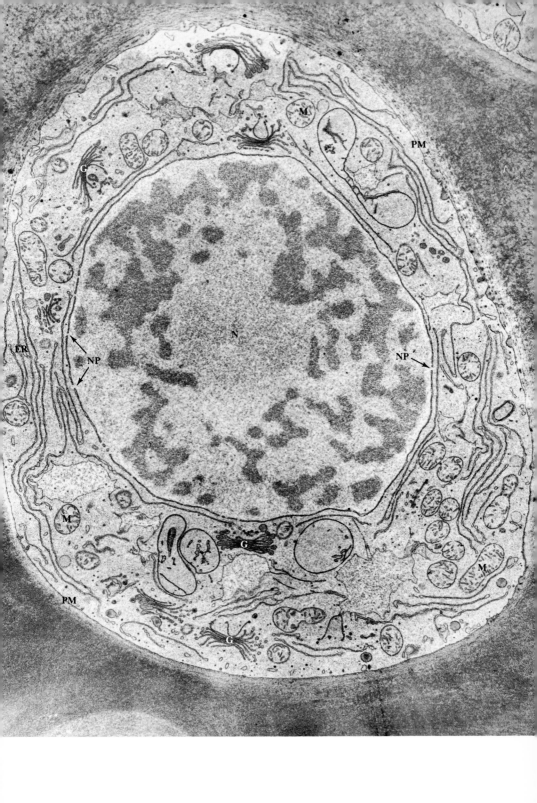

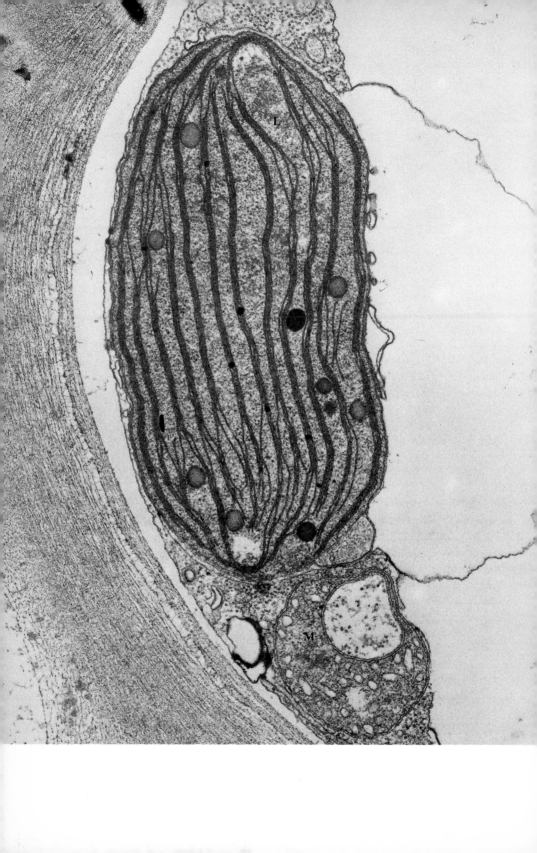

The mitochondria are among the largest cytoplasmic organelles. They appear in the light microscope as rodlike or filamentous structures. Detailed morphological examination under the electron microscope reveals that in cross section the mitochondrion is compartmentalized by internal membranes. With methods described in Chapter 2, it is possible to isolate the components of the cytoplasm and analyze their structure and biochemical activities. In such analyses, the largest cytoplasmic organelle in plant cells, the plastid, also exhibits an internal membranous organization. The major component of the array of membranes found in the cytoplasm is the endoplasmic reticulum. The numerous elements of this network are extensively distributed throughout the cytoplasm but are not visible with the light microscope. Associated with the membranes of the endoplasmic reticulum, and often free in the hyaloplasm, are the smallest recoverable bodies in the cytoplasm, the *ribosomes*. These are recognizable as tiny round particles along the outside of the reticular membranes and are chemically identifiable by their relatively large amounts of ribonucleoprotein. Other elements in the cytoplasm that may have similar membranous origins are the Golgi structures, the *lysosomes,* and the

Figure 1–4. Left: A chloroplast and a mitochondrion of the brown alga *Egregia menziesii* (×29,500). The large body with lamellae (L) is the chloroplast and the smaller one is the mitochondrion (M). Right: A portion of the Golgi structure in a root tip cell of the bean *Phaseolus vulgaris* (×65,000). Left photo from T. Bisalputra and A. A. Bisalputra, *J. Cell Biol.,* **33,** 511 (1967); right photo from H. H. Mollenhauer, W. Evans, and C. Kogut, *J. Cell Biol.,* **37,** 579 (1968).

spherosòmes. These are rather enigmatic organelles, partly because of their apparently limited distribution according to cell type; that is, they have not been found as regular constituents of the cytoplasm of all cells. The Golgi structures may be seen with the light microscope as a reticulate material in certain types of cells, particularly secretory cells. The lysosomes, considerably smaller than mitochondria but larger than ribosomes, are also found in more specialized types of cells. For reasons to be discussed later, the Golgi structures and the lysosomes have in the past posed a problem of identification. Spherosomes, as studied in plant cells, develop as membrane-limited bodies containing fat or oil.

In most animal cells, there are cytoplasmic bodies that serve an important function during cell division. These are the *centrioles,* which are located at one pole of the cell just outside the nuclear envelope. Homologous cytoplasmic structures called *kinetosomes* or *basal bodies* may also be found in certain animal cells just inside the plasma membrane. The kinetosomes are associated with the formation of *cilia* and *flagella* (Figure 1–5), which are actually outside the boundary of the cell but have their origins within the cytoplasm. Cilia, flagella, and kinetosomes are usually large enough to be observed with the light microscope, whereas centrioles are more easily detected with electron microscopy.

Physical Properties

The physical properties of the cell, particularly of the cytoplasm, are functions of the chemical nature and organization of the hyaloplasm. Essentially, the hyaloplasm is a colloidal system of high water content containing particles of varying sizes. Some of the materials are dissolved, but many of them are suspended in solution. The suspension of particles in hyaloplasm is the basis for its colloidal nature. (Examples of particles in suspension in water are oils and fats; they do not dissolve but are present as droplets.) The organic material in greatest abundance is protein, which contributes to the fibrillar nature of the hyaloplasm. Many of the proteins in suspension, and some of the carbohydrates, are *hydrophilic* (water loving) and occur with shells of water surrounding their molecules. This affinity is mutual, in that the electric charges on the protein and on the water produce attractions that hold them together in a particular way. In addition, certain inclusions may or may not be present in the hyaloplasm, depending upon the metabolic state of the cell. These are fat droplets, starch grains, and pigments, such as the carotenoids found in plant cells and some types of animal cells and the melanin pigments found in many animal cells. Plant cells are often characterized by the presence

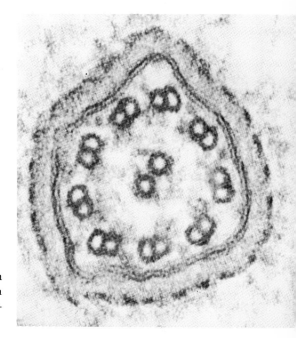

Figure 1–5. Cross section of a flagellum in the developing sperm of the green alga *Nitella* (×194,000). FROM F. R. Turner, *J. Cell Biol.*, **37**, 370 (1968).

of one or more vacuoles containing different kinds of substances. What is generally called the *cell sap* is located within these vacuoles. The cell sap consists of sugars, salts, and sometimes specific pigments, such as the anthocyanins, which are responsible for much of the red and blue coloration of plant parts. The vacuoles may be physically separated from the surrounding cytoplasm by membranes comparable, if not identical, to the other membranes of the cell. There has been some question whether a true membrane is present as a boundary of the vacuole seen in mature plant cells. In some cases no membrane can be detected, whereas in others an envelope or *tonoplast* is found when the vacuole is isolated from the cell. The semipermeable property of the membrane is observed even after isolation.

The physical properties, or mechanical behavior, of the hyaloplasm are due principally to the various chemical inclusions in a gel phase, although it is also possible that the physical and chemical organization of the cytoplasmic membranes contributes to some of these characteristics. A *gel* is a group of suspended particles in a semisolid condition; it might also be described as a jelly-like state. In a gel, molecules are held together by chemical bonds and other attractive forces of different and varying strengths. Bonds may form between hydrogen atoms, between carbon and hydrogen atoms, or between carbon and nitrogen atoms, among others. The *van der Waals force* (Figure 1–6) is a weak, nonspecific force between nonpolar groups of atoms. These forces can hold together long chains of molecules, and the stability of a gel depends upon the type and strength of the attractive forces. Normally, the forces of attraction between long chains of molecules change during the metabolic cycles of the cell. Thus a gel may become less stable and therefore more liquid than solid. This change is known as *solation,* that is, the formation of the *sol* phase. The gel–sol condition is the prime basis for the mechanical behavior of the cytoplasm.

The physical properties include contractility, elasticity, tensile strength, rigidity, cohesiveness, and viscosity. The contractility of gels is important for the absorption and removal of water as they occur in protoplasm generally. Cohesion of particles or molecules is due in large measure to van der Waals forces, and cohesiveness varies with the strength of these forces and influences the degree of solation or gelation. The property of viscosity is one that certainly has important effects on the behavior of the cell. Three well-known and widely observed phenomena are in some way related to the viscosity of the cytoplasm: Brownian movement, amoeboid movement, and cytoplasmic streaming or cyclosis. *Brownian movement* is marked by the agitation of particles in a relatively

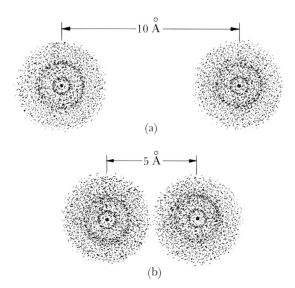

Figure 1–6. Illustration of van der Waals attraction: (a) weak attraction; (b) very strong attraction. Redrawn from *General Chemistry*, 2nd ed., by Linus Pauling. W. H. Freeman and Company. Copyright © 1953.

rapid zigzag pattern. It is due to the bombardment of one particle or molecule by another, setting off a kind of chain reaction of movement. The rate of this movement is dependent upon the size of the particles and the viscosity of the suspension. The higher the temperature, the more rapid the movement, and the viscosity of the cell is decreased. In other words, high viscosity indicates a more gel-like state of the protoplasm, and low viscosity a more sol-like condition. One of the explanations of *amoeboid movement,* as exhibited by the amoebae and certain kinds of blood cells, is based upon the continued changes from gel phase to sol phase and from sol phase to gel phase (sol ⇌ gel). The property of viscosity, in turn, is based upon these changes. No less important is *cytoplasmic streaming* or *cyclosis.* The cause of this phenomenon is not clearly understood, but certain known factors will change its rate or pattern. If there is a decrease in cell metabolism, there is a concomitant decrease in cyclosis. Conversely, an increase in metabolic rate gives rise to an increase in streaming. The streaming of cytoplasm may be related to the changes occurring during solation and gelation, and there is evidence for this in the fact that a decrease in viscosity results in an increase in streaming.

Chemistry

Table 1–1 presents an average chemical composition of protoplasm (the plasma membrane and its contents). The substances listed, found most of the time during the cycle of the cell, provide the chemical basis for the colloidal system and for the physical properties of the cytoplasm.

Table 1–1   Average Chemical Composition of Protoplasm

Substance	*Percent by Weight*	*Location in Cell*
water	90 ± 2	nuclear sap, vacuoles, hyaloplasm
proteins	7 ± 2	membranes, hyaloplasm, as enzymes
carbohydrates	2 ± 0.5	vacuoles, hyaloplasm, cell wall, storage products
lipids	1 ± 0.5	membranes, hyaloplasm, inclusions
inorganic materials	1 ± 0.5	vacuoles, hyaloplasm, as cofactors

The principal chemical component of protoplasm is water. It serves as the medium in which all other materials are contained and also plays an important part in the metabolic activities of the cell. Water may exist as free water or as water bound to proteins or carbohydrates. The most abundant organic constituents are the proteins, of which there are several types. Protein in some form is found in most parts of the cell. Certain types present in the hyaloplasm constitute the principal ingredient of the protoplasmic gels. These include the globulin proteins, which are insoluble in water. Among the proteins occurring in the nucleus are the histone proteins, which are important structurally and functionally in the chromosomes. There are also some complex proteins, called *conjugated proteins,* which consist of protein and another substance. Examples are the nucleoproteins of the nucleus and cytoplasm, the lipoproteins of the cytoplasmic membranes, the chromoproteins (for example, hemoglobin), and many enzymes. Carbohydrates, lipids, and nucleic acids are the other major organic constituents of protoplasm. The carbohydrates include various sugars, starches, and the plant cell wall component cellulose. The lipids are structural components of the cytoplasmic membranes and also appear as insoluble inclusions in the hyaloplasm, often as fat droplets. Phospholipid is an important lipid compound present in various cytoplasmic organelles. There is a great variety of inorganic materials in the cell, although in relatively small amounts, as salts or in combination with the organic constituents. Among the latter are several chromoproteins, which contain one or more metallic ions, such as iron, copper, manganese, and magnesium.

Proteins

Proteins are composed of amino acids, which are characterized by the presence of two specific groupings of nitrogen, hydrogen, carbon, and oxygen atoms—the amino group (NH_2) and the carboxyl group (COOH). The general formula for an amino acid is

$$\overset{\displaystyle R}{\underset{\displaystyle NH_2—CH—COOH}{\mid}}$$

in which R represents a chemical group that differs in the various amino acids. Three specific amino acids are shown in Figure 1-7. One of these, cysteine, contains sulfur, which is found in a few other amino acids as well. A protein consists of a chain of these amino acids, and the number, kind,

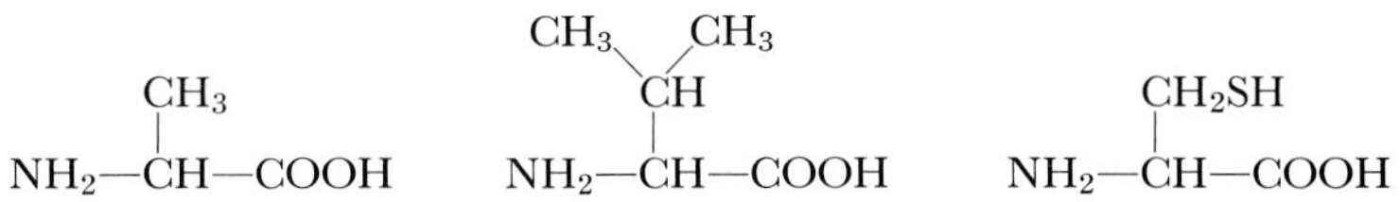

$$CH_3$$
$$|$$
$$NH_2—CH—COOH$$
alanine

$$CH_3\diagdown\diagup CH_3$$
$$CH$$
$$|$$
$$NH_2—CH—COOH$$
valine

$$CH_2SH$$
$$|$$
$$NH_2—CH—COOH$$
cysteine

Figure 1–7. Representative amino acids.

and sequence of the amino acids determine the protein's type and activity in the cell. The chemical basis for this chain organization arises from the amino and carboxyl groups. The amino group is basic, and the carboxyl group is acidic. Formation of a chain depends upon the combination of an amino group of one amino acid with the carboxyl group of another, with the loss of one molecule of water.

$$RCOOH + R'NH_2 \rightarrow R—CO—NH—R' + H_2O$$

The linkage —CO—NH— is known as a *peptide bond;* a combination of two amino acids is called a dipeptide and a chain of several amino acids is a polypeptide. There are over 20 different amino acids and many more proteins of biological importance, some of which are listed in Table 1–2. Proteins are generally rather large molecules with molecular weights ranging from about 12,000 to over 2 million.

Table 1–2 Representative Amino Acids and Proteins

Amino Acids		Proteins	
alanine	lysine	actin	insulin
arginine	methionine	albumins	lysozyme
asparagine	phenylalanine	catalase	myosin
cysteine	proline	cytochrome oxidase	pepsin
glutamine	serine	deoxyribonuclease	peroxidase
glycine	tryptophan	fibrin	protamine
histidine	tyrosine	globulins	ribonuclease
leucine	valine	histone	trypsin

Proteins can be classified according to certain of their chemical or physical properties. For example, albumins are a class of protein soluble in water and dilute salt solutions, whereas globulins are insoluble in water and soluble in neutral salt solutions. Histones and protamines, also soluble in water, differ from albumins in having a rather high content of basic amino acids, such as arginine. These two types of proteins are distinguished from each other by their arginine contents as well as their molecular weights.

The arrangement of the amino acids in a protein is not always linear but may contain one or more turns. Complex proteins often have two or more levels of structure. The first, or *primary*, structure depends on the linear chain of amino acids. A coiled or helical chain provides *secondary* structure, and additional folding gives the protein *tertiary* structure. *Quaternary* structure is also found in some proteins consisting of two or more amino acid chains. Hemoglobin, for example, contains four polypeptide chains and exhibits quaternary structure.

Several of the proteins in Table 1–2 are enzymes. The complete formula for ribonuclease, one of the first enzymes for which the structure was determined, reveals several turns in a chain of 19 different amino acids with a molecular weight of 14,000. There are 124 amino acid units in the chain. A more complete analysis of the three-dimensional structure of an enzyme was carried out with lysozyme. This enzyme causes the destruction (*lysis*) of bacterial cells and is found in many organisms, including man. It acts on the bacterial cell wall by disrupting the components of a polysaccharide chain similar to chitin. Each molecule of the enzyme contains 129 amino acids in a single polypeptide chain.

Some enzymes require a nonprotein addition for activity. If the addition is organic, it is usually called a *prosthetic* group, but if of an inorganic nature, such as a metallic ion, it is more commonly referred to as a *cofactor*. The principle of enzyme activity lies in the specificity of an enzyme for a particular substance, the *substrate,* upon which it acts. The chemical configuration of the substrate probably determines which enzyme effects a specific reaction involving the substrate. An enzyme may influence a chemical reaction by altering its rate or by initiating a change in the substrate.

In the cell, enzymes are found in association with several structures: mitochondria, plastids, the nucleus, and the endoplasmic reticulum. The synthesis of proteins can be cited as an example of the importance of enzymes. The general chain of events in protein synthesis begins in the nucleus, where certain enzymes participate in the synthesis of ribonucleic acid (RNA). The RNA moves into the cytoplasm and to the ribosomes, where the various amino acids are joined together into a protein chain. This union involves the activity of several enzymes at this site. In the cytoplasm, another type of RNA carries the amino acids to the ribosomes, and the transfer mechanism requires its specific enzymes. In many respects, the most important functional aspects of proteins are their structural relations in the cell and their activities as enzymes.

Carbohydrates

Carbohydrates, which are composed of carbon, hydrogen, and oxygen, are most important biologically as a source of energy for the cell. They also provide some structural basis for the cell, particularly in plants. The simplest class of carbohydrates, the monosaccharides, are characterized by the number of carbon atoms in the chain (or ring); for example, a triose has three carbons, a pentose has five carbons, and a hexose has six carbons. A typical, and familiar, sugar is the hexose glucose. Glucose is

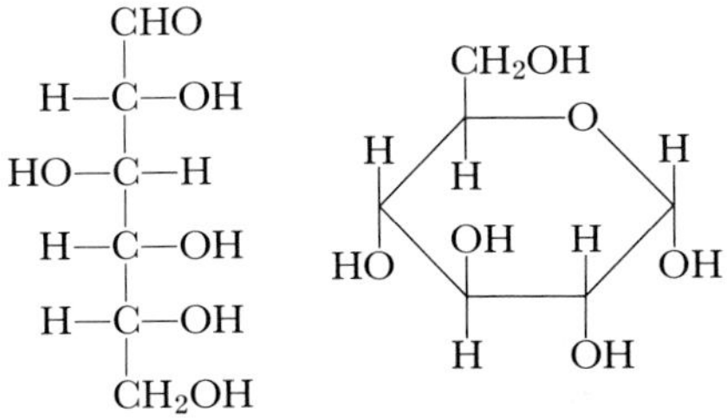

glucose

especially important as a major source of energy for the cell. The second class of carbohydrates consists of the disaccharides, each composed of two monosaccharides. Important members of this group are sucrose and maltose. The third class of carbohydrates contains the polysaccharides, formed by the condensation of many monosaccharides with a loss of water. Examples of biologically important polysaccharides are starch, glycogen, and other storage materials in plant and animal cells, cellulose, which is a

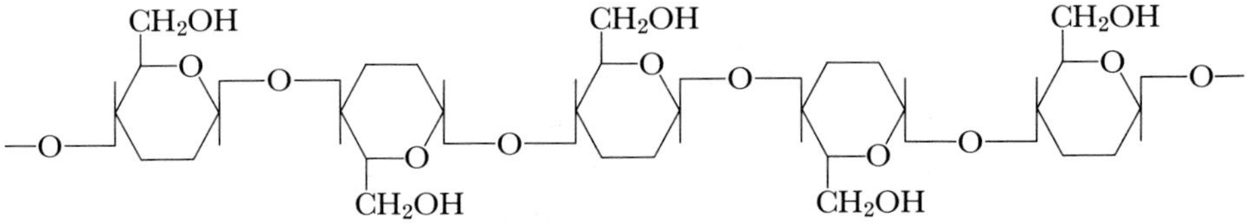

cellulose

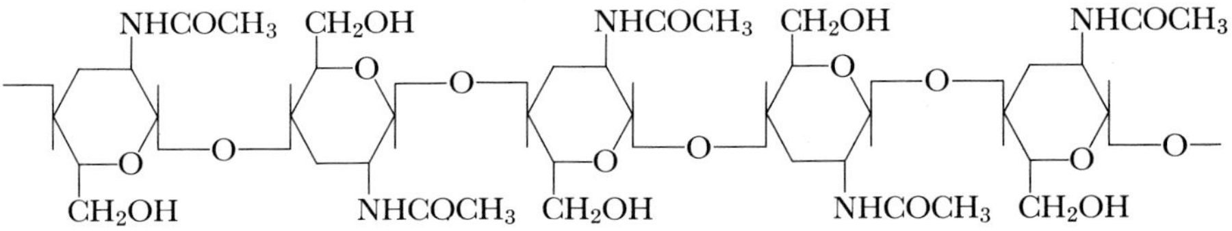

chitin

Figure 1–8. The polysaccharides cellulose and chitin.

major component of plant cell walls, and chitin (Figure 1–8). Other types of carbohydrates may serve as the prosthetic groups of certain proteins. The synthesis of carbohydrates is best known in the process of photosynthesis, in which carbon dioxide and water are utilized as chemical sources and light energy is absorbed by chlorophyll for the several reactions that occur.

Lipids

Lipids are important in several metabolic activities of the cell. Of particular interest is oxidative metabolism, which involves the mitochondria and plastids. The simplest lipids are the triglycerides, which are composed of fatty acids and glycerol.

$$
\begin{array}{llll}
\text{CH}_2\text{OOCC}_{15}\text{H}_{31} & & \text{CH}_2\text{OH} & \text{HOOCC}_{15}\text{H}_{31}\ \text{(palmitic)} \\
| & & | & \\
\text{CHOOCC}_{17}\text{H}_{35} \quad + \quad \text{H}_2\text{O} \xrightarrow{\text{lipase}} & \text{CHOH} \quad + \quad \text{HOOCC}_{17}\text{H}_{35}\ \text{(stearic)} \\
| & & | & \\
\text{CH}_2\text{OOCC}_{17}\text{H}_{33} & & \text{CH}_2\text{OH} & \text{HOOCC}_{17}\text{H}_{33}\ \text{(oleic)} \\
\quad\text{triglyceride} & & \text{glycerol} & \quad\text{three fatty acids}
\end{array}
$$

The more complex lipids include the steroids, such as the sex hormones, vitamin D, bile acids, and cholesterol (Figure 1–9). Other lipids form complexes with other compounds; examples are the phospholipids, lipoproteins, and carotenoids.

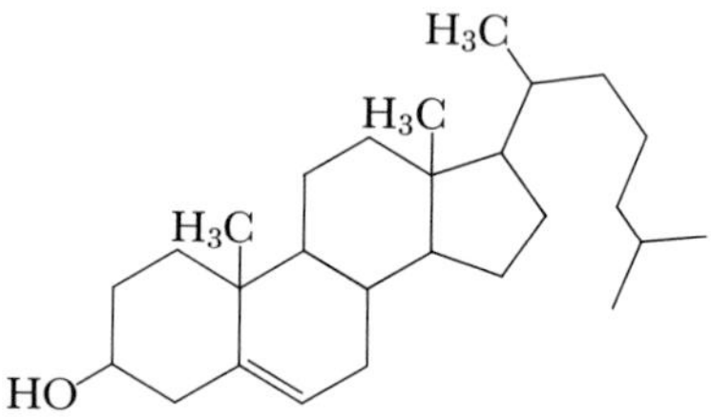

Figure 1–9.   Cholesterol, a complex lipid.

Inorganic Components

Inorganic components occur in ionic states as positively charged particles, cations (for example, Na^+), and as negatively charged particles, anions (for example, Cl^-). The distribution of the ions of various salts inside and outside the cell is important in maintaining the osmotic balance in the cell. Certain ions are of particular importance in the organization of protoplasm and in its metabolic activities. One of the most significant of these is the phosphate group (PO_4^{3-}), which is associated with phosphoprotein, phospholipid, and nucleotides. A major source of energy for the cell is the compound adenosine triphosphate (ATP), in which the linkages of the phosphate groups exhibit high energy levels. Another inorganic constituent, sulfur, is important in the organization of several organic compounds, such as the amino acids, and therefore of several enzymes. Sulfur also provides linkages in the spindle fiber apparatus during cell division. Such inorganic ions as manganese and magnesium may serve as cofactors for the activity of specific enzymes. From a structural standpoint, there is some evidence for the presence of specific ionic linkages in the molecular arrangement of the chromosomes. In support of this is the observation of iron, calcium, and magnesium in the nucleus.

Nucleic Acids

The nucleic acids are an especially significant group of substances found in the nucleus and in the cytoplasm. In the nucleus they are associated with the chromosomes and are important in transmitting information from the nucleus to the cytoplasm. In the cytoplasm they are most closely concerned with the synthesis of proteins. These and other biological functions will be discussed in more detail later. However, the chemical organization of the nucleic acids should come under a discussion of the chemical composition of the cytoplasm and will be presented here, the nuclear and cytoplasmic nucleic acids being treated together for convenience.

A nucleic acid consists of a ribose (pentose) or deoxyribose sugar, nitrogenous bases (purines and pyrimidines), and phosphates. The important nucleic acids biologically are ribonucleic acid and deoxyribonucleic acid (DNA). The bases found in each are shown in Figure 1–10. In RNA the most common bases are adenine, uracil, guanine, and cytosine. In DNA the most common bases are adenine, thymine, guanine, and cytosine, but the nuclear DNA of some organisms may contain 5-methylcytosine in place of cytosine. Another difference between these two nucleic acids is the sugar component. In DNA there is an oxygen atom absent from the carbon-2 position of the ribose sugar.

A nucleic acid is actually composed of chains of nucleotide units, each nucleotide unit consisting of a molecule of sugar, a base, and phosphoric acid. A nucleic acid contains large numbers of nucleotide units and has

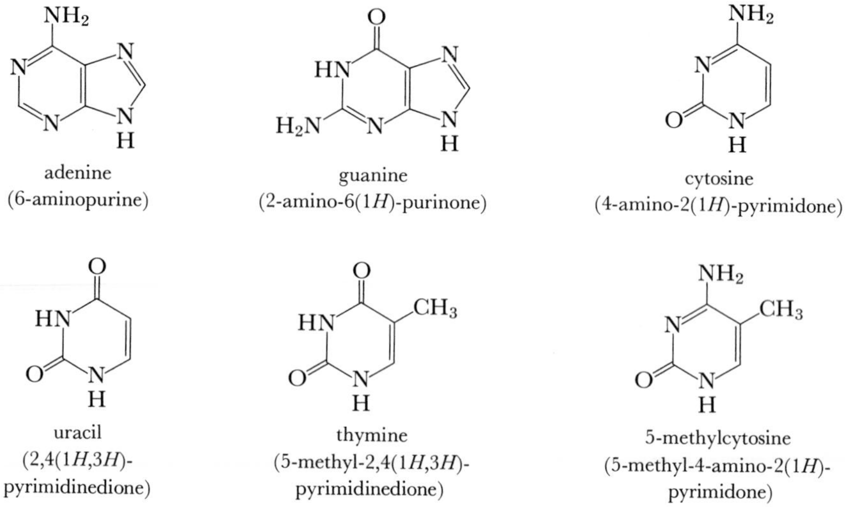

adenine
(6-aminopurine)
guanine
(2-amino-6(1*H*)-purinone)
cytosine
(4-amino-2(1*H*)-pyrimidone)
uracil
(2,4(1*H*,3*H*)-pyrimidinedione)
thymine
(5-methyl-2,4(1*H*,3*H*)-pyrimidinedione)
5-methylcytosine
(5-methyl-4-amino-2(1*H*)-pyrimidone)

Figure 1–10. Purine and pyrimidine bases.

sugar—thymine—adenine—sugar
phosphate phosphate
sugar—adenine—thymine—sugar
phosphate phosphate
sugar—guanine—cytosine—sugar
phosphate phosphate
sugar—cytosine—guanine—sugar
phosphate phosphate
sugar—cytosine—guanine—sugar
phosphate phosphate
sugar—adenine—thymine—sugar
phosphate phosphate

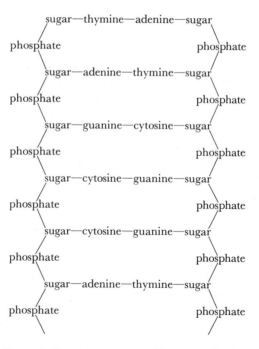

Figure 1–11. Arrangement of base pairs in DNA.

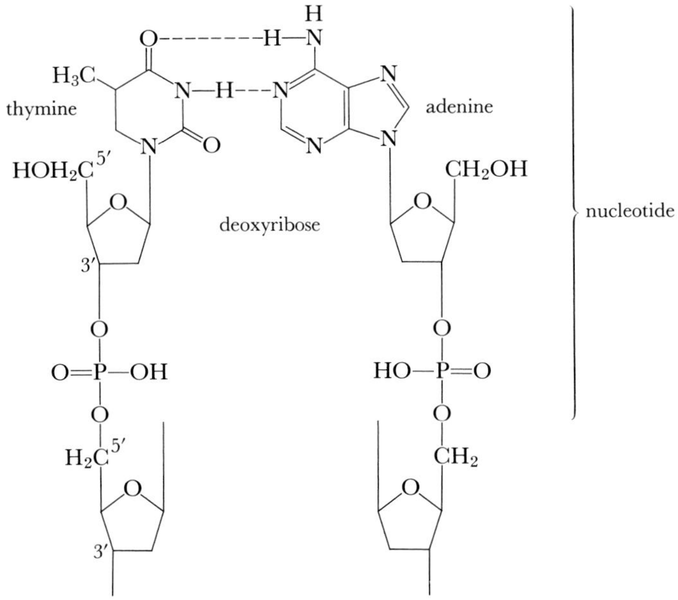

Figure 1–12. Molecular organization of DNA.

a high molecular weight. DNA's isolated from nuclei have molecular weights of 5 million or more, depending upon the species.

There is a specific relationship between the purine and pyrimidine bases in DNA in that a specific purine is always paired with a specific pyrimidine, as shown in Figure 1–11. Thus, the ratio of adenine to thymine is 1 : 1, and the ratio of cytosine to guanine is 1 : 1. However, the ratio of the base pairs adenine–thymine to cytosine–guanine is not always 1 : 1; it ranges from 0.42 : 1 to 1.85 : 1, depending upon the species. For example, the ratio of adenine–thymine to cytosine–guanine in man is 1.53 : 1, whereas that in certain bacteria is 0.42 : 1.

The arrangement of the components of DNA shown in Figure 1–11 indicates two complementary chains of nucleotide units. The molecular organization of these chains is shown in Figure 1–12. The nucleotides are joined by phosphate ester linkages between the 3' position of one deoxy-ribose unit and the 5' position of another deoxyribose unit.

The helical model for DNA as proposed by Watson, Crick, and Wilkins is represented in Figure 1–13. DNA consists of two helixes coiled about each other, such that the chain of each helix is composed of the sugar–phosphate groups and the two helixes are connected by the base pairs via hydrogen bonds. The direction of one helix is opposite to the other. In the synthesis of DNA, one helix serves as a template for the formation of a complementary helix. That is, adenine in one helix directs the formation of thymine in the new helix, and cytosine serves as a template for the formation of guanine in the new helix. As shown in Figure 1–13, the dimensions of the double helix indicate a diameter of

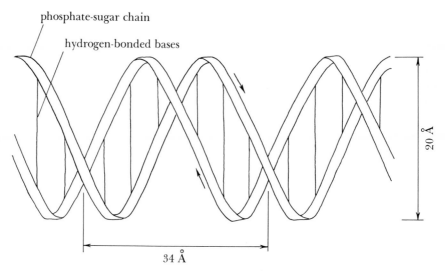

Figure 1–13. Structure of DNA (B configuration).

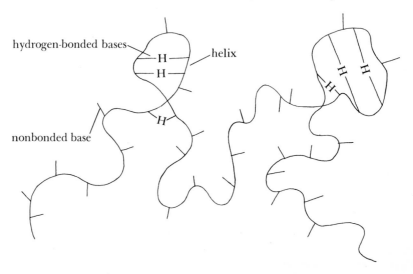

Figure 1–14. Proposed structure of RNA.

20 Ångström units (Å). One full turn of the helix traverses a distance of 34 Å and contains approximately 10 nucleotide pairs.

The differences in chemical constituents between DNA and RNA have been indicated, and there is also a physical difference in the orientations of the molecules. The structure of RNA in most organisms is not based upon a double helix configuration. For the most part, RNA exists as a single strand, but it may be wound back upon itself in several places (Figure 1–14), producing helixes in these places as found in DNA. Approximately 50 to 80% of an RNA molecule from yeast consists of these helical regions. The secondary helical structure is regular rather than random and is important for certain properties of RNA. In the regions of helix formation, the bases are hydrogen-bonded. Evidence suggests that the pairing of the bases is similar to that found in DNA; that is, adenine

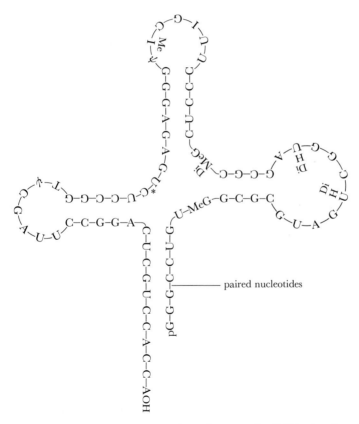

Figure 1–15. Possible conformation of alanine–transfer RNA showing double-stranded regions. FROM R. W. Holley et al., *Science,* 147, 1462 (1965).

pairs with uracil, and guanine pairs with cytosine. The importance of the similarity in the arrangement of bases in DNA and RNA will be discussed later in connection with protein synthesis and nucleic acid synthesis.

In 1965 the structure of an RNA was revealed for the first time (Figure 1–15). The alanine–transfer RNA contains only 77 nucleotides and has a molecular weight of 26,600. One of the significant features of its helical configuration is found in its activity in transferring the amino acid alanine to the site of incorporation into a protein chain.

Examination of the RNA of reovirus (a respiratory and enteric virus of animals) and wound tumor virus of sweet clover points to a double-stranded organization of the RNA in these viruses. In addition, the RNA of reovirus has a molecular weight (10.2×10^6) considerably higher than that of most other RNA-containing viruses. The range of molecular weights for RNA's of a variety of organisms is about 20,000 to 10 million, most of them falling below 2 million.

SELECTED READING

Bourne, G. H., ed., *Cytology and Cell Physiology,* 3rd ed., Academic Press, New York, 1964.

Fresco, J. R., and D. B. Strauss, "Biosynthetic Polynucleotides: Models of Biological Templates," *Am. Scientist,* **50**(1), 158 (1962).

Frey-Wyssling, A., and K. Mühlethaler, *Ultrastructural Plant Cytology,* American Elsevier, New York, 1965.

Gomatos, P. J., and I. Tamm, "The Secondary Structure of Reovirus RNA," *Proc. Natl. Acad. Sci. U.S.,* **49**(5), 707 (1963).

Haggis, G. H., D. Michie, A. R. Muir, K. B. Roberts, and P. M. B. Walker, *Introduction to Molecular Biology,* Longmans, Green, London, 1964.

Holley, R. W., "The Nucleotide Sequence of a Nucleic Acid," *Sci. Am.,* **214**(2), 30 (1966).

McElroy, W. D., *Cellular Physiology and Biochemistry,* 2nd ed., Prentice-Hall, Englewood Cliffs, N.J., 1964.

Morowitz, H. J., and M. E. Tourtellotte, "The Smallest Living Cells," *Sci. Am.,* **206**(3), 117 (1962).

Picken, L., *The Organization of Cells and Other Organisms,* Oxford Univ. Press, Oxford, 1960.

Watson, J. D., and F. H. C. Crick, "The Structure of DNA," *Cold Spring Harbor Symp. Quant. Biol.,* **18**, 123 (1953).

Cytological Methods

In the quest for information about the structure and composition of cells, the cytologist immediately faces two obstacles: the exceedingly small dimensions of cells and their component parts and the transparent nature of cells. This chapter will describe several of the principal methods and tools used by cytologists to overcome these obstacles. Since a number of comprehensive treatments of cytological techniques and instrumentation are readily available, some of which are listed at the close of this chapter, not all methods or types of equipment will be discussed here.

The diameters of the majority of cells fall within a range of 0.2 to 50 μ (1000 μ = 1 mm). Even in large cells, many of the components, or organelles, are less than 0.1 μ in diameter, while the chemical materials comprising the parts of the cell are still smaller (Table 2–1). The human eye, however, is not capable of resolving objects smaller than 100 μ; that is, if two objects are less than 100 μ apart, they will appear as one to the human eye. Thus it is evident that magnification is necessary for any study of cells and subcellular components, and microscopes are among the cytologist's most important tools. Analysis of chemical content (*cytochemistry*) is further complicated because of the minute amounts of substances present in cells. The average dry weight of a single cell, for example, is 2×10^{-10} gram, and there may be no more than 10^{-17} mole of a substance present. The detection of chemical substances (lipids, nucleic acids, enzymes, etc.) in the cell by specific staining reactions has, in fact, been useful for both qualitative and quantitative determinations.

The transparency of cellular material may be overcome by instruments that utilize radiations other than ordinary visible light, or the

**Table 2–1   Scale of Sizes at Atomic, Molecular,
and Cellular Levels**

Substance	Diameter	
	Microns (μ)	Ångström Units (Å)
giant nerve cell	1000	10,000,000
human egg	100	1,000,000
red blood cell	10	100,000
bacterium	1	10,000
virus particle	0.1	1,000
protein molecule	0.01	100
amino acid molecule	0.001	10
hydrogen atom	0.0001	1

material under study may be especially prepared to produce the necessary contrast. Fixation and staining are important techniques in preparation for microscopy for they result in differential absorption of radiant or other energy by different points within the specimen.

Microscopy

The history of lens systems is a long one, dating back as far as the first century A.D.; some of the important developments in microscopy are given in the Summary of Historical Events. The most rapid advances in microscopy, however, have come in recent times, and several kinds of instruments are now available, utilizing a variety of radiations from visible light to X rays.

The first operational light microscope was produced in 1590 by the Janssens. Major developments in microscopy have arisen from extensions and modifications of the use of visible light and from the use of electrons and X rays to permit detailed examination of fine structure and molecular organization. In all cases, the developers of microscopes have had two specific aims: to provide a magnified image as free as possible from optical defects or distortions and to increase the contrast between the object (and its component elements) and the background against which it is observed. The light microscope has a resolution (the minimum distance between two objects allowing their distinction) of about 0.2 μ, enabling the observation of cells and large component elements, such as plastids, nuclei, and chromosomes. The electron microscope has gone even further by refining the resolution to nearly 1 Å, enabling the observation of structures within cells not visible with the light microscope. Molecular structure can now be examined by X-ray-diffraction methods, which produce patterns rather than actual images.

Light Microscopy

It is presumed that the basic construction of the light microscope is familiar to the reader. (Literature describing specific models is available from the several manufacturers and suppliers of microscope equipment.) The most important components of the microscope are the lenses, since the resolution of the microscope is dependent upon their quality. In the ordinary compound microscope, there are three lens systems: those in the *condenser,* which collect and focus light on the specimen; the *objective* lens, which produces the image and magnifies it; and the *ocular* lens, which further magnifies the image. The resolution of the microscope is based on the capacity of the lenses to distinguish detail and to present distinct images of objects that are very close together. More specifically, the limit of resolution is dependent upon the ability of the lens system to collect light and the wavelength of light utilized. The *numerical aperture* (NA) is a numerical rating given to the capacity of the system to utilize a cone of light, and the wavelength is in the range of white or visible light. The limit of resolution is determined according to the relationship

$$r = \frac{0.61\lambda}{NA}$$

where 0.61 is a constant representing the minimum detectable difference in contrast and λ is the wavelength of light. The limit of resolution of the light microscope does not exceed 0.17 μ when the wavelength is 4000 Å (the shortest λ of visible light) and the NA is 1.4. With white light having a wavelength of 5500 Å, the limit of resolution is only about 0.25 μ. The higher the NA, the better the resolution, but there are limits here, since the glass lenses ordinarily used in a light microscope prohibit the passage of shorter wavelengths of light. In general, the smallest detectable detail in the light microscope is equal to about one-half the wavelength of light with which it is observed. Thus, the smaller the object, the shorter the wavelength of light necessary.

Phase-Contrast and Interference Microscopy

In conventional light microscopy, the material under observation is prepared in specific ways to produce the necessary contrast. Preparation involves fixation and staining and results in the differential absorption of light by different points within the specimen. The study of living cells is made difficult because they are mostly transparent to visible light, owing partly to their high water content. Even when most of the water is removed, however, there is little contrast. The observation of living cells has been greatly facilitated by the development of phase microscopy.

A cell is rather heterogeneous in content, and some components are thicker than others. In addition, the medium in which the cell is examined, the cell itself, and the components of the cell have different refractive indexes. (When light passes through one medium and into another at an angle other than 90°, the rays of light are bent if the velocity of light transmission is different in the two media. This is known as *refraction*. Since the component parts of a cell refract light in varying degrees, some parts have higher refractive indexes than others.) A difference in either refractive index or thickness between the cell and its surrounding medium or between one part of a cell and another produces a difference in phase. When the difference between either the refractive indexes or the thicknesses of two objects is small, the magnitude of the phase change is small. The phase-contrast microscope transforms phase differences into variations in brightness. Thus the contrast between the cell and its background or medium is significantly increased. The cell, which is otherwise transparent, is observed in shades of gray, depending on the thickness and refractive index of the background or surrounding medium.

The principle of the phase-contrast microscope, then, is to convert small phase differences into differences in contrast that can be detected visually. An annular phase plate is placed in the objective of the microscope and an annular diaphragm is placed in the condenser (Fig. 2–1). As light is transmitted through the lenses, some of the rays pass through in a direct path while others are diffracted laterally. Diffracted light rays are thus out of phase with the direct light, and an image of strong contrasts is produced. The annular diaphragm illuminates the object with a narrow cone of light, and the annular phase plate produces a variation of $\frac{1}{4}\lambda$ between the diffracted lateral light and the direct light. The phase effect is the result of *interference* between the direct image in the center of the objective and the diffracted lateral image. If the diffracted image is retarded, negative contrast results, whereas if it is advanced, positive contrast results. When the refractive index of the medium is greater than that of the

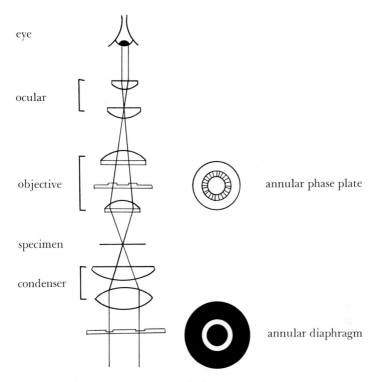

eye

ocular

objective

annular phase plate

specimen

condenser

annular diaphragm

Figure 2–1. Diagram of phase-contrast system.

object, the object is dark, and when the refractive index of the medium is less than that of the object, the object is bright.

The interference microscope is based on the same principle as the phase-contrast microscope, but it has wider application and some decided advantages over the phase-contrast microscope. With the interference microscope, which is also able to detect phase changes in the object, it is relatively easy to vary contrast and to select the most suitable contrast for a given object. It is also possible to obtain color effects in the object because of differences in optical paths. The optical path is the product of the refractive index and the thickness of the object and is a measure of the distance light travels in passing through the object. Measurements of this kind enable the investigator to make quantitative determinations, such as the determination of dry weight. Another advantage of the interference microscope over the phase-contrast microscope is the absence of a halo around the object in view. In the phase-contrast microscope, direct light falls on the annulus and diffracted light falls on the entire phase plate. Thus there is incomplete separation of the two, resulting in a halo around the object. If the detail of the object is dark, the halo is bright, whereas a dark halo surrounds bright object detail. The absence of a halo in interference microscopy is the result of complete separation of direct and diffracted light. Phase contrast, therefore, has been called an imperfect type of interference contrast.

Polarization Microscopy

The polarizing microscope is quite similar to the interference microscope. In the polarizing microscope, Nicol prisms of calcite were formerly added below the condenser and beyond the objective or in the ocular. A simpler and cheaper system utilizes sheets of Polaroid film, or a sheet of polyvinyl alcohol stained with iodine and then stretched over gentle heat. Two rotatable polarizing devices are required: the *polarizer* and the *analyzer*. The polarizer is placed below the condenser and sends only plane-

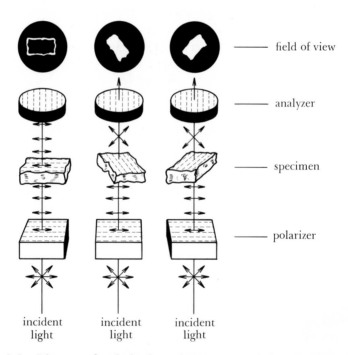

Figure 2–2. Diagram of polarization microscopy. Variations in darkness and brightness of an anisotropic object are shown when rotated ±45°. Reproduced from G. B. Wilson and J. H. Morrison, *Cytology,* 2nd ed., by permission of Reinhold Book Corporation, New York, 1966.

polarized light into the specimen. The analyzer is located above the objective. When it is rotated 360°, the visual field alternates between bright and dark at every 180° turn. When the axes of polarizer and analyzer are parallel to one another, the two positions of maximum light transmission are obtained. Rotation of the analyzer by 90° prevents the passage of polarized light and produces a dark field. The usual test is to rotate the specimen to find the points of maximum and minimum brightness. The maximum brightness is obtained when the axis of the specimen makes a ± 45° angle with those of the polarizer and analyzer (Figure 2–2).

Polarized light may pass through material with the same velocity in all directions, or the velocity may vary with direction. The property of the material or specimen is the determining factor. *Isotropic* material is the kind through which polarized light passes with the same velocity whatever the impinging direction. Such material has the same index of refraction in all directions. The velocity of passage of polarized light through *anisotropic* material, however, varies with direction. Such material is *birefringent,* since it exhibits two different indexes of refraction corresponding to the different velocities of transmission.

If birefringence is a property of the specimen itself, the phenomenon is called *intrinsic* birefringence. *Form* birefringence occurs when particles of one refractive index are oriented in a medium of different refractive index. This can disappear if the medium is changed. Some materials exhibit birefringence only when subjected to mechanical stress. This type is called *strain* birefringence. Birefringence has been observed in several cell organelles, including the spindle apparatus of dividing cells, muscle and nerve fibers, and internal membranes of plastids.

The polarizing microscope is used to measure the retardation of light polarized in one plane relative to that in another perpendicular plane. Measurement is in millimicrons and is facilitated by the use of a compensator in the optical system. Retardation, which depends on the thickness of the specimen, can be measured now to about 0.1 mμ (1 Å). The method is useful for indirect analysis of the ultrastructure of a cell, since the property of birefringence depends on structural properties smaller than the wavelength of light. Analysis depends on changes occurring when the polarizer, specimen, or analyzer is rotated.

The quantitative expression of birefringence is the difference between the two indexes of refraction of the specimen, the indexes of refraction corresponding to the respective different velocities of transmission of the light rays.

$$\text{birefringence} = n_2 - n_1$$

where n_1 is the refractive index associated with the fast ray and n_2 the refractive index associated with the slow ray. Since the compensator read-ing yields a direct value for retardation, the effective birefringence is obtained by dividing the retardation (Γ) by the geometric thickness of the specimen (d):

$$\Gamma/d = (n_2 - n_1)$$

For example, if the measured retardation is 2200 mμ and the thickness of the specimen is 5000 mμ, then

$$(n_2 - n_1) \doteq \Gamma/d$$
$$= 2200/5000$$
$$= 0.44 = \text{birefringence}$$

As a result of these relations, the polarizing microscope provides a tech-nique for the measurement of birefringence and especially molecular orientation.

Dichroism is a phenomenon that depends on differences in the absorp-tion of polarized light passing through material in different directions. Certain colors of light are absorbed when the specimen is oriented in a particular way. Color differences may occur—for example, a red nucleus against a blue cytoplasm. When the specimen is rotated 90°, the material will change color.

Electron Microscopy

The smallest cells have an average diameter of 0.1 μ. Accordingly, their components are considerably smaller and require special methods to bring them to an observable level. Even in large cells, many of the com-ponents, or organelles, are less than 0.1 μ in diameter. Since the resolu-tion of the light microscope is not high enough to make these particles visible to the human eye, it is necessary to go beyond the limits of light microscopy to an instrument that has much greater resolution. The elec-tron microscope utilizes electrons of short wavelength (about 0.05 Å) as a means of illumination in place of visible light (5500 Å). The components of a cell have different masses, each of which causes a scattering of the elec-tron beam. The contrast between the object and its surrounding medium or between one object and another results from this scattering of the electrons by the atoms of the objects in the specimen, which permits the resolution of structures with diameters as small as 1 mμ (10 Å) and, in some instances, less. This represents a resolving power 250 times that of the light microscope.

The preparation of cells or cell parts for study with the electron microscope requires very specialized methods. Since a thick specimen will scatter electrons more than once and will cause poor resolution, extremely thin sections are necessary. The thinner the section, the better the resolution, but, of course, there are lower limits to the thinness that can be achieved in practice. However, it is now possible to prepare sections as thin as 100 Å with techniques that preserve the tissue or cell fragment from physical and chemical damage. The material must also be dry.

In order to increase the contrast produced by electron scattering and to prevent undue damage to the specimen, the investigator must kill and preserve (a process known as *fixation*) the material to be studied in a certain way. The most widely used fixatives in electron microscopy are osmium tetroxide (OsO_4) and formaldehyde. OsO_4 prevents the breakdown of lipid material during drying and protects the specimen against damage from drying or freezing. This fixative is most effective at physiological pH and freezing temperatures. Formaldehyde makes certain lipids insoluble, particularly when used in the presence of calcium ions. Fixation by freeze-drying in a vacuum is another valuable method (see Autoradiography). Potassium permanganate ($KMnO_4$) has proved to be very effective for the preservation of membranous structures in the cell, and it provides high contrast. In a buffered solution at a concentration of 1 to 2%, $KMnO_4$ destroys many proteins, thereby increasing the relative density of phospholipids. Since the membranes in the cell contain appreciable amounts of phospholipids, this fixative provides an effective means for studying them. Another fixative that has achieved widespread use is glutaraldehyde. At a concentration of $6\frac{1}{2}\%$ in phosphate buffer, it has been valuable for the study of enzyme histochemistry. As is the case with many stains and fixatives, however, occasional errors or accidents occur. Figure 2–3 illustrates one of the more attractive artifacts in electron microscopy.

In some cases, it is necessary to use a substance that will produce what is comparable to a stain reaction. For example, certain parts of a cell may selectively incorporate phosphotungstic acid. The heavy metal atoms in this substance cause an increase in electron scattering and thus in contrast. Other substances used in this way include chromium and platinum, which produce what is called a shadowing effect.

After fixation, the specimen is embedded in a plastic material, such as methacrylate, or in a resin, such as Araldite, and thin sections are cut on a specially designed microtome with glass or diamond knives. A section is then placed on a very thin membrane, preferably no thicker than 150 Å. This membrane must be strong enough not to tear and must produce as little electron scatter as possible. Such a membrane may be made from collodion (nitrocellulose), formvar [poly(vinylformal)], carbon, aluminum, or beryllium. The first two materials are the most commonly used, and the last provides the thinnest and most transparent membrane. The membrane is supported by a metal grid, usually of fine-mesh steel or copper, and the entire section-carrying assembly is placed in the electron microscope.

The body of the electron microscope is rather complex, but the main components involved in producing an image are in some ways no more complex than those in the light microscope (Figure 2–4). Since electrons travel long distances only in a vacuum, the instrument must be completely enclosed in a vacuum. The electron source is a cathode filament, which emits a narrow electron beam. This beam is collected and focused on the specimen by an electromagnetic condenser lens. After the electrons pass through the specimen, they are collected again by an electromagnetic

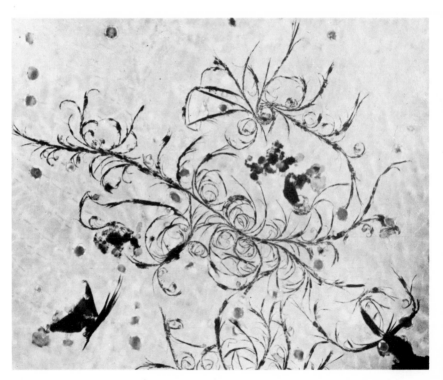

Figure 2–3. Electron micrograph of rat diaphragm muscle tissue fixed in glutaraldehyde and osmium (×800). Accidental crystallization occurred during the staining process with uranyl acetate and lead citrate, producing this artifact. The fine crystals are probably uranyl and the butterfly-like crystals are probably lead. COURTESY Dr. O. James Inashima, Professor of Pharmacology, Northeastern University, Boston, Mass.

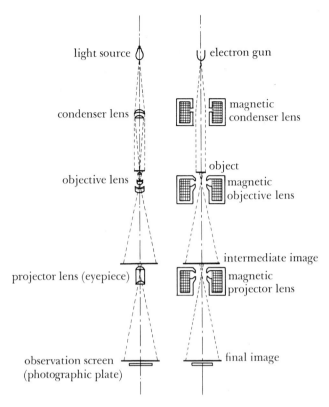

Figure 2-4. Comparison diagram of light and electron microscopes. COURTESY GEC–AEI (Electronics) Ltd., Scientific Apparatus Division, Harlow-Essex.

objective lens, which serves to produce a magnified image. Further magnification is accomplished by an electromagnetic projector lens, which projects the image onto a fluorescent viewing screen or a photographic plate. Focusing of the image can be adjusted by varying the current in the projector lens. The objective and projector lenses contribute almost equally to the magnification, and it is possible to produce a total magnification as high as 160,000 times specimen size in modern instruments.

Ultraviolet and Fluorescence Microscopy

One of the basic principles of microscopy is that the shorter the wavelength of light used for illumination, the greater the resolving power of the microscope. The light microscope utilizes glass lenses that do not transmit wavelengths below 4000 Å. In order to use shorter wavelengths, it is necessary to replace the glass with some substance through which they can pass. The substance most widely used for this purpose is fused quartz, which is transparent to wavelengths as low as 2400 Å, or slightly lower. Other possible lens materials are fluorite (CaF_2) and lithium fluoride, the latter being transparent to wavelengths as low as 2000 Å. Slides and cover slips must also be made of a material, such as quartz, that is transparent to short wavelengths. The range of ultraviolet light applicable to microscopy is thus about 2000 to 4000 Å, with the shorter wavelengths of limited application because of the difficulty of constructing lenses to transmit them. There is little reason for developing ultraviolet microscopes of greater resolution than those now in use because of the availability of the electron microscope for studies of fine structure.

The ultraviolet microscope is a valuable tool for certain kinds of cytological procedures. In particular, because of the ultraviolet absorption characteristics of specific cellular components, this instrument is useful for their qualitative and, in some cases, quantitative determination. For example, the absorption peaks (maximum or principal wavelengths of light absorbed by a substance) of nucleoproteins fall in the ultraviolet range between 2600 and 2700 Å, and it is therefore possible by means of the ultraviolet microscope to observe and photograph nucleoprotein-containing materials, such as chromosomes, in unstained living cells. The image produced by the ultraviolet microscope is usually projected onto a photographic plate but may also be recorded by a photoelectric cell or a television tube. Since the range of ultraviolet absorbed by the cellular components is capable of seriously damaging and even killing the biological specimen, careful adjustments are essential in the operation of the microscope.

Variations and modifications of the ultraviolet microscope are also valuable for quantitative estimations of specific cellular materials. For example, the amounts of nucleoproteins in living (or fixed) cells can be measured because of their specific ultraviolet absorption peaks. Quantitative determinations of this kind fall into the category of *spectrophotometry,* and several types of instruments are available for such purposes. Specific applications are described in Chapter 10.

Ultraviolet light is also the illumination source for the fluorescence microscope. When certain types of chemical substances are illuminated or irradiated with ultraviolet light, excitations are produced in the molecules, causing them to emit light in the visible range. Such a phenomenon is called *fluorescence,* and it is a property of the irradiated material. Some substances readily fluoresce (*autofluorescence*); examples are chlorophyll, which fluoresces red, and riboflavin, which fluoresces yellow-orange. The presence of such substances is easily detectable under proper conditions of illumination. Other substances, such as proteins and carbohydrates, fluoresce weakly or not at all but may be induced to fluoresce by the addition of specific dyes (*secondary fluorescence*). Observations of these reactions in the living cell are possible with the fluorescence microscope.

Ordinarily, the source of illumination in fluorescence microscopes is ultraviolet light at its higher wavelengths, that is, near the lower end of the visible range (3500 to 4000 Å). The light emitted by the object or chemical substance has a wavelength different from that of the ultraviolet light that is absorbed. Therefore, the detection of the presence of the substance is facilitated, and the contrast is quite good. It is possible to adapt the ordinary light microscope for fluorescence studies by relatively simple changes. A special filter capable of transmitting only the ultraviolet wavelengths is used near the light source (a mercury vapor lamp or carbon arc). Another filter, capable of absorbing the ultraviolet rays that are not absorbed by the object and transmitting the visible light of fluorescence, is added to the ocular.

X-Ray Microscopy

Significant improvement in resolution can be obtained with radiations of extremely short wavelengths, and X rays having such wavelengths can be generated as a source of "illumination" for the study of molecular structure. Thin sections, preferably 1 μ or less in thickness, are placed on fine-grain photographic emulsions and exposed to soft X rays in the range 1 to 10 Å. This technique is known as the direct contact method of microradiography. Another technique involves the placement of the specimen between the photographic plate and the source of the X-ray beam, but not in contact with the emulsion. This is the projection method. It results in the enlargement of the shadow produced by the X rays on the film. In an X-ray microscope, electromagnetic lenses or reflecting curved mirrors focus the X-ray beam.

The absorption of soft X rays by biological materials depends on their chemical composition and the physical organization of their chemical components. Therefore, quantitative determinations of dry matter as well as analyses of crystal structure may be made. Since certain chemical elements have definite limits of X-ray absorption, their presence and amounts can also be detected; for example, carbon has a specific absorption at 43.5 Å, nitrogen at 31.8 Å, and oxygen at 23.5 Å. Because of the limitations of X-ray methodology, only preserved materials can be studied, however.

More refined X-ray procedures are based on the diffraction of X rays

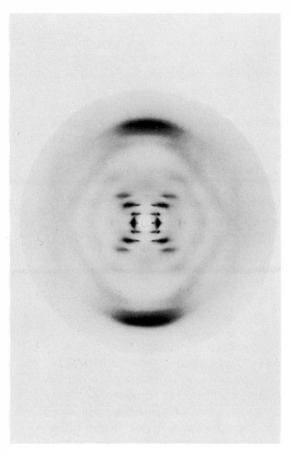

Figure 2–5. An X-ray-diffraction pattern of fibers of Na–DNA in B configuration. FROM M. H. F. Wilkins, *Cold Spring Harbor Symp. Quant. Biol.*, **21**, 75 (1956).

when they encounter small objects. In X-ray diffraction, a narrow beam of short wavelength X rays is passed through the specimen. At a short distance from the specimen, a photographic plate records the diffraction pattern, which appears as a series of concentric rings or spots. The distance between the dark zones of the pattern and the center is a function of the space between regularly repeating objects in the specimen; the smaller the angle of diffraction produced by a given object, the greater the distance between such repeating objects. Thus it is possible to calculate the spacing of objects or units within the specimen. The appearance of the pattern is a measure of the orientation of the units. If they are unoriented, concentric circles are observed, whereas perfect orientation is shown by spots.

In 1962 the Nobel Prize was awarded for the demonstration of DNA structure. The recipients were J. D. Watson, F. H. C. Crick, and M. H. F. Wilkins. The delineation of the molecular structure was based on X-ray-diffraction studies by Wilkins (Figure 2–5).

Autoradiography

A direct use of radiations in the study of biological molecules involves the incorporation of radioactive substances into the molecules and the detection of their presence by photographic techniques (*autoradiography*). The source of radiation in autoradiographic procedures is a radioactive isotope of an element. Most elements occur naturally in more than one form. The most abundant form is stable, while a small amount exists in an unstable form. Unstable isotopes of an element are so described because they disintegrate to a more stable form by losing energy. Thus they are radioactive. With hydrogen, as an example, the stable form contains one proton and one electron, and one of the unstable forms contains, in addition, two neutrons. In this unstable form of hydrogen, known as tritium (^3H), as a neutron changes to a proton and an electron, an energetic electron—a beta particle—is emitted. Accordingly, the kind of radiation emitted by this radioisotope of hydrogen is beta radiation.

Tritium is only one of several radioisotopes used for biological studies. For autoradiography, the most useful ones are beta emitters, including carbon-14, sulfur-35, phosphorus-32, iodine-131, iron-59, and calcium-45. Each of these isotopes has its own characteristic rate of decay or disintegration. The rate is measured as the half-life of the isotope, or the time it takes for one-half the atoms to distintegrate. In other words, the half-life is the time required for a given quantity of isotope to lose half its radioactivity. Tritium has a half-life of 12 years, carbon-14 a half-life of about 5600 years, sulfur-35 a half-life of 87 days, and phosphorus-32 a half-life of 14 days. The relatively weak beta emitters, which emit low energy electrons, are more valuable for autoradiography than the more energetic ones because they give better resolution. Weak beta emitters include tritium, carbon-14, and sulfur-35.

It is possible to substitute a radioactive isotope for its nonradioactive form in many compounds. Since only low level radiation is necessary, labeling a compound by substituting a single atom (or perhaps a few atoms) is usually enough. Radioactivity in a given compound or material can be detected in several ways. An instrument such as a Geiger counter or scintillation counter, which counts the number of disintegrations per unit time, measures the amount of radioactivity present in the material under study. Photographic methods lend themselves well to detection, and these are utilized in autoradiography. Photographic emulsions can be made to register electrons at almost any speed; they are quite sensitive. There is a high concentration of silver bromide (AgBr) in an emulsion, and on exposure to radiation, reduced silver grains appear on the film. The position of these black grains indicates the location of the radioactivity in the biological material, and the number of grains indicates the amount of radioactivity present. The latter relationship is dependent upon the concentration of isotope used, the half-life, the energy of the beta particles, the time of exposure, and the thicknesses of the section and the emulsion. Therefore, photographic methods have decided limitations for quantitative analyses.

When a labeled compound has been made available to a cell long enough for incorporation of the radioactive substance into the cell, the cell is fixed. The method of fixation depends on the chemical nature of the material being studied—whether it is protein, nucleic acid, lipid, or carbohydrate. If it is necessary to retain all of the radioactivity in the cell or to preserve enzymes, fixation by freeze-substitution or freeze-drying is quite successful. In freeze-drying, the cell or tissue is quickly frozen in isopentane at -160 to $-190°C$ and dehydrated in vacuo at -40 to $-60°C$. In freeze-substitution, which is particularly satisfactory, after rapid freezing the specimen is dehydrated in ethanol, methanol, or acetone at -20 to $-60°C$. This method is especially good for preserving phosphates but does not preserve lipids. It is of particular advantage for autoradiography because soluble substances are not extracted and there is relatively little change in chemical content.

It is desirable to have as thin a section of the specimen as possible, generally 5 to 7 μ. The cells may be embedded for sectioning, or, depending on the nature of the tissue, they may simply be smeared onto a slide. The emulsion used should also be quite thin, preferably about 5 μ. The specimen is first mounted on the slide and then coated with the emulsion. Usually the material can be stained prior to application of the emulsion to orient the grains with respect to the specimen. One widely used and effective technique is the *stripping film* method. A film consisting of an emulsion 5 μ thick with a gelatin base 10 μ thick for support is stripped from a glass plate and floated, emulsion side down, on the surface of water. It is then picked up on a slide on which the specimen has been mounted. In this case, the specimen may be stained before or after stripping film is added to the slide. The stripping film method has been especially valuable for the study of chromosome duplication and metabolism (Chapter 14).

The slide is kept in the dark long enough for proper exposure of the film. The time varies according to the isotope used, its concentration, and the thicknesses of the material and the emulsion and ranges from a few days to months. Following exposure, the film is developed with photographic reagents, usually at 18°C. The slide is then ready for microscopic examination.

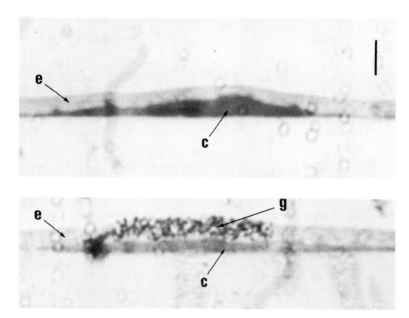

Figure 2–6. Transverse sections of autoradiographs of mouse L strain cells labeled with [³H]thymidine. The cultures were grown on the surface of polymerized Epon, the developed autoradiograph embedded in Epon, and sections cut at 1 μ. Top: Unlabeled cell; bottom: labeled cell. e, emulsion; g, grains; c, cell (line = 10 μ). Reproduced from *Thymidine Metabolism and Cell Kinetics,* by J. E. Cleaver, North-Holland Publishing Company, Amsterdam, 1967.

Recent development of liquid emulsions has been of particular value for combining autoradiography with electron microscopy. In this method, an extremely thin layer of emulsion can be applied to the specimen with a wire loop. Development of silver grains over the electron microscope image can give a resolution as good as 0.1 μ (Figure 2–6). Specimens to be studied with the light microscope can also be coated with liquid emulsion by dipping the slide (with its mounted or smeared tissue) into it.

The basic methodology of autoradiography often involves labeling a compound that is a precursor in the synthesis of another compound. For example, a study of RNA synthesis can be made by using orotic acid labeled with an isotope, since orotic acid is a precursor of RNA. For DNA synthesis, thymidine may be labeled (usually tritiated), and for protein synthesis, a specific amino acid may be labeled (Figure 2–7). With a series of section or smears of labeled tissue, it is possible to follow the fate of the label in different parts of the cell.

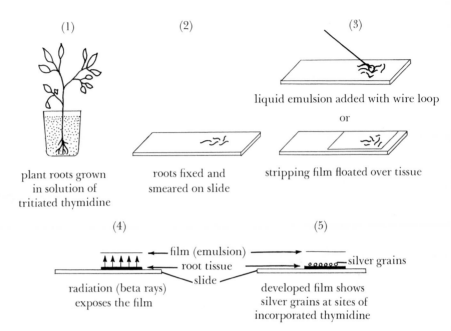

Figure 2–7. Procedure for autoradiography. The method is applicable to studies of proteins as well as nucleic acids.

Isolation of Cellular Components

The recovery of particulate components of cells for biochemical studies or in preparation for electron microscopy can be achieved with some facility. Nuclei, mitochondria, and other cell organelles can be removed from the cell and separated from each other by special methods.

First, the cell must be disrupted by removal of the cell boundaries to permit the release of the component structures. Depending on the material in question, one of three techniques may be used for this purpose: grinding in a mortar, homogenization in ground glass, or exposure to sonic vibrations. In most cases, disruption is best done at low temperatures, between 0 and 4°C, especially for the preservation of metabolic activity for subsequent study.

After cell disruption, the particulate components are separated from each other by high speed centrifugation, their separation being contingent on differences in size and specific gravity. Two principal methods are *dif-*

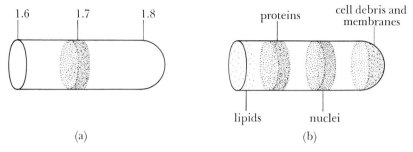

Figure 2–8. Isolation of subcellular components. (a) Cesium chloride (CsCl) density gradient. The density of the solution varies gradually from low to high. Particles having the same density as a specific region of the solution will be located at that point after prolonged centrifugation. An example is shown. (b) The result of centrifugation of homogenized cells layered on the top of a sucrose gradient. Fast-moving particles have reached the bottom of the tube, followed by slower-moving particles according to their rates of sedimentation. Redrawn from H. T. Epstein, *Elementary Biophysics*, 1963, Addison-Wesley, Reading, Mass.

ferential centrifugation and *gradient differential centrifugation*. The former depends on differences in sedimentation rate among the various components; the latter also involves a density gradient. In differential centrifugation, the heavier particles settle first, and then there is gradual separation by sedimentation of the light particles. For example, centrifugation at a speed 700 times gravity of a tissue homogenate suspended in 0.25 M sucrose results in the separation of nuclei. If the supernatant resulting from this centrifugation is centrifuged at about 5000 to 8500 times gravity, the mitochondria settle out of solution. At still higher speeds, other particulate components are separated. For example, the microsomal fraction in 0.25 M sucrose is recovered by 30 minute centrifugation at 100,000 times gravity. In gradient differential centrifugation, the homogenate is placed in a tube on top of a sucrose column, which is stratified— that is, the sucrose solution progressively increases in density from top to bottom. Upon centrifugation, cellular components having different sedimentation rates appear at different levels according to their size and specific gravity (Figure 2–8).

Specific procedures are followed for certain kinds of particulate or chemical components of cells. For example, retention of nucleoprotein material and enzymes of the nucleus is achieved by the method of Behrens. The tissue is lyophilized (freeze-dried) and suspended in a nonaqueous solvent (for nuclei, an ether–chloroform mixture or a benzene–carbon tetrachloride mixture); the cells are disrupted by grinding in a colloid mill or a mortar; and the nuclei are isolated by gradient differential centrifugation.

Fixation

Fixation of cells or tissues may be defined as the selective preservation of morphological organization and chemical content for microscopic observation. The major effects of fixing solutions may be summarized as follows: preventing bacterial decay and autolysis; rendering the cell contents insoluble; reducing cell shrinkage and distortion; increasing the visibility of the cell components; and preparing the cell components for stain.

The most reliable fixatives contain one or more substances that precipitate the proteins of the cell or render them insoluble without precipitating them. Depending upon the fixative and the conditions under which it is used, the solid phase of protoplasm separates from the aqueous phase as fibrils, granules, nets, or vacuoles. The separation of the solid phase is brought about essentially by the production of cross-linkages between the protein molecules, and the molecules are thereby stabilized for further treatment and observation. An important question is how closely the observed fixed structure resembles the structure in the living cell (and, in the extreme, whether this structure actually exists in the living cell or simply represents artifact). Since several methods are available for the observation of both preserved and living cells, an answer to this question is readily obtained.

The fixative used must be selected for its specific chemical activity so that the desired structures are preserved to the exclusion of other materials that might interfere with analysis. It is also necessary to avoid any destruction of the material to be studied and to distribute the effect of the fixative uniformly throughout the cell. Table 2–2 gives the effects and important applications of chemical fixatives. Although the table lists only two mixtures, many others are appropriate for both nuclear and cytoplasmic structures. The purpose of this table is primarily to acquaint the reader with the kinds of effects produced by some common fixing solutions and to indicate that they may be used in different combinations according to the need.

Other methods of fixation have been mentioned earlier, in connection with electron microscopy and autoradiography. These include freeze-drying and freeze-substitution, which are especially valuable for the preservation of enzymes and other protein material. In both techniques, the material is fixed by rapid freezing at temperatures between -160 and $-190°C$ in isopentane or propane cooled by liquid nitrogen. After freezing, the material is dried in a vacuum at -40 to $-60°C$ (freeze-drying) or treated with cold methanol, ethanol, or acetone to dissolve the ice crystals (freeze-substitution). In freeze-substitution, the crystals are replaced by the reagent used. Both of these methods have the advantages of producing little change in the chemical content of the cell after death, causing no shrinkage, and preserving structure.

A newer technique, with some similarities to freeze-drying, is called *freeze-etching*. First developed in 1957 for the electron microscopy of virus particles, it has recently been extended to higher organisms. The specimen is frozen in ice at $-100°C$, then cut under high vacuum at the same temperature. A thin film of ice is sublimated from the surface of the section, and the etched surface of the specimen is coated with carbon to obtain a

Table 2–2 Some Chemical Fixatives and Their Uses

Fixative	*Effects*	*Application*
acetic acid, 0.3–50% (used alone or in mixtures)	does not fix cytoplasmic proteins, precipitates nucleoproteins, destroys Golgi and mitochondria, swells and softens	with basic dyes; nucleus, chromosomes
potassium dichromate, 2–7% (used in mixtures)	renders proteins insoluble in water, fixes lipids, pH dependent	chromosomes, cytoplasmic structures
ethanol, 70–100% (used alone or in mixtures)	precipitates proteins, dissolves lipids, shrinks and hardens	with basic dyes; nucleus
formaldehyde, 4–10% (used in mixtures)	does not precipitate proteins, fixes lipids, hardens with no shrinkage	with basic dyes; Golgi, mitochondria, enzymes
osmium tetroxide 0.5–2% (used alone or in mixtures)	fixes lipids, causes blackening (osmium reduced to black oxides), makes staining difficult	cytoplasm, Golgi, mitochondria, fat
Bouin's solution (5 parts picric acid, 5 parts 40% formaldehyde, 1 part glacial acetic acid)	precipitates all proteins, shrinks and softens	chromosomes
Carnoy's solution (3 parts ethanol, 1 part glacial acetic acid)	combines properties of ethanol and acetic acid	nucleoproteins, chromosomes

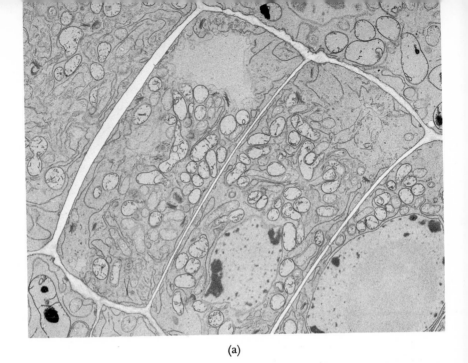

(a)

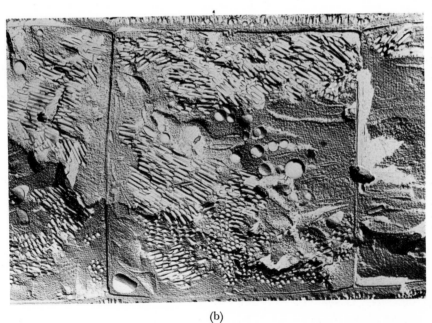

(b)

Figure 2–9. Comparison of conventional fixation with freeze-etching for electron microscopy. (a) Cells of *Vanilla planifolia* roots fixed with $KMnO_4$ ($\times 4200$). (b) Cell of the blue-green alga *Oscillatoria* prepared by freeze-etching ($\times 16,400$). (a) FROM H. H. Mollenhauer and D. A. Larson, *J. Ultrastruct. Res.*, **16**, 55 (1966); (b) FROM M. Jost, Dr. Thesis, ETH, Zurich, 1965.

carbon replica. After removal from the vacuum, and thawing, the specimen is removed from the replica film with concentrated acids. The released film (the carbon replica) is floated on water and prepared in the usual way for electron microscopy. The image produced is quite different from that after conventional fixation (Figure 2–9), and gives a view of ultrastructure in a three-dimensional manner. The advantages of the method include little loss of soluble material, and possibilities for quantitative studies and more precise measurement of dimensions as they occur in the living cell.

Following fixation for light microscopy, a specimen may be embedded in paraffin or some comparable substance and cut into thin sections on a microtome. If sections are prepared in this way, the specimen is stained after being placed on a slide, and the mount may be made permanent with a special mounting medium that gives a hard, protective coating to the section under the cover slip. Mounting media include diaphane, Permount, and balsam. Since each medium is compatible with certain solvents, the slide and specimen must be rinsed in a solvent or solvents before mounting. If diaphane is used, an absolute alcohol rinse is required before the medium is added, and if Permount is used, a toluene rinse is necessary after the alcohol rinse. The details of mounting procedures vary, depending on the methods of fixation and staining. Some tissue may be smeared or squashed directly on the slide instead of sectioned. These procedures will be described fully in Chapter 10.

Staining

The selection of a stain for the study of cells under the light microscope depends upon several factors. These include the nature of the material to be studied, the type and pH of the fixative used, and the chemical reactivity of the dye. In addition, the concentration of the dye and the temperature and pH at which it is most effective are important considerations. In general, the chemical reactions involve mainly the staining of proteins and nucleic acids. The dyes for staining cellular components contain two kinds of active chemical groups, *chromophoric* and *auxochromic* groups. Chromophoric groups impart color to the dye; examples are carboxyl ($-COOH$), azo ($-N{=}N-$), and nitro ($-NO_2$) groups. Auxochromic groups give the dye its ability to attach to the component and to dissolve and dissociate in water.

Dyes are usually classified as acidic or basic. An acidic dye has a greater combining capacity at low pH than a basic dye, and is generally used for staining the cytoplasm, particularly proteins. The net charge on the dye ion of an acidic dye is negative, and the color is carried by the anion. Although the dye, prepared as a sodium or potassium salt, is ordinarily neutral or slightly alkaline in reaction, it reacts with, and stains substances with, a basic reaction. A basic dye is generally used for staining the nucleus, particularly nucleic acids. The net charge on the dye ion is positive, and the color radical is the cation. Basic dyes are prepared as chloride or sulfate salts of mineral organic acids, and stain acidic substances. They are, in effect, dye salts of colorless acids. Some dyes, on the other hand, are neither acidic nor basic, the anion and cation both having the color property. Examples of acidic dyes are Acid Fuchsin, Congo Red, Janus Green B, Orange G, and methyl blue. Basic dyes include basic fuchsin, crystal violet, methyl green, and safranine. A substance that has an affinity for basic dyes is called *basiphilic,* and one that has an affinity for acid dyes is *acidiphilic.*

The acidic or basic character of a dye provides the chemical basis for a staining reaction, but there may be a physical basis as well. This is usually attributed to the adsorption of the dye at the surfaces or boundaries of cellular structures. Although adsorption is largely a physical event, chemical factors may also be involved. Variations in pH, fixation, and the use of mordants influence the adsorption of the stain. In certain instances, an additional substance is necessary to facilitate the dye reaction. Such substances, called *mordants,* normally consist of salts of di- and trivalent metals. The salt is capable of combining with both the protein of the cell and the dye used for staining. The term *lake* describes a combination of dye and mordant. Metallic hydroxides, for example, form lakes with certain dyes and attach the dye to the tissue or organelle. If the lake is insoluble in water, the mordant is used first, followed by the stain; otherwise, the mordant may be combined directly with the dye. The mordant is usually a double salt of potassium or ammonium with aluminum or ferric sulfate, which combines with the dye to produce a basic lake. Ferric ammonium sulfate is also known as iron alum. Examples of stains used in lakes or after mordanting are hematoxylin and carmine.

The fact that certain structures within a cell take up one or more particular dyes only rarely provides chemical or functional information about an organelle. In most instances, the staining reaction is relatively nonspecific in this respect. Moreover, the amount of dye taken up is not necessarily an indication of the amount of substance present, except in very special cases. One example, well documented, is that of a stain reaction for DNA, which will be described in Chapter 10.

Studies of the components of the cytoplasm and nucleus often concentrate on specific chemical composition and metabolic (enzymatic) activity. Stain techniques are available for the location and identification of nucleic acids, proteins, lipids, and carbohydrates. The morphology and behavior of the chromosomes in the nucleus are of particular interest, but consideration of these aspects of stain technology will be deferred until Chapter 10.

Some dyes change color upon reaction with cell components; the absorption spectrum of such a dye is different from that of the dye–substrate combination. This phenomenon is known as *metachromasia,* and the dyes are metachromatic. Most of the useful metachromatic dyes are basic, reacting with acidic substances. The color change appears to be due to the way in which the attachment occurs. The substrate tends to bind the dye as a dimer or polymer; the polymerized form of the dye may be responsible for the color change. The changes are unidirectional; a green dye becomes more blue, a blue dye becomes reddish, and a red dye becomes orange or yellow. Several of the metachromatic dyes, like thionine and Toluidine Blue, stain nucleoproteins. Azure B (trimethylthionine) has been demonstrated to stain sex chromosomes differentially when used at an acid pH. Since metachromatic dyes impart different colors to different substrates, they are helpful in delineating specific chemical substances in cells. A dye may also produce two colors within the cell. For example, with Toluidine Blue, cytoplasm stains blue because of its RNA content, while glycoproteins stain red.

The use of dyes involves two serious problems that have not been satisfactorily resolved. The stain reaction, to have any validity, must be specific, and the location of the colored product of the reaction must remain stable. These limitations should be kept in mind when these cytochemical techniques are employed for the study of chemical composition, organization, or activity of a cell.

Specific types of dyes, which become selectively bound to one or more molecules of a particular substance, are used for the demonstration of proteins, nucleic acids, lipids, and carbohydrates. Dyes producing a color change only in a specific substance are called *chromogenic agents.* Not only may they be used to determine the presence and location of a certain compound, but some are used for quantitative estimations. In this respect, it is often valuable to know how a given substance is related to other substances in the same cell and what, if any, effect its quantity has on the morphology of the structure in which it is located. Unfortunately, the limitations of quantitative cytochemistry are even greater than those of qualitative cytochemistry.

Cells may be stained for cytochemical investigations either with or without fixation, depending upon the chemical nature of the material to be observed. Stains applied to unfixed cells for the detection of specific structures or specific chemical substances are known as *vital* stains. One of the most widely used vital stains is Janus Green B. When it is first introduced into a cell, it stains all of the cell components green, since it is maintained in its oxidized state. After a short time, however, it is reduced to its colorless form in all parts of the cell except the mitochondria, where it is reoxidized by cytochrome oxidase (an enzyme that takes part in the terminal stages of cellular respiration) and retains its color. This is one of several methods for the determination of enzymatic activity in cells. Other vital stains include neutral red, for plant vacuoles, and methylene blue, for dividing cells.

Fixed cells are often required for observations of nonenzymatic proteins. Some of the relevant methods are restricted to specific proteins or amino acids, but others are quite general, measuring only total nonenzymatic protein content or distribution. In any case, the composition and pH of the fixative are important considerations in selecting the stain since they affect the staining capacity of the specimen. For instance, formaldehyde increases the tendency of protein to accept basic dyes, whereas mercuric compounds increase the tendency of protein to accept acidic dyes. Potassium dichromate ($K_2Cr_2O_7$) fixatives are effective in the cytoplasm at a pH higher than 4.6 and in the nucleus at a pH lower than 4.6. Therefore the specificity of a stain for the nucleus or cytoplasm depends in part on fixative pH. The intensity of the stain reaction with an acidic or basic dye depends also on the acidity or alkalinity of the medium; that is, the stain reaction is pH dependent. A striking example is the contrast in effects of Orange G, an acidic dye, which has its greatest binding at a pH of 1 to 2, and methylene blue, a basic dye, which binds best at a pH of 10 to 11. Thus two factors are critical in stain procedures, the fixative and the pH.

Stains for total protein analysis include Naphthol Yellow S and mercuric bromophenol blue. These dyes are specific for the basic amino acids lysine, arginine, and histidine. The complex formed with Naphthol Yellow S has an absorption peak of 4350 Å and can be used quantitatively to some extent in photometric methods, which are based on the theory that

Table 2–3   Some Cytochemical Tests for Protein

Stain	Reacts with
diazonium hydroxide	histidine, tyrosine, tryptophan
mercury orange	protein containing —SH
Millon reagent	tyrosine
Sakaguchi reagent	arginine

the amount of light absorbed is proportional to the number of absorbing molecules present in the sample. Very few stain reactions have been shown to exhibit this relationship. Bromophenol blue, since it is an acidic dye, has a disadvantage in that its reaction with protein is influenced by the presence or absence of RNA. A specific reaction for histone protein is possible with Fast Green at pH 8.1 after the removal of nucleic acid with trichloroacetic acid at 90°C. Other dyes specific for certain amino acids are listed in Table 2–3.

The Feulgen reaction for DNA will be discussed in detail in Chapter 10 in connection with methods for staining chromosomes. There are, of course, other stains that react with DNA. Methyl green–pyronine, for example, stains DNA green and RNA red. The specificity of this reaction can be supplemented by treatment with ribonuclease for the removal of RNA. With other dyes this type of enzymatic treatment is necessary for distinguishing between DNA and RNA, since both may take the same stain. Generally, basic dyes and ribonuclease treatment are used for RNA detection. Azure B has been used for quantitative determinations of RNA, but there are difficulties in this direction because of the relatively wide distribution of RNA in the cell.

Several fat-soluble dyes effectively demonstrate lipid material in the cell. Among these are Sudan Black B, which is relatively specific for phospholipid and has been used as a stain for Golgi structures. Osmium tetroxide also produces a "stain" reaction in Golgi structures, as a result of the formation of black oxides of osmium. Sudan Red is another dye for lipid substances. Fatty acids, such as stearic and palmitic acids, respond to a direct application of Schiff reagent (leucobasic fuchsin); this is called the *plasmal* reaction.

The periodic acid–Schiff (PAS) reaction is utilized for the demonstration of polysaccharide materials, such as starch, cellulose, and hemicelluloses in plant cells and mucoproteins and chitin in animal cells. The reaction involves the hydrolysis of carbon bonds (C—C) by periodic acid (HIO_4) to form dialdehydes (CHO—CHO). Upon addition of Schiff reagent, the specimen takes on a red color due to the presence of the aldehydes.

The cytochemistry of enzymes is somewhat more difficult than that of nonenzymatic material because of enzyme sensitivity to reagents. Chromogenic agents used for enzyme studies may catalyze a specific reaction involving the enzyme or enzymes or accept electrons at a certain step in a series of enzymatic reactions. In many studies of enzyme activity, tissue is incubated with a substrate for the enzyme under consideration. The Gomori method for phosphatases is an example of this approach. A substrate, such as glycerophosphate, is made available to tissue. If alkaline phosphatase is present, hydrolysis of the substrate occurs and a calcium phosphate precipitate forms. The calcium phosphate may be made visible by treatment first with cobalt ion (cobalt nitrate) and then with sulfide ion (ammonium sulfide) to produce a black cobalt sulfide, or the calcium phosphate may be examined directly under the interference microscope. Gomori's method for esterases is based on principles similar to those for the phosphatase determination. Various microscopic methods, particularly fluorescence microscopy, may be utilized in other cytochemical studies.

Methods for the detection of oxidases may involve specific stain reactions. The demonstration of enzyme activity in the mitochondria, which contain a complex of oxidative enzymes, is possible by the following technique. The colorless tetrazolium salt is reduced to the colored form, a formazan, by electrons accepted from dehydrogenases. That is, in the presence of succinic dehydrogenase, for example, tetrazolium is converted into a form that is cytologically detectable. In another technique the oxidation of the Nadi reagent results in the formation of indophenol blue, a colored substance. This reaction is due to the activity of cytochrome oxidase, also present in mitochondria.

SELECTED READING

Baker, J. R., *Principles of Biological Microtechnique*, Wiley, New York, 1958.

Baker, J. R., *Cytological Technique*, 5th ed., Methuen, London, 1966.

Bourne, G. H., ed., *Cytology and Cell Physiology*, 3rd ed., Academic Press, New York, 1964.

Brachet, J., and A. E. Mirsky, eds., *The Cell*, Vol. 1, Academic Press, New York, 1959.

Caro, L., "Progress in High Resolution Autoradiography," in J. A. V. Butler and H. E. Huxley, eds., *Progress in Biophysics and Molecular Biology*, Vol. 16, Pergamon Press, New York, 1966, pp. 171–91.

Danielli, J. F., ed., *General Cytochemical Methods*, Vols. 1 and 2, Academic Press, New York, 1958 and 1961.

Frey-Wyssling, A., "Freeze-etching, a Method of Obtaining True-to-Life Electron Micrographs of Ultrastructures," *Advan. Sci.*, 23(109), 109 (1966).

Gray, P., *The Use of the Microscope*, McGraw-Hill, New York, 1967.

Mellors, R. C., ed., *Analytical Cytology*, 2nd ed., McGraw-Hill, New York, 1959.

Oster, G., and A. W. Pollister, eds., *Physical Techniques in Biological Research*, Vols. 1–3, Academic Press, New York, 1955–1956.

Sharma, A. K., and A. Sharma, *Chromosome Techniques*, Butterworths, London, 1965.

Cell Boundaries

The outermost limits of a cell are composed of living or nonliving materials or both. Whatever their chemical constitution and structural organization, their functions include regulating the flow of materials into and out of the cell and providing some degree of support and maintenance of cell shape and cell size. Every cell has a *plasma membrane,* which is the living boundary of the cytoplasm. The plasma membrane is a thin, delicate structure with specific chemical and physical properties that remain relatively consistent in the great variety of cells and organisms. Some animal cells have one or more layers of nonliving material outside their plasma membranes. Such layers, most of which consist of protein and carbohydrate compounds, comprise walls of varying composition. The eggs of a number of marine animals—for example the sea urchin—are coated with *mucin,* a glycoprotein. In the Crustacea, the cell surfaces produce the substance chitin (Figure 1–8), which is a polymer of glucosamine, another protein–carbohydrate complex. The chitinous walls of Crustacea and certain layers of plant cell walls also require calcium ions for stability. Walls with outer nonliving layers are characteristic of many animals, but they are not essential to the life of the cell, although they may provide protection for the cell under certain environmental conditions, by serving as a filter, for example.

The Plant Cell Wall

The cells of all members of the plant kingdom are bounded by nonliving walls. Cell shape and size and tissue construction depend upon the presence of these walls, and the organization of the wall material determines certain functional attributes of specific cell types. Some cell walls are of greater thickness than others, and the pattern of wall thickening is characteristic for different cells. Parenchyma cells, which are undifferentiated living cells found in a variety of positions in the body of higher plants, have relatively thin cell walls, as do *meristematic* (dividing) cells. The water-conducting cells of the higher plants, found in the xylem tissue, have much thicker cell walls, with more elaborate construction. Still other cells, such as those found in supporting tissue, may have special thickened places in the corners of their cell walls.

The traditional classroom studies of osmosis in plant cells demonstrate that the cell maintains its shape and size even though water may be lost in considerable quantities. This behavior is attributed to the rigidity of the cell wall and to the fact that the water comes from within the limits of the plasma membrane, specifically from the vacuole or vacuoles of the protoplast (living portion of the cell); the cell wall maintains its structure but is quite permeable to liquids, allowing relatively free diffusion through it. In spite of this gross observation made with the light microscope, there may be some alteration in shape or size of the cell due to changes in the water content of the cell wall. Such an alteration, however, is not usually perceived under the light microscope.

Morphology

The initial wall of a plant cell is the *primary wall,* the outermost layer of the cell. The primary walls of adjacent cells do not lie in direct contact with each other, but are separated by a shared wall layer, the *middle lamella* (Figure 3–1). In a young or immature cell, such as is found in

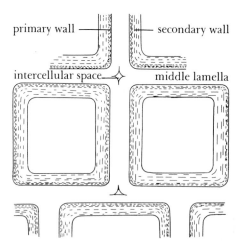

primary wall ——————— secondary wall

intercellular space———⟨⟩   middle lamella

Figure 3–1. Gross structure of a plant cell wall.

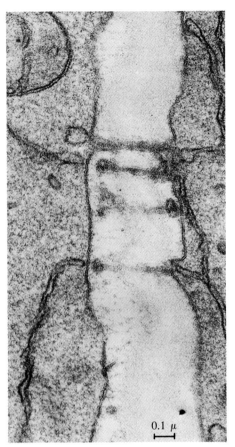

Figure 3-2. Plasmodesmata showing strands of the endoplasmic reticulum in the cell wall of the root
cortex in *Ricinus* (×60,000). FROM
A. Frey-Wyssling and K. Mühlethaler, *Ultrastructural Plant Cytology*, Elsevier, Amsterdam, 1965,
p. 302.

0.1 μ

meristem and parenchyma, the primary wall and middle lamella represent the full extent of wall development. A more specialized cell, such as
a xylem vessel, may exhibit additional wall deposits, which form on the
inner surface of the primary wall. The addition of new layers of wall
material comprises a *secondary wall*. The thickenings mentioned earlier
are due to the development of a secondary cell wall. In tracheids, the principal water-conducting cells of gymnosperms, a *tertiary wall* becomes the
innermost layer of the cell wall. The tertiary wall often bears on its surface "warts" or small swellings. Although the chemical organization of
the tertiary wall is not as clearly defined as that of the primary or secondary wall, it may be composed of the hemicellulose xylan.

When the middle lamella and primary walls develop, there remain
openings in the walls between adjacent cells. These pores allow the passage of materials between cells, and it is often possible to observe cytoplasmic material or strands (*plasmodesmata*) passing through (Figure 3-2).

There is some evidence that the plasmodesmata include actual connections between the cytoplasmic membrane systems of the adjacent cells and that they permit the movement of gases and nutrient materials from cell to cell with relative ease. In young cells, the pores are small. In more mature or specialized cells, such as vessels and tracheids, both of which conduct water in xylem tissue, the pores are large and may have additional wall modifications around their periphery. The large pores in the cell walls are called *pits*.

Chemistry

Water constitutes about 90% of the volume of the material of the cell wall, and, as will be shown later, plays an important part in the potential elastic properties of the wall. The primary cell wall is composed essentially of cellulose and hemicelluloses, complex carbohydrates, but it may have additional carbohydrate substances embedded between the cellulose fibrils (Table 3–1). Cellulose (Figure 1–8) is a polymer of the disaccharide *cellobiose,* of which the basic unit is glucose. Thus the long-chain cellulose is composed of glucose units, which are bound as cellobiose molecules linked at their end hydroxyl groups. Although the length of the chain varies, there may be as many as 3000 glucose residues per cellulose chain. The chain molecules of cellulose occur in parallel bundles of about 2000 chains, each bundle having a diameter of 100 to 250 Å. Each bundle of 2000 comprises a single *microfibril.* Many microfibrils arranged in parallel comprise a *macrofibril,* which can be seen under the light microscope.

Table 3–1   Average Composition of a Primary Cell Wall*

Substance	Fresh cell wall, wt %	Dry, wt %
Water	60.0	
Hemicelluloses	21.2	53.0
Pectic substances	2.0	5.0
Cellulose	12.0	30.0
Protein	2.0	5.0
Lipids	2.8	7.0

* From G. Setterfield and S. T. Bayley, *Ann. Rev. Plant Physiol.,* **12,** 35 (1961).

In the primary walls of higher plants, the microfibrils are somewhat loosely organized and scattered, permitting the deposition of other carbohydrate materials within the spaces between the microfibrils. These other wall materials may include *hemicelluloses, pectins,* and *lignin.* Hemicelluloses consist of pentoses (arabinose and xylose) and hexoses (mannose and galactose), and their presence depends upon the type of cell in question; many cells are devoid of them. The hemicellulose xylan is found particularly in woody tissue, and as much as 50% of the cell wall may be hemicellulose in collenchyma, which is supporting tissue. Whereas the microfibrils of higher plant cell walls are made exclusively of cellulose, those in the algae may contain some hemicellulose. In other cells, hemicelluloses are utilized as storage materials.

The pectins are most commonly found in the middle lamella. The basic chemical unit of pectin is the carbohydrate galacturonic acid, which is capable of forming salts with calcium and magnesium. A calcium-containing pectin is the principal component of the middle lamella of most plant cell walls, but it is also found in the primary walls and the outermost layers of the secondary walls of some cells. In primary walls, pectins occur in layers between the cellulose microfibrils. In secondary walls, which consist primarily of cellulose, there may also be deposits of lignin, especially in the more specialized cells and in places where several cells lie side by side. Other secondary wall materials are cutin and suberin, which are generally found on cells at the plant surfaces, such as the epidermal cells of the leaf and stem.

The fine structure of a cell wall is dependent in part upon its chemical organization and the manner in which additional wall materials are deposited on the inner surface of the primary wall. In the primary wall, the microfibrils lie one on top of the other rather than enmeshed or intertwined. As new microfibrils are formed, they lie on top of the older ones. This pattern of growth provides a rather loose arrangement of fibrils in the primary wall of a higher plant. The formation of the secondary wall also proceeds by the apposition of the microfibrils. However, the fibrils of the secondary wall are more closely packed than those of the primary wall and are usually arranged in parallel order only, because of their high cellulose content. That is, most of the fibrils of the secondary wall lie parallel to each other, which is not necessarily the case in the primary wall (Figure 3–3).

The phenomenon of cell growth and elongation remains a puzzle. The elasticity of the wall is due to the activity of *auxins,* or plant hormones, but it is not clear how the auxins affect the wall. It seems likely that the effect is indirect rather than direct, one possibility being a general

(a)

(b)

Figure 3–3. Fibril arrangements in the cell wall of *Valonia* (×12,000): (a) dispersed in the primary wall; (b) parallel in the secondary wall. FROM A. Frey-Wyssling and K. Mühlethaler, *Ultrastructural Plant Cytology,* Elsevier, Amsterdam, 1965, p. 298.

stimulation of cellular metabolism. In this event, the elasticity of the wall may increase and thus facilitate its uptake of water, which leads to elongation of the cell. Water absorption, however, appears to be more passive than active with respect to the behavior of the wall. Recent studies have provided some information about the chemistry of cell wall expansion. There is evidence that the middle lamella contains, in addition to the carbohydrate material, a protein component. The protein may serve to bind calcium in the middle lamella, and the auxins may bind, or chelate, the metal ion away from the protein. In this way, the elasticity of the wall may be increased. If this hypothesis receives further substantiation, the effect of auxins on cell elongation will be considered as a direct effect on the chemical organization of the cell wall, since certain auxins have chelating activity.

In spite of the fact that no regular correlation exists between cell wall synthesis and cell elongation, some relationships have been found. In general, enlargement of a cell tends to stimulate synthesis of wall material. Although a relatively small percentage of the new wall material is incorporated into the existing structure of the wall (most new material is added by apposition), this tends to encourage expansion of the wall by altering the polysaccharide bonding. An auxin (such as indoleacetic acid) appears to promote the synthesis of new wall material in this manner, and consequently increases the rate of elongation. In addition, the experimental use of ethylenediaminetetraacetic acid (EDTA), a chelating agent, results in the loosening of cell wall material and the separation of cells. This reaction indicates that metal ions (for example, Ca^{++} and Mg^{++}) are important in binding wall materials in the cellulose wall of each cell as well as in the middle lamella. The binding sites include pectins in the middle lamella and protein in the primary and secondary walls.

In algae, the growth or expansion of a cell wall is marked by a tearing of the outer material and the addition of new material on the inner surface. In higher plants, tearing is rare; instead there appear to be a loosening of the fibrils and a reorientation in the direction of elongation. The new fibrils forming on the inner surface become oriented in the same direction.

Origin

In Chapter 1, reference was made to the endoplasmic reticulum as a complex array of double membranes in the cytoplasm of the cell. These membranes are similar in structure and chemical make-up to the plasma membrane and other cell organelles. There is now very good reason to

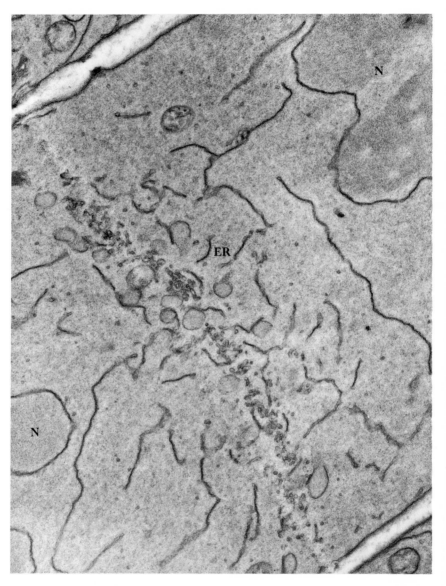

Figure 3–4. Formation of the cell plate during mitosis in the onion root tip. ER, endoplasmic reticulum; N, nucleus. FROM K. R. Porter and R. Machado, *J. Biophys. Biochem. Cytol.,* **7,** 167 (1960).

state that the endoplasmic reticulum plays an important role in the formation of the middle lamella and the new cell wall as cell division is concluded. Electron microscopic studies of cell division in the root tip cells of *Allium cepa* have provided direct observation of the formation of the *cell plate* at the end of cell division. The cell plate develops across the equator of the dividing cell to separate the cytoplasms of the daughter cells and eventually contributes to the formation of the middle lamella. A new primary wall arises on the inner surface of the middle lamella in each of the two daughter cells.

After the chromosomes have separated into two groups at opposite ends of the dividing cell, three types of structures appear to congregate at the equator of the cell. One type consists of short double-membrane units of the endoplasmic reticulum, which have migrated from the periphery of the cell (Figure 3–4). A second type consists of small vesicles of about 20 mμ diameter, which line up along the equator, starting at the center of the cell and gradually developing across it, to separate the cytoplasm into two parts. The vesicles fuse with one another and with small elements of the endoplasmic reticulum to form an almost continuous membrane-like structure across the cell (Figure 3–5). This is the cell plate, the origin of the middle lamella. The vesicles are rich in pectin, as would be expected from the chemical composition of the middle lamella. At a few points along the cell plate, fusion is incomplete, leaving pores between the adjacent daughter cells. Later observation reveals plasmodesmata extending through these pores. Elements of the endoplasmic reticulum seem to be associated with the plasmodesmata. The third type of structure in the

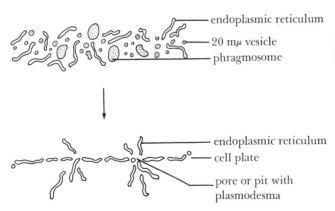

Figure 3–5. Formation of the cell plate in a plant cell.

equatorial region of the cell prior to cell plate formation is the *phragmosome*. Several phragmosomes arise on either side of the row of small vesicles and in association with the elements of the endoplasmic reticulum. The phragmosomes are about 250 mμ in diameter, with an outer membranous layer surrounding rather structureless or slightly granular contents. The density of the phragmosomes is much greater than that of the small vesicles that make up the cell plate. The phragmosomes disappear from the equator with the final separation of the daughter cytoplasms, and one view is that they contribute in some way to the formation of the middle lamella.

The origin of the small 20 mμ vesicles is not known, although studies on the epidermal cells of maize roots indicate that the Golgi apparatus is responsible for their production (Figure 3–6). It has also been suggested that the vesicle membranes contribute, via cell plate formation, to the organization of the new plasma membranes. The phragmosomes may be the result of envelopment of synthetic products of the cell by elements of the endoplasmic reticulum. At the same time, observations on maize roots

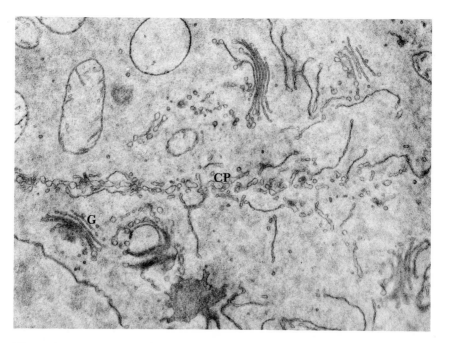

Figure 3–6. Golgi apparatus as the origin of cell plate vesicles in corn root. CP, cell plate; G, Golgi. FROM W. G. Whaley and H. H. Mollenhauer, *J. Cell Biol.,* **17,** 216 (1963).

indicate that the Golgi secretes material into some of the vesicles and that this material can be identified in newly formed cell walls. The entire structural arrangement at the cell equator during division of the cytoplasm may be homologous with the *phragmoplast* of classical botany. The phragmoplast has been described with the light microscope as a barrelshaped structure that appears near the end of cell division perpendicular to the spindle. It has not been observed in this form with the electron microscope.

The Plasma Membrane

Since the cell contains many membranes in varying configurations, and since these membranes are closely related to each other structurally and functionally, the term *cell membrane* is rather ambiguous. Therefore, the term *plasma membrane* will be used to describe that cell membrane which serves as the boundary of the cytoplasm. This membrane lies between the cell wall and the cytoplasm in plant cells, and it is the outer limiting membrane of most animal cells. Many botanists prefer the term *plasmalemma* to plasma membrane. Little doubt remains that every living cell has a plasma membrane, but its structure has not been investigated in every type of cell because of problems of technique; the plasma membrane is extremely difficult to isolate intact from a living cell. The electron microscope has aided greatly, however, in the study of this submicroscopic structure. In most cells the plasma membrane is not readily visible under the light microscope, although it is almost invariably assumed to be present by most observers. If at all visible, it appears simply as a very thin line at the surface of the cytoplasm or just inside the cell wall.

The mammalian red blood cell and the myelin sheath of the nerve fiber (Figure 3–7) have provided the bulk of information regarding the structure and properties of the plasma membrane. Fortunately, through modern techniques permitting observations of many other cell types, considerable evidence is accumulating to support the findings on these two cells as applicable to others. The red blood cell can be so treated as to remove all but the plasma membrane for electron microscopy and physiological studies. The residue of such treatment has been designated as the *ghost,* presumably representing the plasma membrane. Ponder and others, however, have raised objections on the grounds that there is no direct proof that the ghost is a true likeness of the plasma membrane as it occurs in the living cell. At least one author has suggested that the ghost is simply an artifact of the technique used in attempting to recover the plasma membrane. Nevertheless, the abundant studies with the red cell and nerve

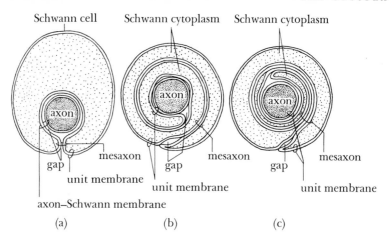

Schwann cell   Schwann cytoplasm   Schwann cytoplasm

axon   axon   axon

gap   mesaxon   gap   mesaxon   gap   mesaxon

unit membrane   unit membrane   unit membrane

axon–Schwann membrane

(a)   (b)   (c)

Figure 3–7. Diagram of the development of the myelinated peripheral nerve. The myelin sheath consists of unit membranes in close apposition. Adaptation of Fig. 7 (p. 72) by J. David Robertson in *Molecular Organization and Biological Function,* edited by John M. Allen, Harper & Row, New York, 1967.

cell and now with other cells have established a basic framework of information about the plasma membrane.

Chemistry

The uptake of osmium tetroxide or lead compounds by the plasma membrane is indicative of the presence of lipid compounds. Lipids identified in the plasma membrane include lecithin, cephalin, and cholesterol. They are arranged in parallel chains in a double (bimolecular) layer, with their hydrophobic, nonpolar ends adjoining each other and their hydrophilic, polar ends associated with protein (Figure 3–8). The double layer of chains may be held together by van der Waals forces at the nonpolar ends. The binding of the protein and lipid components may be by hydrogen bonds, ionic linkages, or electrostatic forces. This arrangement is typical of lipoprotein systems, and although many questions exist concerning its specifics, the description given here is becoming well substantiated experimentally.

Phospholipid is the major type of lipid found associated with the proteins in the plasma membrane. In the red blood cell, the amino acid composition of the protein component of the membrane includes relatively large amounts of arginine and lysine, in addition to histidine, tyrosine, tryptophan, methionine, and a small amount of cysteine. Whereas the amino acid content is apparently constant in one type of cell, it may vary in different cell types or in the same type of cell in different mammals. Moreover, the protein of the outer layer appears to differ from that of the inner layer. The protein is acidic in nature and constitutes from 20 to 74% of the membrane. In the rat, for example, the highest proportion of protein is found in the intestinal microvilli, and the lowest in myelin. This difference also reflects functional specificity, since the membranes of cells lining the intestine are more active in the transport of materials across them. In the mammalian erythrocyte, the ratio of protein to lipid is approximately 1.6 : 1 by weight. More variable than either the lipid or protein content of these membranes is the amount of water present. However, in most examinations, less than 25% of the content is water. Bell has suggested that a polysaccharide is present in the outer protein layer of the plasma membrane and that it serves to confer some stability to the lipoprotein complex. Additionally, he has suggested that the phragmosomes, mentioned in connection with the formation of the middle lamella, may in fact be of polysaccharide composition and aid in the formation of the new plasma membrane on reaction with lipoprotein.

The organization of the lipid and protein components of the membrane shown in Figure 3–8 includes a possible arrangement of small pores. In this figure, the pores have a protein surface, the protein occurring as a continuation of the outer layers in this molecular configuration.

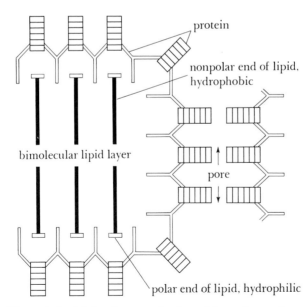

Figure 3–8. Molecular organization of the unit membrane.

Morphology

The molecular model of the plasma membrane in Figure 3–8 is quite consistent with the structure observed under the electron microscope. The *unit membrane* proposed by Robertson consists of two dense layers, each about 20 Å thick, enclosing a less dense area about 35 Å across, for a total thickness of 75 Å or more. Although the plasma membrane is difficult to see in many kinds of cells, Robertson's model fits well other cell membranes, such as the endoplasmic reticulum, with which the plasma membrane is often closely associated. In the application of this unit membrane structure to the lipoprotein organization, the outer and inner dense layers represent the protein, and the interior region the bimolecular layer of phospholipid (Figure 3–9).

Measurements of the plasma membranes of different mammalian cells show that some variations exist. For example, the plasma membrane of a rabbit erythrocyte has a thickness of about 215 Å, somewhat greater than would be expected on the basis of the size of the unit membrane. However, the red cell membranes of mammals may be significantly different in this respect from most other cell types. Furthermore, certain cells may have more complex structures than others, such as the intestinal epithelium in which the plasma membrane is 105 Å thick, with the outer two layers each 40 Å thick and the less dense layer in between 25 Å thick.

The similarity of the plasma membrane to the other membranes of the cell is supported by their chemical composition (lipoprotein) as well as their structural organization. However, the plasma membrane evidently

Figure 3–9. Unit membrane boundary of the human red blood cell (×280,000). FROM J. D. Robertson in M. Locke, ed., *Cellular Membranes in Development,* Academic Press, New York, 1964, p. 3.

(a)

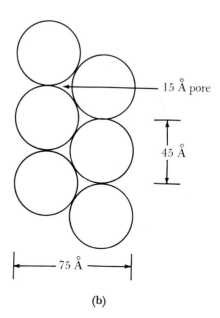

15 Å pore

45 Å

75 Å

(b)

Figure 3–10. Ultrastructure of the plasma membrane. (a) Plasma membrane of yeast prepared by freeze-etching (×118,800). Note the globular arrays and folds in the membrane. (b) Model of substructure of the plasma membrane according to Frey-Wyssling. (a) FROM H. Moor and K. Mühlethaler, *J. Cell Biol.,* **17,** 609 (1963); (b) based on A. Frey-Wyssling and K. Mühlethaler, *Ultrastructural Plant Cytology,* Elsevier, Amsterdam, 1965, pp. 150–52.

varies more in thickness in different cell types than do the other membrane systems. Such differences may be due to variations in the proportion and types of phospholipids present. Another characteristic of some of these membranes, particularly in the nuclear envelope, is the presence of pores or discontinuities in their surfaces. In the plasma membrane only very small pores have been observed, none of greater diameter than 10 Å; the pores of the nuclear envelope are considerably larger. The size of a pore in the plasma membrane actually may vary, however, since it has been postulated that the pores are open or closed depending upon specific metabolic conditions during the transport of materials. The pores may be lined by positively charged groups, since cations are excluded from them.

Recent studies, particularly those employing the freeze-etching technique in electron microscopy, have implied a more complex ultrastructure. According to Frey-Wyssling, the granular pattern at the surface of the plasma membrane illustrated in Figure 3–10a suggests a hexagonal array of globular macromolecules, each 40 to 50 Å in diameter (Figure 3–10b). Robertson, on the other hand, considers that the substructure includes hexagonal subunits with diameters greater than 100 Å involving only the nonlipid layers of the membrane. At present, however, there is no compelling evidence that seriously alters the concept of the unit membrane structure.

Surface Variations

Infoldings or invaginations of the plasma membrane into the cytoplasm are present in many kinds of cells. At certain loci, the infolded plasma membrane may be connected with the endoplasmic reticulum, providing direct channels into and out of the cytoplasm. The cells of intestinal epithelium provide a good example of infolding; the folds at the cell surface are known as *microvilli,* and there may be as many as 3000 in a single cell (Figure 3–11). The microvilli serve in the same capacity as the intestinal villi, namely, they increase the surface area for absorption. In other cells, the invaginated membrane forms pockets or chambers in which are located mitochondria (Figure 3–12). The close association with mitochondria in both cases suggests that the transport of materials across the plasma membrane may be facilitated by the energy available from the mitochondria. The role of energy-rich systems and enzymes in the movement of materials through the membrane will be discussed later. The invaginations of the membrane are involved in the transport of substances, since small droplets are often seen near the membrane and surrounded by elements of the membrane.

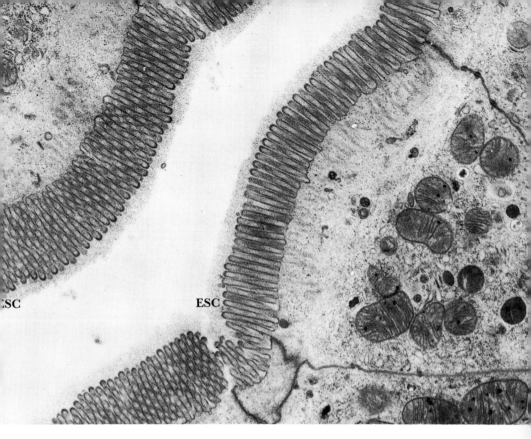

ESC

ESC

Figure 3–11. Microvilli in the intestinal epithelium of the bat (×21,000). ESC, enteric surface coat. Micrograph by S. Ito, from D. W. Fawcett, *J. Histochem. Cytochem.*, **13**, 75 (1965); © 1965, The Williams & Wilkins Co., Baltimore, Md. 21202.

Studies of the relations between the plasma membranes of adjacent cells have revealed several interesting features. The average distance separating the membranes of adjacent cells is 110 to 150 Å. There may be some cementing substance between, but the evidence for this is weak. However, substances like hyaluronic acid or chondroitin sulfuric acid are found as coating material on many cells. Mucopolysaccharide has been suggested as a substance that could account for the specificity of cell association. A curious aspect of cell association is the fact that like cells are found in contiguous relation. The underlying cause of this apparent selection or attraction of like cells is not known, although differences in surface charge may be responsible. Another possibility is that surface antigens of high specificity are present on the membranes; these antigens would be different for different cell types. Presumably, their specifiicity is under nuclear control. Of particular interest is the observation that cancer cells lose the property of specific adhesion. Other forces of possible importance

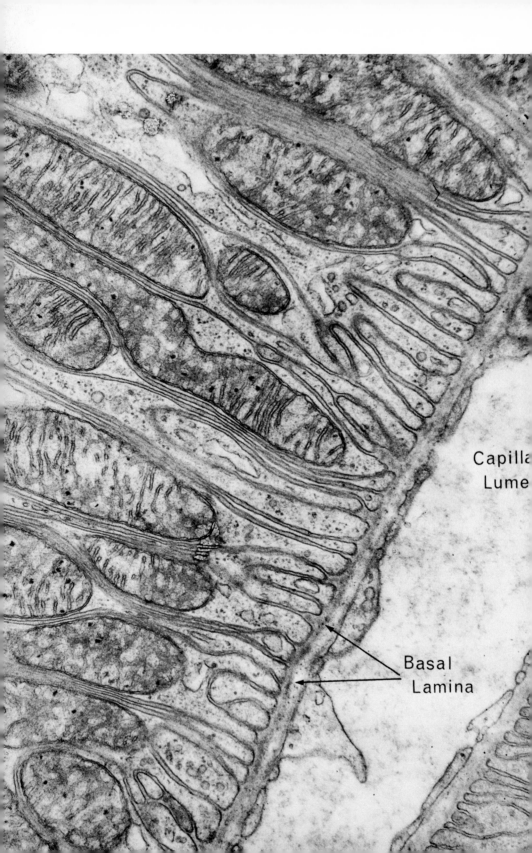

Capilla
Lume

Basal
Lamina

Figure 3–12. Invaginated surface membrane with associated mitochondria in a kidney tubule of the guinea pig ($\times$31,500). CL, capillary lumen. Micrograph by A. Ichikawa, from *An Atlas of Fine Structure: The Cell, Its Organelles and Inclusions* by D. W. Fawcett. W. B. Saunders Company, Philadelphia, 1966.

in cell adhesion include van der Waals forces, surface tension, or specific chemical bonds, for example, with hydrogen or calcium. Yet the 150 Å spacing between cells makes the latter very unlikely.

The membranes of adjacent cells seldom adjoin along a straight line but rather exhibit interdigitations, comparable to the infoldings of a membrane. In some regions the membranes are widely separated, leaving intercellular spaces of wide diameter. In still other regions the cells are so closely and tightly adjoined that early observations gave the impression of direct connections between the membranes. More careful examination has shown that such connections are rare. They do exist as plasmodesmata and in some sperm cells. On the other hand, in many animal cells, thickenings appear on the inner surfaces of adjacent plasma membranes in the regions of strong binding. A number of fine filaments radiate from the thickened areas toward the interior of the cell (Figure 3–13). The thickened regions of the membranes with their extensions or filaments are referred to as *desmosomes*. The desmosomes are located on the inner surface of the membrane in each cell and appear to form through the apposition of some extra material on the membrane rather than through a thickening of the membrane itself. The outer surface of the membrane in each cell remains unaffected.

A report by Fawcett relates that direct cell connections have been observed during spermatogenesis in *Hydra, Drosophila,* the rat, rabbit, cat, pig, monkey, and man. Classically, the descriptions of spermatogenesis have stated that the cells of each succeeding meiotic division are separate and independent throughout the cycle. Fawcett, however, states that the primary spermatocytes (Chapter 13) are joined, as well as the four secondary spermatocytes and the spermatids. Ultimately, the spermatids separate as individual spermatozoa. The cytoplasmic bridges are quite broad, 5000 to 10,000 Å in diameter, and there is only one bridge between any two cells.

Cytoplasmic connections during pollen grain formation in plants have been demonstrated by Heslop-Harrison and others (Figure 3–14). Channels as wide as 15,000 Å occur in pollen mother cells and persist into the early stages of meiosis. In some instances, continuity of the endoplasmic reticulum can be seen between the adjacent cells. Although few plants have been studied in this respect, the pattern may be common to most higher plants.

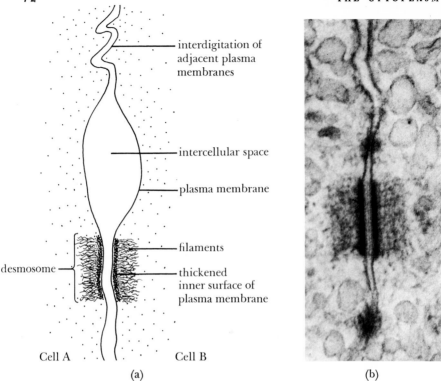

Figure 3–13. (a) Portions of two adjacent cells, showing the intercellular space, a desmosome, and a region of interdigitation of plasma membranes. (b) Desmosome in adjacent plasma membranes of two endothelial cells in an arterial capillary of the *retia mirabilia* of a fish swim bladder. (b) FROM D. W. Fawcett, *Exptl. Cell Res.*, Suppl. 8, 174 (1961).

Function

The principal function of the plasma membrane is to regulate the flow of materials into and out of the cell. This regulation depends upon the membrane's permeability, which is determined in large part by its chemical organization.

A fundamental mechanism is osmosis, by which water diffuses through a membrane from a region of its high concentration to one of low concentration. The plasma membrane is often inaccurately described as semipermeable or differentially permeable because water moves through it with relative ease whereas larger molecules do not. Osmosis does account for the movement of water through the plasma membrane, but it also implies that solutes pass through at a much slower rate, if at all. Thus this mechanism does not explain the movement of the many solutes that do pass through the membrane. Although small molecules like water move with greater facility through the membrane than do large molecules—for example, water passes through 200 to 10,000 times as fast as glycerol— many large molecules are able to penetrate the membrane at certain times during the life of the cell. Other mechanisms of movement must exist to account for their penetration and for changes in the permeability of the membrane. Perhaps the plasma membrane is best described, then, as selectively permeable and relatively labile in permeability.

Certain molecules, particularly nonelectrolytes, have an ability to penetrate that is almost linearly proportional to their lipid solubility. The relationship emphasizes the significance of the lipid components of the plasma membrane and is indirect evidence of their presence. It is believed that such molecules enter the membrane by dissolving in the lipid portion.

Two additional mechanisms are available for substances of low lipid solubility and relatively high molecular weight, such as glucose, which enters the human erythrocyte at a relatively rapid rate, ribonuclease (mol wt 13,000), and protamines and histones (mol wt 2000 to 10,000). Solid particles may be ingested by *phagocytosis* and liquids by *pinocytosis*, two processes involving the physical activity of the plasma membrane.

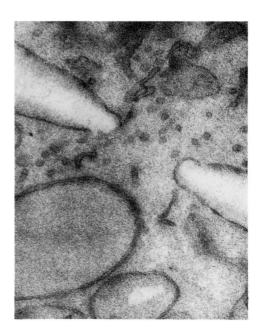

Figure 3–14. A large channel connecting two meiotic cells of hemp (×38,000). Note continuity of the plasma membranes. FROM J. Heslop-Harrison, *Endeavor,* **25,** 65 (1966).

Phagocytosis is exemplified in the amoebae, with the extensions of pseudopodia around a particle and its subsequent incorporation into the cell. The activity of certain white blood cells is similar and is important in the reactions of the body to infection by foreign materials. The leukocytes, for example, are able to ingest bacteria, cell debris, and other large bodies. With the electron microscope it has been possible to observe outpocketings of the plasma membrane in several types of cells around a particle external to the cell. The particle becomes *ad*sorbed at the surface of the membrane and is then taken into the cell by an infolding of the membrane and the formation of a vesicle consisting of the particle enveloped by a pinched-off part of the membrane. Once inside the cell, the particle is released into the cytoplasm by some mechanism as yet unknown. It is possible that small, as well as large, particles are incorporated into cells in this manner.

Pinocytosis brings about incorporation of liquid substances by a method similar to phagocytosis and may be the route for entry of proteins

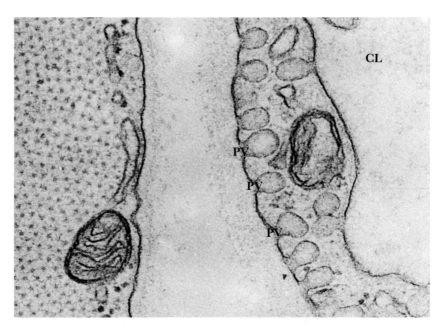

Figure 3–15. Pinocytosis vesicles in a heart muscle capillary (×71,000). PV, pinocytosis vesicles; CL, capillary lumen. Micrograph by D. W. Fawcett, from *An Atlas of Fine Structure: The Cell, Its Organelles and Inclusions.* W. B. Saunders Company, Philadelphia, 1966.

into the cell. Again the substance is adsorbed at the surface of the plasma membrane. An infolding of the membrane then occurs, resulting in the formation of a vesicle containing the droplet by a pinching off of the membrane within the cytoplasm (Figure 3–15). The material is then released in some way from the vesicle inside the cell, and, as in phagocytosis, the membrane that surrounded the droplet may become part of the endoplasmic reticulum. A striking cytological phenomenon is usually apparent during the process of pinocytosis. There is very pronounced activity or motion at the surface of the plasma membrane and the cytoplasm as incorporation takes place. This movement may be related to the normal movements within the plasma membrane or to some unexplained internal cytoplasmic activity.

The elimination of material from a cell is accompanied by surface changes similar in kind to those observed in pinocytosis and phagocytosis, especially the former. Certain cells secrete specific substances, which have various effects upon other cells or tissues of the body, or which are released from the body. *Secretion* is defined as the chemical activity of a cell in producing and releasing a particular substance (for example, an enzyme or hormone). This activity requires energy and is considered an active rather than a passive cell process. It is possible to observe the accumulation of granules, droplets, or vacuoles in secretory cells prior to their expulsion. The accumulation of such materials often involves the activity of the Golgi apparatus, which will be discussed in Chapter 5. In the release of the material from the cell, there may be a disruption of a portion of the plasma membrane, followed by the elimination of the material and a reconstitution of the membrane. This type of change has been noted in the cells of the pancreas and the thyroid gland. The materials may, instead, be incorporated into vesicles developing at the surface of the membrane. Vesicles of this type have been observed. After the material is expelled, the membranes of the vesicles are reincorporated into the framework of the plasma membrane.

The movements of ions and molecules across the plasma membrane by mechanisms other than osmosis, phagocytosis, and pinocytosis appear to involve the active chemical behavior of the membrane itself. This activity requires energy, and the mechanism is known as *active transport*. Active transport has been defined by Stein as "the movement of molecules or ions in a direction opposite to that of a prevailing electrochemical gradient." By this means a cell can maintain a composition different from that of its environment and thus become independent of its environment.

Lipid-soluble substances (and many that are perhaps only slightly miscible) react as follows. The transportant and some chemical com-

ponent of the plasma membrane form a complex. The complex is transferred across the membrane, and the transportant is released on the
opposite side into the cytoplasm. The membrane performs work in this
transport, and energy is required. The source of energy for active transport
is metabolic activities in the cytoplasm and largely from mitochondrial
ATP. The indication that substances interfering with oxidative phosphorylation (thus inhibiting the formation of high-energy phosphate
bonds) decrease the permeability of the membrane provides evidence for
the role of ATP in active transport. In some cells the energy is derived
from oxidative metabolism, such as the oxidation of glucose or its breakdown under anaerobic conditions. In the red blood cells, for example,
the transport of sodium and potassium ions depends on the anaerobic
breakdown of glucose.

The material to be transported undergoes some metabolic change
as it is incorporated into the chemical organization of the membrane and
carried across. This change suggests that a carrier of some kind becomes
activated at the inner surface of the membrane, moves to the outer
surface, picks up the transportant, and carries it across the membrane for
release at the inner surface. Some carriers have been identified in *Escherichia coli* as protein substances. In this connection, carriers have been given
the names *permeases* and *translocases,* with the additional implication that
enzyme activity is necessary for active transport. Evidence for enzymatic
activity is found in the localization of enzymes in the plasma membranes
of several cells. Cholinesterase and proteolytic enzymes have been segregated from the red cell membrane and phosphatase appears to be involved
with the permeability of the membrane to phosphate and glucose in yeast
cells. The transport of β-galactoside into the bacterium *E. coli* is mediated
by β-galactoside permease present on the plasma membrane. Twelve
different permeases appear to serve in the transport of the 20 amino acids
in *E. coli.* Transport systems are indeed quite specific. The specificity of
recognition resides in a surface transport protein, and at least one, M protein, has been isolated from bacteria. It is possible that the surface protein
both recognizes and carries a substance across the membrane. The protein
may undergo either diffusion or a conformational change which might
create an opening in the membrane. Because of this possible mechanism
for transport, and the fact that the term is somewhat misleading, Pardee
has suggested that the word *permease* "should be abandoned."

One of the most intensively studied phenomena has been the transport of sodium and potassium ions through the plasma membrane (Figure
3–16). The interior of a cell is usually high in potassium ions and low in
sodium and chlorine ions. Moreover, heavily hydrated ions like sodium
diffuse less readily than do potassium ions. Thus, neither sodium nor

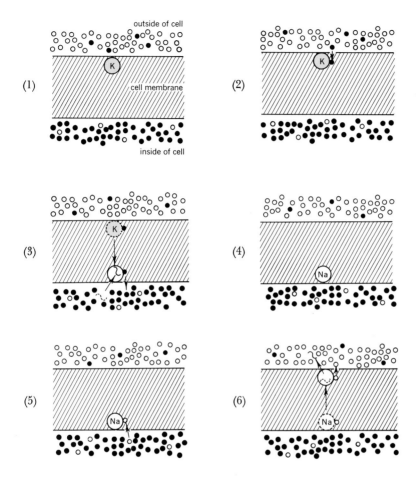

Figure 3–16. Proposed scheme for the active transport of sodium and potassium ions through the plasma membrane. The model employs hypothetical carriers for the ions. The free potassium carrier cannot move across the membrane (1) until it forms a compound with a potassium ion (2). Then the carrier migrates from the outside wall of the membrane to the inside wall (3), where it gives up the potassium ion to the interior of the cell and receives energy from the cell. The energy turns it into a sodium carrier (4), which cannot cross the membrane until it in turn combines with a sodium ion (5). The carrier migrates to the outside wall of the membrane and releases the ion (6). It also gives up energy, probably through the mediation of an enzyme, to become once again a potassium carrier (1). This is called active transport because the cell supplies energy to operate the system against the large concentration gradients of sodium outside and potassium inside the cell. Adapted from "How Things Get into Cells" by H. Holter. Copyright © 1961 by Scientific American, Inc. All rights reserved.

potassium is at equilibrium between the cytoplasm and the environment of the cell; there is a net transport of potassium into the cell and sodium out of the cell. The movement of these ions against the electrochemical gradient requires a system referred to as the "sodium pump." The pump itself appears to be a carrier, as described above, and requires energy for its operation. Some evidence suggests that the pump is located near the 10 Å pores of the membrane. Although most of the investigations of the sodium pump have been with animal cells, there is evidence that a similar system operates in plants. Furthermore, a chlorine pump is presumed to operate in the tonoplast, moving chlorine into the vacuole of the plant cell. Among the significant features of the pumping system are that ion gradients are important in the transmission of the nervous impulse and that many enzymes within cells require potassium as a cofactor.

In summary, active transport involves the incorporation of the material to be transported by some substance in the membrane, a carrier, which moves the material across to the other side of the membrane. The transport of the material requires energy, in the form of ATP, and enzyme activity as well. The carrier moves from the outer surface of the membrane to the inner surface, at which point it releases the transportant. Acquiring energy from the cell on the inner surface of the membrane, the carrier returns to the outer surface to resume its transportation activity. By the same token, the carrier can receive an ion or molecule from the inner surface of the membrane and transport it to the outer surface for release.

If the ability of a substance to penetrate depends upon its size and if transport does not occur by any of the mechanisms presented, it seems quite possible that the material enters and leaves the cell through the tiny pores in the plasma membrane. In some ways, pore conduction is a kind of active transport, especially since the permeability of the membrane is known to change from time to time. In other words, a molecule may be able to penetrate the membrane at one time but not another, depending upon the metabolic state of the cell and the plasma membrane. The pore is either open, and permeable to a substance, or closed, and impermeable. This property may be due to the behavior of the protein component of the membrane, which lines the pores.

In conclusion, it is evident that there are several mechanisms by which materials enter and leave cells. Some of these are rather complex, involving chemical as well as physical changes in the membrane. The membrane is functionally labile; it is not permeable to a given substance at all times, and it may be impermeable to many materials most of the time and permeable to many other materials most of the time.

SELECTED READING

General

De Robertis, E. D. P., W. W. Nowinski, and F. A. Saez, *Cell Biology,* 4th ed., Saunders, Philadelphia, 1965.

Frey-Wyssling, A., and K. Mühlethaler, *Ultrastructural Plant Cytology,* American Elsevier, New York, 1965.

Newcomb, E. H., "Cytoplasm–Cell Wall Relationships," *Ann. Rev. Plant Physiol.,* 14, 43 (1963).

Robertson, J. D., "The Membrane of the Living Cell," *Sci. Am.,* 206(4), 65, (1962).

The Cell Wall

Ginzburg, B. Z., "Evidence for a Protein Component in the Middle Lamella of Plant Tissue: A Possible Site for Indolylacetic Acid Action," *Nature,* 181 (4606), 398 (1958).

Klein, S., and B. Ginzburg, "An Electron Microscopic Investigation into the Effect of EDTA on Plant Cell Wall," *J. Biophys. Biochem. Cytol.,* 7(2), 335 (1960).

Mühlethaler, K., "Ultrastructure and Formation of Plant Cell Walls," *Ann. Rev. Plant Physiol.,* 18, 1 (1967).

Porter, K. R., and R. D. Machado, "Studies on the Endoplasmic Reticulum. IV. Its Form and Distribution During Mitosis in Cells of Onion Root Tip," *J. Biophys. Biochem. Cytol.,* 7(1), 167 (1960).

Preston, R. D., "Wall Organization in Plant Cells," *Intern. Rev. Cytol.,* 8, 33 (1959).

Ray, P. M., "Cell Wall Synthesis and Cell Elongation in Oat Coleoptile Tissue," *Am. J. Botany,* 49(9), 928 (1962).

Robards, A. W., "A New Interpretation of Plasmodesmatal Ultrastructure," *Planta,* 82, 200 (1968).

Setterfield, G., and S. T. Bayley, "Studies on the Mechanism of Deposition of Primary Cell Walls," *Can. J. Botany,* 35, 435 (1957).

Setterfield, G., and S. T. Bayley, "Arrangement of Cellulose Microfibrils in Walls of Elongating Parenchyma Cells," *J. Biophys. Biochem. Cytol.,* 4(4), 377 (1958).

Siegel, S. M., *The Plant Cell Wall,* Pergamon Press, New York, 1962.

The Plasma Membrane

Baker, P. F., "The Sodium Pump," *Endeavor,* 25, 166 (1966).

Bell, L. G. E., "Polysaccharides and Cell Membranes," *J. Theoret. Biol.,* 3(1), 132 (1962).

Burgen, A. S. V., "The Structure and Function of Cell Membranes," *Can. J. Biochem. Physiol.,* 40(9), 1253 (1962).

Campbell, R. D., "Desmosome Formation: An Hypothesis of Membrane Accumulation," *Proc. Natl. Acad. Sci. U.S.,* **58**(4), 1422 (1967).

Fawcett, D. W., "Intercellular Bridges," *Exptl. Cell Res.,* Suppl. 8, 174 (1961).

Finean, J. B., "The Molecular Organization of Cell Membranes," in J. A. V. Butler and H. E. Huxley, eds., *Progress in Biophysics and Molecular Biology,* Vol. 16, Pergamon Press, New York, 1966, pp. 145–70.

Holter, H., "Pinocytosis," *Intern. Rev. Cytol.,* **8,** 481 (1960).

Pardee, A. B., "Membrane Transport Proteins," *Science,* **162** (3854), 632 (1968).

Pethica, B. A., "The Physical Chemistry of Cell Adhesion," *Exptl. Cell Res.,* Suppl. 8, 123 (1961).

Ponder, E., "The Cell Membrane and Its Properties," in J. Brachet and A. E. Mirsky, eds., *The Cell,* Vol. 2, Academic Press, New York, 1961, pp. 1–84.

Stein, W. D., "The Transfer Mechanisms in Active Transport," in P. M. B. Walker, ed., *New Approaches in Cell Biology,* Academic Press, New York, 1960, pp. 125–38.

Stein, W. D., *The Movement of Molecules Across Cell Membranes,* Academic Press, New York, 1967.

Whaley, W. G., and H. H. Mollenhauer, "The Golgi Apparatus and Cell Plate Formation—A Postulate," *J. Cell Biol.,* **17**(1), 216 (1963).

4

Endoplasmic Reticulum
and Ribosomes

As a recent discovery among cellular components, the endoplasmic reticulum has presented a problem of terminology, partly because of the variety of forms in which it is found. For an ordered discussion of this organelle and its associated structures, the endoplasmic reticulum is described as a network of double membranes distributed extensively throughout the cytoplasm. This description is comparable to that of Porter, who has stated that "the endoplasmic reticulum is a complex, finely divided vacuolar system extending from the nucleus throughout the cytoplasm to the margins of the cell." The vacuolar system is represented by the channels or spaces between the double membranes. Thus the endoplasmic reticulum consists of membranes enclosing a series of continuous or discontinuous cavities.

Several important functional features of the endoplasmic reticulum were discussed in the preceding chapter, including the associations observed between these membranes and the nuclear envelope and plasma membrane. There exist in these relations structural and chemical similarities, both of which are significant in the general physiology and developmental characteristics of a particular cell or cell type. In addition, the activities of the endoplasmic reticulum emphasize the importance of the cytoplasm in the regulation of cellular processes. The cytoplasm as well as the nucleus is active in such regulation.

Many of the more modern approaches to cellular biochemistry and differentiation involve studies of the behavior and role of the endoplasmic reticulum. For this reason, the morphology, chemical activities, and functional attributes of this system are presented here in some detail.

Morphology

The hyaloplasm of the cell has been defined as the aqueous portion of the cytoplasm remaining after the removal of all particulate structures. Embedded in the hyaloplasm, or matrix of the cytoplasm, are the membranous units called collectively the endoplasmic reticulum. Although the endoplasmic reticulum has been studied primarily with the electron microscope, there have been a few reports that it has been observed in some living cells of mammalian tissue by the use of phase-contrast microscopy. However, its dimensions are below the limit of resolution of the light microscope. The methods used to prepare cells for observations of the endoplasmic reticulum produce similar or identical results even in different kinds of cells. Not only do microscopic techniques confirm the existence of the endoplasmic reticulum, but physical methods, such as ultracentrifugation, permit the isolation and recovery of the elements from the cell. Therefore, in spite of the comparatively recent discovery of the endoplasmic reticulum, there is now general agreement that it exists and has a characteristic morphology. The techniques do not give rise to artifacts but permit relatively consistent observations in a variety of cells.

Part of the problem in the identification of the endoplasmic reticulum has been its appearance in different forms in the same cell and in different cell types. Cells being prepared for study under the electron microscope are often sectioned in different planes, and consequently the endoplasmic reticulum is cut in several ways—longitudinally, tangentially, and transversely. Even when sections are made in the same plane, the morphology of the endoplasmic reticulum may vary, depending upon the type of cell examined and especially upon the metabolic state of the cell at the time of preparation. Another difficulty has arisen from the fixatives used for the preservation of the endoplasmic reticulum prior to microscopic study. In isotonic fixatives, for example, the two membranes comprising any element of the endoplasmic reticulum are not clearly seen because they tend to become very closely apposed to one another, more or less occluding the space normally found between them. The fixation effects indicate that the membranes are sensitive to osmotic changes and imply that they have physical properties similar to those of the plasma membrane.

The endoplasmic reticulum has been found in all kinds of mature cells except the mature mammalian erythrocyte, which is also devoid of a nucleus. In his classification of the membranes of the cell, Porter categorizes the membranes of the nuclear envelope as the most constant portion of the membrane system. Otherwise, they and the membranes of the endoplasmic reticulum, which are the most variable in form of all membranes during the cycle of the living cell, are quite similar. The three principal forms in which the endoplasmic reticulum occurs are cisternae (lamellae), vesicles, and tubules (Figure 4–1). The cisternae are identified as rather long and flattened units, 40 to 50 mμ thick, often arranged in parallel stacks (Figures 4–2 and 4–3). This arrangement is characteristic of synthetically active cells, such as those in which protein synthesis is taking place; an example is the pancreas, which produces digestive enzymes. The vesicles range in diameter from 25 to 500 mμ and are for the most part rounded in shape. The tubules are more diverse in shape than the cisternae and vesicles and have diameters of 50 to 100 mμ. In all of these forms, the spaces enclosed by the membranes comprise the vacuolar system described by Porter. In some cells, or in certain regions of some cells, the membranes form a continuous array of connecting elements, thus enclosing a system of cavities that provides channels for the movement of materials. The connecting vessels may arise from the cisternae or the tubules, depending upon the cell in question and its state of development. As will be seen, the morphology of the endoplasmic reticulum is often correlated with the state of differentiation of the cell, and the continuity of the membranes and their internal cavities is a function of development.

The unit membrane of the endoplasmic reticulum is comparable to that of the plasma membrane. Evidence for this resemblance is found in the chemical composition of the membranes and the fact that the endoplasmic reticulum may sometimes be continuous with the nuclear envelope or the plasma membrane in certain places. If the membranes

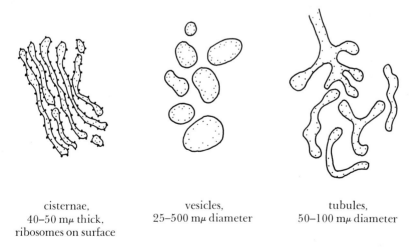

cisternae,	vesicles,	tubules,
40–50 mμ thick,	25–500 mμ diameter	50–100 mμ diameter
ribosomes on surface		

Figure 4–1. Morphology of the endoplasmic reticulum.

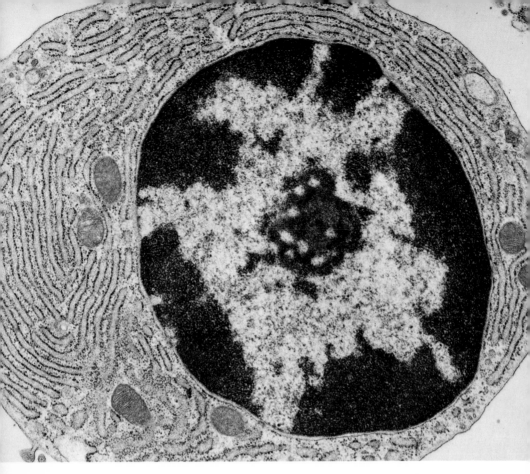

Figure 4-2. Endoplasmic reticulum in plasma cell of guinea pig bone marrow (×20,000). Note the large nucleus with its nucleolus. Micrograph by D. W. Fawcett, from *An Atlas of Fine Structure: The Cell, Its Organelles and Inclusions.* W. B. Saunders Company, Philadelphia, 1966.

were not structurally similar, such connections would be unlikely. Continuities of the endoplasmic reticulum with the nuclear envelope (see Figures 9–5 and 9–6) suggest, in fact, that the latter may actually be a part of the endoplasmic reticulum rather than an independent membrane system. Observations in crayfish oocytes, rat embryonic cells, and other cells have provided evidence that, at least in some cells, the endoplasmic reticulum is derived from evaginations of the nuclear envelope. Homologies have also been suggested between the membranes of the endoplasmic reticulum and mitochondrial membranes (Figure 4–4). On the other hand, direct association of the endoplasmic reticulum with the plasma membrane may occur only during pinocytosis. Moreover, differences in membrane thickness are found among membranes of different organelles. For example, the plasma membrane may be 95 Å thick and mitochondrial membranes only 60 Å thick in the same cell. Although these differences are frequently reported, they may be due to preparative techniques and therefore not biologically significant. Nevertheless, the compositions of the plasma membrane and the endoplasmic reticulum membranes appear to be variable among different organs and species of animals. Differences in membrane thickness, for example, may be due to differences in the proportion and types of phospholipids present in them.

The connections of elements of the endoplasmic reticulum with other membranes in the cell, including those of the Golgi apparatus (Chapter 5), are important in the considerations of some of the functions of the endoplasmic reticulum. For the present, the membrane system of the endoplasmic reticulum may be regarded as composed of lipoprotein with properties of permeability and transport similar to those of the plasma membrane. Although some problems remain in the delineation of the membranes of the cell, it seems safe to state that they are all quite similar from a chemical and structural standpoint and that together they comprise an elaborate system for communications intra- and intercellularly.

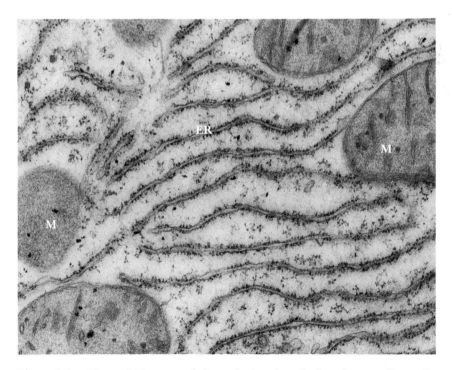

Figure 4-3. Cisternal elements of the endoplasmic reticulum in a rat liver cell. ER, endoplasmic reticulum; M, mitochondrion. Ribosomes are located along the outer surfaces of the membranes, and some are free in the hyaloplasm. FROM K. R. Porter in J. Brachet and A. E. Mirsky, eds., *The Cell*, Vol. 2, Academic Press, New York, 1961, pp. 621-76.

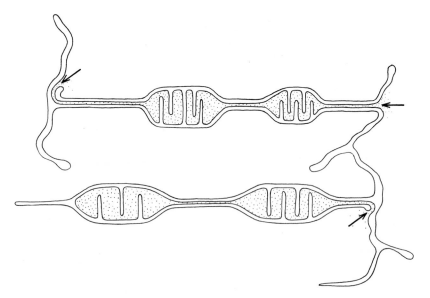

Figure 4–4. Diagram showing a possible mechanism for mitochondrial origin. The arrows point to finger-like invaginations of cytoplasmic matrix into the cavity of a large endoplasmic reticulum cisterna. Two of these meet in the mitochondrion at the upper left, to produce a transverse or continuous septum like the ones frequently seen in liver mitochondria. The two lower mitochondria are very much like those seen in developing nerve fibers. FROM J. D. Robertson in M. Locke, ed., *Cellular Membranes in Development,* Academic Press, New York, 1964, p, 21.

The intercellular relations are particularly evident in observations of membrane behavior during pinocytosis and phagocytosis.

The three forms of the endoplasmic reticulum may appear in a single cell at the same time or at different times during the cell cycle. For a given time in a particular cell, however, the pattern of arrangement is quite characteristic. For example, mammalian liver cells exhibit parallel lamellar elements (cisternae), of more or less uniform size, during metabolic activity, whereas pancreatic cells exhibit a slightly different arrangement of cisternae, with size differences in the individual units. Notochord cells of *Ambystoma* larvae have still another arrangement of cisternae. In striated muscle cells, the endoplasmic reticulum is arranged as a network of tubules, commonly known as the *sarcoplasmic reticulum* (Figure 4–5). There are also species differences in the patterns of the endoplasmic reticulum as well as differences among tissues or cell types. Thus the liver cells of one species may show a different arrangement of the endoplasmic reticulum from the liver cells of another species, but some similarity

(a)

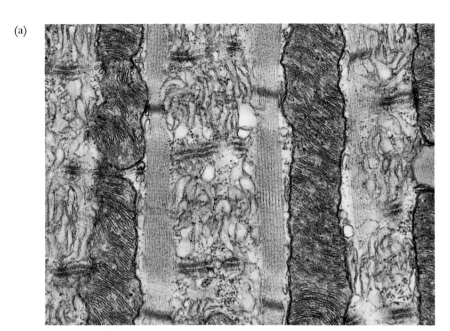

(b)

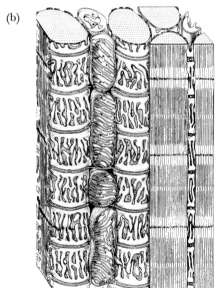

Figure 4–5. Sarcoplasmic reticulum in muscle cells. (a) In the bat cricothyroid muscle (×23,000). The convoluted membranes are the sarcoplasmic reticulum. (b) A three-dimensional representation of the sarcoplasmic reticulum in skeletal muscle. FROM J. P. Revel, *J. Cell Biol.,* **12,** 571 (1962).

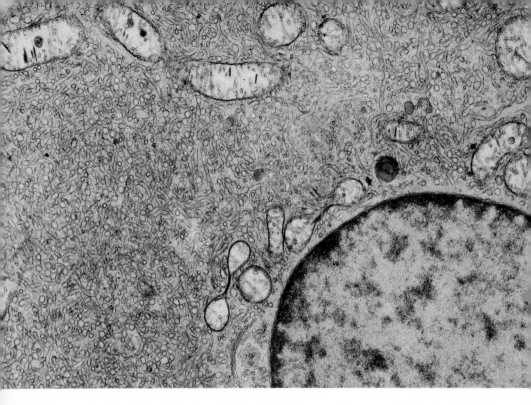

Figure 4–6. Extensive development of agranular endoplasmic reticulum in a steroid-producing cell of opossum testis ($\times$16,600). Micrograph by D. W. Fawcett, from *An Atlas of Fine Structure: The Cell, Its Organelles and Inclusions.* W. B. Saunders Company, Philadelphia, 1966.

of pattern usually exists in cells having the same general functions, in this case secretion (Figure 4–6).

One of the most significant and easily observable differences among the basic morphological elements of the endoplasmic reticulum is that some of the elements are smooth-surfaced while others are rough-surfaced. The elements with rough surfaces are high in ribonucleic acid and are intensely basiphilic. The membranes themselves are not rough, but associated with their outer surfaces are tiny particulate components, 100 to 150 Å in diameter (Figure 4–7). These are called ribonucleoprotein (RNP) particles or *ribosomes* and contain on the average 40% RNA and 60% protein. The elements having ribosomes are usually of the cisternal type and are found in cells active in protein synthesis. Biochemical studies have indicated that the ribosomes are important in protein synthesis, even though the membranes are not always necessary for this activity. These and other functions will be presented in more detail later.

Ribosomes often form patterns in their association with the endoplasmic reticulum. These patterns include spiral, rosette, or circular arrangements of the particles. The presence and the arrangements of the ribosomes with the endoplasmic reticulum have produced some of the difficulties in the physical and chemical identification of the cytoplasmic membranes. The elements with associated ribosomes react strongly with basic dyes, owing to the basiphilic nature of the ribosomes. Highly developed endoplasmic reticulum and ribosomes are especially noticeable in synthetically active cells, including secretory cells, as well as in nerve cells.

Ribosomes appear not only along the membrane surfaces (Figure 4–8) in many cells, such as the meristematic cells of plant tissue and other types of cells with meagerly developed membrane systems; they are also located more or less free in the hyaloplasm (Figure 4–9). A distinction has been made between the role of free ribosomes and that of endoplasmic reticulum–associated ribosomes. The former may predominate in a cell when the protein synthesized is for intracellular use (for example, hemo-

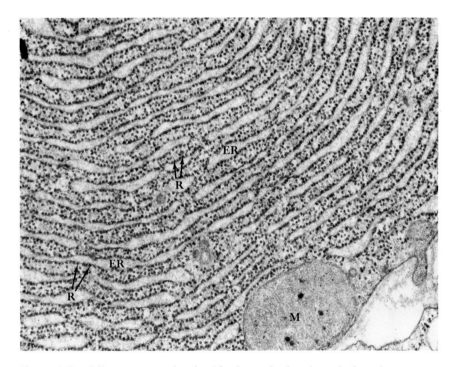

Figure 4–7. Ribosomes associated with the endoplasmic reticulum in an exocrine cell of rat pancreas (×32,000). ER, endoplasmic reticulum; M, mitochondrion; R, ribosomes. Micrograph by G. E. Palade, from *Cell Ultrastructure* by William A. Jensen and Roderic B. Park. © 1967 by Wadsworth Publishing Company, Inc., Belmont, California. Reproduced by permission of the publisher.

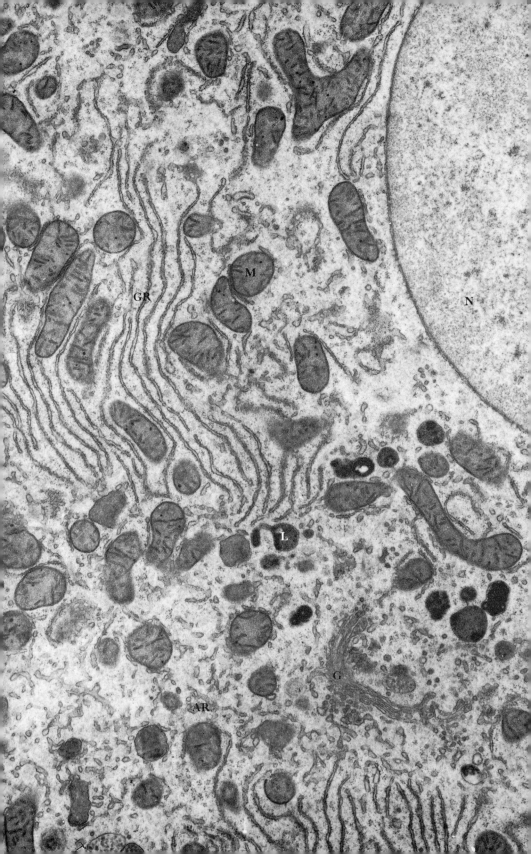

Figure 4–8. Granular and agranular endoplasmic reticulum in a rat liver cell (×16,000). AR, agranular reticulum; G. golgi; GR, granular reticulum; L, lysosome; M, mitochondrion; N, nucleus. FROM K. R. Porter in T. W. Goodwin and O. Lindberg, eds., *Biological Structure and Function,* Vol. 1, Academic Press, New York, 1961, p. 130.

globin, enzymes), and the latter when the proteins are for export (for example, antibodies, digestive enzymes).

On the basis of sedimentation constants derived from high resolution ultracentrifugation, at least three classes of ribosomes can be distinguished: (1) animal cytoplasmic ribosomes, (2) plant cytoplasmic ribosomes, and (3) organelle and bacterial ribosomes. Figure 4–10 illustrates the differences. Isolation of ribosomes in low concentration of magnesium ions results in the separation of the two subunits of a ribosome (80 S or 70 S). (One subunit is nearly twice the size of the other.) Each of the subunits contains RNA and protein and is characterized by the sedimentation constant of the RNA component, as shown in Figure 4–10. The protein components are quite complex, and, in most cases, are rich in the amino acids arginine and lysine. In the bacterium *Escherichia coli,* for example, there are about 10 proteins associated with the 16 S RNA and about 20 with the 23 S RNA. The diameter of a ribosomal particle

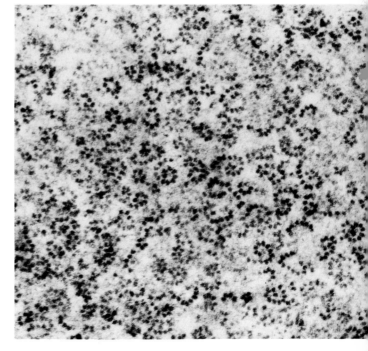

Figure 4–9. Ribosomes from the cotyledon of the ripening seed of *Phaseolus vulgaris* (×50,000). Many of the ribosomes are located on the surface of endoplasmic reticulum lamellae, but the latter are not visible here. Note especially the spiral arrangement of the ribosomes. COURTESY Dr. Helgi Öpik, Department of Botany, University College of Swansea, Wales.

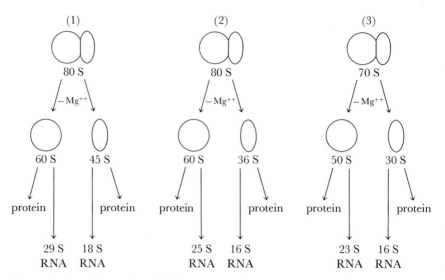

Figure 4–10. Three classes of ribosomes. The Svedberg unit (S) is a measure of the sedimentation velocity of particles in the ultracentrifuge.

is about 200 Å, and its molecular weight is about 3 to 4 million. A further complexity recently demonstrated in several cell types is the presence of a 5 S ribosomal RNA, derived from the large subunit, which may participate in some specific manner during protein synthesis.

Ribosomes are not confined to the cytoplasm, but may also be located within the nucleus, mitochondria, and chloroplasts. Observations of the latter two organelles indicate that their ribosomes fall into class (3) and are similar to bacterial ribosomes. Nuclear ribosomes studied in the cells of calf thymus tissue appear to be closer in size to cytoplasmic ribosomes, class (1), than to bacterial ribosomes, and may contain up to 62% RNA. Ribosomal RNA is usually single-stranded, having unequal amounts of guanine, cytosine, adenine, and uracil, although many bases may be paired through hydrogen bonding to form a few double-stranded regions. The nuclear origin of cytoplasmic ribosomes will be discussed in Chapter 9.

Clusters of ribosomes are often found in synthetically active cells. A cluster, called a *polysome* (or ergosome), consists of three or more ribosomes, held together by a molecule of another type of RNA, messenger RNA. The significance of this arrangement is described in Chapter 19.

Some other specialized membrane elements have been located in certain kinds of cells, but the evidence for their identity with the endoplasmic reticulum is equivocal. One of the most common of these specializations is the Golgi apparatus, which has been found in a number of different plant and animal cells. Since the discussion of this organelle is reserved for a later chapter, the reference here is only to indicate that continuities exist between the Golgi and the endoplasmic reticulum and that there are important structural and functional similarities.

The immature eggs of several animals, and a few other cell types exhibiting active growth, include a membrane system that differs markedly from the endoplasmic reticulum but at the same time suggests at least a similar origin. The specialized structures are the *annulate lamellae,* first described in the eggs of the sea urchin *Arbacia.* An individual lamella consists of two parallel membranes separated by a space of 20 to 40 mμ, the membranes fusing at their edges to form a type of vesicle. The annulate lamellae are not connected with the more typical elements of the endoplasmic reticulum and also differ from the endoplasmic reticulum in having pores. The pores are surrounded by dense material (annuli) and are arranged almost identically to the pores in the nuclear envelope. In some cells the annulate lamellae lie in stacks near the nuclear envelope, but they may also occur as small, unstacked units elsewhere in the cytoplasm (Figure 4–11). Moreover, there is some evidence that they are derived from evaginations of the nuclear envelope. One of the most significant distinctions between these membranes and the endoplasmic reticulum is the presence of RNA in the absence of ribosomes. Thus the membranes of the annulate lamellae are chemically different from those of the endoplasmic reticulum, which are primarily lipoprotein in content. The lamellae are thought to be short-lived and may break up into smaller cytoplasmic vesicles.

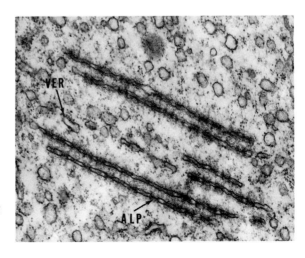

Figure 4–11. Annulate lamellae in sea urchin oocyte (×21,500). VER, vesicle of endoplasmic reticulum; ALP, annulus or pore within lamella. FROM H. W. Beams, Everett Anderson, and J. F. Reger, "Electron Microscope Studies on the Egg of *Abracia punctulata,*" 1962 (unpublished).

Functions

As the form of the endoplasmic reticulum varies according to cell types and cell metabolism, the functions of the endoplasmic reticulum vary with form and location. An outline of the functions follows.

1. The membranes provide for increased surface area within the cytoplasm for metabolic activities. There are, in fact, enzymes on their surfaces. Such an arrangement facilitates the union of an enzyme with its substrate (the substance on which the enzyme acts). An enzyme operates more efficiently when attached to a surface than when in solution.

2. The cavities bounded by the membranes permit the collection of products of synthetic activities of the cell. Such products accumulate in the cavities for storage and later transport to other parts of the cell or for release from the cell in secretion. Perhaps the osmotic properties of the membranes are significant for this activity.

3. The presence of the cavities results in the retention of synthetic materials and their separation from the general matrix of the cytoplasm. Thus there is a conservation of metabolic products.

4. The similarities between the endoplasmic reticulum and other membranes of the cell suggest that the endoplasmic reticulum is the origin of some of these other membranes. Its role as a source of nuclear membrane material during cell division has been established.

5. Specialized arrangements of the endoplasmic reticulum, such as the sarcoplasmic reticulum, may allow for the transmission of impulses or excitations intracellularly.

Of the five general functions outlined, number 1 presents the most complex problem of terminology. A brief review of the components in question is in order as a preface. The endoplasmic reticulum itself is a series of membranes ramifying throughout the cell in one or more forms. These membranes enclose spaces, or cavities, and may have on their outer surfaces associated ribosomes. The smooth endoplasmic reticulum is often continuous with the rough (granular) endoplasmic reticulum, thereby making the absence or presence of ribosomes the only significant difference between the two. The membranes themselves are made of lipoprotein, whereas the ribosomes consist of RNA and protein. Upon high speed centrifugation a fraction containing elements of the endoplasmic reticulum along with ribosomal particles can be recovered from the cell. This fraction represents the *microsomes* and is clearly a functional rather than a normal structural unit for several reasons. The microsomes do not exist as such in the living cell; they represent bits and pieces of the endoplasmic reticulum (and perhaps other cell debris) and associated ribosomes removed from the cell. The ribosomes can readily be dissociated from the endoplasmic reticulum membranes by treatment with deoxycholate. The description of the microsomes is most often related to their biochemical activities outside the living cell (in vitro).

The morphological and chemical distinctions between the membranes and the ribosomes are reflected in their functions. Comparisons of the behavior of cells having abundant associated ribosomes (rough or granular endoplasmic reticulum) with cells having few or no ribosomes (smooth or agranular endoplasmic reticulum) illustrate the functional differences. The incorporation of radioactively labeled amino acids (that is, amino acids labeled with carbon-14 or tritium) into proteins is greater in ribosome-containing fractions than in nonribosome-containing fractions. In other words, a microsomal fraction high in ribosomes shows a high rate of protein synthesis. There is, in fact, a close correlation between the RNA content of the microsomal fraction and the rate of protein synthesis. If the microsomal fraction is treated with ribonuclease (an enzyme that disrupts or inactivates RNA), the incorporation of labeled amino acids into protein is inhibited. Since the ribosomes rather than the membranes are the elements containing RNA, the ribosomes are essential for the synthesis of proteins. The membranes are not entirely superfluous in protein synthesis, however, for it has been found that ribosomes associated with membranes are five or six times more effective in the process than free ribosomes in the hyaloplasm. The role of the endoplasmic reticulum in protein synthesis will be discussed later.

The smooth form of the endoplasmic reticulum (Figure 4–6), in particular the tubular type, is found in cells that are active in the synthesis of steroid compounds, such as cholesterol, glycerides, and the hormones testosterone and progesterone. It is also found in the pigmented epithelial cells of the retina, which are involved in the metabolism of vitamin A in the production of visual pigment. Glycogen-storing cells of the liver contain the smooth, tubular elements of the endoplasmic reticulum, as do plant cells in which new cell wall material is being formed. In the latter, the endoplasmic reticulum is closely associated with the surfaces along which the new wall material is laid down. All of these instances point to the active participation of the membranes in cellular metabolism, apart from protein synthesis as related to the ribosomes. Substantiating evidence is found in the fact that ribonuclease does not disrupt the activity of a variety of enzymes in these cells. These enzymes are associated with the membranes at their surfaces or within their cavities and include esterases, adenosine triphosphatase, glucose 6-phosphatase, NADH–cytochrome c reductase, and enzymes connected with the synthesis of cholesterol. A few conclusions may be drawn from this background of information. The membranes of the endoplasmic reticulum serve as a framework on which enzymes catalyze the synthesis of various steroid substances, including cholesterol. The endoplasmic reticulum also is a site, among others, of ATP synthesis in the cell, the ATP being utilized as a source of energy for the intracellular transport of materials or in RNA metabolism involving the ribosomes. The presence of the cytochrome c reductase enzyme suggests oxidative metabolism (respiration) in the endoplasmic reticulum, although it usually occurs in the mitochondria. In the formation of secondary cell wall material in plants, certain enzymes and metabolites may be carried by the endoplasmic reticulum to the region of wall synthesis.

The point was made earlier that free ribosomes are not as active in protein synthesis as are ribosomes associated with elements of the endoplasmic reticulum. Evidently the membranes contribute in some way to the efficiency of the process. This function is related to general functions number 2 and number 3. One possibility is that the endoplasmic reticulum serves to collect the products of protein synthesis (for example, an enzyme) for later use in the cell or for transport out of the cell. This would occur in the production of enzymes by the pancreas, the protein products ultimately being released into the lumen of the digestive tract, where foods break down. Studies of metabolic activities in the cells of the pancreas have, in fact, delineated in some detail the behavior of the endoplasmic reticulum during and following the synthesis of digestive enzymes. The pancreatic cells responsible for enzyme production have a large number of ribosomal particles associated with parallel arrays of cisternae. In these cells several granules accumulate within the cavities of the cisternae, causing the membranes around the cavities to become somewhat distended (Figure 4–12). Thus the membrane system becomes a repository for the products of synthesis, namely, the *prozymogen* granules, precursors of active enzymes. Later, *zymogen* (also enzyme precursor) granules appear in the region of the Golgi apparatus, where they are enclosed in vesicles by smooth membranes. The prozymogen apparently is transported from the regions of protein synthesis in the granular endoplasmic reticulum to the Golgi region via the endoplasmic reticulum cavities. The enzymes are ultimately secreted into the lumen of the pancreas by a process similar to pinocytosis. The associations between the

Figure 4–12.   In this plasma cell from guinea pig bone marrow, the cisternae of the endoplasmic reticulum are greatly distended owing to accumulation of cell product ($\times 29,700$). Micrograph by D. W. Fawcett, from *An Atlas of Fine Structure: The Cell, Its Organelles and Inclusions.* W. B. Saunders Company, Philadelphia, 1966.

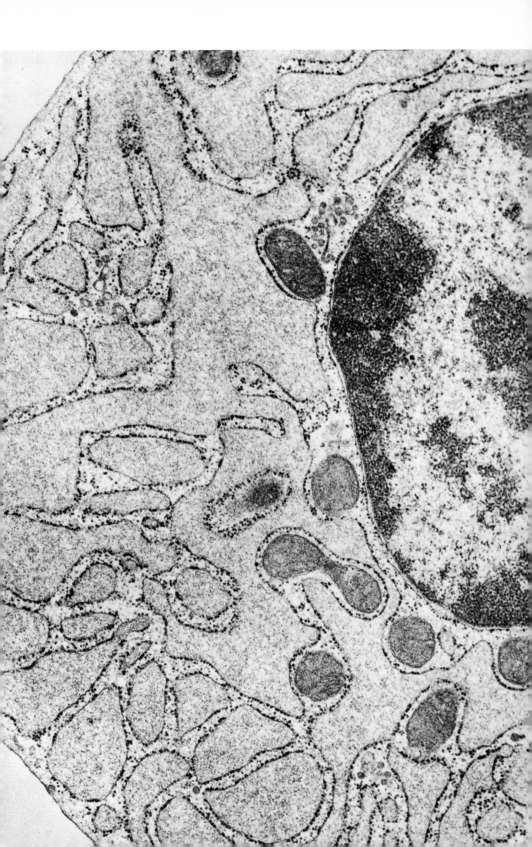

membrane elements of the cytoplasm and the plasma membrane may provide the channels through which the enzymes move within and out of a cell. Materials moving along these passageways are not lost into the hyaloplasm, where they might be degraded or become unavailable for transport out of the cell.

Considering the sizes of some of the protein molecules presumed to move within the cell, a problem of passage through the endoplasmic reticulum cavities might be expected. The spaces between the membranes of the endoplasmic reticulum are on the average 75 to 100 mμ across, a width that would permit the movement of small molecules but not of large molecules. Since large molecules move despite the cavity dimensions, it is possible that, as an alternative to passage of the molecules through the cavities, some of the distended membrane elements move from one part of the cell to another, carrying with them the cavity contents. Studies of the guinea pig pancreas, however, indicate that the movement proceeds through the cavities from the site of protein synthesis to the Golgi region. The movement of fat particles in the intestinal villi appears to occur by pinocytic activity, even though membrane continuities are observable among the nucleus, the cytoplasm, and the cell environment; thus channel size is unimportant in this case. In conclusion, one of the most important functions of the endoplasmic reticulum is to provide a pathway for the intracellular movement of materials, for the release of materials from the cell, and for the incorporation of materials into the cell.

The last general function, number 5, has been well substantiated. In striated muscle cells, the smooth elements of the sarcoplasmic reticulum are characteristic. The nature of these cells and the arrangement of the reticulum are indicative of at least one function. Electrical impulses are transmitted through the nervous system to the muscles, where responses are produced. Since muscles are composed of cells, the impulses must, in some way, be transmitted through the cells to elicit the responses. The membrane elements appear to have some electrochemical properties, and it may be that they provide for the lateral conduction of excitations within the muscle fibers. One of the current views regarding the role of sarcoplasmic reticulum in muscle suggests the release of calcium ions by the sarcoplasmic reticulum. The calcium ions may stimulate enzyme action associated with the contractile protein of muscle, myosin, resulting in the release of energy from ATP. This energy release from the cellular energy pool results in the contraction of the muscle fibrils, and relaxation of the fibrils occurs when the calcium ions are recaptured by the sarcoplasmic reticulum. The source of the ATP is from anaerobic glycolysis (Chapter 6). Additionally, the sarcoplasmic reticulum may also transport the waste product of muscle cell respiration (lactic acid) to the cell surface for release into the bloodstream.

The behavior of the endoplasmic reticulum during cell division has been considered in connection with the formation of the cell plate in plant cells (Chapter 3). An even more striking aspect of endoplasmic reticulum behavior during division is apparent during the formation of the new nuclear envelopes of the daughter nuclei (Figure 4–13). In the

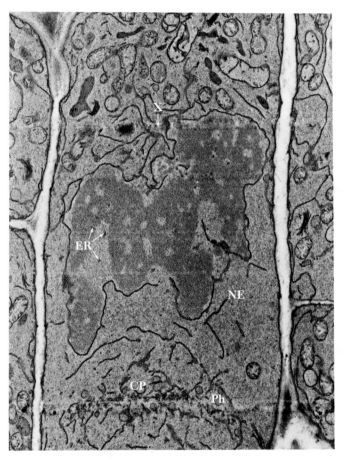

Figure 4–13. Formation of the nuclear envelope from the endoplasmic reticulum during cell division in the onion root tip. CP, cell plate; ER, endoplasmic reticulum; NE, nuclear envelope; Ph, phragmosome; X, polar elements of endoplasmic reticulum. FROM K. R. Porter and R. D. Machado, *J. Biophys. Biochem. Cytol.,* 7, 167 (1960).

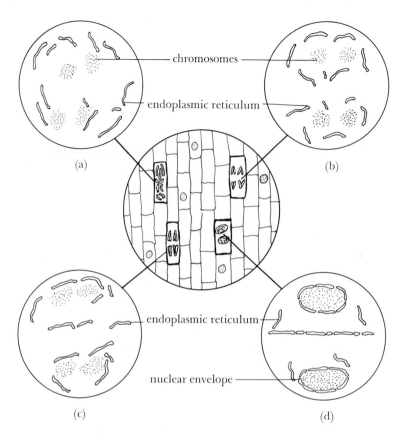

Figure 4–14. Formation of nuclear envelope from the endoplasmic reticulum during cell division. The center of the illustration depicts the appearance of dividing cells under the light microscope. Indicated regions are magnified to show the appearance of chromosomes and endoplasmic reticulum with the electron microscope at each stage. (a) Endoplasmic reticulum elements are mostly peripheral to the chromosomes. (b) As daughter chromosomes congregate at the poles of the cell, elements of the endoplasmic reticulum begin to move around them. (c) As the nuclear envelopes develop, other elements of the endoplasmic reticulum move into the equatorial region of the cell in the initiation of cell plate formation. (d) Nuclear envelopes have formed around the groups of daughter chromosomes, and endoplasmic reticulum elements contribute to the cell plate.

early part of division the nuclear envelope becomes fragmented into small vesicles and some large lamellar units. These units and vesicles move toward the poles of the cell and to the periphery (Figure 4–14), where they are indistinguishable from elements of the endoplasmic reticulum. From the polar ends of the cell, elements of the endoplasmic reticulum migrate into the regions around the chromosomes, which are grouping at the poles. Most of these units of the endoplasmic reticulum join or fuse to produce a nuclear envelope around each group of daughter chromosomes, and a few may actually be caught within the developing nuclei. The observations of the behavior of the endoplasmic reticulum in cell division have been made primarily on plant cells. However, it seems likely that the events leading to the formation of the nuclear envelopes occur in other kinds of cells as well.

The behavior of the endoplasmic reticulum during cell division may be quite random, for it is not possible to follow individual elements throughout the cycle. New elements may even form at this time, but their origin is not known. Although some elements of the endoplasmic reticulum contribute to the new nuclear envelopes, other elements may undergo fragmentation and remain as small vesicles in the cytoplasm, and many cisternal units persist, distributed in about equal proportions between the daughter cells.

Although the origin of the new endoplasmic reticulum membranes has not been fully revealed, certain observations on the development of several cytomembranes have considerable significance in this respect. In fact, one of the possible functions attributed to the endoplasmic reticulum is that of membrane biosynthesis. The protein components of endoplasmic reticulum and other membranes may be assembled by activity of the endoplasmic reticulum. There is certainly convincing evidence that Golgi membranes and many cytoplasmic vesicles can be derived from endoplasmic reticulum. Moreover, endoplasmic reticulum membranes appear to be continuously synthesized, having a relatively high rate of turnover. At the same time, the several elements of endoplasmic reticulum in the cell are asynchronous in this respect; they are not all replaced at the same time or with the same rate. It has also been suggested that membranes of the endoplasmic reticulum are formed not from preexisting elements but from the ground substance of the cytoplasm.

At the opposite end of the cell cycle are the cytoplasmic events following the death of a cell. Whereas the various elements of the endoplasmic reticulum are relatively labile during the life of the cell, in that they may undergo morphological changes, as during cell division and when the cell becomes metabolically active, they are relatively stable at the time of cell death. A variety of experimental procedures has indicated that no significant changes in the morphology of the endoplasmic reticulum occur immediately. The granular endoplasmic reticulum tends to become vesicular, but not until a few hours after the death of the organism, and the agranular form remains intact for a period of several days.

Differentiation

The endoplasmic reticulum has been shown to have different forms at different times and in different cells (Figure 4–1). Its morphology and distribution are characteristic of the cell type, particularly with regard to function. In cells that have not undergone significant development either morphologically or physiologically—that is, have not differentiated—the endoplasmic reticulum itself is not very well developed. For example, relatively few membranes are present in spermatocytes, fat tissue, and very young meristematic cells. On the other hand, cells that have undergone maturation and become active in protein synthesis have extensive, well-developed endoplasmic reticulum membranes. In other words, the formation of the endoplasmic reticulum is very closely related to the process of cellular differentiation. It is in the fully differentiated cell that the endoplasmic reticulum may appear in more than one form.

These facts indicate that the patterns of differentiation of cells and the distribution of structures within the cells during differentiation are closely correlated with the patterns of development of the endoplasmic reticulum. Examinations of undifferentiated cells show that the endoplasmic reticulum is not prominent but that there are often a number of ribosomes free in the cytoplasmic matrix. As cell division ensues in the undifferentiated tissue, the endoplasmic reticulum becomes more and more evident, and at the same time differentiation progresses. Porter has suggested the following sequence of events to describe these changes. During the formation of the new nuclear envelope in a daughter cell, new elements of the endoplasmic reticulum may be formed. These new elements are functional only in the succeeding interphase (nondividing phase of the cell cycle). In the next cell division, new elements of the endoplasmic reticulum are formed that are slightly different in structure and function from those extant in the preceding division, and these new elements replace those formed earlier. With each succeeding cell division, new endoplasmic reticulum is formed and replaces its predecessor. Finally, after the fully differentiated cells are derived, the pattern of the endoplasmic reticulum in the cells is the relatively permanent, characteristic form for the particular cell type.

Some specific instances of development have been studied in detail, most of which confirm the contention that the endoplasmic reticulum is important in the process of differentiation. One of the simplest examples is the pattern of development of the endoplasmic reticulum in the formation of guinea pig sperm. The spermatogonia (which undergo a specialized cell division) have very few elements of endoplasmic reticulum. The products (spermatids) of the divisions of the spermatogonia, however, exhibit networks of tubular elements and a few parallel cisternae, as well as a small number of ribosomes. Each of the spermatids ultimately gives rise to a mature sperm, after several morphological changes. The early spermatids (immature) have mostly tubular elements and few cisternae, the older spermatids eventually lose most of the elements of the endoplasmic reticulum and retain their ribosomal content, and the mature sperm have little or no endoplasmic reticulum but possibly some ribosomes.

In *Hydra,* a primitive coelenterate, small structures called *nematocysts* are projected from the surface of the body for the purpose of stinging or killing prey. The nematocysts are produced in cells called *cnidoblasts,* located in the ectodermal layer of cells. The primitive cnidoblast has very few elements of endoplasmic reticulum, most of which are tubular. As the cnidoblast matures, more extensive tubules and cisternae develop near the region of the cell in which the nematocyst is being formed. When the metabolic activity of the cnidoblast is greatest, the cytoplasm is filled with closely packed cisternae of the granular form. Thus numerous ribosomes are present, indicating that protein synthesis is occurring. It is apparent that the synthetic activities of the cnidoblasts in producing nematocysts are closely correlated with the development and activities of the endoplasmic reticulum and ribosomes. During the development of the cnidoblasts, cytoplasmic bridges containing elements of endoplasmic reticulum connect adjacent cells (Chapter 3). Such connections between the membrane systems of the cnidoblasts may aid in coordinating their differentiation. The phenomenon of coordination of differentiation in identical cells is quite common, and the endoplasmic reticulum may play an important role here as well as in the differentiation of an individual cell.

Studies of the development of the amphibian embryo have produced information that is extremely useful in correlating the process of differentiation with the morphological and physiological changes occurring in the cytoplasm of the developing cells. The time between fertilization of the amphibian egg and observable changes in the morphology of the developing embryo encompasses a number of stages. Many cell divisions follow fertilization, and up to a certain point all of the new cells are identical. Then masses of cells move and reorganize, and the embryo begins to change in shape from a ball of cells to an elongated body. Along one side a plate or ridge begins to form as a forerunner of the nervous system. These events are known as *neurulation.* Beneath the neural plate is the notochord, a rod of cells that establishes the anteroposterior axis of the embryo. Up to the time of notochord formation, the cytoplasm of the cells is almost devoid of structure. There are few organelles present, including little or no endoplasmic reticulum. During the notochord stage, two principal changes are noted: the formation of large intracellular vacuoles and the formation of a fibrous sheath on the exterior of the notochord.

The vacuoles derive from the evagination of the outer membrane of the nuclear envelope, which separates from its inner partner, leaving cavities between. Shortly after the separation, small vesicles appear near the nuclear envelope, suggesting that parts of the envelope give rise to elements of the endoplasmic reticulum. Thus the endoplasmic reticulum seems to have its origin in the nuclear envelope in undifferentiated cells. The notochord cells that produce the sheath contain well-developed endoplasmic reticulum and many ribosomes. It is possible that the contents of the cavities of the endoplasmic reticulum are involved in the formation of the sheath material. In addition, elements of the endoplasmic reticulum are seen to be connected with the nuclear envelope in some places.

These observations indicate that the endoplasmic reticulum contributes in several ways to the development of the amphibian embryo. Connections between the membranes of the nuclear envelope and the endoplasmic reticulum would provide a pathway between the nucleus and the cytoplasm for the passage of such materials as products of gene action, which are necessary for the synthesis of proteins and other building materials. This possibility implies at least two functions attributed to the endoplasmic reticulum: to facilitate intracellular transport and to facilitate protein synthesis. The development of granular endoplasmic reticulum supports the role in protein synthesis. Since the genes are ultimately in control of cellular activities, the endoplasmic reticulum may indirectly implement gene action. Finally, studies of embryonic development provide valuable evidence for the role of the endoplasmic reticulum in differentiation.

SELECTED READING

General

Brachet, J., "The Living Cell," *Sci. Am.*, **205**(3), 50 (1961).
Porter, K. R., "The Ground Substance: Observations from Electron Microscopy," in J. Brachet and A. E. Mirsky, eds., *The Cell*, Vol. 2, Academic Press, New York, 1961, pp. 621–76.

Waddington, C. H., "How Do Cells Differentiate?" *Sci. Am.*, **189**(3), 108 (1953).

Morphology

Barer, R., S. Joseph, and G. A. Meek, "The Origin of the Nuclear Membrane," *Exptl. Cell Res.*, **18**(1), 179 (1959).

Comb, D. G., and N. Sarkar, "The Binding of 5 S Ribosomal Ribonucleic Acid to Ribosomal Subunits," *J. Mol. Biol.*, **25**(2), 317 (1967).

Küntzel, H., and H. Noll, "Mitochondrial and Cytoplasmic Polysomes from *Neurospora crassa*," *Nature*, **215**(5108), 1340 (1967).

Oberling, C., "The Structure of Cytoplasm," *Intern. Rev. Cytol.*, **8**, 1 (1959).

Pappas, G. D., "Electron Microscopic Studies on Amoebae," *Ann. N.Y. Acad. Sci.*, **78**, 448 (1959).

Rose, G. G., and C. M. Pomerat, "Phase Contrast Observations of the Endoplasmic Reticulum in Living Cultures," *J. Biophys. Biochem. Cytol.*, **8**(2), 423 (1960).

Setterfield, G., H. Stern, and F. B. Johnston, "Fine Structure of Pea and Wheat Embryos," *Can. J. Botany*, **37**, 65 (1959).

Whaley, W. G., H. H. Mollenhauer, and J. H. Leech, "Some Observations on the Nuclear Envelope," *J. Biophys. Biochem. Cytol.*, **8**(1), 233 (1960).

Functions

Novikoff, A. B., "Approaches to the in Vivo Function of Subcellular Particles," in T. Hayashi, ed., *Subcellular Particles*, Ronald Press, New York, 1959, pp. 1–22.

Palade, G. E., and P. Siekevitz, "Liver Microsomes," *J. Biophys. Biochem. Cytol.*, **2**(2), 171 (1956).

Porter, K. R., and R. D. Machado, "Studies on the Endoplasmic Reticulum. IV. Its Form and Distribution During Mitosis in Cells of Onion Root Tip," *J. Biophys. Biochem. Cytol.*, **7**(1), 167 (1960).

Porter, K. R., and C. Franzini-Armstrong, "The Sarcoplasmic Reticulum," *Sci. Am.*, **212**(3), 73 (1965).

Siekevitz, P., "The Relation of Cell Structure to Metabolic Activity," in J. M. Allen, ed., *The Molecular Control of Cellular Activity*, McGraw-Hill, New York, 1962, pp. 143–66.

Smith, D. S., "The Organization and Function of the Sarcoplasmic Reticulum and T-System of Muscle Cells," in J. A. V. Butler and H. E. Huxley, eds., *Progress in Biophysics and Molecular Biology*, Vol. 16, Pergamon Press, New York, 1966, pp. 107–42.

Differentiation

Fawcett, D. W., "Changes in the Fine Structure of the Cytoplasmic Organelles

During Differentiation," in D. Rudnick, ed., *Developmental Cytology*, Ronald Press, New York, 1959, pp. 161–89.

Gordon, J. B., and H. R. Woodland, "The Cytoplasmic Control of Nuclear Activity in Animal Development," *Biol. Rev. Cambridge Phil. Soc.*, 43(2), 233 (1968).

Palade, G. E., "Functional Changes in Structure of Cell Components," in T. Hayashi, ed., *Subcellular Particles*, Ronald Press, New York, 1959, pp. 64–83.

Waddington, C. H., "Specificity of Ultrastructure and Its Genetic Control," *J. Cellular Comp. Physiol.*, 60(2), Suppl., 93 (1962).

Dictyosomes, Lysosomes, and Spherosomes

A major feature of plant cells is the central vacuole, occupying in a mature cell the largest part of the cell volume, particularly in parenchymatous cells. Yet the use of the terms *vacuole* and *vacuolar system* has led to some confusion in the identification of specific cell organelles or their origins. A case in point is the cavity system of the endoplasmic reticulum, which is usually described as separate and distinct from the classical vacuoles. The same problem is found upon examination of the vacuole-like large vesicles associated with the Golgi apparatus. In both of these situations, each "vacuole" is membrane-bounded; the membrane is homologous with the plasma membrane. Compounding the apparent lack of distinctions among the various types of vacuoles is the possibility that they are related ontogenetically. The classical plant vacuole, for example, appears to develop in young cells from smaller "bladders." During the period of their development into the large, mature form, connections may be noted with the endoplasmic reticulum, implying that the vacuoles are greatly expanded cavities from the endoplasmic reticulum. Another view is that vacuoles are derived from the Golgi apparatus.

Whatever its origin, the classical vacuole is similar to other vacuole-like bodies in having a unit membrane boundary. Because of its special properties of semipermeability, the membrane is called the *tonoplast*. The vacuole differs from other bodies of this type in its contents; the tonoplast-bound vacuole contains mostly water and varying amounts of secondary metabolites and storage products. Among the secondary metabolites are phenols, flavonols, anthocyanins (blue and red pigments), and alkaloids. The storage materials include sugars and proteins. Although homologies indeed exist between the tonoplast and the membranes of Golgi, endoplasmic reticulum, and plasma membrane, important differences are evident with respect to the permeability properties of the tonoplast. Isolation of the tonoplast from a cell does not destroy its semipermeability, but the plasma membrane retains its functions only in the living cell. Moreover, as mentioned in Chapter 3, an influx chloride pump operates at the tonoplast, whereas a sodium extrusion pump operates at the plasma membrane. In some plant cells, the ion flux is greater through the plasma membrane than through the tonoplast. Variations in this characteristic of the tonoplast are influenced by the salinity of the plant environment. In any event, two major phenomena are revealed through the behavior of the tonoplast: (1) the gross permeability of a plant cell primarily reflects the characteristics of the tonoplast; (2) there exists selectivity of movement of solutes within a plant cell as well as between the cell and its environment.

In the ensuing discussions of Golgi-related vacuoles and other similar bodies in some cells, the use of the term *vacuole* is restricted to these specialized organelles and does not apply to the classical vacuole just described. This is not to imply, however, that they are unrelated; they may, as stated, have similar or identical origins during the development of a young cell to maturity. The restriction is one of function rather than of structure or origin, since the role of the central vacuole is quite different from that of organelle-related vacuoles.

Dictyosomes and Golgi

From the time of its discovery in 1898 to the present, the Golgi apparatus has been the most controversial of cellular constituents. Several shades of interpretation of this cytoplasmic material have been expressed, from disbelief to total acceptance of its existence. Part of the difficulty lay in the lack of refinement of techniques for the observation of cytoplasmic structures, especially those described by Golgi as the internal reticular apparatus. The apparent network of material that responded positively to silver nitrate or osmium tetroxide was rarely consistent in its appearance. It exhibited quite striking variations in size, location within the cytoplasm, and general morphology among different cells and different organisms, and its presence was demonstrated primarily in animal cells. Among the variations noted were those between the Golgi apparatus of vertebrates and invertebrates. These seemed so significant as to suggest organelles of perhaps different origins, and consequently several names were given to the structures in different organisms.

Golgi discovered the cytoplasmic apparatus using the method of silver impregnation in nerve cells of the cat and the barn owl. Impregnation with silver salts or osmium tetroxide detects the presence of lipid material. The use of the vital stain (Chapter 2) neutral red or methylene blue produced stained droplets in a cell, which were considered by some workers to represent a precursor to the Golgi apparatus as seen in a cell fixed with silver or osmium. Because of the great variability in appearance and the observations of similar patterns of morphology with numerous chemicals applied *outside* a living system, many investigators regarded the so-called Golgi apparatus as an artifact resulting from the methods used to demonstrate its presence. Furthermore, although many of the early descriptions of Golgi material referred to it as a network (reticula), no such network has been seen in living cells. This provides additional support for the argument that the classical Golgi apparatus is an artifact of fixation.

Out of all this rather confused and confusing situation there arose a single consistent observation: in most animal cells examined there is a region or portion of the cytoplasm that is able to reduce silver nitrate and/or osmium tetroxide (Figure 5–1). Most workers have identified this region, but often they have described elements that are not characteristic, depending upon the methods, particular tissues, and optical equipment employed in their studies.

Baker examined the region by using Sudan Black stain and suggested that the variations in morphology are due to a series of changes in form during the activity of the apparatus. However, similar changes have been observed with such substances as gum arabic or Toluidine Blue coacervate in the absence of Golgi.

The most convincing evidence for the existence of the Golgi or derivative material (see Figures 5–7 and 5–8) came from observations of living spermatocytes and spermatids. In these cells the structure has been

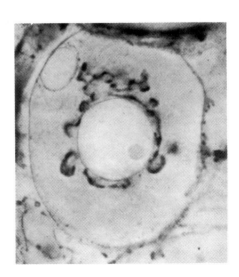

Figure 5–1. Light microscope appearance of a Golgi apparatus in a rat neuron (×2500). FROM G. Bourne, *Cytology and Cell Physiology*, 2nd ed., Clarendon Press, Oxford, 1951, p. 284.

seen under the light microscope in association with the nucleus during the process of spermiogenesis.

Morphology

It has become increasingly clear that the light microscope is inadequate for accurate observations or descriptions of the Golgi apparatus. The diversity in techniques and the morphological differences in different types of cells only compound the difficulty of obtaining good cytological preparations for use with this instrument. Quite simply, consistent results are impossible with light microscope preparations; the characteristics of the Golgi vary with the preparation. In recent years, however, the Golgi controversy has almost dissolved to minor disagreements because of observations with the electron microscope. Reports on a great variety of cells, both plant and animal, in many preparations have been consistent in descriptions of the Golgi apparatus. It is not surprising that these descriptions are rather unlike those forthcoming from light microscope studies.

Although the expected variations appear from one cell to another, the Golgi apparatus does have a definite organization that is common. Most of the variations, which involve shape and size, degree and regularity of branching, and position in the cytoplasm, are seen with the light microscope but quickly resolved with the electron microscope. The features of the Golgi that may be characteristic of a particular cell type are mostly related to the metabolic stage of the cell at the time of observation. Thus the characteristics of the Golgi depend more upon its functional state than upon the kind of cell in which it is located. The position of the apparatus, however, is more likely to be associated with the cell type than with the functional state of the Golgi.

One result of the disagreement over morphology is the plethora of names found in the literature for the same structural complex or parts thereof: dictyosome, lipochondria, idiosome, Golgi body, Golgi substance, Golgi apparatus, Golgi complex. Classically, the material in invertebrates has been called dictyosome, and in vertebrates, Golgi. Objection has been raised to the use of Golgi for all cases, since this term refers to the material described by Golgi in certain brain cells of the owl, which differs from the dictyosomes described in many other types of animal and plant cells. In this discussion the terminology outlined by Mollenhauer and Morré will be followed. *Dictyosome* refers to a stack of lamellae (or cisternae) with its attached tubules and vesicles (Figure 5–2), whereas Golgi apparatus describes the total *associated* dictyosome content of a cell, whether the cell contains one or more dictyosomes. In plant cells there may be

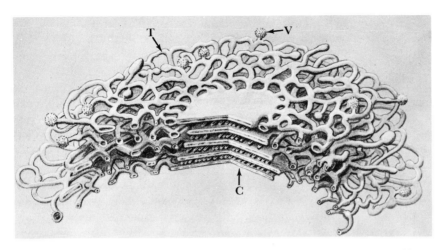

Figure 5–2. Diagrammatic interpretation of the morphology of a plant dictyosome. C, cisterna; T, tubule; V, developing vesicle. FROM H. H. Mollenhauer and D. J. Morré, *Ann. Rev. Plant Physiol.,* **17,** 27 (1966).

several Golgi apparatus entities, each made up of one or more dictyosomes. The basis for this distinction lies in the fact that a group of associated dictyosomes functions synchronously. An estimate of several thousand dictyosomes has been made for cotton synergid cells. At least three types of dictyosomes may be represented, each with a different function; the cell, consequently, would contain three Golgi apparatus. It also follows that in a cell containing a single dictyosome, the dictyosome is the Golgi apparatus.

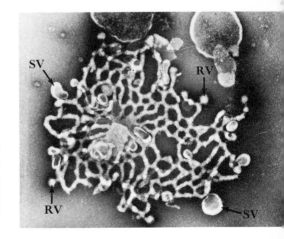

Figure 5–3. A single cisterna of a dictyosome showing two kinds of attached vesicles (×45,000). Stained with phosphotungstic acid. SV, smooth vesicle; RV, rough vesicle. FROM W. P. Cunningham, D. J. Morré, and H. H. Mollenhauer, *J. Cell Biol.,* **28,** 169 (1966).

In fully matured, functional cells, the Golgi apparatus is well developed, whereas in weakly functional or nonfunctional cells, it is poorly developed. In the former, under the electron microscope, a dictyosome consists of three main structural components: cisternae, tubules, and vesicles (Figure 5–3). Although this morphology is generally different from the classic reticulum seen under the light microscope, the reticulum can be produced by impregnation with osmium tetroxide, since all three components reduce it. The reticulum is derived primarily, however, from the tubules that appear in sections as vacuoles (Figure 5–4).

The cisternae are quite similar in appearance to the smooth-surfaced endoplasmic reticulum. In fact, they are stacks of parallel double membranes or lamellae. Each membrane corresponds to the unit membrane described in Chapter 3, with dimensions of comparable magnitude. In the exocrine cells of mouse pancreas, the stacks are arranged in groups, each group consisting of several membrane pairs separated from the neighboring group by a distance of about 130 Å. Each membrane is 60 to 70 Å thick, and the two membranes of a cisterna are separated by a space 60 to 90 Å wide. In other types of cells, the space between cisternal mem-

Figure 5–4. Golgi apparatus producing secretion vesicles in a root cap cell of corn (×47,500). GC, Golgi cisternae; GV, Golgi vacuoles. FROM H. H. Mollenhauer and W. G. Whaley, *J. Cell Biol.,* **17**, 222 (1963).

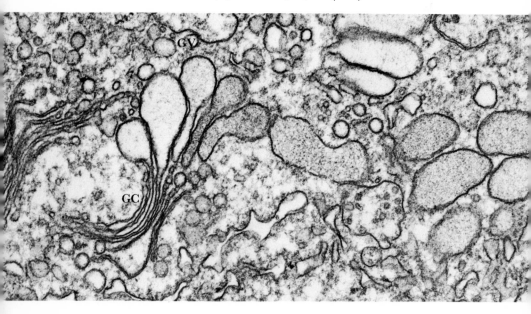

branes varies from 50 to 200 Å. The large vacuoles (Figure 5–4) derive from expanded cisternae; that is, the cisternal space has enlarged to separate the two membranes more widely. The functional aspects of this phenomenon are discussed later. The small vesicles derive from the tubules, but by a different mechanism. They arise through a budding or pinching off of the ends of the tubules and may be only 40 Å in diameter. In such cases, the vesicles are not easily distinguished from the surrounding hyaloplasm.

Plant dictyosomes contain, on the average, two to seven cisternae in a stacked arrangement, and show little or no continuity between adjacent cisternae. Extending sometimes several microns from this central stack are highly branched anastomosing tubules 300 to 500 Å in diameter (Figures 5–2 and 5–3). Two types of vesicles may be connected with the tubules. One is rough-surfaced and spherical, with a diameter of about 500 Å, and is usually found at the ends of the tubules. The other is a smooth vesicle, somewhat flattened, that varies from 200 to 800 Å in diameter. This type may be located within the tubular network, or sometimes near the center of the stack of cisternae. Intercisternal elements, 70 to 80 Å in diameter, may be found between adjacent cisternae (Figure 5–2). They appear to be parallel fibrous elements, and have no known function. Similar dictyosome morphology has been observed in some animal cells, including rat liver.

In an active dictyosome there is evidence from electron microscope studies that the secretion vesicles develop progressively across the cisternae. Synthetic products accumulate at the forming face of the dictyosome (top cisterna of Figure 5–2) where the vesicles first develop. The vesicles, which incorporate the synthetic products, increase in size as they progress across the stack to be released at the maturing face of the dictyosome (Figure 5–5). Since cisternal components ultimately separate from the dictyosome, new ones must form to maintain the dictyosome. The functional significance of such activity will become more apparent in the discussion of Golgi physiology.

The obvious similarity between the dictyosome membranes and the membranes of the endoplasmic reticulum has led to suggestions that the dictyosome is derived from elements of the endoplasmic reticulum. It is difficult to affirm or deny this possibility with confidence. Certainly, both structures are portions of the extensive system of membranes in the cell, which includes the plasma membrane and nuclear envelope as well. There is also evidence that the dictyosome produces plasma membrane. The relationships between the Golgi and the endoplasmic reticulum exist in plant and animal cells alike (Figure 5–6).

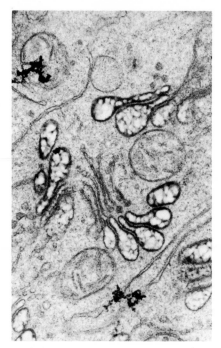

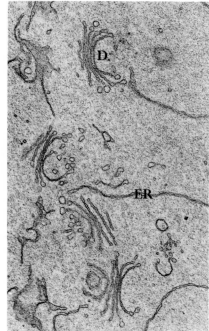

Figure 5–5. Dictyosome in a root cap cell showing forming face at the right and maturation face at the left (×39,000). FROM W. G. Whaley, J. E. Kephart, and H. H. Mollenhauer in M. Locke, ed., *Cellular Membranes in Development,* Academic Press, New York, 1964, p. 162.

Figure 5–6. Associations between dictyosomes and the endoplasmic reticulum (×17,600). D, dictyosome; ER, endoplasmic reticulum. FROM W. G. Whaley, J. E. Kephart, and H. H. Mollenhauer in M. Locke, ed., *Cellular Membranes in Development,* Academic Press, New York, 1964, p. 162.

Morphological Changes During Spermiogenesis

In the spermatids of invertebrates, the cisternae of the dictyosome are arranged in a cup-shaped pattern with as many as 15 lamellar units stacked in parallel. From the periphery of the lamellae, small vesicles or vacuoles are pinched off. During the maturation of the sperm, along with other cytological events (Chapter 13), the dictyosome undergoes several changes. The system of cisternae is gradually replaced by more vesicles and tubules, and within some of these vesicles small granules appear (Figure 5–7). These granules represent secretory products within the dictyosome. Some of the granule-containing vesicles coalesce to form a single *acrosome*

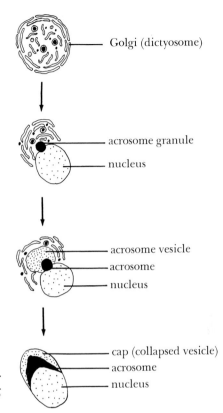

Figure 5–7. Development of the acrosome from the Golgi apparatus during spermiogenesis.

within a large vesicle, which comes to lie on the surface of the sperm nucleus. The vesicle gradually spreads over more of the nuclear surface and eventually collapses on the nuclear membrane to form the cap material (Figure 5–8). The acrosome remains at the apex of the nucleus and contains enzymes involved in the process of fertilization.

Chemistry and Physiology

Study of the chemical composition of the Golgi apparatus reveals the presence of approximately equal amounts of phospholipid and protein. The membranes of the complex undoubtedly consist of lipoprotein, but some of the lipid and protein material identified in Golgi may be storage material and enzymes, respectively. The most significant biochemical property or activity of the Golgi apparatus is due to enzymes that hydrolyze the diphosphates of uridine, guanosine, and inosine in certain plant and animal

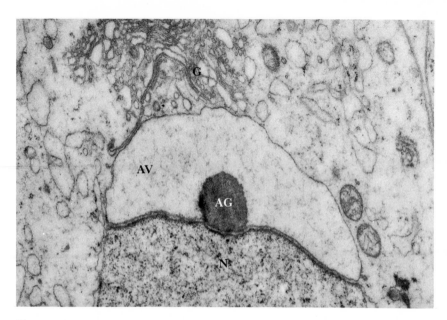

Figure 5–8. Cat spermatid showing the acrosome granule in the acrosome vesicle. AG, acrosome granule; AV, acrosome vesicle; G, Golgi; N, nucleus. COURTESY M. H. Burgos, from D. W. Fawcett in D. Rudnick, ed., *Developmental Cytology,* Ronald Press, New York, 1959.

cells. The general term nucleoside diphosphatase has been used to describe this class of enzyme, although different specific enzymes occur in different kinds of cells. The enzymatic activity appears to be confined to the membranes of the Golgi apparatus, but similar activity has been observed in the endoplasmic reticulum and nuclear envelope in some cells. However, glucose 6-phosphatase, present in endoplasmic reticulum, is absent from dictyosome membranes.

The Golgi apparatus is a discrete and independent cytoplasmic structure; it shares no biochemical activities with the mitochondria, although it shows some direct continuities with the endoplasmic reticulum. Nevertheless, its most important functions are closely related to the activities of these other organelles. The mitochondria are the major sites of ATP formation in the cell. ATP is utilized in the production of proteins and other substances, protein synthesis usually occurring in the vicinity of the rough endoplasmic reticulum (membranes with numerous ribosomal particles on their surfaces). Many products of synthetic activity in cells, including enzymes and hormones, are released or secreted from the cells. In those cells exhibiting high secretory activity, the Golgi apparatus is very well developed. For this reason, the principal function attributed to the Golgi apparatus has been, historically, related to the processes of secretion. In several types of cells (Chapter 4), synthetic products from the rough endoplasmic reticulum are transferred to the Golgi region, whence they are liberated from the cell through the plasma membrane by pinocytosis. Therefore, the secretory function of the Golgi seems to be well founded experimentally; it is responsible for the concentration of synthetic products in membrane-enclosed vesicles, which are transported to the cell surface for export. The proximity of the Golgi and contractile vacuoles in protozoa may confirm the concentration behavior of the Golgi membranes; that is, the Golgi membranes may remove water from the products of synthesis during the formation of the secretory granules. It should be emphasized, however, that the Golgi material remains discrete and independent from the contractile vacuoles. There is no homology between the structures; their relationship is apparently a sharing of the activities involved in water removal.

The products of synthesis in other parts of the cell accumulate within the small vesicles or large vacuoles of the dictyosomes. In some cells the products appear to be carried from the cavities of the endoplasmic reticulum to the dictyosomes. In other cells the small vesicles may collect products for later secretion and then fuse to form larger vesicles or vacuoles. Continuities are observed between the endoplasmic reticulum and the Golgi membranes, and there are transition elements in regions of the cytoplasm where the transfer of products occurs. Small smooth vesicles near the dictyosomes transport secretory proteins from transitional elements of the endoplasmic reticulum to the secretory vesicles of the dictyosomes. After a vesicle has attained maximum size, its membrane fuses with the plasma membrane, and the contents are released through an opening created in the plasma membrane.

Autoradiographic methods provide additional evidence for the activity of Golgi as described. The pancreatic exocrine cells of a guinea pig injected with tritiated leucine show the route taken by the labeled amino acid. Shortly after injection, radioactivity is detected in the vicinity of the rough endoplasmic reticulum. Later it is located in newly synthesized protein in the dictyosome vesicles. Finally the label is found associated with the zymogen granules of the cytoplasm.

Morphological evidence for the role of Golgi in secretion has been obtained in a number of different cells. The Golgi is extremely well developed in cells of the salivary glands, pancreas, and endocrine glands, in bile-secreting cells of the liver, in cells of the silk-spinning glands of insects, and in developing sperm cells. The acrosome in a sperm cell represents a secretory product from the Golgi itself. In many of the cells just mentioned, there is a noticeable change in the morphology and number of dictyosomes during secretory activities, and it is thus possible to trace such changes cytologically during these events.

The Golgi apparatus in plant and animal cells not only is active as a collecting and transporting site for secretory products, but also may ex-

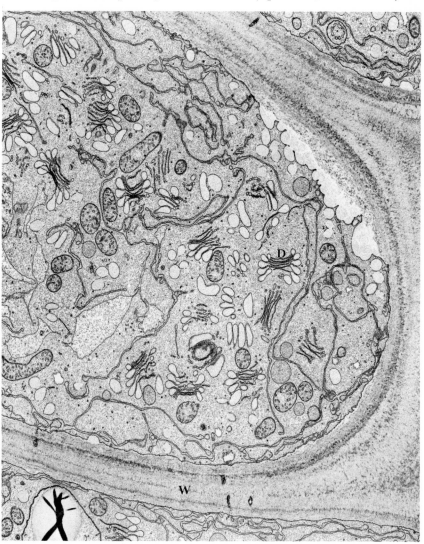

Figure 5–9. Dictyosome-derived secretory product accumulations in root cap cell of corn seedling (×10,600). D, dictyosome; W, cell wall. FROM D. J. Morré, D. D. Jones, and H. H. Mollenhauer, *Planta,* **74,** 286 (1967).

hibit its own synthetic activity. In the cases so far examined, the role of dictyosomes as a synthetically active organelle is in the production of carbohydrates. Labeling studies with animals have shown that [3H]glucose or [3H]galactose becomes incorporated into glycoproteins, whose mono- or polysaccharide moiety is produced in the dictyosomes. Observations in plants demonstrate Golgi-produced pectic materials transported to and incorporated into cell walls. In the outer root cap cells of corn, for example, the contents of large secretory vesicles derived from dictyosome cisternae are released to the cell wall region (Figure 5–9). The vesicle membrane fuses with the plasma membrane, and the vesicle contents accumulate between the cell wall and the plasma membrane. Similar observations have been made of dictyosome activity in the formation of new transverse cell walls through development of the cell plate. Incorporation of [6-3H]glucose, for example, can be demonstrated by autoradiography in the dictyosomes and in the cell plate during telophase of mitosis (Figure 5–10). In many plants the endoplasmic reticulum also contributes to cell

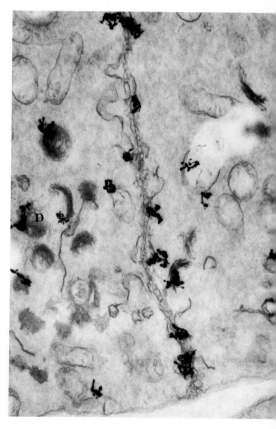

Figure 5–10. Telophase cell of root tip in wheat seedling after exposure to [6-3H]glucose (×13,000). Radioactivity can be seen at the cell plate and in a few dictyosomes. D, dictyosome. FROM J. D. Pickett-Heaps, *J. Ultrastruct. Res.,* **18,** 287 (1967).

plate formation and to the synthesis of cell wall precursor substances. Other carbohydrates produced by Golgi apparatus include mucilage and hemicelluloses. The former has been demonstrated in glandular hairs of insectivorous plants as well as in root cap cells. The slime produced on the root tip is a large acidic polysaccharide containing glucose, galactose, ribose, and other carbohydrate units.

In summary, the major function of the Golgi apparatus is in the secretory activities of specific types of cells, which include the formation of the acrosome during sperm maturation, the production of hormones by endocrine glands, the release of zymogen granules that later are active as digestive enzymes, and the production of cell wall material, and in the storage of protein or lipid material in vesicles and vacuoles. Some of these activities have a physical nature, whereas others are biochemical or enzymatic.

Lysosomes

The lysosomes represent a relatively new discovery among cytoplasmic particles. Consequently, there remain a number of unsolved problems concerning their morphology and physiology. In spite of these questions, however, a considerable quantity of information has been amassed in the past few years. Lysosomes have been found in many animal cells, and similar structures have been observed in plant cells. Although they have been identified primarily by biochemical methods, their morphology can now be studied in detail under the electron microscope.

Morphology

The diameter of a lysosome averages 0.4 to 0.8 μ but may be as great as 5 μ in mammalian kidney cells and is exceedingly large in phagocytes. The shape is often spherical but may be irregular. On the outside is a membrane, composed of lipoprotein, that is homologous with the unit membrane of Robertson. In contrast to the outer membranes of other cytoplasmic components, the lysosome membrane is single.

The internal organization is quite variable. Some lysosomes have a rather solid or very dense content, others have a very dense outer zone with a less dense core, and still others have cavities or vacuoles within the granular material. Generally their content is denser than that of mitochondria. The polymorphic nature of lysosomes has recently been attributed to specific aspects of their major functional activity, namely, intracellular digestion. The name of the bodies, in fact, is derived from this function: lyso- (lytic, digestive) -some (body). Since the contents of the lysosomes vary with the substances they contain and the stage of digestion of these substances, their morphology varies accordingly.

Two types of lysosomes are shown in Figure 5–11, a *digestive vacuole* in the upper right portion and *residual bodies* in the lower portion. The digestive vacuole in this cell from rat kidney is the result of fusion of a primary lysosome with a vacuole containing a substance ingested by the cell. In the residual bodies are myelin figures representing substances that have not been completely digested, such as fat.

The complete range of distribution of lysosomes has not been determined, but they have been observed in kidney, liver, spleen, brain, and thyroid cells of mammals and in some protozoa. It seems likely that they occur in all animal cells. In general, large and numerous lysosomes are found in cells with digestive functions, such as white blood cells.

Several possibilities exist for the origin of lysosomes, and it may be that they have multiple origins depending upon the tissue in which they are located or their function in a specific cell. A lysosome may represent a pinocytosis vacuole, implying extracellular origin. Its enzymatic activities

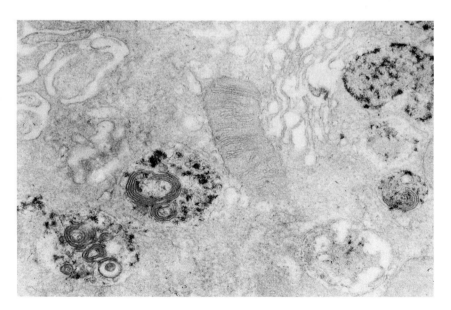

Figure 5–11. Two types of lysosomes in a rat kidney cell (×60,000). Upper right: A digestive vacuole; lower left: residual bodies. Micrograph by Alex B. Novikoff, from C. de Duve, *Sci. Am.,* **208,** 64 (1963).

may then develop after the particle has become part of the cytoplasmic machinery. Lysosomes may also represent inclusions containing remnants of digested material. Observations of digestive activity (Figure 5–11) emphasize this particular possibility. Of even greater significance, as will be demonstrated later, is the evidence that lysosomes originate from the Golgi apparatus and resemble zymogen granules. The problem of establishing an origin for lysosomes stems from their variability in size, shape, and density from cell to cell. However, the delineation of morphological types of lysosomes, as related to their functions, and the evidence that the membranes derive from the Golgi apparatus and the enzymes from ribosomal activity, point to a uniformity of origin even in different cell types.

Chemistry

More definitive identification of the lysosomes has come from the study of their biochemical activities and enzyme content than from observations of their morphology. The simplest chemical definition of a lysosome is "a body rich in acid hydrolase." High levels of acid phosphatase have been found in a number of different tissues, including plant roots, fungi, liver, kidney, and endocrine glands. In the cells of these tissues, acid phosphatase activity is especially pronounced in the region of the Golgi apparatus and is associated with the particles described as lysosomes. Acid phosphatase activity can be demonstrated by the Gomori staining method (Chapter 2), which is quite reliable. Another chemical characteristic of lysosomes is the absence of oxidative enzymes; this property distinguishes

Table 5–1   Enzymes Isolated From Liver Lysosomes*

Enzyme	Substrate
acid deoxyribonuclease	deoxyribonucleic acid
acid phosphatase	phosphate esters of nucleic acid
acid ribonuclease	ribonucleic acid
α-mannosidase	mucopolysaccharides
arylsulfatases A and B	mucopolysaccharides
β-galactosidase	mucopolysaccharides
β-glucuronidase	mucopolysaccharides
β-N-acetylglucosaminidase	mucopolysaccharides
cathepsins A and B	protein
phosphoprotein phosphatase	protein

* Classified generally as acid hydrolases.

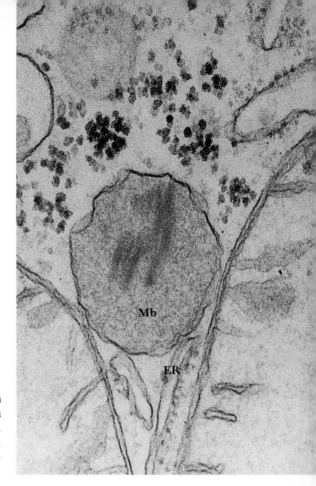

Figure 5–12. A microbody (Mb) from mouse liver showing a dense inclusion (×85,000). ER, endoplasmic reticulum. FROM H. H. Mollenhauer, D. J. Morré, and A. G. Kelley, *Protoplasma,* **62,** 43 (1966.)

them from the mitochondria and implies that they represent a discrete group of cytoplasmic particles. When the lipoprotein membrane of a lysosome is disrupted, all of the enzymes within are released simultaneously and become active (Table 5–1). As long as the membrane is intact or unchanged by contact with other cellular structures, the enzymes are inactive.

Similar particulate components of the cytoplasm, *microbodies,* have been identified by their biochemical activities. They have somewhat different enzyme contents and therefore may be entirely distinct from the lysosomes. These particles are high in uricase, and in rat liver they also contain catalase and D-amino acid oxidase. Often a crystalline inclusion may be present (Figure 5–12). An important difference between these particles and recognized lysosomes is that they exhibit uricase activity even when their membranes are intact. Additionally, some lysosomes (in liver, for example) contain ferritin granules (iron-containing protein), whereas uricase particles do not. Microbodies have been observed in a variety of plant species, from algae and fungi to higher plants. Although they are morphologically similar to animal microbodies (Figure 5–13), plant microbodies do not contain uricase, but may contain catalase and D-amino acid oxidase.

An interesting example of homology arises in the acrosome of a sperm. Since the acrosome shows acid phosphatase activity, it may represent a lysosome that is quite specialized. This observation suggests a Golgi origin for lysosomes, since the acrosome material is derived ultimately from Golgi activity. The function of the acrosomal enzymes (proteases) is to digest the gelatinous materials surrounding the egg, thus facilitating the process of fertilization.

Function

The relationships existing between pinocytic or phagocytic vacuoles and lysosomes have important functional significance, as implied earlier. In the Kupffer cells of liver and in phagocytic cells, the entrance of proteins in pinocytosis vacuoles has been observed. The vacuoles carry the protein material to the regions in which lysosomes are identified. There the lysosomal particles increase in number and exhibit acid phosphatase activity. Lysosomes may be important as the means by which certain kinds of materials gain access to cells. Foreign protein or other material could undergo digestion within the cell as a result of such *endocytosis* (pinocytosis and phagocytosis). Ingested particles enclosed in membranes derived from the plasma membrane (Chapter 3) and forming vacuoles are sometimes called *phagosomes*. It is the behavior of the lysosomes and phagosomes that has been described in the delineation of the various morphological types of lysosomes.

After the entrance of a particle or large body into the cell by endocytosis and the formation of a phagosome, the membranes of the phagosome and a lysosome may fuse to form a single large vacuole. Within this vacuole the lysosomal enzymes begin the process of digestion of the foreign material. Initially the lysosome, known at this time as a primary lysosome, contains the complex of enzymes in an inactive state, but fusion of the type described produces a secondary lysosome with a different morphology (Figure 5–11) and active enzymes. After enzymatic digestion the digested material diffuses out into the hyaloplasm of the cell. Some material may remain in the enlarged lysosome vacuole, in which case the remnant vacuole is described as a residual body, since it contains the residue of the digestive process.

Another example of lysosomal activity can be demonstrated in the white blood cell. A mature white blood cell entering the circulation con-

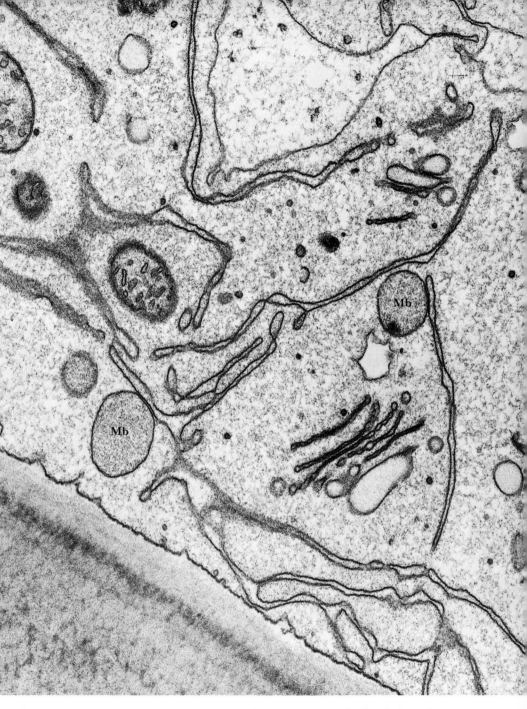

Figure 5–13. Cell from the root cap of corn showing two microbodies (Mb) and endoplasmic reticulum (×35,000). A dense inclusion is in the upper microbody. FROM H. H. Mollenhauer, D. J. Morré, and A. G. Kelley, *Protoplasma,* **62,** 43 (1966).

tains many lysosomes. During the lifetime of the cell, it may ingest a foreign body such as a bacterium. In this event, the lysosomes seem to disappear, releasing their enzymes into the vacuole containing the bacterial cell. The bacterium is destroyed, the lysosomes are lost, and the white blood cell ultimately dies, having carried out its major function in the body. Other kinds of animal cells also have short lives, such as those in the outer layer of the skin and the mucous membrane linings of the body. These cells are continually being replaced, and the activity of the lysosomes in them provides a mechanism by which the dead or degenerating cells are removed. The lysosome membranes rupture in these cells, releasing the enzymes into the body of the cell so that the whole cell may be digested. Lysosomes contain a sufficient complement of enzymes to digest most types of biological or organic materials, and the digestive process (*autolysis*) occurs quite rapidly in dead cells. The process of tissue degeneration, or *necrosis,* can be attributed in part to this lysosomal activity.

A variety of cells undergoing degeneration physiologically and morphologically have large vacuoles containing mitochondria or other cell structures. These vacuoles are enlarged lysosomes, according to their acid phosphatase content, and are called *autophagic vacuoles.* The mitochondria within them are apparently gradually degenerating. Normal cells, such as normal liver and kidney, do not contain mitochondria within large lysosomes, nor are their lysosomes as widely distributed within the cytoplasm as in pathological tissue. Moreover, dividing cells have very few lysosomes. Observations of autophagic vacuoles can be made in cells treated experimentally with a detergent to induce degeneration or under conditions of starvation. The digestion of mitochondria or other cell structures, such as elements of the endoplasmic reticulum, provides a source of energy for these cells, and the digestive process occurring in the vacuoles does not necessarily result in irreparable damage to the cell if normal conditions of maintenance are restored. Following digestion of the cell structure, the autophagic vacuoles may become residual bodies.

There is evidence that the rupture of the lysosome membranes is accelerated in the absence of oxygen and on exposure to various poisons. Oxygen deficiency may prevail during aging or tissue degeneration, and lysosomal activity may account for the destruction of cells and tissues that ensues. In the phenomenon of aging, as observed in liver, heart muscle, and nervous tissue, there is an accumulation of lipofuscin granules (brown pigment) in the lysosomes and a marked increase in esterase and acid phosphatase activity. Aging may also be accompanied by a breakdown of the Golgi apparatus. In fact, the lysosomes are very often found in association with the Golgi, as indicated by the localization of acid phosphatase activity in the region of the Golgi, although not in cells such as those in the proximal convoluted tubules of the kidney.

The effect of cell poisoning is illustrated with an excess of vitamin A, which disrupts the lysosome membrane, causing release of the enzymes into the cell and producing autolysis in cartilage and bone tissue. Damage may also occur in extracellular structures as the enzymes diffuse from the degenerating cell. The lysosome membrane, a most critical element in the activities of the organelle, is thus seen to be sensitive to environmental changes. The efficacy of such drugs as cortisone, which tends to reduce inflammation of tissues, may rest on their capacity to confer stability on the lysosome membrane under conditions of environmental change or stress.

The relations between the lysosomes and the Golgi apparatus are perhaps of utmost significance. Studies have shown that the accumulation of secretory products within the Golgi vacuoles leads to the formation of lysosomes and that the membranes surrounding the products are derived from the Golgi membranes. Thus a portion of the Golgi apparatus is converted into lysosomal particles during the secretory process, and evidence indicates that the change is accompanied by an alteration of enzymatic activity, since the Golgi membranes do not ordinarily contain acid phosphatase. Starved *Euglena,* for example, develop large numbers of lysosomes in the Golgi region, which exhibits high acid phosphatase activity under these conditions.

The complex of connections between the Golgi, endoplasmic reticulum, and lysosomes in the production and distribution of acid hydrolases has been identified by Novikoff as the GERL complex in animal cells. These associations can be observed with the electron microscope, and similar complexes may be found in plants. However, lysosome-like bodies in plants have somewhat different, although homologous, characteristics. The latter are discussed in the following section.

In summary, the lysosomes appear to be involved in both the secretion of synthetic materials, at least those of lysosomal origin, from cells, and the engulfment of foreign materials into cells. In the former instance, lysosome activity is part of a chain of events beginning in the regions of the endoplasmic reticulum, leading to the Golgi apparatus, and ending in the release of protein. The specific activities of the lysosomes, however, are mostly confined within the cell, where proteins (the complex of enzymes capable of digesting various organic substances) are utilized in the destruction of foreign materials, including dead cells, and in the process of tissue degeneration.

Spherosomes

Cytoplasmic bodies containing hydrolytic enzymes have been observed in plant cells, and many of them contain large amounts of lipid (up to 98%). These lipid-containing vacuoles are called *spherosomes*. They have a single limiting membrane and a diameter of 0.5 to 1.0 μ (Figure 5–14). The presence of acid phosphatase has suggested that spherosome enzyme activity is associated with lipid metabolism. Spherosomes do not exhibit as wide a range of lytic action as do lysosomes, but are related as storage bodies for similar kinds of enzymes. One view of spherosomes is that they may develop as precursors of reserve oil droplets. Granular material in spherosomes may represent a protein stroma that is later replaced as oil

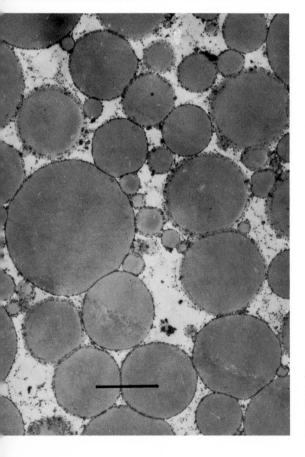

Figure 5–14. Spherosomes isolated from peanut cotyledons and fixed with osmium tetroxide (×17,200). FROM T. J. Jacks, L. Y. Yatsu, and A. M. Altschul, *Plant Physiol.*, **42**, 585 (1967).

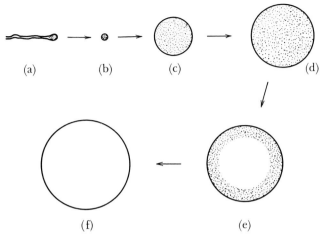

Figure 5–15. Development of spherosomes and oil droplets: (a) terminal strand of endoplasmic reticulum; (b) detached vesicle; (c) juvenile spherosome; (d) spherosome; (e) transition stage; (f) oil droplet. FROM A. Frey-Wyssling and K. Mühlethaler, *Ultrastructural Plant Cytology*, Elsevier, Amsterdam, 1965, p. 171.

accumulates (Figure 5–15). A contrary view is that spherosomes are not precursors to fat or oil bodies. The latter interpretation is based on the observations that there is no coalescence of spherosomes, that fat bodies have no membranes and easily coalesce, and that spherosomes do not contain neutral fat. Whatever the correct interpretation, spherosomes clearly are major sites of lipid storage in plant cells, and resemble lysosomes in having a single membrane boundary and some hydrolytic enzyme activity.

SELECTED READING

General

Allison, A., "Lysosomes and Disease," *Sci. Am.,* **217**(5), 62 (1967).

Dalton, A. J., "Golgi Apparatus and Secretion Granules," in J. Brachet and A. E. Mirsky, eds., *The Cell,* Vol. 2, Academic Press, New York, 1961, pp. 603–20.

Kuff, E. L., and A. J. Dalton, "Biochemical Studies of Isolated Golgi Membranes," in T. Hayashi, ed., *Subcellular Particles,* Ronald Press, New York, 1959, pp. 114–27.

Nath, V., and G. P. Dutta, "Cytochemistry of Protozoa, with Particular Reference to the Golgi Apparatus and the Mitochondria," *Intern. Rev. Cytol.,* **13,** 323 (1962).

Novikoff, A. B., "Lysosomes and Related Particles," in J. Brachet and A. E. Mirsky, eds., *The Cell,* Vol. 2, Academic Press, New York, 1961, pp. 423–88.

Morphology of Golgi

Avers, C. J., "Fine Structure Studies of Phleum Root Meristem Cells. I. Mitochondria," *Am. J. Botany,* 49(9), 996 (1962).

Baker, J. R., "The Golgi Controversy," *Symp. Soc. Exptl. Biol.,* **10**, 1 (1957).

Fawcett, D. W., "Changes in the Fine Structure of the Cytoplasmic Organelles During Differentiation," in D. Rudnick, ed., *Developmental Cytology,* Ronald Press, New York, 1959, pp. 161–89.

Mollenhauer, H. H., and W. G. Whaley, "An Observation on the Functioning of the Golgi Apparatus," *J. Cell Biol.,* **17**(1), 222 (1963).

Whaley, W. G., J. E. Kephart, and H. H. Mollenhauer, "Developmental Changes in the Golgi Apparatus of Maize Root Cells," *Am. J. Botany,* **46**(10), 743 (1959).

Zeigel, R. F., and A. J. Dalton, "Speculations Based on the Morphology of the Golgi Systems in Several Types of Protein-Secreting Cells," *J. Cell Biol.,* **15**(1), 45 (1962).

Chemistry of Golgi

Duncan, C. J., "Properties and Stabilization of the Lysosomal Membrane," *Nature,* **210**(5042), 1229 (1966).

Essner, E., and A. B. Novikoff, "Cytological Studies on Two Functional Hepatomas. Interrelations of Endoplasmic Reticulum, Golgi Apparatus, and Lysosomes," *J. Cell Biol.,* **15**(2), 289 (1962).

Laties, G. G., "Physiological Aspects of Membrane Function in Plant Cells During Development," in M. Locke, ed., *Cellular Membranes in Development,* Academic Press, New York, 1964, pp. 299–320.

Morré, D. J., D. D. Jones, and H. H. Mollenhauer, "Golgi Apparatus–Mediated Polysaccharide Secretion by Outer Root Cap Cells of *Zea mays.* I. Kinetics and Secretory Pathway," *Planta,* **74**(3), 286 (1967).

Pickett-Heaps, J. D., "Further Observations on the Golgi Apparatus and Its Functions in Cells of the Wheat Seedling," *J. Ultrastruct. Res.,* **18**(3–4), 287 (1967).

Sano, M., "Further Studies on the Theta Cell of the Mouse Anterior Pituitary as Revealed by Electron Microscopy, with Special Reference to the Mode of Secretion," *J. Cell Biol.,* **15**(1), 85 (1962).

Sjöstrand, F. S., and V. Hanzon, "Function of the Golgi Apparatus in the Exocrine Pancreas Cell," *Science,* **134**(3488), 1434 (1961).

Lysosomes and Spherosomes

Ashford, T. P., and K. R. Porter, "Cytoplasmic Components in Hepatic Cell Lysosomes," *J. Cell Biol.,* **15**(1), 198 (1962).

De Duve, C., "Lysosomes, A New Group of Cytoplasmic Particles," in T. Hayashi, ed., *Subcellular Particles,* Ronald Press, New York, 1959, pp. 128–59.

De Duve, C., "The Lysosome," *Sci. Am.,* **208**(5), 64 (1963).

Frey-Wyssling, A., and K. Mühlethaler, *Ultrastructural Plant Cytology,* American Elsevier, New York, 1965.

Gahan, P. B., "Histochemistry of Lysosomes," *Intern. Rev. Cytol.,* **21,** 1 (1967).

Jacks, T. J., L. Y. Yatsu, and A. M. Altschul, "Isolation and Characterization of Peanut Spherosomes," *Plant Physiol.,* **42**(4), 585 (1967).

Novikoff, A. B., and E. Essner, "Cytolysomes and Mitochondrial Degeneration," *J. Cell Biol.,* **15**(1), 140 (1962).

Sorokin, H. P., "The Spherosomes and the Reserve Fat in Plant Cells," *Am. J. Botany,* **54**(8), 1008 (1967).

6

Mitochondria

"There is one very good thing about the mitochondria: they certainly exist!" Jean Brachet stated. And they have been observed in almost all plant and animal cells. Whereas only relatively recent studies have verified the existence of the endoplasmic reticulum and associated structures, the mitochondria have been known for some time. In what seems to be a standard cry of objection to claims for new cell components, the mitochondria too were once considered an artifact of fixation. However, there is now no doubt that they exist and play a specific and essential role in cellular metabolism. They can be identified with regularity by their characteristic morphology as well as their biochemical activities. In many ways, more is known about the mitochondria than about any other single cytoplasmic constituent.

Morphology and Occurrence

Mitochondria can be observed in living cells with dark-field or phase-contrast microscopes. They can also be seen with a light microscope after the application of vital stains (Chapter 2). Within the range of magnification of standard optical equipment, the mitochondria usually appear as rodlike or filamentous structures. In most cells they are distributed throughout the cytoplasm, but in certain cells they are localized. The latter situation holds in cells of the kidney tubules, in which they occur in the folds of the basal regions near the plasma membrane (Chapter 3). In other cells the mitochondria are closely associated with the nuclear envelope. In both cases of localization, there is a functional significance to the position, such as in the transport of materials from one region to another. In *Paramecium* most of the mitochondia are located just beneath the surface of the cell, very few being found in the innermost portions of the cytoplasm. Energy for the activity of the *cilia* that line the cell boundary is supplied by the mitochondria near the surface. In nerve fibers the mitochondria are located in the region of the cell transmitting the nerve impulse. Mitochondria change their positions in many cells, perhaps being carried from one part of the cell to another by the streaming of the cytoplasm. Specific instances of movement result in improved access of the mitochondria to various substrates and thus increase the efficiency of mitochondrial function. Those mitochondria that are more or less stationary serve a specific function in their restricted locale (cardiac muscle, kidney tubules).

The number of mitochondria in a single cell varies considerably, according to the species and the functional type. In the amoeba *Chaos chaos*, there may be as many as 500,000 mitochondria, whereas in a rat liver cell there may be as few as 500. It is possible to detect differences in the number of mitochondria within the same tissue. In the rat liver, for example, although there may be as many as 2500 mitochondria per cell, the average number is about 1000. Eggs of sea urchin species contain from 14,000 to 150,000 mitochondria. The function of the cell is often correlated with the number of mitochondria present, as, for example, in salivary gland cells, in which an increase in secretory activity is reflected in the number of mitochondria.

Measurements of mitochondria magnified by the electron microscope have resulted in a general size range with some species variations. The average diameter is 0.2 to 2 μ, with a tendency toward the lower value. The range in length is greater, from 0.3 to 40 μ. Mitochondria in the exocrine cells of mammalian pancreas are about 10 μ long, those in oocytes of *Rana pipiens* are 20 to 40 μ long, and those in rat liver average 3.3 μ in length. Generally the length of the mitochondria is within the range 3 to 5 μ, and the cell environment (pH, osmotic pressure, etc.) has some influence on their size.

Mitochondrial shape is characteristic for a cell or tissue type, but this too is dependent upon environmental or physiological conditions. Although most cells contain rodlike mitochondria, some cells, such as the sperm and eggs of a number of organisms, contain more spherical forms. For a detailed delineation of mitochondrial organization, it is necessary to use the electron microscope. In spite of the excellent methods of preparation now possible and the details of the fine structure that have been detected, there remains the long-standing question: do the methods of preparing the cells for mitochondrial observation (fixation, etc.) significantly alter the structure as it occurs in the living, undisturbed cell? Until

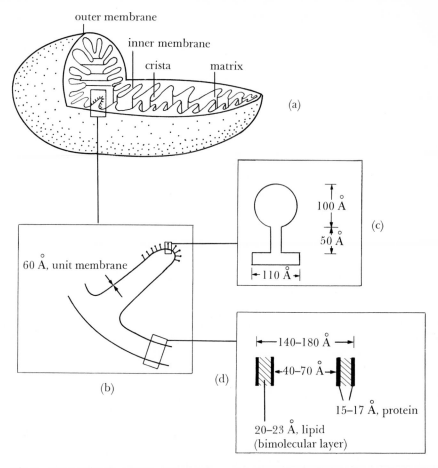

Figure 6–1. Mitochondrial ultrastructure: (a) three-dimensional view; (b) detail of area outlined in (a); (c) dimensions of elementary particle; (d) dimensions of area outlined in (b).

optical or other techniques permit the direct observation of living cells at very great magnifications, this question will be unanswered. Nevertheless, the fine structure of mitochondria as it is now described is, in all likelihood, a very close approximation of the living structure.

The ultrastructure of a mitochondrion is summarized in Figure 6–1.

Figure 6–2. Mitochondria with tubular cristae in hamster kidney (×49,000). Micrograph by D. W. Fawcett, from *An Atlas of Fine Structure: The Cell, Its Organelles and Inclusions.* W. B. Saunders Company, Philadelphia, 1966.

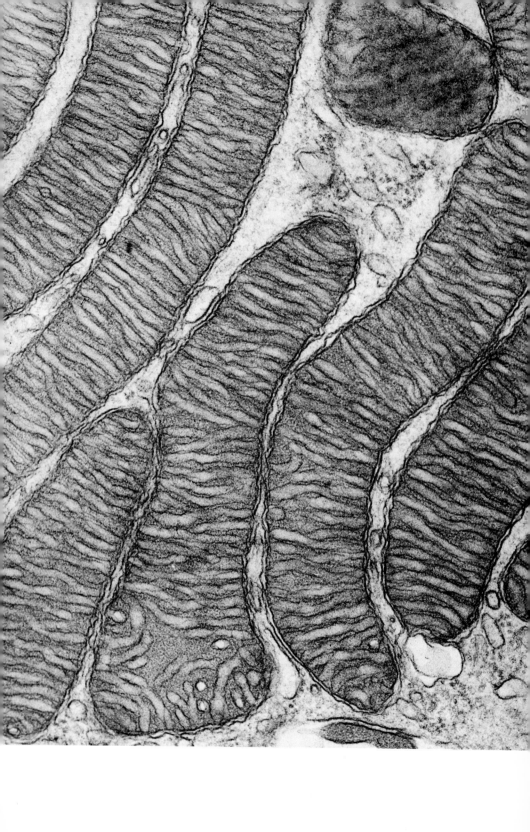

Although the gross morphology of a mitochondrion is considerably different from that of any other cell organelle, the basic components of a mitochondrion are the unit membranes described in Chapter 3. An outer limiting membrane surrounds each mitochondrion and measures about 60 Å in thickness. Just inside this membrane is a less dense region, from 20 to 60 Å thick, which separates the outer membrane from the inner membrane. The inner membrane has approximately the same diameter as the outer membrane and is characterized by a series of infoldings into the cavity of the mitochondrion. These folds are called *cristae,* and they penetrate the *matrix* of the mitochondrion. The outer boundary, then, consists of a double membrane arrangement and an intermediate space, with a total thickness of 140 to 180 Å. There are two cavity systems, the one occupied by the granular matrix and the other between the inner and outer membranes. In a number of cell types, connections have been observed between the inner and outer membranes. The biochemical activities of the membranes and the matrix will be considered later, although it should be indicated at this time that the functions of the mitochondria are very closely related to their structure.

The presence, number, and density of granules within the matrix vary according to cell type and physiological conditions. More variable, however, is the arrangement of the cristae. They may be parallel to the long axis of the mitochondrion (as in neurons and striated muscle) or, more commonly, perpendicular to the long axis. They may be arranged as vesicles, often branched to form a network of connecting chambers (human leucocytes, some protozoa, corn, and parathyroid glands). A tubular arrangement (Figure 6–2) is usual in cells active in steroid secretion (adrenal glands) and has been found in plant meristematic cells and the Malpighian tubules of insects. This is also rather standard in many protozoa. The term *villi* has been used to denote the numerous, interlaced cristae in amoebae (Figure 6–3). In certain spermatids the cristae are arranged concentrically within the matrix. Despite these differences in arrangement according to the type of cell or species, the underlying purpose of the infoldings is to provide an increased surface area within the mitochondrion for enzymatic activity (Figures 6–4 and 6–5).

Related to the differences in cristae arrangement are variations in the number of cristae and the volume of the matrix. Where there are relatively few cristae (mammalian liver), there is much matrix, and a large number of cristae (muscle tissue) reduces the amount of matrix. The number of cristae directly affects the capacity of the mitochondrion to carry on oxidative reactions. In the flight muscle cells of insects, for example, there are more cristae as well as more mitochondria than in any other cells of the body.

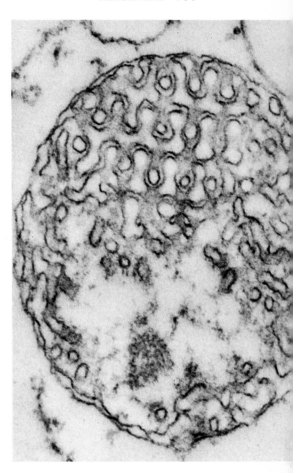

Figure 6–3. Arrangement of cristae in a mitochondrion of *Pelomyxa carolinensis* (×48,000). FROM G. D. Pappas and P. W. Brandt, *J. Biophys. Biochem. Cytol.,* **6,** 85 (1959).

As a consequence of negative staining with phosphotungstate for electron microscopy, small particles are observed along the surfaces of the inner mitochondrial membranes. Discovered by Fernández-Morán, they have been called inner membrane subunits or *elementary particles.* Although there have been claims that the elementary particles represent artifacts of negative staining, they have also been observed in positive contrast preparations by Ashhurst. In spite of some conflicting views about the structure of these subunits, they form an integral part of the inner membrane and play an active part in respiration. In fact, each particle may represent an assembly of respiratory enzymes. According to Fernández-Morán, each of these repeating units consists of three parts: a polyhedral head 80 to 100 Å in diameter, a 50 Å stalk 30 to 40 Å wide, and a cuboid base 40 × 110 Å. The base forms a part of the inner membrane

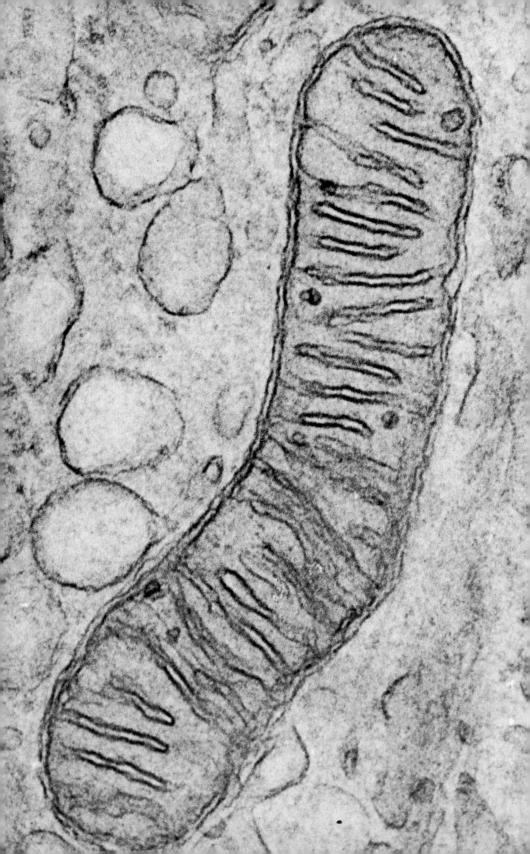

Figure 6–4 Mitochondrion from mouse epididymis (×175,000). Micrograph by D. W. Fawcett, from *An Atlas of Fine Structure: The Cell, Its Organelles and Inclusions.* W. B. Saunders Company, Philadelphia, 1966.

surface (Figure 6–6). Depending upon the size and type of mitochondrion, there are from 10,000 to 100,000 elementary particles per mitochondrion.

Functionally the particles are associated with the presence of enzymes for oxidative phosphorylation and with mitochondrial adenosine triphosphatase. Green has calculated that a single respiratory assembly consists of one molecule each of nicotinamide adenine dinucleotide dehydrogenase, succinic dehydrogenase, and cytochromes a, b, c, and c_1, with a total molecular weight of 1.3 million. On the basis of the estimated molecular weight of an elementary particle (740,000), more than one would be required to provide the electron transport pathway from nicotinamide adenine dinucleotide to oxygen (see the following sections). Green and Silman

Figure 6–5. Mitochondria from adipose tissue of a bat (×14,000). Micrograph by D. W. Fawcett, from *An Atlas of Fine Structure: The Cell, Its Organelles and Inclusions.* W. B. Saunders Company, Philadelphia, 1966.

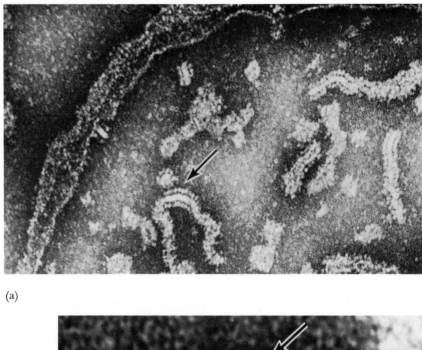

(a)

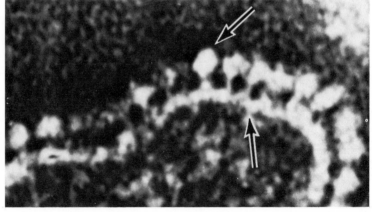

(b)

Figure 6–6. Mitochondrion isolated from beef heart and prepared with phosphotungstate. (a) Arrays of elementary particles appear on the cristae surfaces (×100,000). (b) Structure of elementary particles showing headpiece, stalk, and base (×600,000). FROM H. Fernández-Morán et al., *J. Cell Biol.,* **22,** 63 (1964).

consider that the electron transfer chain is located exclusively in the base pieces and that the stalk and headpiece are concerned with the terminal stages of oxidative phosphorylation. Moreover, Green's view is that the complete electron transfer assembly corresponds in size to the elementary particle. On the other hand, Chance suggests that each elementary particle carries a single electron carrier component and possibly additional protein. Adjacent elementary particles may interact by diffusion from one to another. Chance and Parsons have suggested the term *oxysome* to represent a factor for coupling phosphorylation to respiration. The elementary particle then would consist of oxysomes or parts thereof. There may also be some homologies between elementary particles of mitochondria and *quantasomes* of chloroplasts (Chapter 7).

Chemical Composition

The permeability of the mitochondrial membranes is partly a function of their lipid content. This is particularly true of the outer membrane, which is quite permeable to lipid-soluble substances. The composition of the membranes is similar to that of the plasma membrane and the endoplasmic reticulum, namely, phospholipid and protein. The protein is present on the two surfaces, with a bimolecular layer of lipid between (Figure 6–1). Analysis of the entire mitochondrial body, including the resident enzyme systems, indicates that about 70% (dry weight) is protein and 25 to 30% is lipid. Of the lipid component, 90% is phospholipid, and 10% carotenoids, cholesterol, vitamin E, and other traces. Also present in small amounts in the mitochondrion are sulfur, iron, copper, and some vitamins, most of which are related to enzyme activities. The nucleic acid contents of mitochondria are discussed later.

Some of the metallic ions in mitochondria are associated with specific functions of the cell in question. Certain of these elements have been located in the matrix and may account for the dense particles often observed. Silver has been found in some liver cells and retinal epithelium, iron in erythrocytes, and sodium and potassium in duodenal cells. These and other substances may be present only at a given time during mitochondrial activity, to be released into the cytoplasm at another time, or they may be stored indefinitely. The localization of particular substances in the mitochondria may produce morphological changes, such as alterations in the number and arrangement of the cristae, and storage of certain materials is sometimes accompanied by a reduction in the size and number of cristae, with their eventual disappearance. After a substance is released from a mitochondrion, the normal structure is restored, or the mitochondrion degenerates.

The structure and chemical composition of the mitochondria are so closely related to their functions or biochemical activities that it is not possible to discuss one aspect without making reference to the other. The chemical composition of the mitochondria depends in large part upon the enzymes present for oxidation, phosphorylation, and electron transfer. The enzyme systems are somewhat separated from each other in the sense that certain enzymes (mainly the electron carriers) are intimately associated with the membranes while others (the oxidative enzymes of the Krebs cycle) are located within the matrix. The next section outlines the major pathways of cellular respiration as a background for the consideration of mitochondrial functions.

Metabolic Pathways

The cycle of respiration involves the breakdown of carbohydrates, fatty acids, and amino acids, with the bulk of the activity affecting the carbohydrates. The basis of the biochemical reactions, which lead to the ultimate liberation of energy along with carbon dioxide and water, is oxidation. This is best defined as the loss of electrons but can also be described as the loss of hydrogen or the addition of oxygen. Since certain of the respiratory reactions occur in the absence of oxygen (anaerobic) whereas others require oxygen (aerobic), the first definition seems soundest. The major product of the complex series of biochemical events is energy. This energy may be stored in chemical form as ATP (Figure 6–7), it may be released as heat (as in muscle contraction), or it may be utilized in a variety of chemical reactions, including those of the respiratory cycle, nervous transmission, protein and nucleic acid syntheses, cell division, active transport, and secretion. Although most of the cellular ATP is produced within the mitochondria, it is used both inside and outside these organelles.

The general scheme of cellular respiration is shown in Figure 6–8. The enzymes necessary for glycolysis are not located in the mitochondria but are apparently present in the hyaloplasm. On the other hand, the enzymes responsible for the remainder of the cycle are in the mitochondria. Therefore, most of the oxidative enzymes are specifically, although

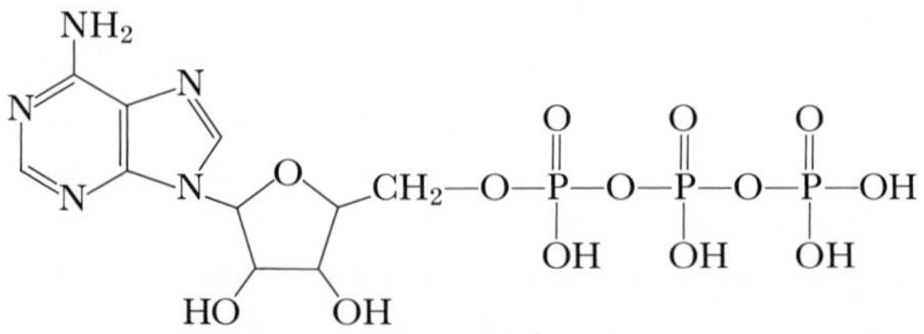

Figure 6–7. Structure of adenosine triphosphate.

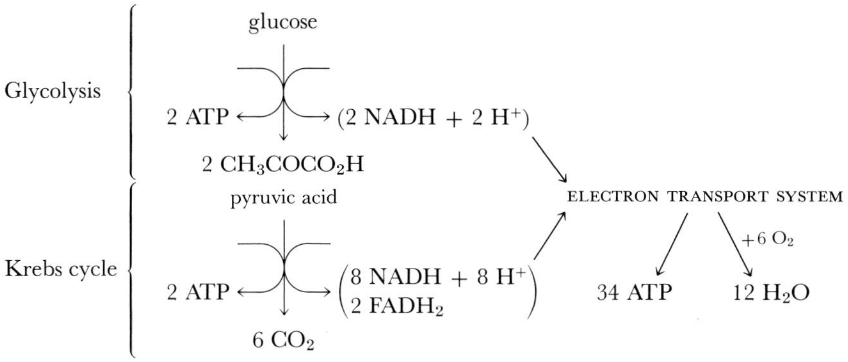

Figure 6–8. A general scheme of cellular respiration.

not exclusively, associated with the mitochondria. The entire complex of enzymes present in the mitochondria and associated with oxidative metabolism was once known as the *cyclophorase system*. Since some alteration of protein occurs on isolation from the mitochondria, not all of the enzymes have been purified, especially those bound into the framework of the membranes themselves.

The activity of the oxidative enzymes is quite specific, and they are easily inactivated. In addition, a large number of them depend upon the presence of particular prosthetic groups for their activity. A prosthetic group readily dissociated from the protein enzyme is known as a *coenzyme*. Several of the coenzymes involved in oxidative metabolism are B vitamins, such as thiamine (B_1), necessary for pyruvate metabolism, and riboflavin (B_2), necessary for electron transport. Coenzyme A (CoA), which is important in the Krebs cycle, is also known as pantothenic acid plus ATP.

Glycolysis

Although the enzymatic reactions of the glycolytic cycle do not occur within the mitochondria, they are important as background, since the product, pyruvic acid, is oxidized to carbon dioxide and water in the presence of oxygen in the Krebs cycle. Glucose is the principal substrate for the glycolytic reactions; it is phosphorylated and ultimately broken down to the three-carbon compound pyruvic acid. In the process some small amount of energy is liberated, as two high energy phosphate groups. These combine with adenosine diphosphate (ADP) to form two molecules of ATP. The energy, then, is stored in the phosphate bonds of ATP or

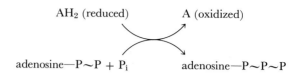

Figure 6–9. Oxidative phosphorylation. P_i, inorganic phosphate; $\sim$, high energy bond.

released as heat, as during muscle contraction. During the glycolytic cycle ATP donates high energy phosphate to another compound, thus enabling that compound to react chemically. Consequently, energy is both utilized and released in the cycle, the net gain being two molecules of ATP. This reaction is oxidative phosphorylation (Figure 6–9), the most important of all the reactions involving the mitochondria. It confers upon the mitochondrion its role as a fundamental unit of secretion and absorption for the cell. Storage of energy in ATP is possible only when oxidation is coupled with phosphorylation; uncoupling these two events results in the liberation of heat without concomitant ATP formation. The glycolytic cycle makes a very small contribution to the pool of ATP in the cell in comparison with the later phases of respiration. The glycolytic cycle is outlined in Figure 6–10.

Krebs Cycle

Although the major substrate for oxidative reactions is carbohydrate (glucose), which enters the Krebs cycle (tricarboxylic acid cycle) after breakdown to pyruvate, fatty acids and amino acids may also enter the cycle. For example, the amino acid glutamic acid becomes α-ketoglutaric acid on deamination and is included in the reaction cycle. At the same time fatty acids and amino acids may be derived from one or more of the tricarboxylic acids present in the Krebs cycle. On amination, α-ketoglutaric acid is converted to glutamic acid. Thus both the formation and the decomposition of organic materials may be related to the same metabolic system in the cell.

The Krebs cycle is outlined in Figure 6–11. Carbon dioxide is split from the carboxyl group of pyruvic acid (decarboxylation), leaving a two-carbon residue or fragment, which is then bound to coenzyme A to form acetyl-CoA. Coupling with oxaloacetic acid (a four-carbon compound) produces citric acid (a six-carbon compound). Concurrently two hydrogens are liberated from pyruvic acid and carried to the electron transport system. A specific dehydrogenase enzyme catalyzes the removal of the hydrogen. During the Krebs cycle five pairs of hydrogens are donated to the trans-

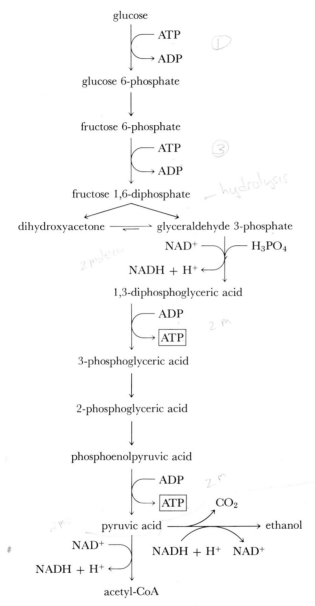

glucose

— ATP

→ ADP

① glucose 6-phosphate

fructose 6-phosphate

— ATP

③ → ADP

fructose 1,6-diphosphate — hydrolysis

dihydroxyacetone ⇌ glyceraldehyde 3-phosphate

NAD⁺ — — H₃PO₄

NADH + H⁺ ←

2 molecu

1,3-diphosphoglyceric acid

— ADP

→ [ATP] 2 m

3-phosphoglyceric acid

2-phosphoglyceric acid

phosphoenolpyruvic acid

— ADP 2 m

→ [ATP] CO₂

pyruvic acid → ethanol

NAD⁺ — NADH + H⁺ NAD⁺

NADH + H⁺ ←

acetyl-CoA

Figure 6–10. The glycolytic cycle. The major products of the cycle are enclosed in boxes. The hydrolysis of fructose 1,6-diphosphate results in dihydroxyacetone and glyceraldehyde 3-phosphate. These two 3-carbon products are in an equilibrium that favors glyceraldehyde 3-phosphate. Each glyceraldehyde 3-phosphate then leads to the formation of four molecules of ATP, two molecules of NADH, and two molecules of pyruvic acid.

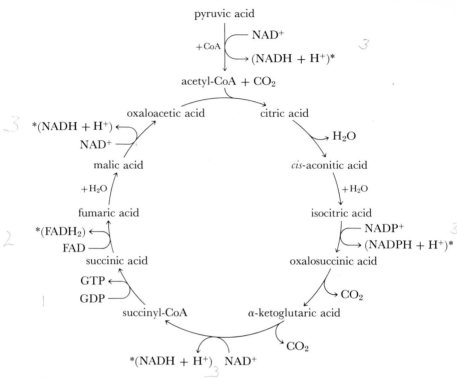

pyruvic acid

$+CoA$ — NAD⁺

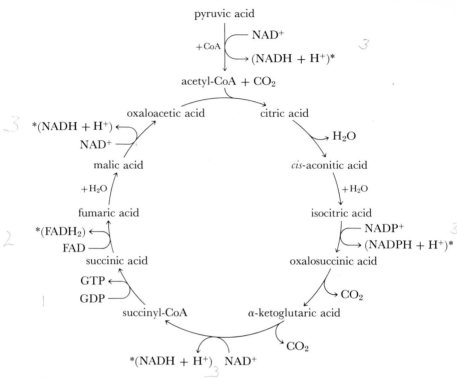

Figure 6–11. The Krebs cycle. Starred molecules indicate points of electron entry to the electron transport system.

port system, which gives rise to the bulk of the ATP in the cell. The hydrogens are carried in the form of reduced coenzymes nicotinamide adenine dinucleotide ($NADH + H^+$) and flavine adenine dinucleotide ($FADH_2$). The coupling of the Krebs cycle with the electron transport cycle provides a much more efficient system for energy production than the glycolytic cycle. In fact, 36 molecules of ATP are produced from this combination, as against 2 molecules in glycolysis, yielding a total of 38 ATP molecules for the whole respiratory pathway. As shown in the two cycles, carbon dioxide and water are also liberated.

Electron Transport System

The dehydrogenase that removes two hydrogens from the substrate undergoing oxidation in the Krebs cycle passes them to flavoprotein, a hydrogen acceptor, which carries them through the *cytochrome system* for the ultimate coupling with oxygen to form water. The terms electron transport system and cytochrome system are used here synonymously. The hydrogens are released into the cytoplasm by the flavoprotein enzymes while electrons, thus removed from the substrate of the Krebs cycle, are transferred to the cytochromes. The electrons pass from one cytochrome to another as along a chain until they reach oxygen, which becomes activated. The oxygen then combines with the free hydrogen to produce water. Figure 6–12 outlines the electron transport system.

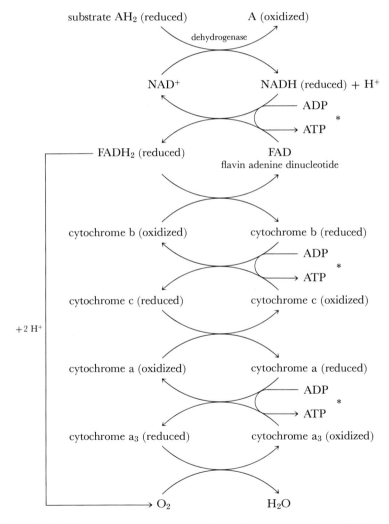

Figure 6–12. Electron transport system. Asterisks mark points of ATP production via oxidative phosphorylation.

The cytochromes are pigments containing iron, which are capable of transferring electrons by a series of oxidations and reductions. From flavoprotein the electrons pass to cytochrome b, which in turn passes them to cytochrome c; thence they pass to cytochrome a and finally to cytochrome a_3 (cytochrome oxidase). At some point in the system, another substance, coenzyme Q, is involved in the transfer mechanism, but it is not yet clear whether this coenzyme always participates. From cytochrome oxidase the electrons are transferred to oxygen. During each step in the transfer of electrons from dehydrogenases to flavoproteins to cytochromes, inorganic phosphates are raised to high-energy organic phosphates in ATP, as indicated by the asterisks. Thus phosphorylations accompanying the specific reactions in this system of oxidations give rise to 36 molecules of ATP.

In summary, the numerous chemical reactions that break down carbohydrates, fat, and protein involve oxidations requiring a series of specific oxidative enzymes. A number of these enzymes operate in conjunction with a prosthetic group or coenzyme. The most significant product of these reactions is energy, and its liberation depends upon the coupling of oxidation with phosphorylation.

Function

Several enzymes of the respiratory cycle are located exclusively within the mitochondria; these are the enzymes linking oxidation to phosphorylation, enzymes for fatty acid and amino acid oxidation, and cytochromes c, a, and a_3. All of the enzymes of the Krebs cycle are found in the mitochondria, but only some of them are located there exclusively. The chief site for respiratory activity in the cell, then, is in the mitochondria. Of special interest is the observation that the resident enzymes are arranged in the mitochondrion in a specific pattern. Certain phases of oxidative metabolism occur along the membranes, or cristae, whereas others are localized within the matrix. The electron transport enzymes are bound in some way, perhaps by protein, to the lipoprotein of the membranes, whereas the Krebs cycle enzymes, which are soluble, are within the matrix, although closely associated with the membranes.

It has often been stated that the morphological integrity of the mitochondrion is necessary for the maintenance of its function, namely, enzymatic activity. This is correct, but only with respect to particular enzymes. If mitochondrial structure is disrupted, the oxidations of the Krebs cycle are lost, or, more precisely, the enzymes of this cycle become inactivated. As long as some double membrane organization remains, oxidative phosphorylation and electron transport continue. If the membranes are disrupted to the extent that only single membranes remain, then only electron transport reactions take place. These results, obtained from in vitro studies, confirm the specific arrangement of the various enzymes within the mitochondrion. The significant factor in the relationships of the enzymes to the membranes and matrix is that the functions of the mitochondrion are dependent upon its structural organization (Figure 6–13).

In addition to its other activities in the cell, ATP is utilized in the secretion and absorption of water and electrolytes by the mitochondria and may be important in maintaining the mitochondrial morphology. These phenomena have been demonstrated in several ways. A number of agents have been shown to cause swelling of mitochondria in vitro; these include thyroxine, inorganic phosphate, calcium ion, zinc ion, arsenate, and hypotonic solutions. Agents interfering with the coupling of oxidation and phosphorylation, of which thyroxine is an example, tend to cause swelling. Conversely, enzymes catalyzing oxidative phosphorylation tend to cause contraction. These same enzymes may participate as well in active transport and the water relations in cells. Liver mitochondria isolated in hypertonic solution are rod-shaped (as they are in normal tissue) and exhibit limited oxidative phosphorylation but considerable adenosine triphosphatase activity. On the other hand, on isolation in isotonic solution, they exhibit active oxidation and phosphorylation but no adenosine triphosphatase activity.

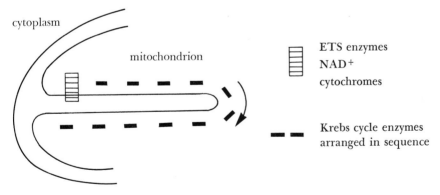

Figure 6–13. The relations between mitochondrial membranes and enzymes of respiratory reactions. The glycolytic reactions (glucose → pyruvic acid) occur outside the mitochondrion, and the pyruvic acid then enters the mitochondrion where Krebs cycle enzymes and electron transport system (ETS) reactions complete the respiration process. The ETS reactions are closely associated with the mitochondrial membranes in this model.

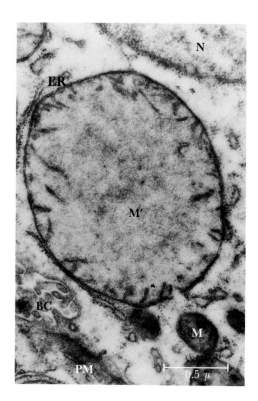

Figure 6–14. Swelling of a mitochondrion in a liver cell of a starved rat (×32,000). BC, bile canaliculus; ER, endoplasmic reticulum; M, normal mitochondrion; M', swollen mitochondrion; N, nucleus; PM, plasma membrane. FROM C. Rouiller, *Intern. Rev. Cytol.,* 9, 227 (1960).

Swelling of mitochondria induced by phosphate appears to be associated with the inactivation of NAD-dependent oxidations and a loss of NAD. If oxidative phosphorylation is resumed, the swelling effects may be reversed. If a restoration of activity does not occur, the upset in water balance (uptake versus release) may lead to a further degeneration of mitochondrial structure. The shape may change from rodlike to spherical to cylindrical, and the cristae may also change shape and, with extreme swelling, fragment and eventually disappear. Once the cristae or internal membranes are disrupted, no recovery of mitochondrial form or function is possible, since membrane disturbances are accompanied by either a loss of material from the matrix or an increase in its granular content. Other environmental factors reducing phosphorylating activity and producing swelling include radiation, low temperature, thiamine deficiency (Figure 6–14), and old age. Gross morphological changes may include a tendency of the mitochondria to stick together or fuse in an end-to-end or side-to-side manner as in scurvy (due to a deficiency of vitamin C). Extensive swelling can lead to lysis (bursting) or fragmentation.

The swelling and contraction of a mitochondrion are, as indicated, the result of changes in the balance between the amount of water diffusing into it and that diffusing out. Changes in the permeability of the membranes, then, will bring about changes in morphology. Generally, when ATP is present in the cell in very high amounts, water is released at a greater rate than it enters, and the mitochondrion shrinks. Conversely, when the concentration of ATP is low in the cytoplasm, the permeability of the mitochondrial membranes increases, and they expand. There is considerable evidence that the outer membrane is relatively stable, whereas the inner membrane is not so stable. It is quite likely that the outer membrane is more permeable, especially to lipid-soluble substances, and the inner membrane more selective.

Nucleic Acid Content

No longer can DNA be considered a special property of the cell nucleus; DNA is found in mitochondria, chloroplasts, and other cytoplasmic organelles. Mitochondrial DNA, comprising about 1% of the total cell

Figure 6–15. Mitochondria from a brown alga (×75,000). Arrows indicate the fibrils of DNA in clear areas. FROM T. Bisalputra and A. A. Bisalputra, *J. Cell Biol.*, **33,** 511 (1967).

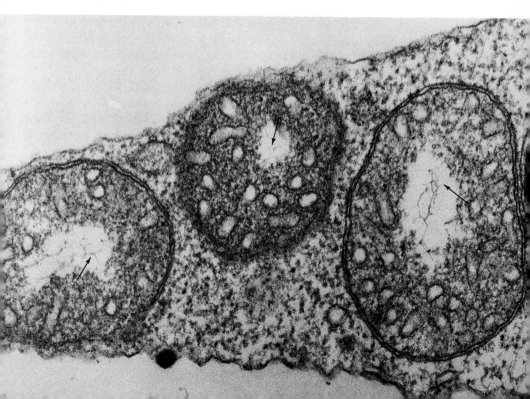

Table 6–1   Sedimentation Properties of Nuclear and Mitochondrial DNA's (in Cesium Chloride)

Organism	Nuclear DNA, g/cm^3	Mitochondrial DNA, g/cm^3
Gallus domesticus (chicken)	1.698	1.707
Paramecium aurelia	1.689	1.702
Saccharomyces cerevisiae (yeast)	1.697	1.682
Allium cepa (onion)	1.688	1.706
Ipomoea batatas (sweet potato)	1.692	1.706
Swiss chard	1.690	1.705

DNA, has been identified in most plant and animal phyla, and has properties that distinguish it from nuclear DNA. Proof of its presence rests on the observation that mitochondrial DNA is Feulgen-positive, incorporates [^{3}H]thymidine, and is digested by deoxyribonuclease. Fibrils having diameters of 25 to 100 Å are seen in clear areas within the mitochondrial matrix (Figure 6–15); these are the structures that respond to Feulgen and deoxyribonuclease treatments. Sometimes the fibrils show connections with the inner mitochondrial membranes.

The semiautonomous nature of mitochondrial DNA is supported by several kinds of evidence, including the observation that uptake of precursors is not necessarily synchronous with nuclear DNA synthesis. Moreover, in most organisms the guanine–cytosine content of mitochondrial DNA is different from that of nuclear DNA. Sedimentation in cesium chloride demonstrates additional differences between nuclear and mitochondrial DNA's (Table 6–1); mitochondrial DNA generally has a greater density. Renaturation experiments have shown that mitochondrial DNA renatures faster and more readily than does nuclear DNA.

Examination of isolated mitochondrial DNA has revealed some interesting features about the molecule. Most mitochondrial DNA studied so far is in the form of a circle having a circumference of about 5 μ and a molecular weight of 9 to 10 million. These characteristics appear to be similar in different organs as well as among many species. The native form of the molecule appears to be as highly twisted, double-stranded circles (Figure 6–16), although open circles are sometimes observed. More than one molecule of DNA may be present in a single mitochondrion; yet a molecular weight of 10 million is sufficient to determine a sequence of 25 proteins with an average molecular weight of 20,000.

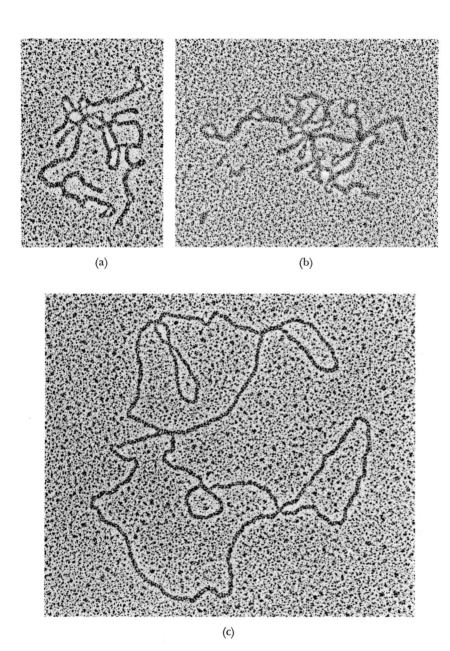

(a)   (b)

(c)

Figure 6–16. Molecules of mitochondrial DNA (×85,000): (a, b) twisted circles (*Xenopus laevis*); (c) an open circle (*Xenopus laevis*). FROM I. B. Dawid and D. R. Wolstenholme, *J. Mol. Biol.,* **28,** 233 (1967).

The significance of this last statement is underscored by the evidence for the presence in mitochondria of the machinery necessary for protein synthesis. Not only is mitochondrial DNA replicated within the mitochondrion (DNA polymerase is present), but some RNA is also produced there (DNA-dependent RNA polymerase is present). The RNA produced in the mitochondrion is a messenger RNA that carries the code for protein synthesis. Ribosomal RNA may also be produced, although typical ribosomal particles may not be present. However, ribosomes have been located in *Neurospora crassa* mitochondria, and have a sedimentation value of 81 S. This unit consists of two subunits that contain respectively a 25 S and a 19 S RNA. These compare to 28 S and 18 S ribosomal RNA in the cytoplasm. Another difference is noted in the lower guanine and cytosine contents of the mitochondrial fractions. *Neurospora* mitochondria also contain transfer RNA (tRNA) molecules (18 different transfer RNA's have been identified), and their specific aminoacyl–tRNA synthetases. However, as a result of hybridization studies with DNA (see Chapter 19), these transfer RNA's appear to be of nuclear rather than mitochondrial origin. Ribosomal and messenger RNA's, on the other hand, show significant hybridization with mitochondrial DNA in *Tetrahymena*.

In summary, the control of mitochondrial structure and function resides at least partly in the mitochondrion itself. Present are the required materials for DNA, RNA, and protein synthesis, and several of these events have been shown to occur within the organelle. Earlier evidence has established that the nucleus also exerts some control over the mitochondria.

Physiological and Morphological Changes

Changes in mitochondrial morphology often correlate with the various activities of the cell at different times during the cell cycle. These changes may affect the number of mitochondria present, mitochondrial size or shape, or the membrane organization in the mitochondria. Moreover, differences in mitochondrial morphology may be apparent in cells of the same tissue at the same time, reflecting differences in the biochemical activities of the cells in question. In mammalian liver, for example, the mitochondria in the peripheral cells are generally long in shape, while those in the cells at the center of the tissue are rounded. The peripheral cells exhibit a high level of Krebs cycle enzymatic activity; malic dehydrogenase activity is much more concentrated there than in the central cells. In contrast, glutamic dehydrogenase activity is greater in the central cells, in which there is less Krebs cycle activity, than in the peripheral cells. These differences within one tissue are relatively insignificant in comparison with those between different tissues, however, and, for the most part, one tissue is rather homogeneous from a biochemical standpoint.

In secretory cells a decrease in the number of mitochondria occurs with an increase in fat or glycogen deposits. When such deposits decrease, the number of mitochondria increases. A decrease in the number of mitochondria is also noted during the development of red blood cells; as the amount of hemoglobin increases in these cells, the number of mitochondria decreases. In mature erythrocytes there are no mitochondria. A similar relationship has been found in many plant cells during the development of plastids, although mitochondria persist in most mature cells along with the plastids.

Experiments with starved animals have been of some value in the study of possible correlations between cell physiology and cell fine structure. In general, changes in the nutrition of an animal (and consequently of its cells) result in marked changes in the morphology of the mitochondria. Mitochrondria in the liver cells of a starved rat swell and exhibit a decrease in matrix density and cristae number after a few days. If a starved animal is refed, there is recovery of normal mitochondrial morphology after several hours. Starvation may also result in the formation of rather oddly shaped mitochondria, and if its effects are extreme (complete disruption of the cristae, for example), recovery will not occur. The pancreas as well as the liver of a starved animal may show changes in mitochondrial appearance. Very often mitochondria surround lipid droplets, especially during cell degeneration. It was once believed that this close association was an indication that mitochondria were transformed into lipid droplets. More careful analysis has disproved this interpretation. The outer membrane of a mitochondrion seems to disappear as it comes in close contact with lipid, and the number of granules within the matrix increases. This suggests that fatty acid oxidases are operating in the utilization of fat and the breakdown of fat by way of the Krebs cycle.

In the oocytes of the frog (*Rana pipiens*) and the fresh water snail (*Planorbis*), there is evidence that some of the mitochondria are transformed into yolk bodies. Yolk platelets accumulate inside these mitochondria and tend to displace the cristae toward the periphery. Eventually little of the typical morphology of the mitochondria remains, and the mitochondria become identifiable as yolk bodies.

Among the most striking changes in mitochondrial morphology are those taking place during the maturation of a spermatid into a spermatozoon (Chapter 13). Many arthropods and vertebrates lose their mitochondria prior to or during this maturation process, so that mitochondria are not present in the mature sperm. In other organisms the mitochondria contribute materially to the development of the mature sperm. In the snail *Helix pomatia,* the mitochondria of a spermatid have longitudinally arranged cristae. The cristae separate from the external membranes of the mitochondria and reposition themselves concentrically, fused end to end. The mitochondria in *Helix* and many vertebrates eventually form a sheath that is part of the tail of the sperm. The sheath develops by a fusion of the mitochondria around the filament or axis of the tail and may be as long as 200 μ in *Helix,* although it is shorter in other organisms.

Pathology

Several aspects of mitochondrial degeneration have already been presented, particularly the morphological changes occurring under certain physiological conditions, both in vivo and in vitro. The presence of storage material, produced either in the mitochondria or elsewhere, may inhibit the normal functioning of the mitochondria and lead to their degeneration. In most cases the appearance of a substance within a mitochondrion does not mean that it was produced there; it is quite likely of foreign origin, for example, a result of poisoning of the cell or extramitochondrial damage to the cell. Owing to the permeability of the mitochondrial membranes, poisoning, fasting, or changes in hydration may cause swelling of the mitochondria by increasing the rate of water uptake. In addition, certain substances may accumulate within the mitochondria because of the selective permeability of the membranes to them (for example, iron, melanin pigments, potassium).

The behavior of the mitochondria and their possible function in cancer cells are somewhat ambiguous. Some cancer cells are no different from normal cells in mitochondrial morphology, whereas other cancer cells display quite remarkable differences. In the latter instances, there may be a great increase in the number of mitochondria, or the mitochondria may degenerate to reduce their number. Degeneration, size irregularity, and swelling seem to be the most common properties of mitochondria in cancer cells. The main difficulty is that there is little consistency in such anomalies, nor are they specific for one or more types of cancer. In mammary tumors, for example, which are associated with the presence of virus particles, some of the mitochondria are affected while others are not. The viruses are capable of multiplying within the mitochondria, thereby producing a change in mitochondrial morphology, but these morphological changes are absent in some mitochondria. Concerning the biochemical activities of mitochondria in cancer cells, again there is inconsistency; respiration may be normal, subnormal, or greater than in normal cells. It is possible that certain of the agents inducing cancer (carcinogens) affect one or more enzymes in the mitochondria and lead to changes in morphology or number. However, at most, the role of the mitochondria in cancer development is secondary.

Origin

At the outset, one point should be made clear about the origin of the mitochondria: they are not derived from nor do they give rise to plastids. Although there is some similarity in morphology between the two organelles at certain times during the cell cycle, they arise independently of each other and eventually achieve structural and functional distinction. Moreover, differences in their DNA contents argue against a common origin. On the other hand, the possibility exists that both organelles develop from similar precursor bodies. Robertson has suggested a scheme whereby mitochondria may arise from invaginations of the plasma membrane (Figure 6–17) or by development of the endoplasmic reticulum (Figure 4–4). There have also been suggestions of mitochondrial deriva-

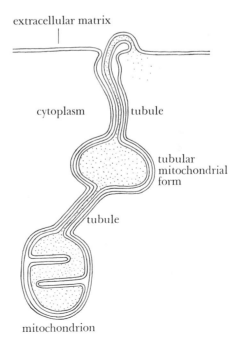

extracellular matrix

cytoplasm

tubule

tubular mitochondrial form

tubule

mitochondrion

Figure 6–17. A possible mechanism for the formation of mitochondria from the plasma membrane. FROM J. D. Robertson in M. Locke, ed., *Cellular Membranes in Development,* Academic Press, New York, 1964, p. 17.

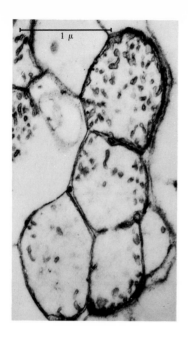

Figure 6–18. Septa development in a mitochondrion of *Elodea,* just prior to separation. FROM A. Frey-Wyssling and K. Mühlethaler, *Ultrastructural Plant Cytology,* Elsevier, Amsterdam, 1965, p. 225.

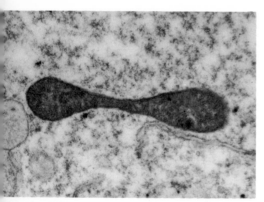

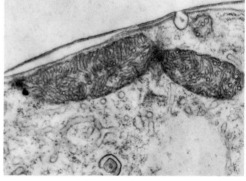

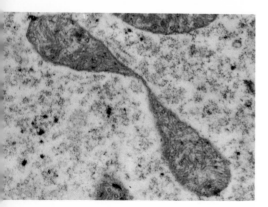

Figure 6–19. Stages in mitochondrial division by constriction in *Tetrahymena pyriformis.* FROM A. M. Elliott and I. J. Bak, *J. Cell Biol.,* **20,** 113 (1964).

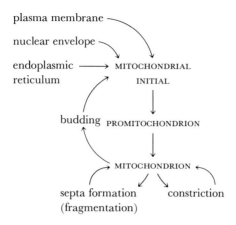

Figure 6–20. Outline of possible mitochondrial origins.

tion from the nuclear envelope. Although such origins have not been well documented with specific observations, mitochondria must at least have membrane origins as opposed to a *de novo* synthesis.

In differentiated or dividing cells with mature mitochondria, replication has been observed through septa formation (Figure 6–18) or by constriction (Figure 6–19). During cell division mitochondria are nearly equally distributed between the daughter cells. Studies with *Tetrahymena pyriformis* demonstrated that one-half of the tritium-labeled thymidine is distributed to each group of mitochondria in the daughter cells. Budding of mitochondria may occur in dedifferentiated or undifferentiated cells, giving rise to mitochondrial *initials*. These can then increase in size and develop cristae until a mature, functional state is achieved. Initials may also represent derivations from the nuclear envelope or the plasma membrane. Figure 6–20 illustrates the several possibilities for mitochondrial origins and development.

Associations with Other Organelles

The relationships between the plasma membrane and the mitochondria have been discussed previously. By way of review or reemphasis, these relationships in the kidney tubules can be cited. The tubules are involved in the resorption of water and glucose, and there may be an accumulation of proteins in the cells. The role of the mitochondria in both respects is as a reservoir of energy for the implied activities. It is as a source of energy for cellular activities that the mitochondria are most important. Several examples can be mentioned. In the flight muscles of insects, the mitochondria (called *sarcosomes* here) are in great supply and are intimately associated with the endoplasmic reticulum. It is possible that the energy derived from the mitochondria is a requirement for the development of the endoplasmic reticulum in several kinds of cells, as, for example, rat liver cells.

The associations of the mitochondria with the nuclear envelope suggest their role in the transport of materials between the nucleus and the cytoplasm, namely, as a supplier of energy. The relation between the nucleus and the mitochondria may be so close as to indicate a continuity of their membranes. This has, in fact, been observed in some trypanosomes (protozoa). In *Pelomyxa* close associations are apparent both during and following cell division. In other organisms the mitochondria are in evidence near the nuclear envelope especially when material appears to be leaving the nucleus and entering the cytoplasm, particularly material of nucleolar origin. Whether the mitochondria aid in the transport of materials from the nucleus into the cytoplasm and from the cytoplasm into the nucleus remains to be determined, but their function as a source of energy for such activities has been definitely established.

SELECTED READING

General

Green, D. E., "The Mitochondrion," *Sci. Am.,* **210**(1), 63 (1964).
Green, D. E., and I. Silman, "Structure of the Mitochondrial Electron Transfer Chain," *Ann. Rev. Plant Physiol.,* **18**, 147 (1967).
Lehninger, A. I., *The Mitochondrion,* W. A. Benjamin, New York, 1965.
Novikoff, A. B., "Mitochondria (Chondriosomes)," in J. Brachet and A. E. Mirsky, eds., *The Cell,* Vol. 2, Academic Press, New York, 1961, pp. 299–422.
Racker, E., "The Membrane of the Mitochondrion," *Sci. Am.,* **218**(2), 32 (1968).

Morphology

Ashhurst, D. E., "Mitochondrial Particles Seen in Sections," *J. Cell Biol.,* **24**(3), 497 (1965).
Brandt, P. W., and G. D. Pappas, "Mitochondria. II. The Nuclear Mitochondrial Relationship in *Pelomyxa carolinensis* Wilson (*Chaos chaos* L.)," *J. Biophys. Biochem. Cytol.,* **6**(1), 91 (1959).
Chance, B., and D. F. Parsons, "Cytochrome Function in Relation to Inner Membrane Structure of Mitochondria," *Science,* **142** (3596), 1176 (1963).
Green, D. E., and O. Hechter, "Assembly of Membrane Subunits," *Proc. Natl. Acad. Sci. U.S.,* **53**(2), 318 (1965).

Løvtrup, S., and T. Zelander, "Isolation of Brain Mitochondria," *Exptl. Cell Res.,* **27**(3), 468 (1962).

Pappas, G. D., and P. W. Brandt, "Mitochondria. I. Fine Structure of the Complex Patterns in the Mitochondria of *Pelomyxa carolinensis* Wilson (*Chaos chaos* L.)," *J. Biophys. Biochem. Cytol.,* **6**(1), 85 (1959).

Parsons, D. F., "Mitochondrial Structure: Two Types of Subunits on Negatively Stained Mitochondrial Membranes," *Science,* **140**(3570), 985 (1963).

Parsons, D. F., W. D. Bonner, Jr., and J. G. Verboon, "Electron Microscopy of Isolated Plant Mitochondria and Plastids Using Both the Thin-Section and Negative-Staining Techniques," *Can. J. Botany,* **43**, 647 (1965).

Pease, D. C., "Demonstration of a Highly Ordered Pattern upon a Mitochondrial Surface," *J. Cell Biol.,* **15**(2), 385 (1962).

Revel, J. P., D. W. Fawcett, and C. W. Philpott, "Observations on Mitochondrial Structure. Angular Configurations of the Cristae," *J. Cell Biol.,* **16**(1), 187 (1963).

Tedeschi, H., "The Structure of the Mitochondrial Membrane: Inferences from Permeability Properties," *J. Biophys. Biochem. Cytol.,* **6**(2), 241 (1959).

Physiology and Pathology

Chance, B., D. F. Parsons, and G. R. Williams, "Cytochrome Content of Mitochondria Stripped of Inner Membrane Structure," *Science,* **143**(3602), 136 (1964).

Green, D. E., "Mitochondrial Structure and Function," in T. Hayashi, ed., *Subcellular Particles,* Ronald Press, New York, 1959, pp. 84–103.

Green, D. E., and Y. Hatefi, "The Mitochondrion and Biochemical Machines," *Science,* **133**(3445), 13 (1961).

Krebs, H. A., "Control of Metabolic Processes," *Endeavour,* **63**, 125 (1957).

Kroll, A. J., and T. Kuwabara, "Prevention of Phosphate-Induced Mitochondrial Swelling," *J. Cell Biol.,* **15**(1), 29 (1962).

Novikoff, A. B., "Approaches to the in Vivo Function of Subcellular Particles," in T. Hayashi, ed., *Subcellular Particles,* Ronald Press, New York, 1959, pp. 1–22.

Palade, G. E., "Functional Changes in Structure of Cell Components," in T. Hayashi, ed., *Subcellular Particles,* Ronald Press, New York, 1959, pp. 64–83.

Rouiller, C., "Physiological and Pathological Changes in Mitochondrial Morphology," *Intern. Rev. Cytol.,* **9**, 227 (1960).

Nucleic Acids

Barnett, W. E., and D. H. Brown, "Mitochondrial Transfer Ribonucleic Acids," *Proc. Natl. Acad. Sci. U.S.,* **57**(2), 452 (1967).

Green, B. R., and M. P. Gordon, "The Satellite DNA's of Some Higher Plants," *Biochim. Biophys. Acta,* **145**(2), 378 (1967).

Nass, M. K., S. Nass, and B. A. Afzelius, "The General Occurrence of Mitochondrial DNA," *Exptl. Cell Res.,* **37**(3), 516 (1965).

Parsons, P., and M. V. Simpson, "Biosynthesis of DNA by Isolated Mitochondria: Incorporation of Thymidine Triphosphate-2-C^{14}," *Science,* 155(3578), 91 (1967).

Sinclair, J. H., B. J. Stevens, P. Sanghavi, and M. Rabinowitz, "Mitochondrial-Satellite and Circular DNA Filaments in Yeast," *Science,* 156 (3779), 1234 (1967).

Sinclair, J. H., B. J. Stevens, N. Gross, and M. Rabinowitz, "The Constant Size of Circular Mitochondrial DNA in Several Organisms and Different Organs," *Biochim. Biophys. Acta,* 145(2), 528 (1967).

Suyama, Y., "The Origins of Mitochondrial Ribonucleic Acids in *Tetrahymena pyriformis,*" *Biochemistry,* 6, 2829 (1967).

van Bruggen, E. F. J., et al., "Circular Mitochondrial DNA," *Biochim. Biophys. Acta,* 119(2), 439 (1966).

Wolstenholme, D. R., and I. B. Dawid, "Circular Mitochondrial DNA from *Xenopus laevis* and *Rana pipiens,*" *Chromosoma,* 20(4), 445 (1967).

7

Plastids

One of the standard distinguishing characteristics of most plant cells is the presence of plastids. A number of unicellular organisms, particularly among the algae and protozoa, have presented problems in classification because of exceptions to this general phenomenon. Some organisms, for example, contain plastids but have other characteristics ordinarily associated with animal cells. Whether the cell is plant or animal is immaterial in this discussion, however; of primary concern is the fact that the morphology and physiology of plastids vary according to cellular function and behavior.

The variations found among plastids involve pigment content, size, and number. Such variations usually represent specific properties of the cells in which the plastids are located. These can be considered variations of a gross nature in contrast to variations in fine structure. The latter variations are due to physiological conditions or changes in the cells and are best studied with the electron microscope.

As might be expected, the gross structure of the plastids is quite different from the fine structure as delineated by the electron microscope. In accordance with the discussions of mitochondria, Golgi, and the other cytoplasmic organelles, emphasis here will be placed on plastid fine structure and function.

Classification

The most obvious variations among plastids are those in color or pigment content. For purposes of introduction and orientation, a classification based on pigments is presented. However, since any classification is some-

what arbitrary and does not of necessity imply other functional or morphological characteristics, there is not always a direct correlation between
pigment content and other significant plastid features.

Plastids may contain one or more pigments or no pigment. The most
familiar type of plastid is the *chloroplast,* which contains chlorophyll
pigments and is instrumental in initiating the process of photosynthesis.
Those plastids containing both chlorophyll and carotenoid pigments are
active in photosynthesis, whereas the plastids containing carotenoid pigments but lacking chlorophyll are photosynthetically inactive. A summary
of the major types of plastids and their occurrence appears in Table 7–1.

Table 7–1   Major Types of Plastids and Their Occurrence

Type	*Major Pigment*	*Occurrence*	*Function*
chromoplast			
chloroplast	chlorophyll *a* and *b*	algae; higher plants	photosynthesis
phaeoplast	fucoxanthin	brown algae; dia-toms; dinoflagel-lates	absorbs light
rhodoplast	phycoerythrin	red algae	absorbs light
chromatophore			
blue-green	phycocyanin; phycoerythrin	blue-green algae	photosynthesis
bacterial	bacteriochlo-rophyll bacterioviridin	purple-sulfur bacteria green-sulfur bacteria	absorbs in far red region
carotenoid	lycopene; cap-santhin	tomato; red pepper; flower parts; fungi; bacteria	
leucoplast			
amyloplast	none	food storage cells	starch storage
elaioplast	none	certain monocoty-ledons	oil storage
proteinoplast (aleurone-plast)	none	seeds (Brazil nut)	protein storage

In the *chromoplasts,* or pigmented plastids, the pigments listed in the
table are not necessarily the only ones present but are the ones primarily
responsible for the color of the cell or group of cells. For example,

fucoxanthin is a carotenoid pigment present in the phaeoplasts of brown algae; it masks the color of chlorophyll *a,* which is also present. Phycoerythrin is responsible for the color of the red algae, although other pigments are present. The carotenoids, such as xanthophyll and carotene, are present in most green plants, but are not always visible, owing to the masking effect of chlorophyll.

Certain pigments other than chlorophyll are capable of absorbing light for the photosynthetic reaction. In the brown algae, fucoxanthin absorbs light and transfers the energy to chlorophyll *a.* Phycoerythrin performs the same function in the red algae, and a similar, but not identical, reaction occurs in certain of the pigmented bacteria.

In the blue-green algae the term *chromatophore* is used instead of plastid, since the pigments are not organized within a discrete plastid body but are often arranged on lamellar structures in concentric rings or plates within the algal cell.

Leucoplasts are plastids devoid of the pigment and membranous structures distinguishing the chromoplasts. The leucoplasts serve primarily for the storage of starches, oils, and proteins.

Morphology

The plastid is the largest cytoplasmic structure yet mentioned; it can readily be seen in most plant cells at low magnification under the light microscope. Although some variation in size is evident from species to species, the average plastid is 4 to 10 μ in diameter and 1 to 3 μ thick. Its shape may be spherical or somewhat ovoid, depending upon the type of cell under observation. Studies of plastids under the electron microscope have shown that their primary structure is based on the unit membranes described previously. Thus, even though the plastid is more elaborate than the other organelles, it is still part of the system of cytoplasmic membranes.

The description of ultrastructure that follows is applicable to most chloroplasts (Figure 7–1). The mature plastid is limited by a double membrane, each unit of which is 40 to 60 Å thick. This functions as a semipermeable membrane as well as a boundary. In higher plants, sucrose and larger molecules penetrate it with difficulty. Inside the membrane is a proteinaceous matrix, called the *stroma,* containing starch grains and sometimes osmiophilic droplets. As the plastid ages or becomes inactive, the number of osmiophilic droplets may increase.

Also embedded in the stroma are several *grana,* each granum consisting of a stack of double membrane discs or *lamellae.* Unstacked,

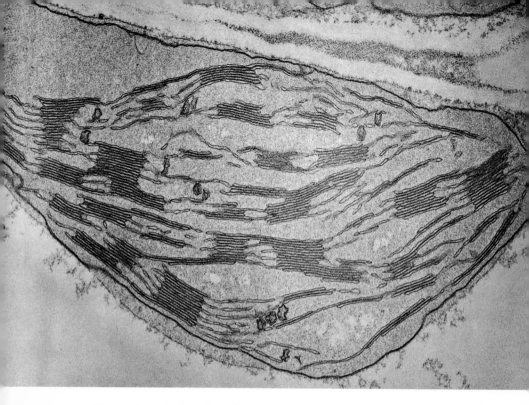

Figure 7–1. Chloroplast from a mesophyll cell of a mature spinach leaf (×39,000). FROM R. B. Park in J. Bonner and J. E. Varner, eds., *Plant Biochemistry,* Academic Press, New York, 1965, p. 133.

intergranal lamellae are stroma lamellae. The lamellar membranes are composed of about 55% lipid and 45% protein, and the chlorophyll is associated with the lipid portions. The lamellae vary in thickness, yet these differences may be more apparent than real, since different techniques for the preparation of plastids for electron microscopy can produce changes in membrane thickness. Moreover, as Weier has stated, "Plastids are dynamic organelles whose structure changes in response to changes in environment." The spaces between the double membranes of the lamellae may vary in width from 25 to 75 Å.

Descriptions of chloroplast ultrastructure have led to a rather complex terminology, especially for the lamellar units. A double membrane disc or lamella is also called a *thylakoid* (Greek, sac-like), smaller, stacked thylakoids comprising grana (grana lamellae), and large thylakoids, (stroma lamellae) providing connections between the stacks. Weier and others have used the term *fret* to describe a stroma lamella as a flattened tubular channel connecting adjacent grana (Figure 7–2). Recent studies have provided evidence that the membranes within the chloroplast form a continuum and that the *loculi* (cavities of the thylakoids) of the grana communicate via fretwork connections (Figure 7–3). The complexity of

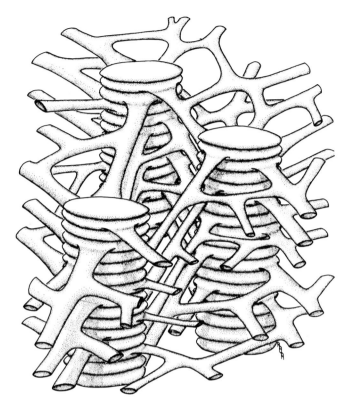

Figure 7–2. A three-dimensional diagram of chloroplast grana connected by a number of frets. FROM T. E. Weier et al., *J. Ultrastruct. Res.,* **8,** 122 (1963).

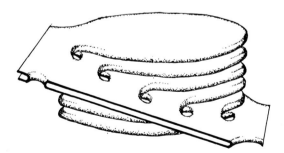

Figure 7–3. An interpretation of the relationships between a stroma lamella (fret) and six thylakoids of a granum. FROM J. Heslop-Harrison, *Sci. Progr. London,* **54,** 519 (1966).

these connections is illustrated in Figure 7–4, in which is shown the helical winding of the frets around the grana. The frets are not simply flat plates intersecting the cylindrical grana.

The discovery of a subunit pattern of organization in the thylakoid membranes has prompted a reevaluation of the view that they are unit

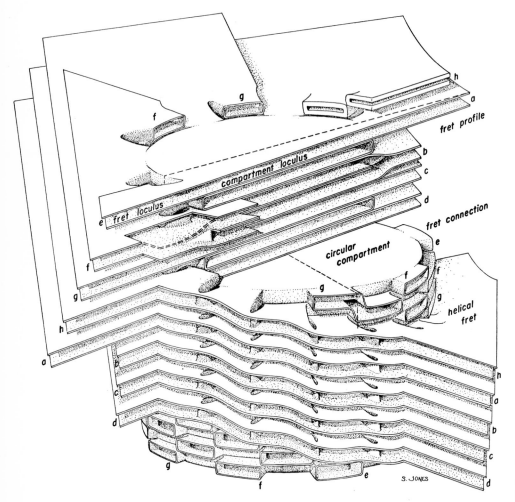

Figure 7–4. A three-dimensional diagram of a granum with fretwork connections. The model is based on the hypothesis that each fret is attached to each compartment of a granum thylakoid by tubular fret connections. Membrane thickness is drawn to scale only at the upper right (h). Note the helical frets. Reproduced by permission of the National Research Council of Canada from D. Paolillo and J. R. Reighard, *Can. J. Botany,* **45,** 733 (1967).

Table 7–2 Representative Distribution of Chemical Substances in the Quantasome*

	Molecular Weight	
Lipid (composition, moles/mole quantasome)		
230 chlorophylls		206,000
160 chlorophyll *a*	143,000	
70 chlorophyll *b*	63,400	
48 carotenoids		27,400
14 β-carotene	7,600	
22 lutein	12,600	
6 violaxanthin	3,600	
6 neoxanthin	3,600	
46 quinone compounds		31,800
16 plastoquinone A	12,000	
8 plastoquinone B	9,000	
4 plastoquinone C	3,000	
9 α-tocopherol	3,800	
4 α-tocopherylquinone	2,000	
4 vitamin K_1	2,000	
116 phospholipids (phosphatidylglycerols)		90,800
14 glycerophosphorylinositol		
52 glycerophosphorylglycerol		
6 glycerophosphorylethanolamine		
42 glycerophosphorylcholine		
2 glycerophosphate		
144 digalactosyldiglyceride	134,000	
346 monogalactosyldiglyceride	268,000	
48 sulfolipid	41,000	
? sterols	15,000	
unidentified lipids	175,600	
		990,000
Protein		
9,380 nitrogen atoms as protein	928,000	
2 manganese	110	
12 iron (1 iron as cytochrome b_6)		
(1 iron as cytochrome f) +		
10 nonheme irons	672	
6 copper	218	
		930,000
Lipid + protein		1,920,000

* From R. B. Park, "The Chloroplast," in J. Bonner and J. E. Varner, eds., *Plant Biochemistry*, Academic Press, New York, 1965, p. 142.

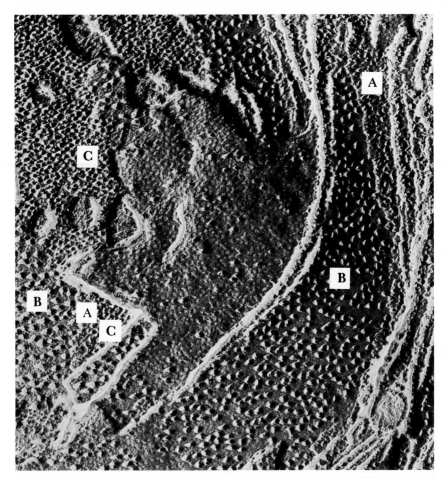

Figure 7–5. Freeze-etched preparation of spinach chloroplast lamellae showing particles (up to 200 Å diameter) on surfaces B and C of the thylakoid membrane (×120,000). Refer to Figure 7–6 for model. FROM D. Branton and R. B. Park, *J. Ultrastruct. Res.*, **19**, 283 (1967).

membranes. Several investigators have observed small, sometimes globular, units on or within the thylakoid membranes. They seem to occur primarily in the stacked thylakoids where there are two membranes lying in apposition. Freeze-etched preparations of spinach chloroplast lamellae show how the particles may be arranged in the membrane (Figure 7–5). A model of this arrangement is presented in Figure 7–6 for reference.

Membrane subunits have an average diameter of 90 Å, although they have been reported as smaller in some species. Aggregates of these particles account for the larger ones observed in Figure 7–5. Each of the sub-

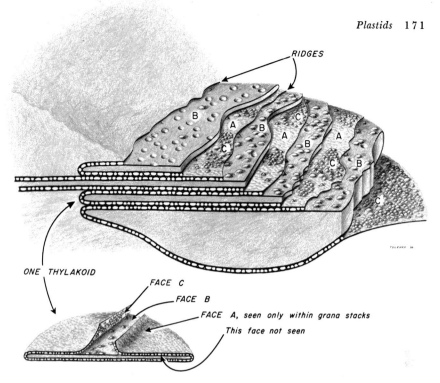

Figure 7–6. Model of chloroplast lamellae based on freeze-etched preparations. Compare faces B and C for locations of particles in Figure 7–5. FROM D. Branton and R. B. Park, *J. Ultrastruct. Res.*, **19**, 283 (1967).

units consists of protein and lipid, the protein matrix binding chlorophylls and lipids. A subunit may swell or shrink in response to changes in the tonicity of a medium containing salt or sugar. This arrangement is clearly a departure from the unit membrane concept of a protein–lipid sandwich; it is thicker and may represent an important functional modification of the unit membrane. Within the thylakoid membrane, in fact, four subunits appear to be arranged as a functional entity, the *quantasome*. It is 180 Å long, 150 Å wide, and 100 Å thick. A quantasome is also defined as the morphological unit capable of absorbing a mole quantum of light. It has a molecular weight of about 2 million, and contains 230 chlorophyll molecules (Table 7–2).

In effect, the quantasome is the unit of photosynthesis, and has certain homologies with the mitochondrial elementary particle (Chapter 6). Both of these particles demonstrate an association of the electron transport system with the unit membranes. Electron transport in both is accompanied by phosphorylation, and both transport systems contain cytochromes b and c, nonheme iron, and quinones. Three types of quantasome packing have been observed in thylakoid membranes: random,

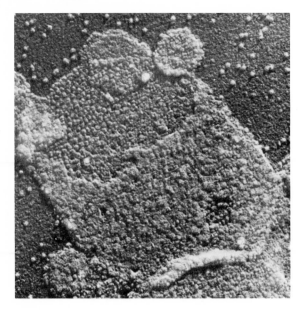

Figure 7–7. Random packing of quantasomes in spinach chloroplast lamella (×68,000). FROM R. B. Park in J. Bonner and J. E. Varner, eds., *Plant Biochemistry*, Academic Press, New York, 1965, p. 138.

linear, and paracrystalline. Random packing is the most common (Figure 7–7), and paracrystalline packing is the least common (Figure 7–8). The activities of quantasomes in photosynthesis will be examined later in other respects.

Figure 7–8. Paracrystalline array of quantasomes in spinach chloroplast lamella. FROM R. B. Park in J. Bonner and J. E. Varner, eds., *Plant Biochemistry*, Academic Press, New York, 1965, p. 140.

There is considerable variation in the number of grana in a single plastid, depending upon the species. The more primitive forms tend to have fewer grana than the higher forms; examples are *Euglena,* which has 1 granum per plastid, and spinach, which has 40 to 60 grana per plastid.

Differences in the relations of the outer limiting membrane with other cytoplasmic membranes have been noted. In the unicellular green alga *Chlamydomonas,* the plastid envelope is sometimes continuous with elements of the endoplasmic reticulum. Connections with other cytoplasmic membranes are, in fact, quite common in cells with single plastids, such as *Chlamydomonas* and *Ochromonas.* In *Ochromonas danica* (Chrysophyceae), which has a single bilobed chloroplast, there is a double membrane envelope *outside* the usual outer limiting membrane. This outer envelope is continuous with the nuclear envelope but does not contain pores. Similar structural relationships exist in other groups of algae, including the Phaeophyta, Euglenophyta, and Cryptophyceae, even though many of these have more than one plastid. An additional outer envelope has not been found, however, in the Rhodophyta or Chlorophyta.

Origin and Development

Although there are similarities in their precursor bodies (initials), mitochondria and chloroplasts are independent organelles, and do not arise one from the other (Chapter 6). However, the origin of the several plastid types has been an enigma. It is now possible to construct a general scheme of the relationships of most plastid types with respect to their origin. Every plastid arises from an existing plastid or proplastid body; in lower plants chloroplasts are formed by division of the mature chloroplasts, and in higher plants they arise from division of a proplastid. The proplastid may be regarded as the "stem" plastid, giving rise to metabolically active leucoplasts or chloroplasts. The latter may develop into other types of chromoplasts, perhaps through a kind of degeneration. Certain kinds of plastids arise from other mature plastids. In monocotyledons, elaioplasts develop from old chloroplasts that lose their chlorophyll and accumulate oil. Chromoplasts, including chloroplasts, may develop from amyloplasts, as in the carrot root. The pathways of development depend upon such external factors as light and such internal factors as reside in the cytoplasm or the nucleus. That is, the basic pattern of development is under genetic control.

Plastids are transmitted directly to daughter cells during cell division, providing a genetic continuity in plastid lineage. Although the origin of initials that develop into proplastids is not entirely clear, some observa-

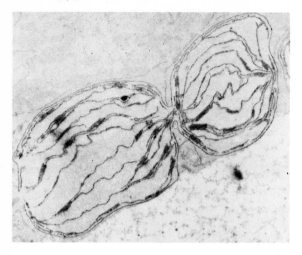

Figure 7–9. Young chloroplast of germinating corn embryo showing equal division (×13,800). FROM M. Vesk, F. V. Mercer, and J. V. Possingham, *Australian J. Botany*, **13**, 161 (1965).

tions in ferns suggest the nuclear envelope as a possible source. Differences between nuclear and chloroplast DNA, however, would tend to argue against nuclear origin. Division of proplastids and developing chloroplasts has been demonstrated in a number of higher plants, and division of mature chloroplasts has been seen in lower plants like the algae. Initials do not divide in higher plants. Division begins with an infolding of the inner membrane of the limiting chloroplast envelope, proceeding like a constriction through the chloroplast. Later the outer membrane invaginates until the chloroplast is divided into two. The daughters may be of about equal size (Figure 7–9) or of unequal size (Figure 7–10). Proplastid division is similar to that of young chloroplasts (Figure 7–11).

In higher plants the development of a mature plastid from a pro-

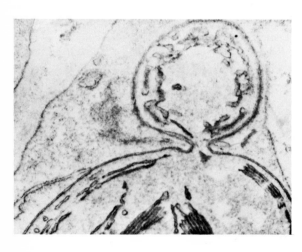

Figure 7–10. Young chloroplast of germinating corn embryo showing unequal division (×34,200). FROM M. Vesk, F. V. Mercer, and J. V. Possingham, *Australian J. Botany*, **13**, 161 (1965).

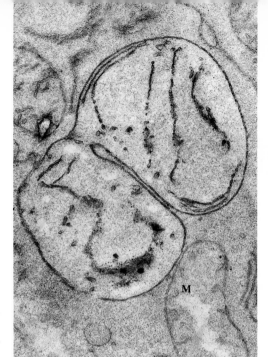

Figure 7–11. Dividing proplastid in first leaf of corn embryo (×28,000). M, mitochondrion. FROM M. Vesk, F. V. Mercer, and J. V. Possingham, *Australian J. Botany,* **13,** 161 (1965).

plastid in the light is characterized by the elaboration of the lamellar membranes from the inner limiting membrane. Several stages in the development of a mature plastid of the type shown in Figure 7–1 are presented in Figure 7–12. As the plastid increases in size, the inner limit-

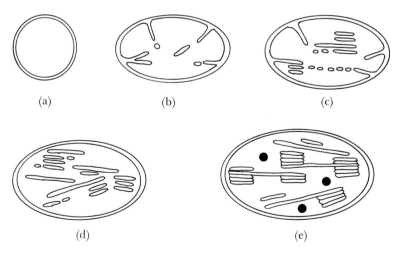

(a)   (b)   (c)

(d)   (e)

Figure 7–12. Development of a chromoplast in the light: (a) proplastid; (b) formation of vesicles; (c) differentiation, development of color; (d) differentiation, development of lamellae; (e) maturation.

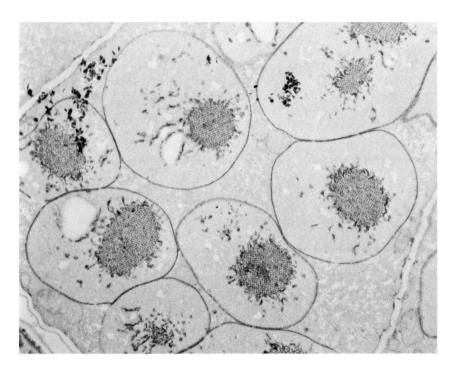

Figure 7–13. Proplastids with prolamellar bodies in a leaf cell of an etiolated red kidney bean plant (×10,000). FROM S. Klein, G. Bryan, and L. Bogorad, *J. Cell Biol.,* **22,** 433 (1964).

ing membrane invaginates in several places, producing small vesicles that pinch off as discrete units. These vesicles aggregate in several arrangements to form the lamellae of the mature plastid.

The absence of light has a distinct effect on plastid development and maturation. In the dark the lamellar pattern appears as a cluster of discs, a prolamellar body, or a series of concentric rings (Figures 7–13 and 7–14). This effect is also produced in plastids of etiolated plants. The proplastids of monocotyledons enlarge in the absence of light, but the proplastids of dicotyledons do not.

Chemistry

The chemical composition of a chloroplast is summarized in Table 7–3. A significant portion of the lipid content can be attributed to the phospholipid component of the membranes of the outer envelope and

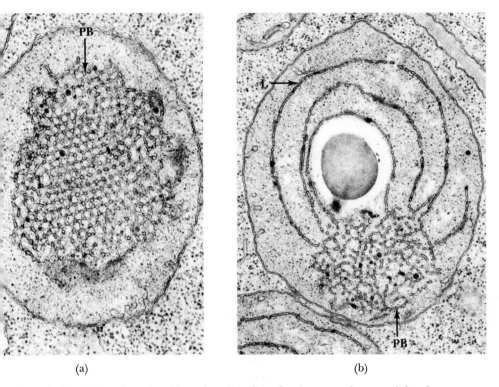

(a)   (b)

Figure 7–14. Alterations in chloroplast lamellar development in an etiolated seedling of the red kidney bean plant: (a) prolamellar body (×40,000); (b) pro-lamellar body and concentric, perforated lamellae (×30,000). L, lamella; PB, prolamellar body. COURTESY E. H. Newcomb, from *J. Cell Biol.*, **33**, 143 (1967).

lamellae. In contrast to other cytomembranes, there is no cholesterol in chloroplast membranes. The protein content represents not only the protein of the membranes but also the chloroplast enzymes. The particular enzymes present may vary somewhat, according to the level of maturity and the metabolic state of the plastid. Enzyme constituents include those involved in the synthesis of protein, lipid, and nucleic acids. Among the latter are RNA polymerase and DNA polymerase. The RNA polymerase appears to be dependent on the chloroplast DNA for RNA synthesis (see below) and messenger as well as transfer RNA may be found. As the maturation of the plastid proceeds, other enzymes may be found, including those necessary for the synthesis of chlorophyll (Figure 7–15), carotenoid, or other pigments and for the synthesis of carbohydrate. The mature chloroplast contains the several enzymes and other substances utilized during photosynthesis (Table 7–2).

Table 7–3   Chemical Composition of a Chloroplast

Substance	Percent by Dry Weight
protein	30–55
lipid	20–30
chlorophyll (75% a, 25% b)	9
carotenoids (75% xanthophyll, 25% carotene)	4.5
RNA	3–7
DNA	0.5
cytochrome f	0.1
vitamin K	0.004
vitamin E	0.08
Mg, Fe, Cu, Mn, Zn, P	trace

Photosynthesis

The photosynthetic reactions in chlorophyll-containing cells require several specific enzymes, among them those catalyzing the decomposition of water and the liberation of oxygen, the reduction of carbon dioxide, and the oxidation of cytochrome f. These enzymes appear to occupy certain positions in the chloroplast fine structure, and accordingly a model has been proposed to correlate plastid morphology and biochemical function. The stroma is considered to contain the soluble enzymes for the

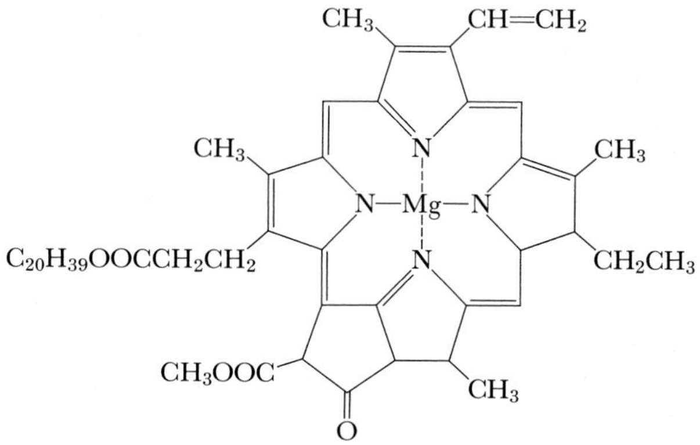

Figure 7–15.   Structure of chlorophyll a. Note that $C_{20}H_{39}OH$ is phytol.

conversion of reduced carbon dioxide to sugar and starch, whereas the lamellae are represented as the sites of enzyme activities associated with the conversion of light energy to chemical energy (Figure 7–16). The latter reactions are mediated, in part, by the chlorophyll localized in the lamellae.

The general photosynthetic equation

$$6CO_2 + 12H_2O \rightarrow C_6H_{12}O_6 + 6O_2 + 6H_2O$$

does not show the complexity of the 20 to 30 reactions involved. Chlorophyll serves in the capture of light energy and in the transfer of this energy to an electron acceptor. What is commonly called the light reaction (Hill reaction) includes several chemical steps. A high energy electron from the chlorophyll molecule is transferred to nicotinamide adenine dinucleotide phosphate (NADP), resulting in its reduction to NADPH. The electron transfer is coupled with the splitting of water and followed by the liberation of oxygen from the water. The oxygen atoms combine to produce molecular oxygen, which is released as a gas. These reactions are localized in the quantasomes.

NADPH undergoes oxidation via the electron transport system, which, in the plastid, includes cytochrome f and vitamin K as part of the biochemical chain. The events occurring in the plastid resemble those of oxidative phosphorylation in mitochondria. The electron transport reactions are coupled with the phosphorylation of ADP to form ATP in the chloroplast. This mechanism of energy transfer is known as *photophosphorylation* and occurs in the quantasomes. One difference between mitochondrial oxidative phosphorylation and photophosphorylation is that the former is inhibited by temperatures below $0°C$. Another important difference is that mitochondria can produce ATP in the light and in the dark, whereas plastids can carry out this activity only in the light. Mitochondria and chloroplasts provide two separate sites for ATP formation in the cell.

The events of phosphorylation may be dependent upon the presence of specific cations. Studies on spinach chloroplasts have indicated that manganese is an essential ingredient; in its absence the light reactions are somewhat reduced. In addition, a manganese deficiency results in few chloroplasts in the cells, and the lamellae are poorly developed.

The fixation of carbon dioxide produces 3-phosphoglyceric acid. These reactions are driven by the energy derived from photophosphorylation. An intermediate product is converted to triose phosphate, with energy from ATP. Two of these units unite to produce a six-carbon sugar or lead to the production of amino acids. The two light-absorbing systems

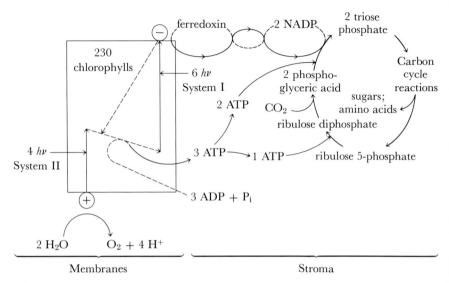

Figure 7–16. Schematic representation of photosynthesis. FROM R. B. Park, *Intern. Rev. Cytol.,* **20,** 67 (1966).

(systems I and II in Figure 7–16) are distinguished as the chlorophyll *a*–absorbing system (683 mμ) and the chlorophyll *b*–absorbing system (670 mμ). Cytochrome f and plastocyanin are associated with system I and cytochrome b$_6$ and plastoquinone with system II. These substances serve as carriers for the transfer of electrons absorbed by system II to system I. Thus the chloroplast contains a variety of enzymes and, along with other cytoplasmic structures, permits the synthesis of the basic chemical requirements of the cell, not only sugars but other carbohydrates, proteins, and lipids. In fact, there is some evidence that certain proteins are synthesized within the chloroplast during the photosynthetic process.

Nucleic Acid Content

Substantiation for the occurrence of protein synthesis in plastids is afforded by the presence of ribosomal particles. In *Euglena gracilis* the ribosomes inside the chloroplast differ from those outside it, as reflected in their respective nucleotide compositions. Ribosomes have also been isolated from spinach chloroplasts, the particles having an RNA content of about 45%. Studies in tobacco have shown that both the 70 S ribosomes and the polyribosomes of the chloroplasts are capable of protein synthesis, but nearly twice as much is produced by the polysomes as by the monosomes. There is also evidence in *Euglena* that chloroplast DNA contains from 20 to 45 genetic sites for the synthesis of ribosomal RNA. In fact, most of the chloroplast RNA is synthesized at the sites of chloroplast DNA, using the latter as template. RNA formed by chloroplast preparations has a higher ratio of adenine to guanine (1.67) than nuclear RNA (1.54), supporting their separate and independent origins.

In addition to RNA, DNA is a regularly occurring chemical constituent of chloroplasts. It has been located in one or more regions of the chloroplast stroma in several kinds of plants including *Chlamydomonas, Euglena,* tobacco, and spinach. The DNA fibrils have an average diameter of 25 Å, are degraded by deoxyribonuclease, and the chloroplast demonstrates incorporation of [³H]thymidine. Although chloroplast DNA is a small proportion of total cell DNA, a sufficient quantity is present to code for several hundred genes. In *Acetabularia,* for example, there is approximately 1×10^{-16} g DNA per plastid. In addition to differences measured by sedimentation properties in cesium chloride (Table 7–4), chloroplast DNA tends to have a higher adenine-thymine content than nuclear DNA. For example, *Euglena* chloroplast DNA has an adenine–thymine content amounting to 80% of its total base composition. Compelling evidence for the independence of chloroplast DNA from the nucleus has been found in *Acetabularia;* chloroplast DNA can be synthesized in the absence of the nucleus. Studies of DNA synthesis in isolated spinach chloroplasts indicate that a significant proportion of the chloroplast DNA is replicated within the chloroplast independently of the nucleus. This system was also shown to be capable of messenger RNA synthesis. Further support for independence has been provided by the experiments with ultraviolet irradiation. Exposure of the cytoplasm or the whole cells of *Euglena* to ultra-

Table 7–4   Comparison of Buoyant Densities of Nuclear, Chloroplast, and Mitochondrial DNA's

Organism	Nucleus, g/cm^3	Chloroplast, g/cm^3	Mitochondrion, g/cm^3
Euglena	1.707	1.686	—
Chlamydomonas	1.721	1.694	—
Chlorella	1.716	1.695	—
Acetabularia	—	1.704	1.714
spinach	1.695	1.705	1.719
Swiss chard	1.689	1.700	1.705
turnip	1.692	1.700	1.706

violet light interferes with plastid differentiation. Ultraviolet causes a bleaching of the plastid that is not produced if only the nucleus is exposed.

Mutant Plastids

Despite a degree of autonomy in plastid development and replication, the patterns of plastid inheritance are dependent upon both nuclear and cytoplasmic factors. The study of mutant forms of plastids indicates such nucleocytoplasmic interdependence. A large number of plastid mutations have their basis in nuclear genes, but some of them are nevertheless under extranuclear control. The yellow mutant produced by streptomycin treatment of *Chlamydomonas* is a case in point. This mutant, which has its genetic origin in the nucleus, has lost the ability to execute a particular step in chlorophyll synthesis. Consequently, its cell is unable to carry on photosynthesis. Several variations in plastid morphology in mutants of nuclear origin have been studied with the electron microscope. The xantha mutants in barley illustrate these variations. In the xantha-3 mutant, lamellar development is meager, whereas in the xantha-10 mutant the lamellae develop in a concentric pattern similar to that in etiolated plants. Another group of mutants in an allelic series (xantha-12, xantha-15, xantha-18, and xantha-22) exhibits giant, widely spaced grana in its plastids. Cells containing such plastids usually die. In the albina-20 mutant (white) no grana develop in the plastids. Lamellar development is evidently independent of chlorophyll synthesis, since in this mutant chlorophyll is synthesized in the light, although it is rapidly degraded. Other examples of plastid mutants under extranuclear control will be considered in Part Three.

SELECTED READING

General

Bassham, J. A., "The Path of Carbon in Photosynthesis," *Sci. Am.*, **206**(6), 89 (1962).

Bogorad, L., "The Organization and Development of Chloroplasts," in J. M. Allen, ed., *Molecular Organization and Biological Function,* Harper & Row, New York, 1967, pp. 134–85.

Goodwin, T. W., ed., *Biochemistry of Chloroplasts,* Vols. I and II, Academic Press, New York, 1966 and 1967.

Granick, S., "The Chloroplasts: Inheritance, Structure, and Function," in J. Brachet and A. E. Mirsky, eds., *The Cell,* Vol. 2, Academic Press, New York, 1961, pp. 489–602.

Kirk, J. T. O., and R. A. E. Tilney-Bassett, *The Plastids,* Freeman, San Francisco, 1967.

Morphology

Branton, D., and R. Park, "Subunits in Chloroplast Lamellae," *J. Ultrastruct. Res.,* 19(3–4), 283 (1967).

Heslop-Harrison, J., "Structural Features of the Chloroplast," *Sci. Progr. London,* 54, 519 (1966).

Hohl, H. R., and A. Hepton, "A Globular Subunit Pattern in Plastid Membranes," *J. Ultrastruct. Res.,* 12(5–6), 542 (1965).

Paolillo, D., and J. Reighard, "On the Relationship Between Mature Structure and Ontogeny in the Grana of Chloroplasts," *Can. J. Botany,* 45, 773 (1967).

Park, R. B., "Substructure of Chloroplast Lamellae," *J. Cell Biol.,* 27(1), 151 (1965).

Ris, H., "Ultrastructure and Molecular Organization of Genetic Systems," *Can. J. Genet. Cytol.,* 3, 95 (1961).

Weier, T. E., and A. Bensen, "The Molecular Organization of Chloroplast Membranes," *Am. J. Botany,* 54(4), 389 (1967).

Weier, T. E., T. Bisalputra, and A. Harrison, "Subunits in Chloroplast Membranes of *Scenedesmus quadricauda,*" *J. Ultrastruct. Res.,* 15(1), 38 (1966).

Origin and Development

Epstein, H. T., E. Boy de la Tour, and J. A. Schiff, "Fluorescence Studies of Chloroplast Development in *Euglena,*" *Nature,* 185(4716), 825 (1960).

Gibbs, S. P., "Nuclear Envelope–Chloroplast Relationships in Algae," *J. Cell Biol.,* 14(3), 433 (1962).

Vesk, M., F. V. Mercer, and J. V. Possingham, "Observations on the Origin of Chloroplasts and Mitochondria in the Leaf Cells of Higher Plants," *Australian J. Botany,* 13, 161 (1965).

Von Wettstein, D., "Developmental Changes in Chloroplasts and Their Genetic Control," in D. Rudnick, ed., *Developmental Cytology,* Ronald Press, New York, 1959, pp. 123–60.

Von Wettstein, D., "Nuclear and Cytoplasmic Factors in Development of Chloroplast Structure and Function," *Can. J. Botany,* 39, 1537 (1961).

Photosynthesis

Calvin, M., and G. M. Androes, "Primary Quantum Conversion in Photosynthesis," *Science,* 138(3543), 867 (1962).

Hall, D. O., and D. I. Arnon, "Photosynthetic Phosphorylation Above and Below 0°C," *Proc. Natl. Acad. Sci. U.S.,* 48(5), 833 (1962).

Mercer, F. V., M. Nittim, and J. V. Possingham, "The Effect of Manganese Deficiency on the Structure of Spinach Chloroplasts," *J. Cell Biol.*, 15(2), 379 (1962).

Park, R. B., "Subunits of Chloroplast Structure and Quantum Conversion in Photosynthesis," *Intern. Rev. Cytol.*, 20, 67 (1966).

Provasoli, L., S. S. Hutner, and I. J. Pintner, "Destruction of Chloroplasts by Streptomycin," *Cold Spring Harbor Symp. Quant. Biol.*, 16, 113 (1951).

Rabinowitch, E. I., and Govindjee, "The Role of Chlorophyll in Photosynthesis," *Sci. Am.*, 213(1), 74 (1965).

Nucleic Acids

Brawerman, G., "The Isolation of a Specific Species of Ribosomes Associated with Chloroplast Development in *Euglena gracilis*," *Biochim. Biophys. Acta*, 72(2), 317 (1963).

Chen, J. L., and S. G. Wildman, "Functional Chloroplast Polyribosomes from Tobacco Leaves," *Science*, 155(3767), 1271 (1967).

Chun, E. H. L., M. H. Vaughan, Jr., and A. Rich, "The Isolation and Characterization of DNA Associated with Chloroplast Preparations," *J. Mol. Biol.*, 7(2), 130 (1963).

Gibbs, S. P., "Synthesis of Chloroplast RNA at the Site of Chloroplast DNA," *Biochem. Biophys. Res. Commun.*, 28(4), 653 (1967).

Gibor, A., and S. Granick, "Ultraviolet-Sensitive Factors in the Cytoplasm That Affect the Differentiation of *Euglena* Plastids," *J. Cell Biol.*, 15(3), 599 (1962).

Heber, U., "Protein Synthesis in Chloroplasts During Photosynthesis," *Nature*, 195(4836), 91 (1962).

Heilporn-Pohl, V., and J. Brachet, "Net DNA Synthesis in Anucleate Fragments of *Acetabularia mediterranea*," *Biochim. Biophys. Acta*, 119(2), 429 (1966).

Kirk, J. T. O., "Studies on RNA Synthesis in Chloroplast Preparations," *Biochem. Biophys. Res. Commun.*, 16(3), 233 (1964).

Lyttleton, J. W., "Isolation of Ribosomes from Spinach Chloroplasts," *Exptl. Cell Res.*, 26(2), 312 (1962).

Ris, H., and W. Plaut, "Ultrastructure of DNA-Containing Areas in the Chloroplast of *Chlamydomonas*," *J. Cell Biol.*, 13(3), 383 (1962).

Sager, R., and M. G. Hamilton, "Cytoplasmic and Chloroplast Ribosomes in *Chlamydomonas*: Ultracentrifugal Characterization," *Science*, 157(3789), 709 (1967).

Sager, R., and M. R. Ishida, "Chloroplast DNA in *Chlamydomonas*," *Proc. Natl. Acad. Sci. U.S.*, 50(4), 725 (1963).

Scott, N. S., and R. M. Smillie, "Evidence for the Direction of Chloroplast Ribosomal RNA Synthesis by Chloroplast DNA," *Biochem. Biophys. Res. Commun.*, 28(4), 598 (1967).

Spencer, D., and P. R. Whitfield, "DNA Synthesis in Isolated Chloroplasts," *Biochem. Biophys. Res. Commun.*, 28(4), 538 (1967).

8

Cilia, Flagella, and Basal Bodies

In the brief catalog of cytoplasmic organelles in Chapter 1, cilia and flagella were cited as structures mostly external to the cell but arising from the cytoplasm. The fact that they originate in the cytoplasm and also make physical connections with the plasma membrane is sufficient justification for their inclusion in a discussion of the cytoplasm. Cilia and flagella are not fundamental appendages of all cells, but they are widespread in their distribution among plant and animal cells. In the animal kingdom these organelles are quite common in protozoa as well as in specific tissues of most metazoa. In plants they are restricted to the unicellular algae and certain reproductive cells of higher forms.

Although the most obvious function of cilia and flagella is related to movement, they serve other important purposes, especially in higher animals. The protozoa and some flatworms provide conventional examples of organisms in which locomotion is the prime function of cilia and flagella, as do sperm and certain spores of a number of plants and animals. In mammals the removal of bacteria and inhaled foreign material is facilitated by the activity of cilia within the respiratory passages. Ciliated epithelium lines the reproductive tubes or ducts, also, setting up currents that move the gametes. Finally, modifications of cilia as nonmotile structures occur in the development of certain cells with a sensory function. Examples are the photosensitive elements of the retina of the mammalian eye.

Before the structure of cilia and flagella is described, some distinction should be made between the two. Fortunately for the cell morphologist, the distinction is a simple one. The only significant and valid difference that can be perceived between cilia and flagella is based on their number and size. A cell with very few appendages, which are quite long (up to 150 μ) in proportion to cell size, is said to have flagella, whereas a cell with numerous short (5 to 10 μ) appendages is considered to be ciliated. The most common numbers of flagella are 1 and 2, although there may be more. The number of cilia may vary from as few as 300 per cell to as many as 14,000 in some protozoa. An additional distinction can sometimes be made with regard to patterns of movement. Cilia generally exhibit a sweeping or pendular stroke, and the several cilia present are often coordinated in their movement. Flagella, on the other hand, generally have an undulant motion and usually move independently of one another. No physiological differences between the structures have been observed, and since they are also morphologically similar, the terms cilia and flagella are often used interchangeably. Except where specific reference is made to one or the other, then, the description that follows is essentially applicable to both cilia and flagella.

Morphology

Cilia and Flagella

This discussion of the morphology of cilia and flagella deals with the portions of these structures that are strictly external to the surface of the cell. The internal portions, those within the cytoplasm, will be treated in the section on basal bodies. This is not to imply, however, that the cytoplasmic portions of cilia or flagella are necessarily physically separate from their external parts.

   Although the fine structure of cilia and flagella has been described with accuracy only recently, there were intimations of their structure as early as 1887, when Jensen observed a fraying of the end of the sperm flagellum. Later, similar observations were made on the cilia and flagella of protozoa. There were also suggestions that the component fibrils of a flagellum had contractile properties. More detailed analyses of fine structure came in the 1950's, with the studies of Hodge on the flagella of spermatozoa and Manton on the cilia of higher plants. In each instance the structures appeared to consist of 11 fibrils, two of which were centrally located with the other nine arranged around them. Manton indicated that each outer fiber was composed of two halves surrounded by a sheath and that the two central fibers were enclosed together in a common sheath.

   These studies are remarkable in many respects, and the organization described has since been substantiated by several investigators using refined techniques of electron microscopy on a variety of organisms. The investigations of Gibbons and Grimstone have provided some exceptional preparations of flagella from three genera of Protozoa, and it is this study on which most of the discussion here is based. There are certainly variations in structural detail in cilia and flagella of different organisms and some of these variations will be examined, but the fundamental arrangements are considered by most authorities to be quite similar. The accepted pattern consists of 11 longitudinal fibrils in a plan commonly known as $9 + 2$.

The average diameter of the appendage is 2000 Å, with a typical tapering toward the distal end (away from the cell surface). The component fibrils run longitudinally within the shaft, perpendicular to the surface of the cell. In some cells the fibrils extend into the cytoplasm below the cell surface, whereas in others two or more of the fibrils end outside the cell surface. Nine of the fibrils are arranged in a cylinder around the two central fibrils, and this entire *axial complex* is enclosed by a double membrane envelope, which is continuous with the plasma membrane. The envelope has an average diameter of 90 Å, the inner membrane being about 40 Å thick and the space between the two membranes about 30 Å across. Each of the nine outer fibrils is composed of two halves, each 180 to 250 Å in diameter, for an overall diameter of at least 360 Å. The two halves are surrounded by a wall and separated from each other by a continuation of the wall with a thickness of 45 Å (Figure 8–1). In the cylinder of nine double fibrils, there is a separation between each doublet of about 200 Å, and each doublet is approximately 250 Å from the envelope.

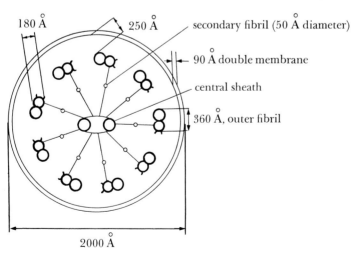

Figure 8–1. Cross section of a flagellum outside the plasma membrane. AFTER Gibbons and Grimstone.

Several investigators have confirmed the existence of arms or extensions from one of the two members of the doublet in each of the nine outer fibrils. There are two arms, each about 50 Å thick and 150 Å long, separated by a space of 130 Å. The subfiber that bears the arms is slightly smaller than its partner and lies somewhat closer to the center of the flagellum. The arms are all oriented in the same direction around the cylinder.

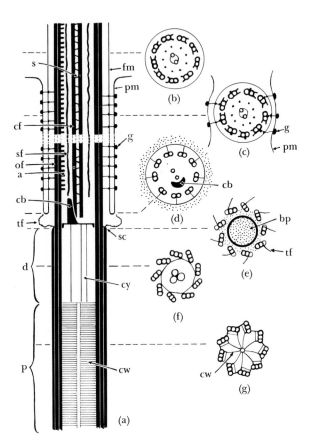

Figure 8–2.   Longitudinal (a) and transverse (b–g) sections showing the organization of a flagellum and basal body of *Pseudotrichonympha*. a, arm; bp, basal plate; cb, crescentic body; cf, central fiber; cw, cartwheel structure; cy, cylinder; d, distal region of basal body; fm, flagellum membrane; g, anchor granule; of, outer fiber; p, proximal regions of basal body; pm, plasma membrane; s, sheath; sc, subfiber c; sf, secondary fiber; tf, transitional fiber. FROM I. R. Gibbons and A. V. Grimstone, *J. Biophys. Biochem. Cytol.,* **7,** 697 (1960).

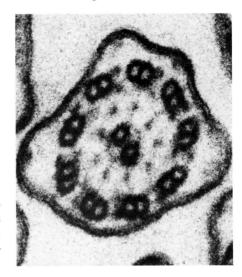

Figure 8–3. Cross section of a flagellum of *Pseudotrichonympha* (×220,000). FROM I. R. Gibbons and A. V. Grimstone, *J. Biophys. Biochem. Cytol.,* **7,** 697 (1960).

The two central fibers differ in several ways from the nine outer ones. As noted, each central fibril is single rather than a doublet, and the two central fibrils are clearly separated from each other although enclosed in a common sheath. In longitudinal section, cross striations are seen on each central fibril, suggesting that they are helical in form and perhaps two- or three-stranded.

Observations of *Pseudotrichonympha* (Figure 8–2) and other flagellates have shown that the submicroscopic morphology of a flagellum varies according to the level of the flagellum at which a cross section is made. In the distal portions of the flagellum, additional fibers are seen between the two central fibers and the nine outer fibers. These secondary fibers are considerably smaller in diameter than either of the other two kinds but can be identified in electron microscope preparations (Figure 8–3). There are nine secondary fibers, each with a diameter of about 50 Å, and they tend to occur in close alignment with the arm-bearing subfibers of the nine outer fibrils. Upon examination in longitudinal section, the secondary fibers appear to be not perfectly straight but somewhat wavy or irregular (Figure 8–2). Some studies have indicated that they represent connections between the central fibers and the nine outer fibers.

Near the distal end, or tip, of the flagellum, there is a tapering off or reduction of fiber structure. Grimstone and Gibbons have described the related morphological changes in flagellated protozoa in some detail. In these organisms the arms of the outer nine fibers disappear first, and then the double nature of the outer fibrils is lost as one of the two members ends. However, this arrangement is certainly variable from one organism to another, and fibers may terminate at different levels along the length of the flagellum. Similar differences are apparent at the proximal end of the flagellum, in the transition zone near the cell surface between the flagellum proper and its basal component within the cytoplasm.

Basal Bodies

The cilium or flagellum may or may not be directly connected with its cytoplasmic portion beneath the cell surface, depending on the level or levels at which the component flagellar fibrils end. In any event, the cytoplasmic portion is a regularly occurring structure found in association with the external appendage. Several names have been used to define the basal structures in a variety of plant and animal cells: *kinetosomes, blepharoplasts, basal granules, centrioles,* and *basal bodies.* Current interpretation of these structures is that they have common or identical origins, and similar or identical structures and functions. As a consequence, it is desirable to discard all but one of the terms for general usage, particularly since they do not contribute significantly to any descriptions. The most widely accepted term now is basal body, and it will be used freely here.

Since connections frequently exist between the basal body and the cilium or flagellum, it is often difficult to determine the extent of the basal body itself. The basal body is embedded in a layer of relatively clear cytoplasm, just beneath the plasma membrane, and in case of a number of external appendages, the several basal bodies are arranged uniformly in parallel rows under the cell surface.

The basic pattern of fibril composition and arrangement in a basal body is somewhat different from that in a cilium or flagellum (Figure 8–2). The nine outer fibrils are composed of three units rather than the two present in the distal portion of the organelle. Two of these subfibers of the triplet extend into the flagellum to form the doublet. The third subfiber ends somewhere between the basal body proper and the flagellum. It has been suggested that the third unit gives rise to the nine radial, transitional fibers that appear to attach the basal body to the surface of the cell. Although there are no central or secondary fibers directly comparable with those in the flagellum in the basal bodies of some cells, such as the termite flagellates, this arrangement is not universal. The outer fibers of the basal body often show fine, fiber-like connections between adjacent triplets as well as between each triplet and a single central fibril. This central fibril has a diameter of about 250 Å. The fine connections among the fibril components make up a pattern resembling a cartwheel, shown especially well in an electron photomicrograph of *Pseudotricho-*

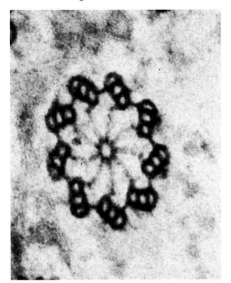

Figure 8–4. Cross section of a basal body of *Pseudotrichonympha,* showing the linkage of outer fibrils and the cartwheel pattern (×195,000). FROM I. R. Gibbons and A. V. Grimstone, *J. Biophys. Biochem. Cytol.,* **7**, 697 (1960).

nympha (Figure 8–4). "Spokes" connecting the outer and central fibrils are also found in cilia (Figure 8–1).

The region near the surface of the cell within which the external portion of the organelle is associated with the basal body has been referred to as a zone of transition. In mammals and protozoa there is no clear-cut separation between a cilium, for example, and its basal body. However, not all of the fibers in the cilium continue into the basal body; the central fibers usually end above its upper end (Figure 8–5a). In molluscs and amphibians the two structures are separated in the zone of transition by a *basal plate,* which appears to be continuous with the outer fibrils (Figure 8–5b). Between the basal plate and the basal body proper is a clear region. Even in those cells without a well-defined separation of the cilium or

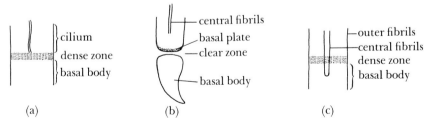

Figure 8–5. Relations between a cilium and a basal body: (a) in mammals and protozoa—continuous fibrils; (b) in molluscs and amphibians—basal plate; (c) in *Tetrahymena.*

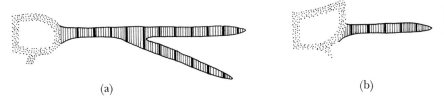

Figure 8–6. Basal bodies with rootlets and knobs: (a) double rootlet, as in some molluscs; (b) single rootlet, as in the frog *Rana.*

flagellum and the basal body, there may be a dense region in the transition zone, suggesting a separation (Figure 8–5c).

Metazoa, with the exception of mammals, have additional structures arising from the basal bodies and extending farther into the cytoplasm. These are called *rootlets,* and they are commonly found in ciliated epithelial cells. Their principal function seems to be the support or anchoring of the basal body and cilium. One or more rootlets are present, depending on the species, and the number is constant for any given species (Figure 8–6). Striations 600 to 1000 Å wide are visible on the surfaces of the rootlets. Between the major cross-striations are spaces of 550 to 700 Å in which narrower bands may be seen. In addition to rootlets, short knobs may project from one side of the basal body.

Centrioles

Chapter 11 considers the role of the centriole during cell division. The discussion here deals primarily with the submicroscopic morphology of the centriole and its relation to the basal bodies of cilia and flagella. Earlier in this section the term centriole was included among those used for the general structure now called the basal body. The inference, of course, is that the two structures are homologous, and analysis of their fine structure has confirmed this interpretation. However, whereas basal bodies are usually close to a cilium or flagellum, centrioles tend to lie nearer the nucleus of a cell. Moreover, centrioles always occur as pairs, whereas basal bodies may not.

The location of the centriole (or centrioles) varies somewhat according to the cell being studied but is generally just beneath the cell surface. Under the light microscope a clear region is seen in some cells, apparently defining the site of the centriole; however, investigations with the electron microscope have not verified this observation. This region (the *centrosphere*) may correspond to the pericentriolar structures often observed near the centriole surface under the electron microscope. The pericentriolar bodies are not always present; they may be associated with the centriole at one time but not at another. Their significance is not clear. Whatever their locations, centrioles are usually seen as paired cylinders, 3000 to 5000 Å long and 1200 to 1500 Å in diameter, open at one or both ends and lying at right angles to each other. As a corollary, a daughter centriole (Chapter 11) arises at right angles to the centriole serving as its origin (Figure 8–7).

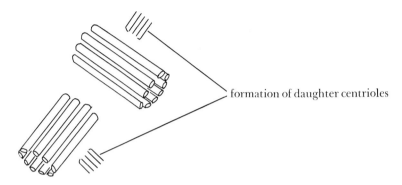

formation of daughter centrioles

Figure 8–7. Orientation of paired centrioles.

The most telling witness for the homology of centrioles and basal bodies is the identity of their submicroscopic fibrils. A dense wall surrounds each cylinder, and within it is a cavity containing longitudinal fibers arranged in the conventional pattern. In those cells in which the centrioles are associated with cilia or flagella, the nine outer fibrils may be triplets as in the basal bodies of protozoa. In these same cells there are connections between the centriolar fibrils and the ciliary or flagellar fibrils. Such connections are particularly obvious between the animal sperm flagellum and the centriole from which it arises. In the formation of the sperm flagellum, one of the two centrioles present produces the axial complex of the flagellum and serves as the basal body of the flagellum; the other centriole is incorporated into the connecting piece between the nucleus and the tail of the sperm. Inasmuch as centrioles are also found in cells that are devoid of cilia and flagella, there is some justification for retaining the term centriole along with the term basal body.

Microtubules

Cytoplasmic structures commonly associated with centrioles, especially in dividing cells, are identified as *microtubules*. They are 200 to 270 Å in

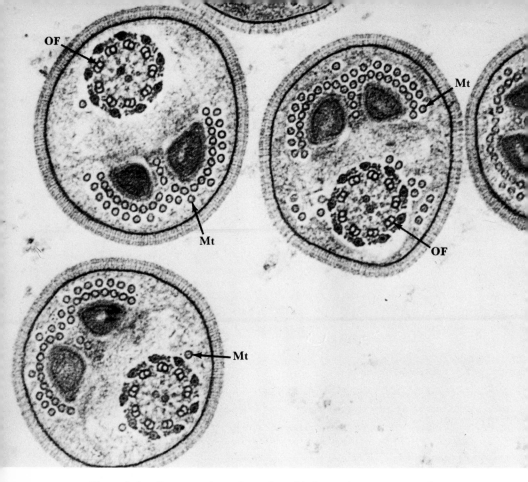

Figure 8–8. Cross section through midpiece of mature grasshopper sperm (×91,000). Compare the outer fibers (OF) of the flagellum with the microtubules (Mt). FROM R. G. Kessel, *J. Ultrastruct. Res.*, **18**, 677 (1967).

diameter and have a dense wall 50 to 70 Å thick. Their low density center gives them a hollow appearance. In plants, the walls of the microtubules are composed of 13 longitudinal filaments, with a center-to-center spacing of 55 to 60 Å. Arrays of microtubules form the *spindle fibers* during cell division (Chapter 11), although microtubules have also been found oriented at random in some nondividing cells.

Striking homologies are found between flagellar and centriolar fibrils and microtubules. Similarity of size and cross-section appearance can be seen in the midpiece of grasshopper sperm in which microtubules develop in association with the flagellum during spermiogenesis (Figure 8–8). Moreover, the presence of subunits in the microtubule wall (10 to 13 longitudinal filaments) is similar to the subunits found in the walls of basal body and flagellar fibers. Examination of the flagella of *Chlamydomonas*

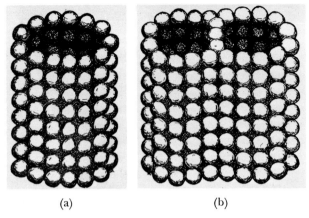

(a)   (b)

Figure 8–9. Model of flagellar-fiber subunit arrangement: (a) a single fiber; (b) a doublet fiber. See text for explanation. COURTESY D. L. Ringo, The Cell Research Institute, The University of Texas, from *J. Ultrastruct. Res.*, **17**, 266 (1967).

reinhardi reveals the presence of 13 longitudinal chains of spherical subunits per fiber (Figure 8–9), each with a diameter of about 50 Å. Each subunit appears to be a protein with a molecular weight of about 40,000. A single fiber then would consist of a tubule of 13 chains of subunits, whereas a doublet (as in the outer fibers) would share 3 of the 13 for a total of 23 chains (Figure 8–10). Similar subunit arrangements have been found in basal bodies. In effect, an interpretation of these several observations is that the fibers in cilia, flagella, and basal bodies are microtubules consisting of longitudinal arrays of globular protein units, possibly also associated in some way with lipid. Furthermore, the microtubules that

Figure 8–10. Cross section of a flagellum of *Chlamydomonas reinhardi* showing the subunits in the outer and central fibers (×186,000). COURTESY D. L. Ringo, The Cell Research Institute, The University of Texas, from *J. Ultrastruct. Res.*, **17**, 266 (1967).

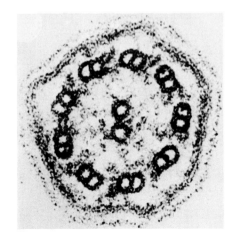

appear to comprise the spindle fibers are closely associated with centrioles during cell division. Since centrioles apparently can give rise to cilia and flagella, additional support is given to the contention that the centrioles produce at least some of the spindle fibers. The significance of microtubules in spindle fibers will be pursued in Chapter 11. More remarkable, and at the same time puzzling, are the similarities that can be noted between the globular subunits here and those in the elementary particles of mitochondria and quantasomes of chloroplasts.

Origins and Variations

The most perplexing question that arises in connection with cilia, flagella, and basal bodies concerns their origins. The problem is compounded by the differences in fine structure along the length of a cilium or flagellum. Most of the evidence suggests that cilia and flagella are derived from basal bodies and that basal bodies have the capacity to reproduce themselves. In ciliates the number of basal bodies in a row increases during the growth of the individual from one cell division to the next, indicating some process of replication. The nature of this self-duplication, however, is not known. The mechanism is definitely not fission.

Replicative capacity of basal bodies has been corroborated by the discovery of DNA in them and their ability to make protein. Basal bodies (often called kinetosomes) of ciliated protozoa incorporate [³H]thymidine as well as labeled amino acids. Their chemical make-up includes 50% protein, 2% RNA, and 3% DNA. DNA has also been identified in centrioles and basal bodies of other organisms.

In both plant and animal cells, basal bodies have been the apparent sources of cilia and flagella. In the liverwort *Marchantia*, for example, the sperm develops two flagella, both of which appear to arise from one of the two centrioles after cell division has occurred. In earlier descriptions the centriole was said to give rise to a basal body (blepharoplast), from which the two flagella developed. Flagellar origin from centrioles has been observed in a variety of cells, including certain reproductive cells of ferns and gymnosperms. The origin of the sperm flagellum in animals has already been mentioned.

Certain nonmotile structures in plants and animals may also originate in either the basal bodies or the centrioles. There is increasingly good evidence that the photoreceptor components of the rods and cones of the eye derive from cilia. The fibrils become modified greatly in the mature photoreceptor cells to form stacks of membranes on which the visual pigments are found. It is possible that these membranes of ciliary origin conduct excitations in the transmission of visual stimuli.

In Chapter 4 there was a brief description of the origin of nematocysts from cnidoblasts in coelenterates. The cnidoblast has a hairlike sensory extension, the *cnidocil,* which projects from the surface of the cell near the opening for the nematocyst. This structure is a device for the opening of the cell and the release of the nematocyst. The fine structure of the cnidocil suggests strongly that it is derived from a flagellum or that it represents a modification of a flagellum.

Movement

The phenomenon of ciliary or flagellar motion has two aspects: the mechanism of movement and the coordination of movement among several organelles, especially in the case of cilia. Neither of these aspects has been explained in a fully satisfactory manner, although a few theories have been advanced. Some consideration has been given to the chemical composition of the structures as at least a partial basis for an explanation of their movement. A protein with adenosine triphosphatase activity has been isolated from the flagella and cilia of several different organisms, including *Tetrahymena pyriformis.* In this protozoon most of the adenosine triphosphatase activity is in the fibers of the cilium, with only a small amount in the membrane. Isolation of the protein, called *dynein,* permits its characterization by sucrose density gradient centrifugation. Two components, 14 S and 30 S units, together exhibit adenosine triphosphatase activity. The latter, with a molecular weight of 5.4 million, is a linear polymer of globular 14 S subunits. It is located not in the outer fibers themselves, but in the arms that extend from them. Although myosin, a muscle protein, has about the same molecular weight as 14 S dynein, it is highly asymmetrical in contrast to globular dynein. Other differences also argue against significant similarity between dynein and contractile proteins of skeletal muscle. On the other hand, dynein resembles myxomyosin, a protein associated with protoplasmic streaming in slime molds. Similarities with spindle protein also suggest its role in movement. The presence of ATP in cilia represents a source of energy for the movement they exhibit. If ATP is added to flagella excised from their cells, the flagella begin to move in rhythmic patterns. Recent evidence from studies of sea urchin spermatozoa suggests that one molecule of dynein dephosphorylates one molecule of ATP during each beat cycle of the flagellum. Complete analysis of the chemical content also indicates the presence of lipoprotein material, presumably derived from the membrane components of the organelle. However, the lipid and protein here may be involved in movement and co-ordination of movement.

The orientation of the fibers in cilia and flagella has a constant relation to the direction of their beat. The fibrils are parallel to each other within the organelle and perpendicular to the direction of beat of the organelle. Since nerve nets or comparable structures have been observed underlying the rows of cilia in many cells, for some time it was thought that movement was controlled by and dependent on nervous activity, but there are few data of a convincing nature to support this theory. On the contrary, cilia removed from their cells and kept in a physiological salt solution retain their ability to move. Fibrous connections between basal bodies (Figure 8–11) have suggested that there may be some nervous control of coordination of movement, also. Whether these connections truly indicate nervous control remains to be determined, but they may nevertheless be involved in coordination.

One of the several theories of ciliary movement has fairly general support among workers in the field. In simplest terms, this theory states that the movement of a cilium or flagellum depends on unequal contractions or localized shortenings of the longitudinal fibrils. The hypothesis of movement proposed by Bradfield is based on several assumptions, namely, that the nine outer fibrils are able to contract and send waves of contraction from the base to the tip of the flagellum, that the central fibrils are not contractile, and that the origin of the impulse causing contraction is

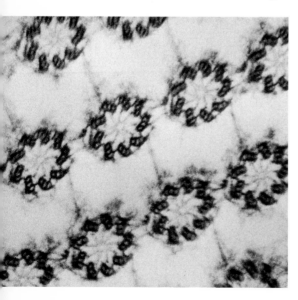

Figure 8–11. Linkage of basal bodies in *Trichonympha* (×89,000). FROM I. R. Gibbons and A. V. Grimstone, *J. Biophys. Biochem. Cytol.,* 7, 697 (1960).

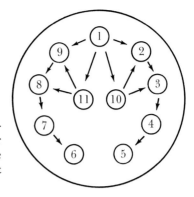

Figure 8–12. Possible scheme for the transmission of a contractile impulse in flagellar fibrils. Once it is initiated, the impulse spreads from one fibril to the next adjacent one.

in the basal body beneath one of the outer fibrils. In the initial movement or beat, a wave of contraction starts in the first fibril (which can be called number 1) and spreads to fibrils 2, 9, 10, and 11 (the central pair) (Figure 8–12). From fibrils 10 and 11, waves of contraction move up and stimulate fibrils 2, 3, 8, and 9 so that they contract simultaneously. The shortening of the fibrils resulting from the contractions makes the cilium bend in a forward direction as if it were a rigid body. On the return beat, the fibrils participating in the initial movement relax, and contractions occur at a slower rate in fibrils 4, 5, 6, and 7, to pull the cilium back to its original upright position. The cycle is repeated when a new impulse arises under fibril number 1.

Although the mechanism of coordination of such movement is not known, the pattern of coordination can be observed. Cilia do not usually beat simultaneously, but tend to move in groups so as to produce waves of movement that sweep along the surface of the cell. In effect, each cilium moves slightly before the next, all of them moving in sequence. The movement of flagella is more undulant than that of cilia, partly because of their greater length.

SELECTED READING

Bradfield, J. R. G., "Fibre Patterns in Animal Flagella and Cilia," *Symp. Soc. Exptl. Biol.,* **9,** 306 (1955).
Brokaw, C. J., "Adenosine Triphosphate Usage by Flagella," *Science,* **156**(3771), 76 (1967).
Child, F. M., "Some Aspects of the Chemistry of Cilia and Flagella," *Exptl. Cell Res.,* Suppl. 8, 47 (1961).

Ehret, C. F., and E. L. Powers, "The Cell Surface of *Paramecium,*" *Intern. Rev. Cytol.,* **8,** 97 (1960).

Fawcett, D. W., "Cilia and Flagella," in J. Brachet and A. E. Mirsky, eds., *The Cell,* Vol. 2, Academic Press, New York, 1961, pp. 217–97.

Gibbons, I. R., "The Organization of Cilia and Flagella," in J. M. Allen, ed., *Molecular Organization and Biological Function,* Harper & Row, New York, 1967, pp. 211–37.

Gibbons, I. R., and A. V. Grimstone, "On Flagellar Structure in Certain Flagellates," *J. Biophys. Biochem. Cytol.,* **7**(4), 697 (1960).

Gibbons, I. R., and A. J. Rowe, "Dynein; a Protein with Adenosine Triphosphatase Activity from Cilia," *Science,* **149**(3682), 424 (1965).

Mizukami, I., and J. Gall, "Centriole Replication. II. Sperm Formation in the Fern *Marsilea* and the Cycad *Zamia,*" *J. Cell Biol.,* **29**(1), 97 (1966).

Parducz, B., "Ciliary Movement and Coordination in Ciliates," *Intern. Rev. Cytol.,* **21,** 91 (1967).

Ringo, D. L., "The Arrangement of Subunits in Flagellar Fibers," *J. Ultrastruct. Res.,* **17**(3–4), 266 (1967).

Satir, P., "On the Evolutionary Stability of the 9 + 2 Pattern," *J. Cell Biol.,* **12**(1), 181 (1962).

Sleigh, M. A., *The Biology of Cilia and Flagella,* Pergamon Press, New York, 1962.

Sorokin, S., "Centrioles and the Formation of Rudimentary Cilia by Fibroblasts and Smooth Muscle Cells," *J. Cell Biol.,* **15**(2), 363 (1962).

Yanagisawa, T., S. Hasegawa, and H. Mohri, "The Bound Nucleotides of the Isolated Microtubules of Sea Urchin Sperm Flagella and Their Possible Role in Flagellar Movement," *Exptl. Cell. Res.,* **52**(1), 86 (1968).

part two

The Nucleus

9

Morphology and Chemistry

A cell typically contains a single nucleus. There are, however, a number of exceptions in which more than one nucleus is present. Plant cells with more than one nucleus, such as certain algae and fungi, are called *coenocytes,* whereas animal cells with this characteristic are called *syncytia.* *Vaucheria,* an alga commonly found in fresh water, is a large cell containing hundreds of nuclei, and the Phycomycetes (fungi) are composed of mycelia with no cross walls between nuclei. A familiar example is the black bread mold, *Rhizopus nigricans.* Some Protozoa, such as *Plasmodium vivax,* the malarial parasite, pass through syncytial stages in their development, and the striated muscle cells of higher animal forms exhibit a syncytial condition.

The position of the nucleus in the cell varies according to cell type, although it is often in the center of the cell. Whatever its location, the nucleus is surrounded on all sides by cytoplasm, from which it is separated by the nuclear envelope. The relative constancy of nuclear position in a particular cell type is illustrated by the green alga *Acetabularia.* This is a single cell with considerable differentiation, and the nucleus is almost invariably found in the basal region of the cell except during reproduction.

Morphology

The shape of the nucleus varies according to the species or cell type. The range of variation is limited, although in addition to the common spherical nuclei, ellipsoid or flattened nuclei occur. In the majority of cells, the

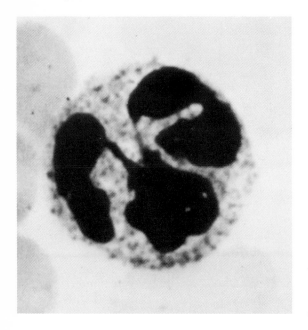

Figure 9–1. Nucleus in a neutrophil of the human male
(×5100). FROM J. L. Hamerton,
Intern. Rev. Cytol., **12**, 1 (1961).

margin of the nucleus is quite regular, but some cells, such as leukocytes,
contain nuclei with lobes or infoldings of their margins (Figure 9–1). The
shape of the nucleus is not necessarily related to the shape of the cell (see
Chapter 1).

As might be expected, the nucleus is not the same size in every cell,
nor does it always maintain a constant size during the lifetime of a given
cell. However, a ratio exists between nuclear volume and total cell volume
that is characteristic for each cell type. Nuclear size is a function of
chromosome number. A *diploid* cell is one in which two sets of chromosomes are present in the nucleus, one set representing the *haploid* number.
The haploid number of chromosomes is constant for each species, ranging
from 1 to as many as 800 (Chapter 16). Cells with more than the diploid
number of chromosomes usually have larger nuclei, especially when they
contain more than two whole sets of chromosomes. Since the number of
chromosomes has a direct bearing on the amount of DNA in the nucleus,
the size of the nucleus is also correlated with the DNA content.

Variation in nuclear size is observed at different times during the
cycle of cellular activities. While the cell is growing, there is an accompanying increase in the size of the nucleus, but just prior to the onset of
cell division, there may be a decrease. Changes in size as well as specific
morphological changes are best described by considering the individual
components of the nucleus.

The Nuclear Envelope

The organization of the nuclear envelope is vital to the functions of the cell as a unit. It is particularly so in terms of providing a pathway for the transport of materials between the nucleus and the cytoplasm. Observations of direct membrane connections between the nuclear envelope and the endoplasmic reticulum, and the evidence that during cell division the nuclear envelope develops from elements of the endoplasmic reticulum, raise an interesting question. Is the nuclear envelope part of the nucleus, or is it a cytoplasmic constituent? Since the cell operates as a unit and does not organize itself into independent parts, the question does not merit an answer. For convenience, however, the nuclear envelope will be treated here as a part of the nucleus.

Heretofore, much emphasis has been placed upon the use of the electron microscope for the study of cell fine structure. Although a number of morphological features of the nucleus can be observed with the light microscope, electron microscopy has been very helpful in delineating nuclear ultrastructure. Under the light microscope the nuclear envelope is barely perceptible; at best, it appears as a thin line between the nucleus and the cytoplasm. Under the electron microscope the nuclear envelope is seen to have a double membrane structure, broken at numerous intervals by pores or openings (Figures 9–2 and 9–3). Each membrane is about 90 Å thick, and each pore opening is 200 to 400 Å in diameter. The inner and

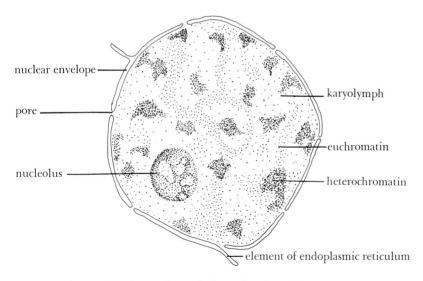

Figure 9–2. General morphology of an interphase nucleus.

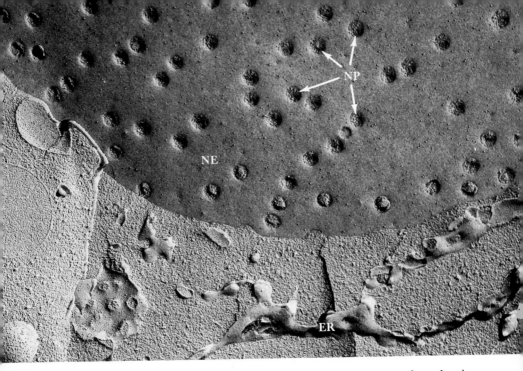

Figure 9–3. Freeze-etched preparation of an onion root nucleus showing nuclear envelope (NE) and pores (NP) in surface view (×38,400). FROM *Cell Ultrastructure* by William A. Jensen and Roderic B. Park. © 1967 by Wadsworth Publishing Company, Inc., Belmont, Calif. Reproduced by permission of the publisher.

outer unit membranes enclose the *perinuclear space,* which is 100 to 300 Å across.

At the margins of the pores, the two unit membranes are continuous (Figures 9–4 and 9–5). In many places the nuclear membranes join the membranes of the endoplasmic reticulum (Figure 9–6). In turn, certain parts of the endoplasmic reticulum may connect with the plasma membrane. In the apothecial (reproductive) cells of the ascomycete fungus *Mollisia,* there are also places at which the nuclear envelope makes direct contact with the plasma membrane. It has been suggested that in such primitive cells the plasma membrane may be the origin of the nuclear membranes.

The permeability of the nuclear envelope is difficult to categorize. Substances may move through the pores of the envelope or through the channels created by the connections with the cytoplasmic membrane system. Since less than 10% of the total surface area of the nuclear envelope is porous, a considerable amount of exchange of materials between the nucleus and the cytoplasm probably occurs through the membranes themselves. In this respect the nuclear membranes are selectively permeable,

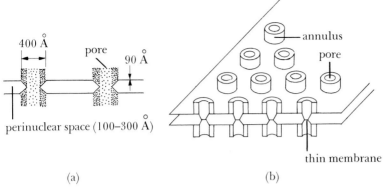

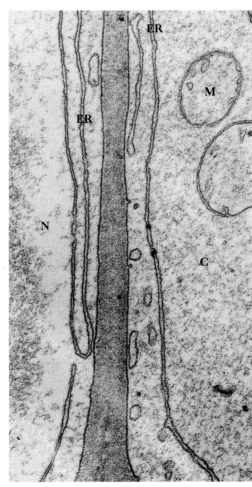

(a)   (b)

Figure 9–4. Fine structure of the nuclear envelope: (a) double membrane and pores; (b) pore complex, or annuli. (a) AFTER Watson; (b) after Afzelius.

Figure 9–5. Nuclear envelope in a corn root cell, showing pores and connections with the endoplasmic reticulum (×42,000). C, cytoplasm; ER, endoplasmic reticulum; M, mitochondrion; N, nucleus; NE, nuclear envelope; PM, plasma membrane. FROM W. G. Whaley, H. H. Mollenhauer, and J. H. Leech, *J. Biophys. Biochem. Cytol.,* **8,** 233 (1960).

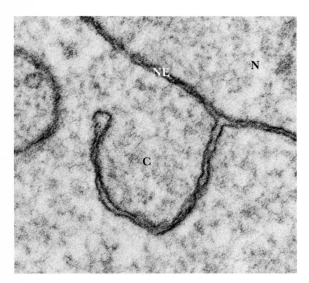

Figure 9–6. Nuclear envelope in a corn root cell, showing the membrane extension into the cytoplasm (×46,000). C, cytoplasm; N, nucleus; NE, nuclear envelope. FROM W. G. Whaley, H. H. Mollenhauer, and J. H. Leech, *J. Biophys. Biochem. Cytol.,* **8**, 233 (1960).

and the mechanisms of transport described in Chapter 3 may apply to them as well as to the plasma membrane (for example, pinocytosis). Support for this contention comes from several observations, including one on the penetration of rather large protein molecules into the nucleus. Ribonuclease and deoxyribonuclease, for example, are usually able to move from the cytoplasm into the nucleus, although at certain times during the metabolic cycle of the cell, the nucleus is impermeable to them.

Variations in membrane thickness from one part of a cell to another and among different species are only partially the result of variations in technique in the preparation of cells for electron microscopy. Measurement of membranes in mitochondria, endoplasmic reticulum, and chloroplasts, for example, have demonstrated real differences in thickness. The unit membranes of the nuclear envelope are composed of protein and lipid, as are other cytomembranes. This similarity in chemical composition among the cell membranes provides support for their basic morphological similarity, but not necessarily identity. With regard to membrane permeability, the passage of materials between the nucleus and the cytoplasm no doubt depends in part on the chemical organization of the nuclear membranes. For this reason the membranes must be considered as active rather than passive in terms of transport. As with the plasma membrane, the movement of substances across the nuclear envelope involves more than simple diffusion.

One additional aspect of membrane structure should be examined. Afzelius has indicated that the pores in some localities of the nuclear envelope are bounded by cylindrical structures. If the double membrane is cut tangentially to the surface of the nucleus, these cylindrical structures, or *annuli,* can be seen (Figure 9–4). Each pore appears to be covered by a thin membrane extending across the annulus. Other investigators have observed cytoplasmic extrusions between the cytoplasm and the nucleus in the pores. The inference is that there is some freedom of movement of materials through the pores. It may be possible to interpret the annuli as cytoplasmic materials extending through the pores rather than as specialized organizations of the nuclear envelope around the pores. On the other hand, Franke's demonstration of annuli in pores of onion root nuclei reveals a subunit structure, each annulus consisting of about eight globular subunits. Moreover, several lines of investigation provide evidence that the pore complex is a dynamic one. The diameter of the pore opening, as well as the number of pores and the state of annular material, varies according to activities during the cell cycle.

Chromatin

The chemistry and morphology of the chromosomes will be presented in Chapter 14, but a few words should be said about the nature of *chromatin* in the interphase nucleus. The term chromatin is somewhat ambiguous and requires explanation or definition. During interphase the chromosomes are usually long and exhibit little coiling or spiraling. They resemble very fine threads so entangled among themselves that discrete, individual ones are not distinguishable. Although each chromosome consists of one or more thin strands, the nucleus looks rather granular, owing to hydration and the tangling of the strands. The chromosomes stain readily with basic dyes, and particularly with basic fuchsin, in the Feulgen method (Chapter 10), which is specific for DNA, a major constituent of the chromosomes. The term chromatin refers to the Feulgen-positive material observed in the interphase nucleus and later during the division of the nucleus and is thus a general term for the substance of the chromosomes.

Certain areas of the chromatin mass stain darker than others during interphase, depending on the specific portions of the chromosomes involved. Those chromosomal regions that stain darker than others during interphase, and often lighter during cell division, are known as *heterochromatic* regions or *heterochromatin.* They are usually located near the centromere (kinetochore), the nucleolus organizer, and the ends of chromosomes, but are not restricted to these locations. In fact, all chromosomal regions may be potentially capable of heterochromatization. The differential staining reaction is due primarily to the degree of coiling in the strands of the chromosomes. Where the strands are highly condensed, there is greater density of chromatin material and therefore a darker stain. Often the denser regions appear as small beadlike bodies along the chromosomes, called *chromomeres*. Studies of the larval salivary gland chromosomes of *Drosophila melanogaster* and the chromosomes of certain mealy bugs suggest that the distribution of DNA along the chromosomes may not correlate proportionately to that of protein. There may be a higher content, for example, of histone protein in heterochromatin than in other chromosomal regions. Examination of patterns of DNA synthesis in several different organisms has established that heterochromatic regions are late in their replication, compared with other regions. Moreover, late-replicating chromatin tends to be genetically less active or inactive. This point will be illustrated in the following section on sex chromatin.

In certain types of cells, such as the salivary gland cells in dipteran larvae (*Drosophila, Sciara*), one or more large areas of the nucleus may stain very densely with the Feulgen reaction. These areas are distinguished from chromomeric regions primarily by their large size and are called *chromocenters*. A chromocenter represents an association of heterochromatic regions of several chromosomes, or, in some cases, an association of particular heterochromatic regions of all of the chromosomes in the nucleus. The latter situation prevails in the salivary gland cells of larval *Drosophila*. Owing to their more diffuse organization, however, chromocenters may stain only faintly in *Drosophila*.

Comprising the bulk of the chromosome is *euchromatin,* which stains less intensely than heterochromatin during interphase, as a consequence of its being less condensed. A classical view was that euchromatin represents the genetically active portions of chromosomes; it remains a valid description. The information now available about heterochromatin, however, indicates that a chromosomal region may be active at one time as euchromatin, but inactive at another (heterochromatin). Therefore, the staining response of chromatin may be considered as a cytological expression of its metabolic state in addition to a reflection of its state of condensation. Whereas some heterochromatic regions may in fact have few genes, the heterochromatization process may represent in others a mechanism for controlling gene action.

Sex Chromatin

With many types of mammalian cells, it is possible to determine the sex of the individual by the presence or absence of specific heterochromatic bodies at interphase. The phenomenon can be considered as a cellular sexual dimorphism. *Sex chromatin bodies* (also called *Barr bodies*, after their discoverer) characterize the nuclei of the majority of female cells but occur at very low frequencies, if at all, in male nuclei; when stained with eosin, Feulgen, or some other nuclear stain, 50 to 80% of the cells in various tissues of the female exhibit such bodies, whereas no more than about 15% of male cells, and in some tissues none, show them. A variety of tissues has been examined, from several mammals, including man, dog, cat, rabbit, opossum, rat, and mouse. In all but one of these organisms, the sex chromatin is restricted essentially to the nuclei of females. In the opossum both male and female cells contain sex chromatin bodies, but they are smaller in the male than in the female. No sex chromatin bodies have been found in molluscs, reptiles, amphibians, or birds. In the domestic chicken, however, in which the female has only one X chromosome, there is some ambiguity on this question.

Certain cells in some of the mammals studied offer exceptions to the general rule relating sex chromatin to sex. Nuclei of the neutrophils (blood cells) in both males and females of the C3H strain of mice contain sex chromatin bodies. The bodies are found in female somatic cells of *Rattus norvegicus* but not during the meiotic divisions giving rise to the egg. This is related to the fact that genetic inactivation of the X chromosome (see below) does not occur until at least the 12th day of embryonic development.

The use of culture techniques for mammalian tissues and cells has made possible the study of more kinds of tissues than ever before and has also permitted better cytological investigations of mammalian cells. Many types of mammalian tissue have been grown under culture conditions in the laboratory, including skin, blood, oral mucosa, embryonic membranes, kidney, heart, and spleen. Since cells from the oral mucosa can be obtained rapidly for immediate observation, this tissue has been used extensively for studies of sex chromatin in humans. Clinical analysis of human tissue for the presence of sex chromatin has proved very valuable in the diagnosis of a number of abnormalities in sexual development and of certain types of mental disorders (Chapter 16).

The sex chromatin body is most often found near the periphery of the nucleus, or near the nuclear envelope (Figure 9–7), but it may appear in other locations, depending upon the species or cell type; different types of cells in the same animal may have different locations for the sex chromatin body or bodies. There is, however, relatively little variation in the size of the structure among various species or among tissues of the same species. The average diameter of the sex chromatin body is 0.8 to 1.1 μ.

A somewhat different appearance of the sex chromatin body is observed in polymorphonuclear leukocytes. The main body has a slightly

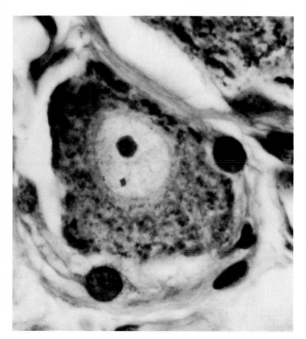

Figure 9–7. Sex chromatin body, below the nucleolus and near the nuclear envelope, in a sympathetic ganglion cell of a female cat (×1600). FROM J. L. Hamerton, *Intern. Rev. Cytol.,* **12,** 1 (1961).

Figure 9–8. Polymorphonuclear neutrophil leukocyte from a human female showing a drumstick (×3600). FROM J. L. Hamerton, *Intern. Rev. Cytol.,* **12,** 1 (1961).

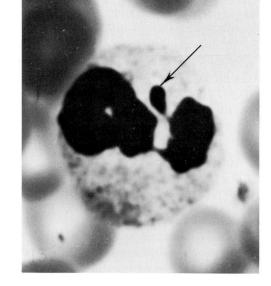

larger diameter than the typical one in other cells, and is attached to the nucleus by a filament (Figure 9–8). The average frequency of occurrence in humans is one per 38 neutrophils in the female, and none in the male. In leukocytes, the sex chromatin body is called a *drumstick*.

For each two sets (one diploid set) of chromosomes, there is usually only one sex chromatin body in the nucleus. If more than two sets of chromosomes are present, more than one sex chromatin body is found. In the human female the nucleus of a cell having four sets of chromosomes (*tetraploid*) contains two sex chromatin bodies; with a doubling of chromosome number, there is a doubling of the amount of sex chromatin. Some tetraploid cells of the human male contain sex chromatin bodies, but few diploid cells do. Such differences in sex chromatin content are readily observable, since certain tissues in the human body often include cells with more than the diploid number of chromosomes. Examples are liver, amnion, and bronchial epithelium.

The basis for the existence of the sex chromatin body is the sex chromosomes of the organism. It was once believed that the female showed a positive test for sex chromatin because each of her cells had two sex (X) chromosomes, whereas each cell of the male, in most mammals studied, had only one X chromosome. It now appears, however, that the heterochromatic body is due to the presence of a single, specific X chromosome. In humans, for example, the two X chromosomes of the female demonstrate different staining properties during interphase, one showing a darker stain reaction than the other. The dark-staining X chromosome exhibits what is referred to as positive *heteropycnosis;* it contains relatively large amounts of heterochromatic material. Other differences between the X chromosomes will be discussed later in connection with the duplication of the chromosomes, but it may be interjected here that the positively heteropycnotic X chromosome duplicates later than its partner. Thus the late-replicating X chromosome is responsible for the origin of the sex chromatin body in the human female. The significance of genetic inactivation of the late-replicating X chromosome is explained in Chapter 16.

Karyolymph

In the unstained cell at interphase, the nucleus appears to contain a granular yet homogeneous material in which discrete chromosomal bodies are almost impossible to discern. The matrix, or *karyolymph* (known also as *nuclear sap*), in which the chromosomes lie at this time is not easily defined. It is, however, a fluid substance, which escapes if the nucleus is punctured; it fills the nuclear space around the chromosomes and the nucleolus. The karyolymph is composed primarily of protein materials and is the site of certain enzymes in the nucleus. Among the chemical constituents are acidic protein and RNA rich in the bases adenine and uracil. The latter is related to RNA elaborated by the chromatin in the expression of gene action. Some evidence has been presented to support the contention that the karyolymph contributes to the formation of the spindle apparatus during cell division in plants, but more recent studies suggest that the spindle material is derived mainly from cytoplasmic substances.

The Nucleolus

The nucleolus is a relatively large, generally spherical body within the confines of the nucleus (Figures 9–9 and 9–10). The number of nucleoli present in each nucleus depends upon the species and the number of chromosomes or sets of chromosomes. In many plant and animal cells, there is one nucleolus for each haploid set of chromosomes. In *Vicia faba,* for example, there are two nucleoli in each diploid nucleus. As a consequence, it is often possible to correlate the number of nucleoli with the number of sets of chromosomes. However, in other organisms there may be two or more nucleoli for each haploid set, and in some organisms the number of nucleoli changes as the cell ages.

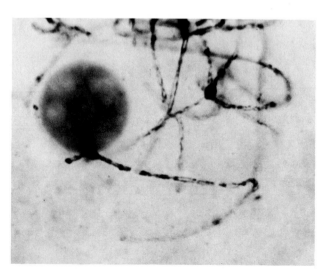

Figure 9–9. Nucleolus of a corn cell (×1400). FROM B. McClintock, *Z. Zellforsch. Mikroskop. Anat.,* **21,** 297 (1934).

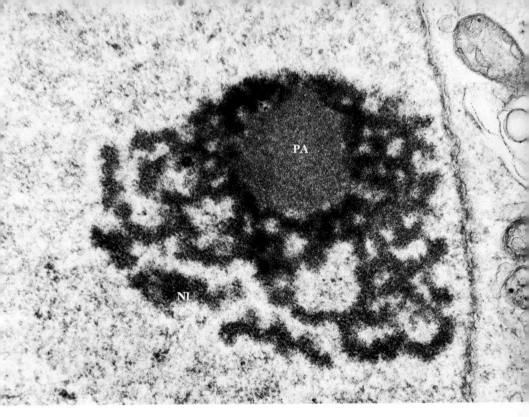

Figure 9–10. Nucleolus from spermatogonium of opossum testis. The pars amorpha (PA) is surrounded by nucleolonema (Nl) (×28,000). Micrograph by D. W. Fawcett, from *An Atlas of Fine Structure: The Cell, Its Organelles and Inclusions.* W. B. Saunders Company, Philadelphia, 1966.

The location of the nucleolus within the nucleus depends upon the chromosomes or chromosome areas associated with it. Certain heterochromatic portions of specific chromosomes are found in contact with the nucleolus during interphase. These are called the *nucleolus-organizing* regions of the chromosomes, and are responsible for producing much of the nucleolar RNA.

Although nucleoli may look different when compared in a variety of organisms, their fine structure is remarkably similar. Four major components are normally observed: particulate, fibrillar, amorphous, and chromatin. The particulate portion is made up largely of ribonucleoprotein, organized as ribosome-like particles 150 to 200 Å in diameter. Although quite similar in form and chemical content to cytoplasmic ribosomes, these particles tend to be slightly smaller than those ribosomes. Protein-containing fibrils 50 to 150 Å in diameter comprise the fibrillar portion. This portion, and the particulate segment, may exhibit vacuole-like regions. These two major components make up the microscopically identifiable *nucleolonema*. The amorphous part (*pars amorpha*) is mostly protein and may consist of tightly packed fibrils and granules in some organisms. In animals the nucleolonema may appear embedded in the pars amorpha, whereas the pars amorpha is usually central to the nucleolonema in plants (Figure 9–11). In either arrangement, the nucleolonema is the part of the nucleolus that tends to be associated with chromosomal heterochromatin. The fourth component, nucleolus-associated chromatin, is a tangled network penetrating the body of the nucleolus, but attached to the nucleolus organizers of the chromosomes.

Except in the algae *Spirogyra* and *Euglena*, the nucleolus disappears during the mitotic cycle, reappearing at the end of division in each daughter nucleus. Evidence for the persistence of some of the nucleolar material throughout the cell cycle has come from investigations with the electron microscope. In the root meristem of *Vicia faba* and in cultured cells of the Chinese hamster, material similar in density and structure to the mature nucleolus, but less organized, is observed among the chromosomes or free in the cytoplasm during the division of the nucleus. This *prenucleolar* material is associated with the chromosome surfaces until the end of division when it coalesces into the body of the reorganizing daughter nucleolus. The nucleolus then assumes its interphase organization. One of the most significant features of this behavior is that a continuity of at least part of the nucleolar material is maintained from one cell generation to the next. Other studies have indicated that not only is some of the persistent nucleolar material incorporated into the daughter nucleoli but that new nucleolar material is included, as a result of the resumption of RNA synthesis in the daughter nuclei.

The nucleolus may play a significant part in mitosis. Grasshopper neuroblasts have two nucleoli in each nucleus. If one of these nucleoli is exposed to ultraviolet radiation for a very short time between a late stage of one division and an early stage of the subsequent division, mitosis is almost permanently stopped. Apparently both nucleoli must be intact for mitosis to proceed.

Although the major component of nucleoli is protein (about 69%), the presence of a substantial amount of RNA (about 20%) makes it possible to stain the nucleolus with certain dyes for light microscopy. Spec-

Figure 9–11. Electron micrograph of two polar nuclei in the embryo sac of cotton (×41,000). One of the nuclei contains a prominent nucleolus. PA, pars amorpha; NE, nuclear envelope; Nl, nucleolonema. FROM *Cell Ultrastructure* by William A. Jensen and Roderic B. Park. © 1967 by Wadsworth Publishing Company, Inc., Belmont, Calif. Reproduced by permission of the publisher.

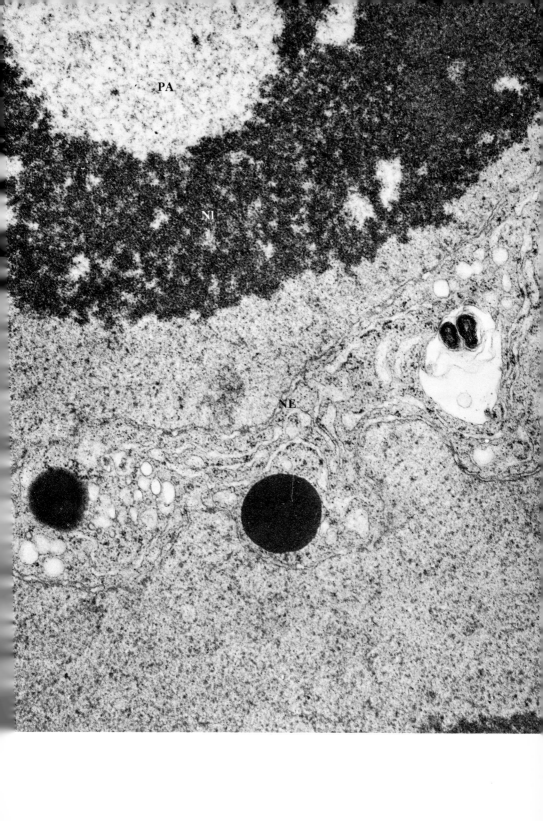

ificity of stain for cellular component is, at best, a relative matter, with the possible exception of the Feulgen reaction for DNA. Nevertheless, some stains tend to be bound preferentially by RNA or by RNA–protein complexes. As a consequence, the nucleolus can be studied with the light microscope by staining it with either azure B or the acidic dye methyl green. Biochemical analysis has indicated that as much as 25% of nuclear RNA resides in the nucleolus. At least one major fact has emerged from recent studies on nucleolar RNA: a significant proportion of it is produced in the nucleolus, and most of this is precursor material to cytoplasmic ribosomal RNA. Similarity in base composition between nucleolar and cytoplasmic RNA (guanine–cytosine rich) provides additional support for this relationship. The ribosomal RNA precursor is identified by density gradient centrifugation as 45 S RNA. This is converted to 35 S and 28 S RNA, which later moves to the cytoplasm for ribosome formation. An 18 S RNA may also be found in the nucleolus (derived from the 45 S RNA), but is rapidly transferred to the cytoplasm. There is also some evidence that the nucleolus may synthesize the precursors to the 50 to 60 S ribosomal subunits.

The synthesis of these ribosomal RNA precursor molecules depends upon the presence of genetic loci in the chromosomes to direct it. The sites of active DNA have now been established in the nucleolus organizers. Evidence for this derives from studies in *Drosophila* and in several amphibian species, as follows. The onset of ribosomal RNA synthesis in amphibians correlates exactly with the first appearance of visible nucleoli at gastrulation. As development proceeds, nucleoli increase in size and ribosomal RNA synthesis increases. A lethal mutant gene in the toad *Xenopus* results, in the homozygous condition, in the absence of nucleoli and nucleolus organizers. The cells are capable of the synthesis of DNA, transfer RNA, and messenger RNA, but no ribosomal RNA is produced. Moreover, nucleolar RNA hybridizes with ribosomal cistrons (genetic loci) of DNA located in the nucleolus organizers. Stocks of *Drosophila melanogaster* have been developed with more than the standard number of nucleolus-organizing regions of the chromosomes. If these regions are specifically involved in the synthesis of ribosomal RNA, the amount of RNA able to hybridize with DNA should be proportional to the dose of nucleolus organizers. This indeed was found, indicating that DNA sequences complementary to ribosomal RNA are in these chromosomal regions. There is also evidence, in the anucleolate mutants of *Xenopus laevis,* for the nucleolar synthesis of some of the lysine-containing fractions of histone protein, since these fractions are absent or in reduced quantities in the mutants. Investigations in pea seedlings have also suggested that some ribosomal protein may also be made in the nucleolus, but this is not under direction of the nucleolus organizer cistrons. Although there is little support for its synthesis in the nucleolus, transfer RNA has been found there and is likely stored only temporarily in the nucleolus before its transfer to the cytoplasm for its activity in protein synthesis.

The genetic material of *Xenopus* contains from 1000 to 2000 cistrons for each of the 28 S and 18 S ribosomal RNA's, whereas the number in *Drosophila* is about 130. In both cases the number represents more than would be required for the synthesis of ribosomal RNA, and the redundancy of these genetic loci is not yet understood. As C. H. Waddington said, after a conference on the nucleolus in 1965, "Possibly many of us thought . . . that we had the nucleolus pretty well under control, and that a general consensus would emerge. Few of us can still suffer from such optimistic delusions."

Redundancy in *Xenopus* oocyte nuclei stems largely from the appearance of multiple nucleoli during the development of the eggs. In this and other amphibians, like the newt *Triturus,* as many as 1000 nucleoli are present, but not directly associated with the chromosomes. It has been suggested that in meiotic prophase of the oocyte, the nucleolus-organizing region undergoes differential replication to produce 1000 copies free of the chromosomes, and that the DNA contained therein codes for the ribosomal RNA. This DNA represents a DNA separate from that introduced into the nucleolus by the nucleolus-associated chromatin described earlier. Each of these peripheral nucleoli has a fibrous core surrounded by a granular cortex. Since deoxyribonuclease digests the core fibrils, this appears to be the location of the nucleolar DNA. In *Xenopus* and *Bufo* (a toad), the DNA content of the nucleus increases by 100% in the early stages of meiosis, indicating that over half of the nuclear DNA at that time is nucleolar. As the oocytes mature, the nucleoli extend into a ring or necklace shape, and in the mature oocytes they revert to the conventional spheroidal form. The latter exhibits a DNA-containing core with a ribonucleoprotein hull or cortex. Synthesis of RNA occurs in the core, and the RNA is transferred to the cortex where it is built into ribonucleoprotein particles. The DNA of *Triturus* oocytes is a rather long fiber with a diameter of about 30 Å. Several species of *Drosophila* also exhibit a nucleolar DNA capable of incorporating [^{3}H]thymidine in larval salivary gland cells. In these species of *Drosophila,* connecting fibers are observed between the nucleoli and the chromosomes. Homologies may exist between this nonchromosomal DNA in amphibian oocytes and in *Drosophila* salivary glands. All of these observations support the interpretation that the site of localization of nucleolar DNA is the same as that for RNA synthesis.

In contrast to these cases, the nucleolus is nearly inactive in RNA synthesis during early meiotic stages of corn anthers and locust testes. Moreover, the nucleolar apparatus is lost prior to meiosis in male reproductive cells of a marine worm, *Urechis*. These observations suggest that the nucleolar genes are switched off prior to or during meiosis in the male.

Chemistry

The chemical substances predominant in the nucleus are the nucleic acids (DNA and RNA) and proteins. Both basic and acidic proteins are present. The former consist either of histones or protamines, both characterized by the presence of the basic amino acids lysine, histidine, and arginine. However, they differ in their proportions of these amino acids. Protamine contains no lysine, arginine residues make up two-thirds of it, and there are only five or six different amino acids present in protamine. On the other hand, histone contains many different amino acids. Histones are widely distributed among cells, whereas protamines are more restricted, for example, to the sperm of certain animals. The acidic proteins in nuclei include the residual proteins of the chromosomes (Chapter 14). Their amino acid content differs in several respects from that of basic protein of the nucleus, resembling that of ribosomal proteins. Moreover, acidic proteins contain tryptophan, whereas histones do not. Histones appear to be most closely associated with the chromosomes, while the acidic proteins are found in the nucleolus and karyolymph as well.

The nucleic acids comprise from 20 to 40% of the nuclear material, with DNA primarily in the chromatin and RNA distributed throughout the nucleus. The protein content is considerably higher than that of the nucleic acids (Table 9–1), and proteins are also found widely distributed. Nuclear DNA content is directly related to the chromosome number and to the stage in the cell cycle during which it is measured. Spectrophotometric analyses of Feulgen-stained nuclei (Chapter 10) have demonstrated that the DNA content per chromosome set is constant and that total nuclear DNA content doubles during interphase prior to mitosis or meiosis

Table 9–1   Chemical Constituents of the Nucleus

Organism	DNA, wt %	RNA, wt %	Protein, wt %		
			Basic	Acidic	Total
pea seedling	14.0	12.1	22.6	51.3	73.9
rat liver	28.8	5.3	—	—	65.9

Table 9–2 Chemical Composition of Chromatin*

Source	Content, Relative to DNA			
	DNA	Histone Protein	Nonhistone Protein	RNA
pea vegetative bud	1.00	1.30	0.10	0.11
pea growing cotyledon	1.00	0.76	0.36	0.13
rat liver	1.00	1.00	0.67	0.043
human HeLa cells	1.00	1.02	0.71	0.09
sea urchin blastula	1.00	1.04	0.48	0.039

*From J. Bonner et al., *Science*, **159**(3810), 47 (1968). Copyright 1968 by the American Association for the Advancement of Science.

and halves during the formation of gametes. Interphase may be separated into three stages with regard to DNA synthesis. During the stage prior to synthesis (G_1), the DNA content has what is called the $2C$ value, corresponding to the DNA content of the diploid genome. DNA synthesis occurs during the S stage, by the end of which the DNA content has a $4C$ value. Prior to division, the interphase occupies a G_2, or postsynthetic, stage during which protein and RNA synthesis continue. After mitotic division each daughter nucleus contains the $2C$ DNA content, and following the end of meiosis, each product contains a $1C$ value.

Proportions of the principal constituents of chromatin relative to DNA are given in Table 9–2. As shown, the bulk of chromosomal material consists of DNA and basic protein, with some variations in contents according to cell or tissue type. Most of the available evidence indicates that the chromosomal RNA is bound to the chromosomal protein. It is possible that some of this RNA is an impermanent constituent, rather than a stable, structural one. Discussion of the synthesis of RNA by chromosomal DNA will be found in later chapters. The role of protein will also be considered.

The next most abundant nuclear substances are the lipids, which comprise from 3 to 10% of the nuclear mass and occur principally as lipoproteins or phospholipids. The phospholipid of the nucleolus differs qualitatively from the phospholipid of the chromosomes.

The most interesting components of the nucleus are the enzymes, primarily because they pose the greatest problem in chemical and functional analyses. One of the difficulties in isolating specific enzymes from the nucleus is technical, since the methods used often result in contamination by cytoplasmic materials or in the loss of nuclear substances. Recent refinements, however, have provided somewhat improved techniques for enzyme analysis. A method for the isolation of nucleoli can be cited as an example. With various modifications appropriate to the tissue under study, it has been utilized for a number of cell types, including the eggs of *Rana pipiens:*

> The jelly coat is removed from the eggs, which are then homogenized in 0.2 M sodium phosphate at pH 7.4. The homogenate is centrifuged at 50 times gravity for 14 minutes, and the residue is discarded. The remaining supernatant is centrifuged at 16,500 times gravity for 45 minutes, and the residue is discarded. After adjustment to 0.02 M with respect to magnesium chloride, the supernatant is centrifuged at 500 times gravity. The sediment contains the nucleoli, which can be subjected to biochemical analyses.

Nicotinamide adenine dinucleotide synthetase, an enzyme necessary for the synthesis of NAD, a coenzyme important in protein synthesis and other chemical reactions in the cell, is found in the nucleus, or more specifically in the nucleolus. Although the enzyme systems have not been entirely isolated, the nucleus also contains enzymes concerned with the synthesis of RNA, DNA, and proteins. These include nucleoside phosphorylase and ribonuclease. The synthesis of RNA in the nucleus, including the nucleolus, is supported by several lines of investigation. At present, most studies suggest that the major portion of the RNA produced in the cell is synthesized in the nucleus and moves thence to the cytoplasm. Some enzyme localization has been found within the nucleus. For example, RNA polymerase and ribonuclease show greater activity in the nucleolus than elsewhere, whereas deoxyribonucleases and adenosine triphosphatase B are located preferentially outside the nucleolus. This information derives largely from studies of isolated rat liver nuclei and nucleoli. That protein synthesis occurs in the nucleus is supported in several ways. Present in the nucleus are the required activating enzymes, transfer and messenger RNA's, and ribosomes. Furthermore, labeled amino acids can be incorporated into nuclear histones and other proteins. Ribosomes, however, are not present in all kinds of nuclei. Also located in the nucleus are certain enzymes involved in the respiratory cycle. Some of these provide a mechanism for the formation of an energy source such as ATP. Evidence for ATP production in the nucleus comes in large part from biochemical studies of calf thymus nuclei.

The inorganic content of the nucleus is quite low but of great biochemical significance. The inorganic materials, such as salts of calcium, magnesium, iron, and zinc, are either bound to the proteins of the nucleus or necessary for enzyme activity. The roles of specific divalent metallic ions, as related to the organization of the chromosomes, will be discussed in Chapter 14.

SELECTED READING

General

Brachet, J., *Biochemical Cytology*, Academic Press, New York, 1957.

Mirsky, A. E., and S. Osawa, "The Interphase Nucleus," in J. Brachet and A. E. Mirsky, eds., *The Cell*, Vol. 1, Academic Press, New York, 1961, pp. 677–770.

Mitchell, J. S., ed., *The Cell Nucleus*, Proceedings of the Faraday Society, Butterworths, London, 1960.

Mitchison, J. M., "Some Functions of the Nucleus," *Intern. Rev. Cytol.*, **19**, 97 (1966).

The Nuclear Envelope

Afzelius, B. A., "The Ultrastructure of the Nuclear Membrane of the Sea Urchin Oocyte as Studied with the Electron Microscope," *Exptl. Cell Res.*, **8**(1), 147 (1955).

Fisher, H. W., and T. W. Cooper, "Electron Microscope Observations of the Nuclear Pores of HeLa Cells," *Exptl. Cell. Res.*, **48**(3), 620 (1967).

Franke, W. W., "Isolated Nuclear Membranes," *J. Cell Biol.*, **31**(3), 619 (1966).

Merriam, R. W., "Some Dynamic Aspects of the Nuclear Envelope," *J. Cell Biol.*, **12**(1), 79 (1962).

Moore, R. T., and J. H. McAlear, "Fine Structure of Mycota," *Exptl. Cell Res.*, **24**(3), 588 (1961).

Watson, M. L., "Further Observations of the Nuclear Envelope of the Animal Cell," *J. Biophys. Biochem. Cytol.*, **6**(2), 147 (1959).

Whaley, W. G., H. H. Mollenhauer, and J. H. Leech, "Some Observations on the Nuclear Envelope," *J. Biophys. Biochem. Cytol.*, **8**(1), 233 (1960).

Chromatin and Sex Chromatin

Atkins, L., P. D. Taft, and K. P. Dalal, "Asynchronous DNA Synthesis of Sex Chromatin in Human Interphase Nuclei," *J. Cell Biol.*, **15**(2), 390 (1962).

Barr, M. L., "Sex Chromatin and Phenotype in Man," *Science*, **130**(3377), 679 (1959).

Barr, M. L., "The Significance of the Sex Chromatin," *Intern. Rev. Cytol.*, **19**, 35 (1966).

Brown, S. W., "Heterochromatin," *Science*, **151**(3709), 417 (1966).

De Mars, R., "Sex Chromatin Mass in Living, Cultivated Human Cells," *Science*, **138**(3544), 980 (1962).

Fraccaro, M., and J. Lindsten, "Observations on the So-called Sex Chromatin in Human Somatic Cells Cultivated in Vitro," *Exptl. Cell Res.*, **17**(3), 536 (1959).

Hay, E. D., and J. P. Revel, "The Fine Structure of the DNP Component of the Nucleus," *J. Cell Biol.*, **16**(1), 29 (1963).

Hsu, T. C., "Differential Rate in RNA Synthesis Between Euchromatin and Heterochromatin," *Exptl. Cell Res.*, **27**(2), 332 (1962).

Klinger, H. P., and H. G. Schwarzacher, "The Sex Chromatin and Hetero-chromatic Bodies in Human Diploid and Polyploid Nuclei," *J. Biophys. Biochem. Cytol.,* **8**(2), 345 (1960).

Kosin, I. L., and H. Ishizaki, "Incidence of Sex Chromatin in *Gallus domesticus,*" *Science,* **130**(3366), 43 (1959).

La Cour, L. F., and J. A. Chayen, "A Cyclic Staining Behavior of the Chromosomes During Mitosis and Meiosis," *Exptl. Cell Res.,* **14**(3), 462 (1958).

Miles, C. P., and S. D. Storey, "Nuclear Chromocenters of Cultured Chicken Cells," *Exptl. Cell Res.,* **27**(3), 377 (1962).

Moore, K. L., *The Sex Chromatin,* Saunders, Philadelphia, 1966.

Ohno, S., W. D. Kaplan, and R. Kinosita, "X Chromosome Behavior in Germ and Somatic Cells of *Rattus norvegicus,*" *Exptl. Cell Res.,* **22**(3), 535 (1961).

The Nucleolus

Barr, H. J., and W. Plaut, "Comparative Morphology of Nucleolar DNA in *Drosophila,*" *J. Cell Biol.,* **31**(2), c17 (1966).

Berlowitz, L., and M. L. Birnstiel, "Histones in the Wild-type and the Anucleolate Mutant of *Xenopus laevis,*" *Science,* **156**(3771), 78 (1967).

Birnstiel, M., "The Nucleolus in Cell Metabolism," *Ann. Rev. Plant Physiol.,* **18**, 25 (1967).

Brinkley, B. R., "The Fine Structure of the Nucleolus in Mitotic Divisions of Chinese Hamster Cells *in vitro,*" *J. Cell Biol.,* **27**(2), 411 (1965).

Brown, D. D., and I. B. Dawid, "Specific Gene Amplification in Oocytes," *Science,* **160**(3825), 272 (1968).

Gabrusewycz-Garcia, N., and R. G. Kleinfeld, "A Study of the Nucleolar Material in *Sciara coprophila,*" *J. Cell Biol.,* **29**(2), 347 (1966).

Gaulden, M. E., and R. P. Perry, "Influence of the Nucleolus on Mitosis as Revealed by Ultraviolet Microbeam Irradiation," *Proc. Natl. Acad. Sci. U.S.,* **44**(6), 553 (1958).

Georgiev, G. P., and J. S. Chentsov, "On the Structural Organization of the Nucleolo-chromosomal Ribonucleoproteins," *Exptl. Cell Res.,* **27**(3), 570 (1962).

Herich, R., "The Nucleolus Structure. II. Differentiation, Morphological Build-up, and Development of Nucleolar Structures," *Nucleus (Calcutta),* **7**(1), 59 (1964).

Hyde, B. B., "Changes in Nucleolar Ultrastructure Associated with Differentiation in the Root Tip," *J. Ultrastruct. Res.,* **18**(1), 25 (1967).

La Cour, L. F., "Ribose Nucleic Acid and the Metaphase Chromosome," *Exptl. Cell Res.,* **29**(1), 112 (1963).

La Fontaine, J. G., and L. A. Chouinard, "A Correlated Light and Electron Microscope Study of the Nucleolar Material During Mitosis in *Vicia faba,*" *J. Cell Biol.,* **17**(1), 167 (1963).

Lane, N. J., "Spheroidal and Ring Nucleoli in Amphibian Oocytes," *J. Cell Biol.,* **35**(2–1), 421 (1967).

Macgregor, H. C., "Pattern of Incorporation of [³H]uridine into RNA of Amphibian Oocyte Nucleoli," *J. Cell Sci.*, 2(2), 145 (1967).

Muramatsu, M., J. L. Hodnett, W. J. Steele, and H. Busch, "Synthesis of 28 S RNA in the Nucleolus," *Biochim. Biophys. Acta*, 123(1), 116 (1966).

Ritossa, F. M., and S. Spiegelman, "Localization of DNA Complementary to Ribosomal RNA in the Nucleolus Organizer Region of *Drosophila melanogaster*," *Proc. Natl. Acad. Sci. U.S.*, 53(4), 737 (1965).

Sirlin, J. L., "The Nucleolus Problem," *Nature*, 186(4721), 275 (1960).

Sirlin, J. L., "The Nucleolus of the Cell Nucleus," *Endeavour*, 20, 146 (1961).

Vincent, W. S., and O. L. Miller, Jr., eds., "The Nucleolus: Its Structure and Function," *Natl. Cancer Inst. Monograph*, 23 (1966).

Wallace, H., and M. L. Birnstiel, "Ribosomal Cistrons and the Nucleolar Organizer," *Biochim. Biophys. Acta*, 114(2), 296 (1966).

Chemistry

Alfert, M., and H. Swift, "Nuclear DNA Constancy: A Critical Evaluation of Some Exceptions Reported by Lison and Pasteels," *Exptl. Cell Res.*, 5(2), 455 (1953).

Allfrey, V. G., and A. E. Mirsky, "Some Aspects of Ribonucleic Acid Synthesis in Isolated Cell Nuclei," *Proc. Natl. Acad. Sci. U.S.*, 43(9), 821 (1957).

Allfrey V. G., A. E. Mirsky, and S. Osawa, "Protein Synthesis in Isolated Cell Nuclei," *Nature*, 176(4492), 1042 (1955).

Amano, M., "Metabolism of RNA in the Liver Cells of the Rat. I. Isolation and Chemical Composition of Nucleus, Nucleolus, Chromatin, Nuclear Sap and Cytoplasm," *Exptl. Cell Res.*, 46(1), 169 (1967).

Le Blond, C. P., and M. Amano, "Synthetic Activity in the Nucleolus as Compared to That in the Rest of the Cell," *J. Histochem. Cytochem.*, 10(2), 162 (1962).

Plaut, W., and R. C. Rustad, "Cytoplasmic Incorporation of a Ribonucleic Acid Precursor in *Amoeba proteus*," *J. Biophys. Biochem. Cytol.*, 3(4), 625 (1957).

Prescott, D. M., "Nuclear Synthesis of Cytoplasmic RNA in *Amoeba proteus*," *J. Biophys. Biochem. Cytol.*, 6(2), 203 (1959).

Rho, J. H., and J. Bonner, "The Site of Ribonucleic Acid Synthesis in the Isolated Nucleus," *Proc. Natl. Acad. Sci. U.S.*, 47(10), 1611 (1961).

Siebert, G., "Enzymes of Cancer Nuclei," *Exptl. Cell Res.*, Suppl. 9, 389 (1963).

Siebert, G., et al., "Enzymatic Studies on Isolated Nucleoli of Rat Liver," *J. Biol. Chem.*, 241(1), 71 (1966).

Stern, H., F. B. Johnston, and G. Setterfield, "Some Chemical Properties of Isolated Pea Nucleoli," *J. Biophys. Biochem. Cytol.*, 6(1), 57 (1959).

10

Cytological Methods

In Chapter 2 the principles of staining and fixing cells were described, as well as some of the specific methods for the detection and study of cytoplasmic structures. It is the purpose of this chapter to present a few specific methods for the study of the nucleus, especially the chromosomes and the nucleolus. Only methods widely used in conventional laboratory procedures are given, and, for that matter, relatively few of the stains and fixatives available for use are mentioned. Although a great variety of plant and animal tissues can be studied cytologically, some lend themselves most readily to the procedures. Plant tissues providing particularly good cytological preparations include the reproductive organs (anthers and ovules) of flowering plants and root meristems, since the behavior of the nucleus during cell division can be studied easily in these cells. Among the animal tissues studied extensively are the male reproductive tissues, oogonia, and certain glandular tissues in insect larvae, since such tissues are relatively simple to isolate and usually contain large numbers of dividing cells. Thus, in both plants and animals, somatic and germinal cells are suitable for cytological analysis.

Fixation

Some of the basic fixing solutions for nuclear contents are listed in Table 2–2. Most widely used for the selective preservation of the nucleus are ethanol, acetic acid, chromic acid, and osmium tetroxide. Carnoy's solution is the simplest and fastest-acting medium for the fixation of chromosomes in either somatic or germinal cells of plant tissues. The cytoplasm is cleared, and excellent contrast results following the application of stain, of which several kinds may be used. Flemming's solution is another good mixture for the fixation of somatic and germinal cells, especially in animal tissues. It consists of osmium tetroxide, chromic acid, and acetic acid and preserves the entire nucleus and its contents. The preparation of certain animal tissues is possible with a weak solution (2%) of osmium tetroxide alone. This may be used, for example, in fixing insect testes that have been smeared on a microscope slide. After treatment with the solution, the material on the slide is rinsed in 1% chromic acid, washed in distilled water, and stained. In many types of cells only the nucleolus is successfully preserved by the osmium tetroxide alone.

An osmium-containing fixative that is a good preservative of root tissue has been developed by Ford. The solution consists of 2% chromic acid (2.5 ml), 2% osmic acid (1.6 ml), and distilled water (3 ml). Roots are fixed at 0°C overnight, after which they are rinsed several times in distilled water. They are then treated for 1 hour with a mixture of ammonium oxalate and hydrogen peroxide (7 parts saturated aqueous ammonium oxalate to 1 part 40% peroxide) for bleaching and maceration. After being washed in distilled water, they may be stained with the Feulgen method for chromosomes.

Newcomer's fixative is also desirable for plant chromosomes and can be used with the Feulgen method or other stains. Its particular advantage is that the tissues may be stored in it for several months. (Tissues may also be stored successfully in Carnoy's fixative or 70% ethanol.) Newcomer's solution is made of 6 parts isopropanol, 3 parts propionic acid, 1 part petroleum ether, 1 part acetone, and 1 part dioxane.

Special methods have been utilized for the demonstration of certain morphological or chemical features of the chromosomes. For example, the spiraling or coiling of the chromosomes, to be described later, can sometimes be emphasized for cytological study by special treatment of the cells prior to fixation. The observation of the chromosome spirals is particularly good in cells with large chromosomes. For this reason the reproductive cells of *Tradescantia, Trillium,* and *Fritillaria* in the plant kingdom and grasshopper testes in the animal kingdom have been widely studied. The methods that have effectively shown the chromosome spirals include treatment with ammonia vapor and treatment with potassium cyanide solution.

Cold treatment (0°C) of the reproductive tissues of such plants as *Fritillaria pudica* results in a sharp distinction between the heterochromatic and euchromatic regions of the chromosomes. The heterochromatic region stands out as either clear areas (negative heteropycnosis) or dark areas (positive heteropycnosis), depending upon the nature of the fixation and staining procedures and the time during the cell cycle at which the nucleus is observed (Chapter 9). This clarification of the heterochromatin was once attributed to a decrease in heterochromatic DNA, suggesting a certain lability of the DNA in heterochromatic regions as compared with euchromatic regions. Recent studies, however, have established that the cold effects are mainly due to differential coiling of the chromosomes.

Staining

Among the nuclear stains cited in Chapter 2 were methyl green and pyronine. These stains are useful for distinguishing between DNA and RNA. Methyl green produces a green color in deoxyribonucleoprotein, and pyronine produces a red color in ribonucleoprotein. Pyronine is therefore a valuable stain for nucleoli, which are normally high in RNA content. When tissues are treated with ribonuclease, they lose their capacity to stain with pyronine, thus demonstrating the reaction of ribonucleic acid. Treatment with deoxyribonuclease, on the other hand, prevents a staining reaction with methyl green and other stains specific for DNA. Methyl green–pyronine is also known as the Unna-Pappenheim stain. In some instances methyl green stains RNA. Protein may inhibit its effect with either nucleic acid.

Other nuclear stains include Toluidine Blue, which stains both RNA and DNA, alkaline Fast Green, which stains histone protein, and crystal violet, which stains ribonucleoprotein in some cells and chromosomes in others.

The Feulgen-Rossenbeck method, developed in 1924, is one of the most effective staining procedures for chromosomes in most kinds of tissues. Not only has it been of value in qualitative cytology; it can also be adapted to quantitative determinations, since the chemical reactions depend on the presence of deoxyribonucleoprotein. Generally, the *Feulgen-nucleal reaction* is specific for DNA. The dye component used, a chloride of pararosaniline (Figure 10–1), is commonly known as basic fuchsin. It is

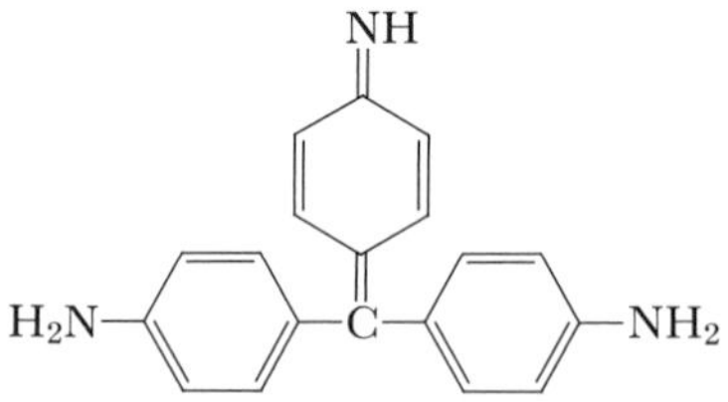

Figure 10–1. Structure of pararosaniline.

made by boiling together small quantities of aniline, *p*-toluidine, and mercuric chloride and then adding the mixture to 70% ethanol. The basic fuchsin is mixed with 1 N HCl and sodium or potassium metabisulfite in water in the following proportions: 1 g basic fuchsin, 2 g metabisulfite, 10 ml 1 N HCl, and 200 ml distilled water. The solution is allowed to stand in the dark for about 24 hours and is then shaken with activated charcoal, which decolorizes it, and filtered. The filtrate is stored in a dark bottle, which prolongs its stability. The solution is leucobasic fuchsin, a clear colorless liquid otherwise known as Schiff reagent.

The tissue to be stained must be hydrolyzed before the stain reaction can take place. Hydrolysis is usually carried out in 1 N HCl at 60°C for 12 minutes. The purine bases of DNA are separated from the deoxyribose components, liberating aldehyde groups on the sugar moiety. In addition, RNA is removed, so that only DNA will respond to the subsequent staining. The insoluble product *(apurinic acid)* reacts with the decolorized Schiff reagent to stain the chromosomes magenta. The cytoplasm and the RNA-containing portions of the nucleus are Feulgen-negative. Although DNA is found in mitochondria and chloroplasts, the amount is too small to be detectable with ordinary light microscopy in most cells.

Since the nucleic acids have characteristic wavelengths of absorption in the ultraviolet region of the spectrum (about 2600 Å), their identification is possible by means of ultraviolet microscopy or spectrophotometry (Figure 10–2). (The absorption spectra of DNA and RNA are based on

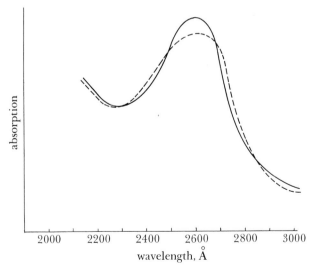

Figure 10–2. Ultraviolet absorption spectra of DNA and RNA: ———, DNA; – – –, RNA.

the presence of purine and pyrimidine bases.) Certain staining procedures can be used in conjunction with photometric techniques for the quantitative determination of these substances. Lambert's law states that the proportion of incident light absorbed by a stained specimen is directly related to its thickness, and Beer's law states that the proportion of light absorbed is directly related to the concentration of absorbing molecules (Beer-Lambert law). Either ultraviolet or visible light may be utilized in cytophotometry, and their use depends on these relationships. Moreover, the amount of stain retained must be proportional to the amount of material being measured. Model systems have established a linear proportionality between amount of color and amount of DNA in the Feulgen reaction. However, it is not possible as yet to convert *directly* the amount of color to the *absolute* amount of DNA by cytophotometry. Such measurements provide for a determination of *relative* amounts of DNA; when coupled with biochemical analysis, absolute amounts can be calculated. A critical test for the stain reaction is provided by treatment with deoxyribonuclease; a negative response to Schiff reagent occurs when DNA is removed.

Specimens stained in the Feulgen method for DNA can be studied with a microscope using monochromatic light (about 5500 Å, which corresponds to the maximum absorption of the DNA–dye complex). The intensity of the light transmitted by the stained specimen is determined by projecting an enlarged image onto a photocell, which measures the current produced. A reading is also taken of a clear area on the slide, and the difference between the two readings is used in calculating the amount of absorbing material present. Such a method has proved useful for the correlation of DNA content with chromosome number; the two values are directly related.

The photometric calculation of absorbance assumes the existence of a uniform, random distribution of stained objects (chromophores) in the measuring field. As a consequence of the nonuniform distribution of chromophores in most nuclei, considerable error is introduced into the measurement of total nuclear DNA content. This is called *distributional error,* and three methods of measurement have been developed to minimize it: *scanning aperture photometry, two-wavelength microspectrophotometry,* and *photographic colorimetry.* With the first method, a small, moving spot of monochromatic light scans the nucleus and an integrated, total absorbance is obtained. Since distributional error increases with an increase in optical density, it is detectable in terms of distortion of the absorption spectrum. In the two-wavelength method, the absorption spectrum is first measured in a region of the specimen having low absorbance where the error is negligible (a uniform distribution). Two wavelengths are then selected such that the absorbance at one is equal to one-half that at the other ($E_1 = \frac{1}{2}E_2$). The value obtained by measurement at two wavelengths will depart from the expected ratio of 2 : 1 by an amount dependent on the extent of distributional error, and from which the true value for average absorbance can be calculated. These calculations have been simplified by the use of tables. In the method of photographic colorimetry, absorbance by the specimen is determined by the amount of color eluted from a cut-out photograph of it, as measured with a colorimeter. Density standards are essential to correct for errors from one photograph to another. These include cellulose films impregnated with a dye, or with DNA. If the latter is used, absolute amounts of DNA can be determined for individual nuclei. The major advantages of this technique are that it requires relatively simple equipment, and that it can be used for measurement of irregularly shaped objects like chromosomes or parts thereof.

When methyl groups are substituted for the amino groups in the colorless substance pararosaniline, the violet-colored stain crystal violet (methyl violet) results. It has six methyl groups. As indicated earlier, crystal violet may be used as a stain for nucleic acid, and it is particularly suitable for staining chromosomes in animal cells. Another widespread application is in the preparation of bacterial cells. The Danish bacteriologist Gram adapted it to the *gram-stain* method, which distinguishes certain bacteria from others. Some bacteria treated with crystal violet and iodine retain the stain after an alcohol rinse, while others do not. Gram-positive bacteria apparently differ from gram-negative ones in their RNA metabolism, since the stain reaction is dependent upon the presence of RNA and its associated basic protein.

Two other dyes are important in chromosome staining: hematoxylin and carmine. The former is obtained from the wood of the tree *Haematoxylin campechianum* Linn. Very often this dye is used with a mordant, such as potassium alum, $KAl(SO_4)_2 \cdot 12H_2O$, or iron alum, $NH_4Fe(SO_4)_2 \cdot 12H_2O$, to form a lake. Although the combination is most successful in staining chromosomes, it may also be used for centrioles and mitochondria. The stain may be made with the mordant or applied separately, as follows.

1. Dye-lake combination: hematoxylin, 0.1 g; water, 100 ml; sodium iodate, 0.02 g; and potassium alum, 5 g.

2. Dye and mordant separate: apply $2\frac{1}{2}\%$ iron alum mordant, rinse with water, and stain with a mixture of hematoxylin, 0.5 g; 96% ethanol, 10 ml; and water, 90 ml.

Carmine is obtained from the female scale insect *Coccus cacti* (Homoptera), which lives on the cactus *Opuntia coccinellifera*. The bodies of the dried females make cochineal, and carminic acid (Figure 10–3) is pro-

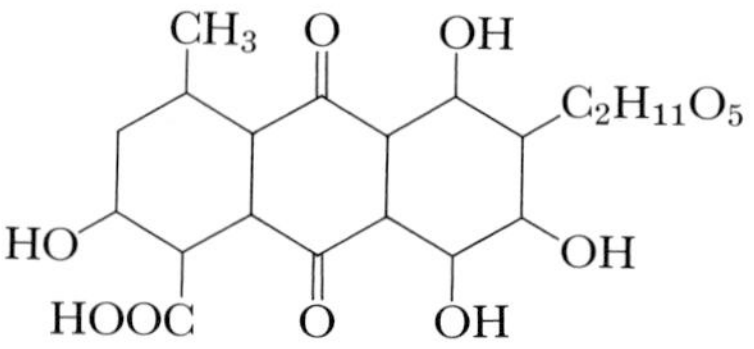

Figure 10–3.   Structure of carminic acid.

duced by extracting cochineal with boiling water, treating it with lead acetate, and treating the resultant lead carminate with sulfuric acid. The dye, carmine, is formed by mixing an alum with the carminic acid. The stain is prepared by saturating a solution of acetic acid (45%) with carmine. Carmine is a good chromosome stain, behaving like a basic dye.

Specific Techniques

This section presents some of the common methods of preparing tissues for nuclear studies. Most of the methods are designed for the preservation and staining of chromosomes, but they may be adapted to other purposes by the substitution of appropriate stains as described earlier in this chapter and in Chapter 2.

   The two main preparation techniques are sectioning and smearing. Sectioning is most useful for studies of the organization of tissues, smearing for studies of individual cells and cell components. Material to be sectioned is fixed with Flemming's or Carnoy's or some other suitable solution and embedded in paraffin. It is cut in thin sections on a microtome. Staining is usually performed directly on the slide, and the section may be made permanent wtih balsam, diaphane, or some other mounting medium. One of the disadvantages of sectioning is the danger of losing portions of the cellular or nuclear contents if the section is cut too thin or at an oblique angle. Even with the most careful handling, some constituent materials are lost. Smearing is not only simpler and faster than sectioning but also results in complete recovery of all the cellular components desired for observation. That is, entire cells are retained on the slide. This is especially important if, for example, chromosome counts are to be made. In smearing, the tissue or cells are applied directly to the slide before or after fixation. Plant tissues lend themselves more readily to this technique than do most animal tissues, although it is effective for both. The procedures of fixation and staining for chromosomes are basically the same with smearing and sectioning. The major difference between the two techniques is that sectioning involves embedding the tissue and cutting it in thin slices, whereas smearing involves direct application of the tissue to a slide. Since smearing is widely used for a great variety of tissues, it is emphasized here.

Feulgen

Tissue is fixed in Carnoy's solution at room temperature for 12 to 24 hours or at 60°C for 15 to 30 minutes. If preferred, Ford's or Newcomer's fixative may be used, depending upon the tissue. The tissue is then washed thoroughly in distilled water so that all fixative is removed. With Carnoy's solution as fixative, the tissue is next hydrolyzed in 1 N HCl at 60°C for 12 minutes. After a brief water rinse, Schiff reagent is added until a deep purple color develops. The dividing regions of the tissue are then smeared on a clean slide in 45% acetic acid, and a cover slip is applied. Pressure is usually necessary to flatten and separate the chromosomes. The slide may be retained for a few days if the edges of the cover slip are sealed with paraffin or Glycomastic, a special preparation that is easily removed with the fixative solution. If a permanent slide is desired, the cover slip may be removed by soaking in 10% acetic acid followed by successive rinses in ethanol–acetic acid mixtures as follows: 1 : 1, 3 : 1, 9 :1, 95% ethanol, and finally 100% ethanol. Mounting medium is applied to the slide, and the cover slip is replaced over the specimen. The slide is allowed to dry for 1 or 2 days.

An easier and quicker technique for the preparation of permanent slides utilizes the dry-ice method of Conger and Fairchild. After the initial smear is made, the slide with cover slip is placed on a block of dry ice to freeze for a few minutes. The cover slip is removed with a thin blade, and the slide is rinsed in 95 or 100% ethanol. A second ethanol rinse is followed by rinses in toluene or some other solvent, depending upon the mounting medium. Another advantage of this method is a reduction in loss of material, as all of the specimen adheres to the slide when the cover slip is discarded. A fresh cover slip is used for the permanent mount.

With Ford's fixative, the material is bleached and macerated after the washing in distilled water and before hydrolysis. The dry-ice method is also suitable in this case, for example, with root tips, pollen, and the salivary glands of insect larvae.

Acetocarmine and Acetoorcein

Either acetocarmine or acetoorcein may be used for animal tissues, root material, and cells undergoing division in the formation of pollen grains. Acetoorcein often produces the more intense reaction. One of the greatest benefits of these stains is their combination with a fixing fluid. Thus only one step is necessary; staining and fixing are accomplished simultaneously. However, preservation is sometimes improved if the material is fixed beforehand, and hydrolysis facilitates a better stain response. Otherwise, whether it is anther material, root tips, or salivary glands, it is squashed on the slide in a drop of stain, and a cover glass is applied. Temporary or permanent slides may be made as explained earlier.

Crystal Violet

The method described by Newton for staining chromosomes utilizes crystal violet in a 1% aqueous solution. After fixation and rinsing, the material is stained, rinsed in water, and treated with 1% iodine in a solution of 1% potassium iodide (made up in 80% ethanol). Following an ethanol rinse, a permanent slide is prepared with clove oil. Since crystal violet is relatively easily removed by ethanol, clove oil is used for dehydration instead of the usual alcohol series. Mounting procedures are typical. This general method is valuable in preparing sectioned material, especially animal tissue, and smeared material.

Colchicine

For determinations of chromosome number and morphology, it is necessary to obtain preparations in which the chromosomes are flattened and well spread and in which numerous divisions are occurring. In somatic cells the best stage of division for observations of this kind is metaphase, during which the chromosomes are shortest and are preparing to separate to the poles of the cell. They can often be distinguished from each other because of their relatively short lengths and their thickness. Yet in cells containing many small chromosomes, individuals are difficult to identify. Therefore, some special treatment is required for the accumulation of many metaphases containing well-spread, clearly defined chromosomes.

The substance most frequently used for such preparations is colchicine, a drug obtained from the crocus plant and used historically to treat gout. The effect of colchicine is primarily to disrupt the spindle apparatus of the cell during division, thereby preventing the movement of the chromosomes to the poles of the cell. Thus colchicine treatment results in the retention of all or most of the cells in metaphase. If cells are treated with colchicine for an extended period of time, divisions of the chromosomes continue without divisions of the cells. Consequently, the number of chromosomes is doubled, quadrupled, etc., producing *polyploid* cells. This effect has been noteworthy in certain agricultural practices.

Microtubules (Chapter 8) comprising the spindle fibers during cell division, and those near the plasma membrane, appear to be the structures specifically affected by colchicine. The latter microtubules assume a pattern that mirrors the orientation of cellulose microfibrils in the cell wall. Colchicine treatment of xylem cells in wheat seedling coleoptiles, for example, results in the nearly total disappearance of these microtubules. In treated root meristem cells, the spindle microtubules are absent and cell plates are missing. Colchicine also inhibits the elongation of regenerating cilia in *Tetrahymena;* no ciliary shafts regenerate in its presence, but do so when colchicine is removed. At a concentration of 4 mg/ml, colchicine does not immobilize normal cells nor affect RNA or protein synthesis. It has been suggested, therefore, that colchicine interferes with the assembly of ciliary precursor proteins. In fact, evidence in several systems shows that colchicine binds to these protein subunits comprising the microtubules of cilia, flagella, and spindles. Thus, the fundamental action of colchicine seems to be a prevention of the assembly of protein into a microtubule. Gout symptoms result from the phagocytic action of leukocytes on urate crystals deposited in the joints. Colchicine may relieve this condition by interfering with the microtubules on which phagocytic activity depends.

Secondary effects of colchicine include a tendency to cause additional condensation of the chromosomes, making them shorter and thicker than normal. This is helpful in spreading the chromosomes apart and also may produce a repulsion between the arms of the chromosomes. More extreme effects, resulting from extended treatment with high concentrations of the drug, include stickiness of the chromosomes, breakage of the chromosomes, and, at worst, liquefaction of the chromosomal material.

The production of colchicine metaphases (c-metaphases) is achieved prior to fixation; tissues are treated with colchicine for 2 to 6 hours before they are killed and preserved. Ordinarily very low concentrations, from 0.02 to 1% solutions in water, are used. Other agents, such as *p*-dichlorobenzene, with similar effects have been employed, but colchicine remains the most popular.

Cell and Tissue Culture

Methods for the growth of mammalian cells in vitro are not new in experimental biology. Yet in recent years refinements and modifications of these techniques have permitted the cytological study of a great variety of tissues with more clarity of detail than ever before.

Present procedures incorporate several of the basic methods for the preparation of chromosomes for cytological analyses. As will be shown later in more detail, the improvement of culture methods led to the validation of the chromosome number in humans as 46 rather than the earlier determined 48. It is now possible to grow cells and tissues outside of the body of the organism and under laboratory conditions with relative ease, and this situation benefits both the cytologist and the pathologist. A variety of tissues from humans and other mammals, especially those in the primate group, has been studied. Examples are embryonic and adult bone marrow, skin, spleen, kidney, and testis. A general scheme of tissue culture is given here to provide background for the later discussion.

A few tissue pieces are collected from a living subject and placed in a sterile chamber with a physiological saline solution for washing and brief storage. The cells are dissociated from each other by treatment with an enzyme, usually trypsin in low concentration (about 0.2%) in a buffered solution.

After dissociation of the cells by trypsinization, the cell suspension is centrifuged and resuspended in a special medium containing all the nutritional requirements for cell division and maintenance. (Various media have been used, including Eagle's, which is cited in the reading list.) The cells suspended in the growth medium are placed in bottles or special test tubes (Leighton tubes) and incubated at 37°C. A depression in the Leighton tube allows for the introduction of a cover slip, to which the cells may adhere, facilitating later cytological preparation. Otherwise, the cells eventually adhere to the surfaces of the glass containers and proliferate there. Subcultures or transfers are made by taking small samples from the tubes and placing them in other tubes with the appropriate medium.

After a suitable time it is possible to recover cell samples from the growing culture for cytological study. Often colchicine in very low concentration is added to the medium to accumulate metaphases over a period of 12 to 24 hours, or less, depending upon the duration of the division cycle in the particular tissue. Following colchicine treatment, the cell suspension may be submitted to treatment with a hypotonic salt solution, which causes spreading and separation of the chromosomes. This is essential in tissues of organisms with high chromosome counts, as is the case ordinarily with mammals. Spreading is also especially helpful because the chromosomes are often quite small.

Accumulation of large numbers of dividing cells can be enhanced by application of 5-aminouracil or excess thymidine prior to colchicine treatment. In effect, a relatively large proportion of cells in a population can be synchronized. The agent acts by slowing down the rate at which cells progress through the S stage of interphase, so that many cells in S accumulate during exposure to the agent. Upon removal from the agent, the cells then proceed through S and G_2 and into mitosis. Consequently, timing of the cycle allows one to collect the cells when most of them are dividing. With 5-aminouracil there may also be an induced delay of exit of the cells from G_2, but there is no effect on G_1. This technique is also applicable to plant tissue, like root meristems, in which as much as 80% of the cell population may be in synchrony as a result of 5-aminouracil treatment.

Fixation is accomplished by one of the standard methods, and staining is usually by the Feulgen reaction, acetocarmine, or acetoorcein. The details of fixation, staining, and the preparation of permanent slides differ only slightly from those of the conventional techniques.

Other methods of handling tissues include the growth of tissue explants on slides or cover slips, resulting in monolayers of new cells growing outward from the tissue slice on the glass surface. In addition, smears can be made of cells from an accessible part of the living organism. For example, examination of sex chromatin bodies can be made on scrapings from the mouth lining smeared on a glass slide and stained with acetoorcein or the Feulgen method. Blood can also be collected and prepared to permit the proliferation of the leukocyte portion in short-term culture. This method is advantageous for a study of chromosomes in peripheral blood. Phytohaemagglutinin, a plant product, is used to stimulate division of the leukocytes, and conventional treatments with colchicine, hypotonic solution, fixative, and stain are followed.

Thus it is now possible to prepare mammalian cells for an analysis of chromosome number and chromosome morphology with considerable facility and to achieve a quality comparable to that with other kinds of cells. Advances in the cytogenetics of mammals, particularly humans, owe much to the development of these cytological methods.

SELECTED READING

Alfert, M., "Studies on Basophilia of Nucleic Acids: The Methyl Green Stainability of Nucleic Acids," *Biol. Bull.,* **103**(2), 145 (1952).
Borisy, G. G., and E. W. Taylor, "The Mechanism of Action of Colchicine," *J. Cell Biol.,* **34**(2), 525 (1967).
Christensen, E., "An Improved Sealing Wax for Temporary Smear Preparations," *Stain Technol.,* **29,** 197 (1954).
Chu, E. H. Y., and N. H. Giles, "Comparative Chromosomal Studies on Mammalian Cells in Culture. I. The HeLa Strain and Its Mutant Clonal Derivatives," *J. Natl. Cancer Inst.,* **20**(2), 383 (1958).

Cohn, N. S., and P. van Duijn, "Constancy of DNA Content in Adrenal Medulla Nuclei of Cold-Treated Rats," *J. Cell Biol.,* **33**(2), 349 (1967).

Conger, A., and L. Fairchild, "A Quick-Freeze Method for Making Smear Slides Permanent," *Stain Technol.,* **28,** 281 (1953).

Darlington, C. D., and L. F. La Cour, "Nucleic Acid Starvation of Chromosomes in *Trillium,*" *J. Genet.,* **40,** 185 (1940).

Darlington, C. D., and L. F. La Cour, *The Handling of Chromosomes,* 3rd rev. ed., Macmillan, New York, 1960.

Davidson, J. N., *The Biochemistry of Nucleic Acids,* 4th ed., Wiley, New York, 1960.

Eagle, H., "Nutritional Needs of Mammalian Cells in Tissue Culture," *Science,* **122**(3168), 501 (1955).

Eigsti, O. J., and P. Dustin, "Colchicine Bibliography III," *Lloydia,* **12,** 185 (1949).

Glick, D., "Quantitative Microchemical Techniques of Histo- and Cytochemistry," in J. Brachet and A. E. Mirsky, eds., *The Cell,* Vol. 1, Academic Press, New York, 1959, pp. 139–60.

Jakob, K. M., and J. E. Trosko, "The Relation Between 5-Aminouracil-Induced Mitotic Synchronization and DNA Synthesis," *Exptl. Cell Res.,* **40**(1), 56 (1965).

Mellors, R. C., ed., *Analytical Cytology,* McGraw-Hill, New York, 1955.

Newcomer, E. J., "A New Cytological and Histological Fixing Fluid," *Science,* **117**(3038), 305 (1953).

Prensky, W., and H. H. Smith, "The Mechanism of 5-Aminouracil-Induced Synchrony of Cell Division in *Vicia faba* Root Meristems," *J. Cell Biol.,* **24**(3), 401 (1965).

Prescott, D. M., ed., *Methods in Cell Physiology,* Vol. 1, Academic Press, New York, 1964.

Puck, T. T., "Single Human Cells in Vitro," *Sci. Am.,* **197**(2), 91 (1957).

Reitalu, J., "Preparation of Human Chromosomes by the Whole Blood Technique, A Convenient Procedure in the Teaching of Cytogenetics," *Hereditas,* **52**(2), 235 (1964).

Richards, B. M., "Cytochemistry of the Nucleic Acids," *Protoplasmatologia,* **5,** 1 (1966).

den Tonkelaar, E. M., and P. van Duijn, "Photographic Colorimetry as a Quantitative Cytochemical Method," *Histochemie,* **4,** 1 (1964).

White, P. R., "The Cell as Organism, 'Tissue Culture,' Cellular Autonomy, and Cellular Interrelations," in J. Brachet and A. E. Mirsky, eds., *The Cell,* Vol 1, Academic Press, New York, 1959, pp. 291–326.

Wied, G. L., ed., *Introduction to Quantitative Cytochemistry,* Academic Press, New York, 1966.

Woodard, J., M. Gorovsky, and H. Swift, "DNA Content of a Chromosome of *Trillium erectum:* Effect of Cold Treatment," *Science,* **151**(3707), 215 (1966).

11

Cell Division

The division and replication of cells are the basis for both sexual and asexual reproduction in most organisms. Even such primitive cell types as bacteria exhibit cell division, although the details of the process are not always recognized. With the exception of such cells (Chapter 17), the mechanisms of cell replication are similar or identical in plants and animals. The multiplication of cells occurs principally by *mitosis*. This term refers to the division of the nucleus into two daughter nuclei of about equal size, each of which has the same number of chromosomes as the parent cell. Following *cytokinesis,* the daughter cells also have more or less equal distribution of the cytoplasmic constituents, such as mitochondria. Mitosis is commonly associated with (but not confined to) *somatic* tissue, in contrast to *germinal* tissue, and is the principal mechanism of asexual reproduction and vegetative propagation. Aside from the aspect of reproduction, mitosis is fundamental to the replacement of old and dying cells and therefore to the regeneration of tissues in the adult organism. In this respect it is possible to categorize the times and sites of mitotic activity in living tissues.

The transformation of a zygote (the product of the union of egg and sperm) into an embryo and the growth and development of the embryo can be considered stage one. During this period an increase in the size of the immature organism and a gradual differentiation into cell and tissue types occur. These events are ultimately dependent upon multiple mitoses, primarily because of the significance of the duplication of genetic material within the nucleus. Stage two is represented by the adult organism, with its mitotically active centers. In higher animals such centers include the blood-forming tissue, epithelial linings of the gut, epidermal cells, and damaged tissue. In plants such centers are called *meristems* and are characterized by the presence of numerous undifferentiated dividing cells. These meristematic regions are found in the apical portions of roots and stems and in the leaf and flower buds of higher plants. In woody plants additional mitotic divisions occur in lateral meristems, such as the cambium, for the production of secondary tissues. Stage three refers to the reproductive life of the organism, as related to asexual reproduction or to certain events in sexual reproduction. The latter will be discussed in connection with the phenomenon of meiosis in the next chapter. Some acellular or unicellular animals and plants, such as amoebae, reproduce solely by asexual means, that is, by a form of cell division, presumably mitosis in the usual sense. The plant kingdom has the greatest capacity for asexual reproduction. A number of animals have remarkable powers of regeneration of lost parts, for which the mitotic process is basic. These examples leave little doubt of the significance of mitosis from the standpoint of the maintenance and reproduction of biological systems.

Mitosis

The behavior of the chromosomes is the most important feature of mitosis. The strongest evidence for this is that only those cells containing nuclei are capable of reproducing themselves. This is not to imply, however, that the cytoplasm does not have a role in cell division. It too must divide, and it contributes to certain aspects of mitosis. Nevertheless, the continuity of genetic material and the control of cell functions and behavior rest with the nucleus, and more precisely with the chromosomes.

Although the organization is in some ways artificial, there is a traditional subdivision of the mitotic events into several specific stages. These include *prophase, metaphase, anaphase,* and *telophase* (Figure 11–1), and during each, characteristic changes take place. The stages are described and illustrated below.

Interphase

In spite of the fact that *interphase* (the period between nuclear divisions) is not listed as a stage of mitosis, it is a critical time in terms of preparation for division of the cell. It is a time of important metabolic reactions both in the nucleus and in the cytoplasm, marked by DNA replication as well as the effective duplication of the chromosomes in mitotic cells. Interphase occupies the time between the end of telophase and the beginning of the

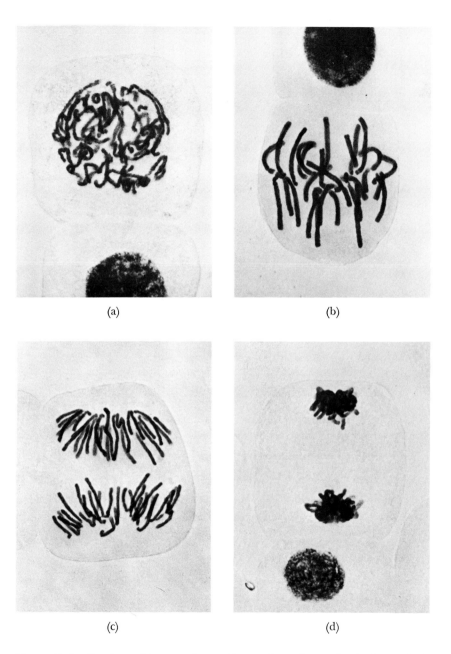

Figure 11–1. Prophase (a), metaphase (b), anaphase (c), and telophase (d) in *Lilium regale* root tip (×2400). Reproduced from J. McLeish and B. Snoad, *Looking at Chromosomes,* Macmillan, London, 1958.

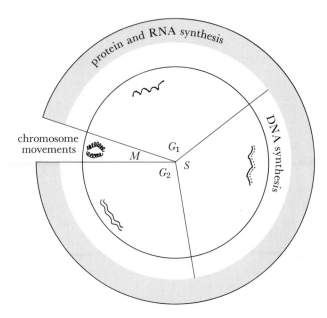

Figure 11–2. The cycle of events in a mitotic cell.

next prophase, and its duration varies from organism to organism. Interphase is discussed here in terms of premitotic preparations.

A typical cell cycle, including interphase, lasts from 20 to 24 hours.
Interphase is the longest period in the cell cycle, and may last for several
days in cells with intermittent or relatively low rates of mitosis. The first
major nuclear event in cell division is the duplication of the chromosomes
through replication of DNA and chromosomal protein. Although DNA
synthesis must precede mitosis, it does not necessarily lead to mitosis. On
the basis of synthetic activities, interphase is divided into three substages:
G_1, S, and G_2 (Figure 11–2). DNA synthesis occurs during S, and has a
relatively constant duration among similar cells of a species, occupying 35
to 40% of interphase time. The duration of S in the root tip cells of *Vicia
faba* is 6 to 8 hours in a total cycle time of 19 hours, and in grasshopper
spermatogonia S lasts 12 hours in a 28 hour cell cycle. Cultured human
cells have an 18 hour cycle with an S period of 6 to 8 hours. In some cells,
however, there is a very short or absent G_1 period, S occupying most of the
interphase time. The most variable in time of the interphase substages is
G_1, which occupies from 25 to 50% of interphase time. It is the period preceding S and following mitosis. Some cells may be in a permanent G_1 interphase, whereas those carrying on cell division exhibit specific activities in
G_1 in preparation for S. These include the synthesis and organization of
the substrates and enzymes necessary for DNA synthesis. Therefore G_1 is

marked by the synthesis of RNA and protein. G_2, the period following S and preceding mitosis (M), is often characterized by an increased nuclear volume, and has an average duration similar to that of M (1 to 4 hours). More significantly, G_2 is the time during which certain metabolic and organizational events occur as prerequisites to mitosis. The inhibition of protein synthesis, for example, results in the inhibition of entry of cells into M. Among the proteins produced at this time are those required for the formation of spindle fibers. Although RNA is synthesized during G_2, not all of it is essential for the entry of the cell into M. Nucleolar RNA synthesis immediately prior to M is not required. On the other hand, early interference with the nucleolus produces a mitotic delay (Chapter 9). Since the nucleolus participates in the production of ribosomal RNA, it appears that the supply of ribosomes in late interphase is sufficient to support the synthesis of the protein required for division. In fact, there is evidence that ribosomes made in early G_2 are reserved for the *subsequent* cell cycle. Messenger RNA is also made in G_2, and is one of the essential types in the preparation for M.

Prior to DNA synthesis (in G_1), each chromosome usually appears as a single strand with the light microscope. Following S (in G_2), the chromosome consists of two strands or *chromatids* (Figure 11–2). However, finer resolution of a chromosome in many higher plants and animals demonstrates the presence of two or more strands prior to duplication and four or more after duplication. This question of the organization of chromosomal subunits will be examined in greater detail in Chapter 14. As noted earlier, total DNA content doubles during the S period, and a nucleus is designated as having the $2C$ value prior to and the $4C$ value after DNA synthesis. Chromosomal protein has been somewhat more difficult to study with respect to its organization and time of synthesis. In several cell types, including root tip cells, liver fibroblasts, and HeLa cells, the synthesis of histone protein occurs concurrently with that of DNA. Although some may be produced in G_1, most of it is synthesized during the S period. It is not yet clear for many cells whether histone is synthesized exclusively in the nucleus or in the cytoplasm. In HeLa cells, whose nuclei lack ribosomes, histones are produced in the cytoplasm in the vicinity of small clusters of ribosomes (polysomes). Calf thymus nuclei, however, are capable of protein synthesis.

The synthesis of RNA occurs during most of the cell cycle, but is depressed at two periods, during S and M. In regenerating rat liver, for example, there is a marked synthesis of RNA in G_1 and G_2, but a considerable reduction in it during the time of DNA synthesis. It increases immediately after the end of S, continues into prophase in most cells, becomes almost completely suppressed during late prophase through metaphase and anaphase, and resumes at some time during telophase. Virtual cessation of RNA synthesis corresponds with the dissolution of the nucleolus in prophase, and resumption coincides generally with nucleolar reconstruction in telophase. Protein synthesis is also suppressed during the same period. These changes in synthetic activity are consistent with the view that condensed chromosomes cannot serve as templates for RNA synthesis, which is necessary for protein synthesis; if no messenger RNA is available to the ribosomes, protein cannot be produced. Moreover, studies in HeLa cells have shown that polysomes disaggregate to single ribosomes during mitotic metaphase, coincident with a depression of protein synthesis. The decrease of protein synthesis in mammalian cells is most pronounced during metaphase and anaphase.

The appearance of the interphase nucleus is shown in Figure 9–2 (page 205). The chromosomes exhibit a minimum degree of condensation or coiling and are so entwined that they cannot be distinguished individually. The slight coiling evident in the chromosomes is a holdover from the previous mitosis. The coils are thus known as *relic* coils. The nucleolus is at maximum size, and the volume of the nucleus may increase during this phase.

No single event seems to be responsible for the initiation of mitosis. The cell is quite active metabolically during interphase, and the several processes, including DNA synthesis, occurring at the time so affect the cell that there is apparently no alternative to division. Ultimately the preparatory processes must be under genetic control. In any case, at the end of interphase a series of changes begins in the physical and chemical organization of the chromosomes that is cytologically observable.

Prophase

Prophase is usually the longest mitotic stage. According to tissue type, it lasts anywhere from several minutes to more than an hour (Table 11–1).

Table 11–1 Duration of Mitotic Stages in Various Tissues

Tissue	*Time, minutes*			
	Prophase	*Metaphase*	*Anaphase*	*Telophase*
onion root	71	6.5	2.4	3.8
pea endosperm	40	20.0	12.0	110.0
grasshopper neuroblast	102	13.0	9.0	57.0

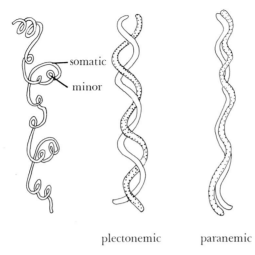

plectonemic   paranemic

Figure 11–3.   Levels of chromatid coiling during prophase.

The visible changes in the chromosomes in prophase are due primarily to an increase in the state of condensation. The duplicated chromosome now consists of two chromatids, each of which undergoes a regular cycle of coiling. Condensation results from this coiling of the individual chromatids as well as a coiling of the two chromatids about each other. Two levels of coils develop in the chromatid, large *somatic* coils, and small *minor* coils (Figure 11–3). The somatic coils, small at first, decrease in number as prophase progresses but increase in diameter, causing an apparent thickening of the chromosome. In the early stages of prophase, the two chromatids of each chromosome are coiled about each other *relationally*. In most cells they cannot be easily separated; they are actually twisted together. This association is called *plectonemic* coiling, and it differs from the type of relational coiling occurring in meiotic prophase. There the coiling is *paranemic,* and the chromatids are easily separated laterally. In mitotic prophase, then, the chromosomes become distinct as individual units owing to increased coiling and a consequent thickened appearance (Figure 11–4). As the coiling cycle continues, the nucleolus decreases in size, until it disappears at the end of prophase.

The final step or event of prophase is the breakdown of the nuclear envelope. The evidence of observations with the electron microscope indicates that the nuclear envelope disperses into the cytoplasm as elements of the endoplasmic reticulum, from which it may have been initially derived.

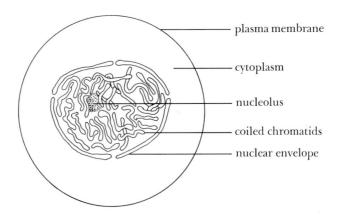

Figure 11–4. Prophase.

Metakinesis

Just prior to metaphase there is movement of the chromosomes, which are now free in the cytoplasm, toward the central region of the cell. *Metakinesis* refers to these movements to an oriented arrangement. In both plant and animal cells, regardless of its origin, the spindle fiber apparatus can be seen. The movement of the chromosomes toward the center of the cell and their axis of orientation there are determined partly by the fibers. The *kinetochore* (centromere) of each chromosome is attached in some way to the spindle fibers, and the attachment may be instrumental in directing the chromosome to the cell equator. Although the chromosome movements are synchronized, each chromosome behaves independently of the others. Mechanical disturbance or displacement of individual chromosomes in a living cell has demonstrated a chromosomal autonomy in movement. Some factor intrinsic to the chromosome may determine spindle orientation and chromosome movement, which suggests that the energetics of the chromosome may be more important than the behavior of the spindle in metakinesis. The nature of associations between kinetochore and spindle fibers is described later.

Metaphase

In metaphase proper the chromosomes lie at the equator of the cell with the kinetochore of each chromosome serving as its point of orientation (Figure 11–5). That is, the kinetochores lie along the equator, while the

arms of the chromosomes extend freely in any direction into the surrounding cytoplasm. This orientation is related to the spindle fiber at-
tachments at the kinetochores. During all of the mitotic stages, the
chromosomes move independently of each other, and in metaphase they
are independently oriented on the equator. Metaphase chromosomes are
the most sharply defined of mitotic chromosomes. They exhibit a high level
of coiling and may therefore be at their shortest and thickest physical state.
The somatic coils are now at their greatest diameter and smallest number,
and there is no longer much relational coiling. The reduction in relational
coiling is due primarily to the shortening of the chromosomes effected by
the changes in the somatic coils. The chromatids are, as a result, no longer
twisted about each other but lie side by side.

Metaphase is considerably shorter than prophase but slightly longer,
on the average, than anaphase. Within a comparatively short time the
kinetochore regions of each chromatid separate so that the sister chromatids become independent of one another. Up to this point they were in
close apposition.

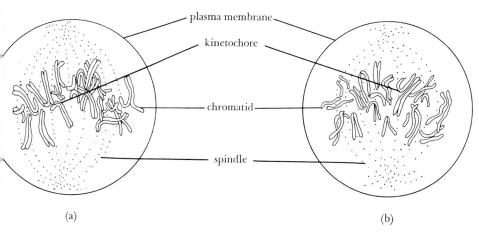

plasma membrane

kinetochore

chromatid

spindle

(a)   (b)

Figure 11–5.   (a) Metaphase. (b) Early anaphase.

Anaphase

Anaphase is the shortest of all stages in the mitotic cycle and is recognized
by the separation of sister chromatids toward opposite poles of the cell.
The part of the chromatid moving first is the kinetochore, which proceeds

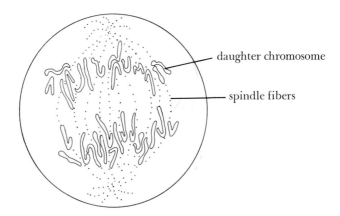

Figure 11–6.   Late anaphase.

along the spindle axis, carrying with it the chromatid (Figure 11–6). The end of anaphase is marked by the arrival of all of the daughter chromosomes (formerly identified as chromatids) at their respective poles. There are now two groups of chromosomes, one at each pole of the spindle. There may be a continuation of the coiling cycle during anaphase, so that the chromosomes become even more condensed than at metaphase. In some cells there is a decrease in coiling with observable slight increases in the lengths of individual chromosomes.

Telophase

The chromosomes are at the poles in telophase and become less distinguishable as individual strands, owing to their uncoiling, which increases their length, and to their entanglement with each other within the restricted polar regions (Figure 11–7). Several events of importance occur during telophase, and it may last as long as prophase. As the chromosomes uncoil, the nucleolus begins to reappear. It is not yet possible to state unequivocally what happens to the nucleolus after prophase, or specifically how it reforms. However, the available information indicates that much of the nucleolar material becomes scattered among the chromosomes by the end of prophase and that this material is reconstituted or reorganized during telophase (Chapter 9). Furthermore, there is evidence that new nucleolar material also develops during telophase, as RNA synthesis resumes at this time. The function of the nucleolus in mitosis may be related to the re-

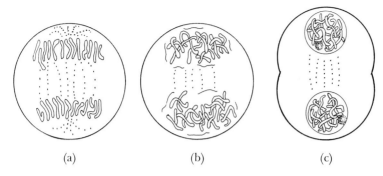

Figure 11–7. Telophase: (a) early; (b) middle; (c) late.

production of the physiological mechanisms of the cell, since the nucleolus is absent during the mechanical phenomena of mitosis and reappears in telophase, when metabolic activity resumes.

A nuclear envelope forms around each group of daughter chromosomes, this "new" envelope originating with elements of the endoplasmic reticulum that have migrated into the polar regions. Although the chromosomes are almost completely uncoiled, the remaining relic coil persists through the succeeding interphase.

Cytokinesis

The end of telophase coincides with the division or separation of the cytoplasms of the daughter cells. The endoplasmic reticulum also contributes to this event. The formation of the cell plate in a plant cell depends upon the presence of elements of the reticulum and dictyosome products, which gather in the equatorial region of the cell between the two groups of chromosomes (or the daughter nuclei) and form the "phragmoplast" (Chapter 3). A similar or identical event probably occurs in animal cells as well. The cell plate in the plant cell is the basis for the new cell wall, more specifically, the middle lamella. In plants the separation of the cytoplasm begins in the center of the cell and gradually extends outward on each side in a plane perpendicular to the axis of the spindle. In animals the division of the cytoplasm begins with a furrowing. There appears to be a pinching in of the plasma membrane from both sides simultaneously until the cytoplasms of the daughter cells are completely isolated from each other. Ultimately the new plasma membrane provides a physical separation between the cytoplasms. Remnants of the spindle fibers visible in late telophase degenerate completely by the end of telophase. Thus the result of the mitotic division is the production of two new cells, each with the same number of chromosomes as the parent cell and with approximately the same physiological potential. Following division, each daughter cell grows in size until it approximates the size of the parent cell.

It was stated earlier that the cytoplasm makes a contribution to certain aspects of mitosis. Specifically, spindle fibers form in the cytoplasm of both plant and animal cells during prophase and metaphase, and their origin is probably cytoplasmic rather than nuclear. The most compelling evidence for this theory is that in animal cells the spindle apparatus develops before the breakdown of the nuclear envelope. In most plant cells the spindle does not become fully organized until the nuclear envelope has dispersed.

The Centriole

In animals, at one pole of the interphase cell just outside the nuclear envelope lie two pairs of centrioles. (Their chemistry and morphology are described in Chapter 8.) The centrioles exhibit a regular cycle of behavior

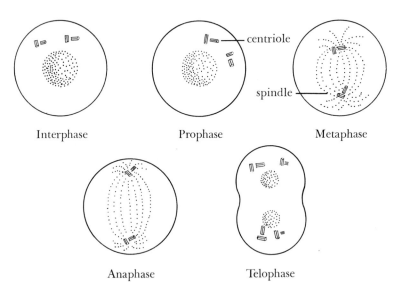

Interphase   Prophase   Metaphase

Anaphase   Telophase

Figure 11–8. The centriole cycle during cell division.

during the division of the cell (Figure 11–8). During interphase they lie at one side of the nuclear envelope. In prophase one centriole pair begins to migrate around the periphery of the nucleus while the other remains in place. At the same time, small elements of the spindle appear between the separating centrioles. By the end of prophase the migrating centriole pair has reached the pole opposite its twin, and there is a continuous array of spindle fibers between the two poles. In addition, fibers radiate from each pole in all directions, with their free ends lying in the cytoplasm. These fibers around each centriole comprise the *aster,* or astral rays. During metaphase and anaphase the centriolar structures remain relatively unchanged. In telophase, however, each centriole duplicates itself. On the other hand, recent studies with mammalian cells have demonstrated that the centrioles commence replication at about the time of DNA synthesis, and complete it by the end of *S.* The new centrioles remain associated until the next mitotic prophase. Since centriolar division occurs in advance of mitotic division, it can be considered the first significant event in the preparation of the cell for division.

The Spindle

Whether or not centrioles are present in mitotic cells, spindle fibers are oriented between the polar regions of the cell by the time of metaphase. The fibers are formed in the cytoplasm even before the disruption of the nuclear envelope, although a few exceptional cells have exhibited spindle development within the nucleus. Polar orientation of the cell at this time depends on the mutual interaction between migration of centrioles (when they are present) and the formation of fiber elements along the cell axis. The axis of orientation of the chromosomes during metakinesis and metaphase is determined by the polar orientation of the spindle fibers. Moreover, the microtubule components of the fibers may play an active role in metakinetic orientation at the equator.

Major properties of the spindle apparatus are polarity, contractility, and birefringence. All three appear to depend mainly on the physical and chemical properties of the microtubules that comprise the spindle. Included in the mitotic (spindle) apparatus (Figure 11–9) may be ribosome-like particles and small vesicles whose functions remain equivocal. The mitotic apparatus can be studied after isolation from the cell or *in situ* in the living cell. Some differences are noted as a consequence of the techniques used for observation. A question arises regarding the magnitude of the contribution of microtubules to birefringence. Birefringence, however, is commonly observed in unfixed preparations with polarization

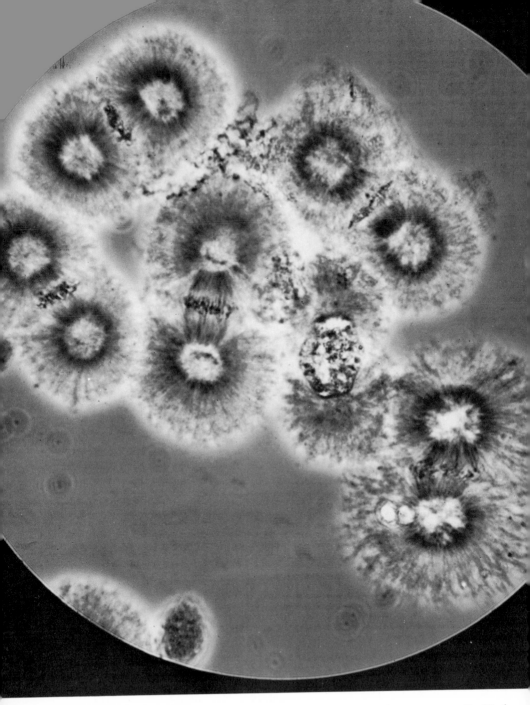

Figure 11-9. Isolated mitotic apparatus from sea urchin eggs. FROM D. Mazia in J. Brachet and A. E. Mirsky, eds., *The Cell,* Vol. 3, Academic Press, New York, 1961, p. 244.

Figure 11–10. Spindle fibers of living crane fly cells during meiosis (×1690). Birefringence of the spindle is demonstrated by the polarizing microscope. Dark bodies at the center are chromosomes. FROM A. Forer, *Chromosoma*, **19**, 44 (1966), with permission of Springer-Verlag.

microscopy (Figure 11–10). The birefringence is primarily positive form birefringence, with a residual positive intrinsic birefringence (Chapter 2). According to Forer, the spindle consists of two components, a birefringent fiber and a traction fiber. With living crane fly spermatocytes as experimental material, Forer used microbeam ultraviolet irradiation to reduce the birefringence in localized areas. One of his conclusions was that the interzonal region (between separating chromosomes at anaphase) is the major site of traction or force for chromosomal movements. The independence of the movement of individual chromosomes may be mediated by a property of the kinetochore region. Any upset in spindle orientation or function, however, is due to changes imposed on the spindle microtubules. Colchicine, for example, binds specifically to the microtubule protein subunits, inhibiting their assembly into functional elements. The final orientation of the precursor subunits may also be facilitated by hydrogen bonds.

The production of spindle protein occurs just prior to mitosis (during G_2) and is one step in the preparation of the cell for division. The bonding between the protein groups in the fibers is still not quite clear. In the initial polymerization of the protein material, sulfhydryl groups (SH) may be involved. The protein —SH groups are present in prophase but not in anaphase when the fibers are at their functional peak. It is possible that disulfide (S—S) linkages maintain fiber integrity once the fibers are formed.

Physically, the spindle fiber substance resembles a highly elastic gel. During metaphase and anaphase the fiber region is generally free of large particles such as mitochondria, which might interfere with fiber behavior,

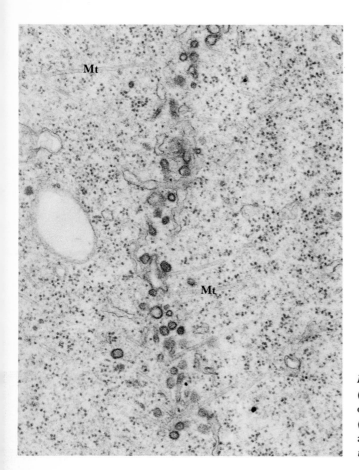

Figure 11–11. Microtubules (Mt) in the cell plate zone of *Phaseolus* root tip cells (× 38,000). FROM P. K. Hepler and E. H. Newcomb, *J. Ultrastruct. Res.,* **19,** 498 (1967).

but often a zone of such particles lies just outside of the fiber region. Electron microscopy has delineated a microtubular structure for an individual fiber. A single microtubule has a diameter of 150 to 200 Å, and as many as 100 are arranged in a bundle to form the fiber as seen with the light microscope. Although differences have been found among microtubules of cilia, flagella, and spindle fibers in several organisms, their general organization indicates the presence of 12 or 13 subfilaments comprising the wall of a spindle microtubule (Chapter 8). The subfilaments are arranged around a hollow core about 100 Å in diameter and have a center-to-center spacing of 45 to 50 Å.

Microtubules are also abundant during early stages of cell plate formation, when vesicles begin to aggregate and fuse (Figure 3–5). The microtubules occupy the region through which the vesicles must pass to reach the zone of plate formation (Figure 11–11). They disappear later as the plate grows laterally. Colchicine disrupts vesicle fusion and subsequent plate alignment, possibly through its effect on the microtubules.

At the light microscope level, three types of fibers have been observed between the poles or centriole regions. Some fibers are *continuous* from one pole to the other, some extend from the kinetochore of a chromosome to one pole (*chromosome* fibers), and a few intervene between the kinetochores of the separating chromatids (*interzonal* fibers). Chromosome fibers are actually attached to the kinetochores. Kinetochore ultrastructure, at least in some animal cells, appears rather complex and quite different from the rest of the chromosome. Each chromosome has two disc-shaped sister kinetochores located on opposite sides of the kinetochore region. At metaphase, the disc consists of a dense core or inner layer next to the chromosomal material and a less dense outer zone. In Chinese hamster, the core may show a pair of axial fibrils coiled together helically. Microtubules appear to extend outward at right angles to the core axis, and several are attached to the chromosome in the disc region (Figure 11–12). It has been

Figure 11–12. Kinetochore (Kc) region of a chromosome in a rat kidney mesenchymal cell (×35,800; inset ×83,500). FROM P. T. Jokelainen, *J. Ultrastruct. Res.,* **19,** 19 (1967).

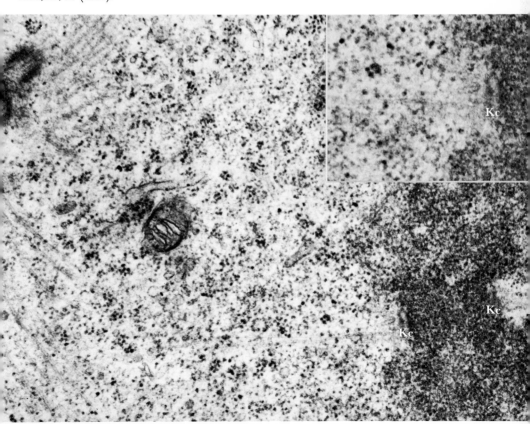

postulated that the kinetochore participates in the organization of micro-tubule subunits into spindle filaments. Whether kinetochores are actual sites of microtubule assembly remains unsettled, and it is not known how the spindle fibers establish contact with the kinetochore.

The behavior of the spindle fibers in the movement of the chromo-somes to the poles is an unsolved problem. A number of theories have been proposed to account for this movement, but no one theory can be con-sidered as the final explanation. The most logical possibility is that invoking a contraction and expansion of the various fiber elements. Be-cause of their physical and chemical organizations, the fibers would stretch or contract, according to their positions. Those fibers extending from the chromosomes to the poles would, on contracting, tend to draw the chromo-somes to the poles. At the same time, the interzonal fibers would, on ex-panding, tend to push the chromosomes to the poles. In animal cells there is an elongation of the entire spindle apparatus during anaphase, which would involve a lengthening or stretching of certain continuous fibers as well. This is less pronounced in plant cells owing to the restrictions im-posed by the rigid cell wall. If the hypothesis is correct, the movement of the chromosomes depends primarily on the contraction and expansion of the appropriate fibers in the apparatus.

More than conjecture suggests that energy is involved, and of course necessary, for the movement of the chromosomes along the spindle fibers in anaphase. Recent studies of adenosine triphosphatase activity in the mitotic apparatus during the separation of the chromosomes imply that ATP provides the energy required for movement, but verification is lack-ing. Consistent with the findings that the cell undergoes several prepara-tory steps prior to mitosis is the concept that the energy for cell division becomes available before division and is stored until later in ATP.

Summary

Mitosis in the biological system is significant for many reasons, among them its role in the reproductive devices of the organism. Of particular importance is the distribution of the genetic material to succeeding cell generations. The maintenance of the genetic integrity of the cell popu-lation and ultimately of the organism and its descendants depends upon the mechanisms of cell division.

The cell cycle usually takes several hours, and the mitotic events are divided into stages related to changes in the nucleus and the cytoplasm. The events of mitosis include the duplication of the chromosomes and their separation to opposite poles of the cell in two equal groups. This separation is effected by the behavior of a number of spindle fiber elements that extend between the poles or centriole regions of the cell. Although there are physical differences between plant and animal cells during division, the basic phenomena of mitosis are the same in most cells.

SELECTED READING

General

Hughes, A. F. W., *The Mitotic Cycle,* Academic Press, New York, 1953.

Mazia, D., "How Cells Divide," *Sci. Am.,* **205**(3), 100 (1961).

Mazia, D., "Mitosis and the Physiology of Cell Division," in J. Brachet and A. E. Mirsky, eds., *The Cell,* Vol. 3, Academic Press, New York, 1961, pp. 77–112.

Stern, H., "The Regulation of Cell Division," *Ann. Rev. Plant Physiol.,* **17**, 345 (1966).

Mitosis

Donnelly, G. M., and J. E. Sisken, "RNA and Protein Synthesis Required for Entry of Cells into Mitosis and During the Mitotic Cycle," *Exptl. Cell Res.,* **46**(1), 93 (1967).

Evans, H. J., and J. R. K. Savage, "The Effect of Temperature on Mitosis and on the Action of Colchicine in Root Meristem Cells of *Vicia faba,*" *Exptl. Cell Res.,* **18**(1), 51 (1959).

La Cour, L. R., and J. A. Chayen, "A Cyclic Staining Behavior of the Chromosomes During Mitosis and Meiosis," *Exptl. Cell Res.,* **14**(3), 462 (1958).

Lafontaine, J. G., "Structure and Mode of Formation of the Nucleolus in Meristematic Cells of *Vicia faba* and *Allium cepa,*" *J. Biophys. Biochem. Cytol.,* **4**(6), 777 (1958).

Moser, H., "The Mode of Timing of DNA Replication and of Mitosis in Cultured Animal Cells," *Experientia,* **23**(11), 913 (1967).

Porter, K. R., and R. D. Machado, "Studies on the Endoplasmic Recticulum. IV. Its Form and Distribution During Mitosis in Cells of Onion Root Tip," *J. Biophys. Biochem. Cytol.,* **7**(1), 167 (1960).

Rebhun, L. L., and G. Sander, "Ultrastructure and Birefringence of the Isolated Mitotic Apparatus of Marine Eggs," *J. Cell Biol.,* **34**(3), 859 (1967).

Robbins, E., and T. W. Borun, "The Cytoplasmic Synthesis of Histones in HeLa Cells and Its Temporal Relationship to DNA Replication," *Proc. Natl. Acad. Sci. U.S.,* **57**(2), 409 (1967).

Scharff, M. D., and E. Robbins, "Polyribosome Disaggregation During Metaphase," *Science,* **151**(3713), 992 (1966).

Terasima, T., and M. Yasukawa, "Synthesis of G_1 Protein Preceding DNA Synthesis in Cultured Mammalian Cells," *Exptl. Cell Res.,* **44**(2–3), 669 (1966).

Cytokinesis

Bajer, A., "Notes on Ultrastructure and Some Properties of Transport Within the Living Mitotic Spindle," *J. Cell Biol.,* **33**(3), 713 (1967).

Behnke, O., and A. Forer, "Evidence for Four Classes of Microtubules in Individual Cells," *J. Cell Sci.,* **2** (2), 169 (1967).

Brinkley, B. R., and E. Stubblefield, "The Fine Structure of the Kinetochore of a Mammalian Cell in Vitro," *Chromosoma,* **19**(1), 28 (1966).

Forer, A., "Characterization of the Mitotic Traction System, and Evidence That Birefringent Spindle Fibers Neither Produce Nor Transmit Force for Chromosome Movement," *Chromosoma,* **19**(1), 44 (1966).

Harris, P., "Some Structural and Functional Aspects of the Mitotic Apparatus in Sea Urchin Embryos," *J. Cell Biol.,* **14**(3), 475 (1962).

Kawamura, N., and K. Dan, "A Cytochemical Study of the Sulfhydryl Groups of Sea Urchin Eggs During the First Cleavage," *J. Biophys. Biochem. Cytol.,* **4** (3), 615 (1958).

Ledbetter, M. C., and K. R. Porter, "Morphology of Microtubules of Plant Cells," *Science,* **144**(3620), 872 (1964).

Mazia, D., R. R. Chaffee, and R. M. Iverson, "Adenosine Triphosphatase in the Mitotic Apparatus," *Proc. Natl. Acad. Sci. U.S.,* **47**(6), 788 (1961).

Mazia, D., P. Harris, and T. Bibring, "The Multiplicity of the Mitotic Centers and the Time Course of Their Duplication and Separation," *J. Biophys. Biochem. Cytol.,* **7**(1), 1 (1960).

Mazia, D., J. M. Mitchison, H. Medina, and P. Harris, "The Direct Isolation of the Mitotic Apparatus," *J. Biophys. Biochem. Cytol.,* **10**(4), 467 (1961).

Pickett-Heaps, J. D., "The Effects of Colchicine on the Ultrastructure of Dividing Plant Cells, Xylem Wall Differentiation and Distribution of Cytoplasmic Microtubules," *Develop. Biol.,* **15**, 206 (1967).

Robbins, E., G. Jentzsch, and A. Micali, "The Centriole Cycle in Synchronized HeLa Cells," *J. Cell Biol.,* **36**(2), 329 (1968).

Rustad, R. C., "An Interference Microscopical and Cytochemical Analysis of Local Mass Changes in the Mitotic Apparatus During Mitosis," *Exptl. Cell Res.,* **16**(3), 575 (1959).

Sato, S., "Electron Microscope Studies on the Mitotic Figure. III. Process of the Spindle Formation," *Cytologia* (Tokyo), **25**(1), 119 (1960).

Went, H. A., and D. Mazia, "Immunochemical Study of the Origin of the Mitotic Apparatus," *Exptl. Cell Res.,* Suppl. 7, 200 (1959).

12

Meiosis

The evolution of *meiotic* division was of utmost significance for the development of sexual reproduction in plants and animals. This kind of cell division provides a mechanism that reduces the chromosome number by half from the diploid to the haploid condition. The meiotic cycle also incorporates events by which an orderly distribution of the genetic material occurs from generation to generation and permits great genetic diversity by relatively frequent reorganization of the genetic complement. This has resulted in increased evolutionary potential in the population. In metazoan organisms meiotic divisions produce the gametes (eggs and sperm). These are the ultimate products of the meiotic process in the higher plants, too, but in certain fungi and algae meiosis takes place *after* the production of the gametes and their fusion in fertilization. Nevertheless, even in these organisms meiosis is related to the sexual method of reproduction. The products of meiosis have half as many chromosomes as the parent cell. Consequently, fertilization (union of egg and sperm) restores the original, parental number of chromosomes. Thus the meiotic cycle is the basis for the maintenance of genetic continuity and chromosome number in a particular species of plant or animal.

With reference to the biochemical properties of the cells, the conditions necessary for the initiation or induction of meiosis are no better recognized than those for mitosis. However, certain physiological changes are doubtless essential for the transition of a particular cell from mitotic behavior to meiotic behavior. Several proposals have been made regarding the possible events leading to meiotic division. One states that adjacent somatic tissue may be responsible for the production of specific meiosis-initiating substances. Such somatic tissue includes the nonsporogenous tissue surrounding the megaspore mother cells, which divide by meiosis to produce megaspores in plants, and the nongerminal tissue in association with the seminiferous tubules, in which sperm are produced in animals. The nature of the chemical substances active in the initiation is not suggested, but a hormone or hormones are good possibilities. In fact, there is a case of a parasitic flagellate protozoon in which meiotic events were initiated by an insect molting hormone, ecdysone. Another proposal involves the relation between RNA and DNA; it states that if the ratio of RNA to DNA is high, the cells will undergo mitosis, and that if this ratio is low, meiosis will take place. The latter relationship has been found in the potential meiotic cells of several plants. Whatever physiological conditions are requisite for meiosis in the sexually mature organism, the cells subject to this type of division are determined during the development of the embryo. That is, certain cells of the embryo are destined to become oogonia, spermatogonia, megaspore mother cells, or antheridia. In the final analysis, meiosis, as well as mitosis, is under genetic control. How the genes exert control over specific meiotic events remains to be discovered.

Although there are a number of characteristic differences between meiosis and mitosis, both are dependent on the activities of the nucleus and the chromosomes and on the organization of particular cytoplasmic materials. The behavior of the spindle apparatus during meiosis is comparable to that during mitosis and will not be discussed in this chapter. The major differences between the two types of cell division concern the chromosomes, and the meiotic cycle will be described from this standpoint. Meiosis is characterized by chromosome pairing, delayed kinetochore division, and the exchange of genetic material by crossing over. Another significant difference is that a meiotic cell is differentiated, whereas a mitotic cell is not.

The Meiotic Cycle

Meiosis consists of two divisions in which the chromosomes duplicate only once, but the nucleus and cytoplasm divide twice to produce four daughter cells. Again, although it is difficult to state exactly when one stage ends and another begins, an organization of the cycle into specific stages is very useful. Thus there is a premeiotic interphase; this is followed by a sequence somewhat comparable to the stages of mitosis and called prophase I, etc. After a second interphase another division occurs (prophase II, etc.). Several of these stages are illustrated in Figure 12–1.

Figure 12–1. Leptotene (a), pachytene (b), diplotene (c), metaphase I (d), anaphase I (e), metaphase II (f), and anaphase II (g) in a pollen mother cell of *Lilium regale* ($\times$1700). Reproduced from J. McLeish and B. Snoad, *Looking at Chromosomes,* Macmillan, London, 1958.

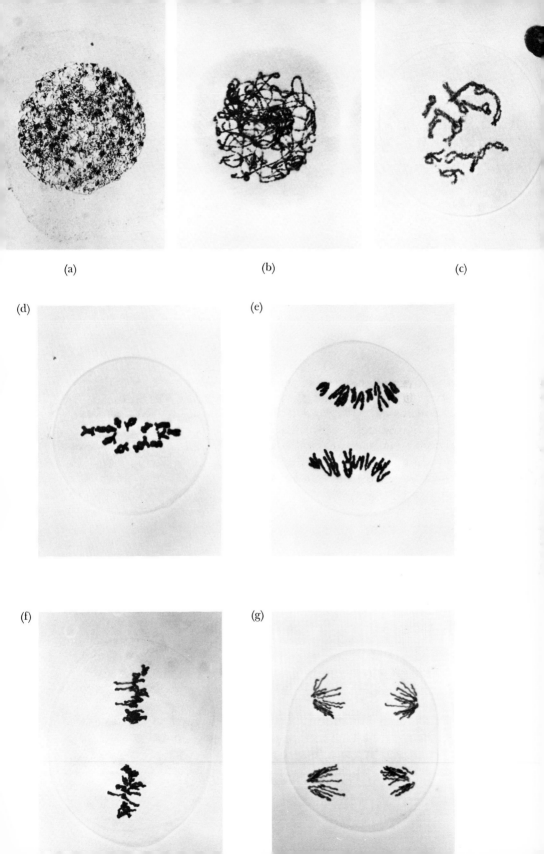

(a)

(b)

(c)

(d)

(e)

(f)

(g)

Premeiotic Interphase

Investigations of the division behavior of *Trillium* microsporocytes in culture have shown that there is no irreversible commitment to meiotic division until after the S substage of interphase. The events that channel cells into meiosis occur during the premeiotic G_2 substage, when the chromosomes are already replicated. G_2 must be completed before normal meiotic events take place. Therefore the characteristic features of meiosis cited above are determined in G_2. As expected, an inhibition of nucleic acid or protein synthesis prevents or impairs normal meiotic progress. RNA synthesis occurs during most of the premeiotic interphase, and DNA synthesis is restricted to the S substage. Compared with mitotic S in interphase, meiotic S is longer. Among the proteins synthesized during interphase are histones, and their time of synthesis usually corresponds with that of DNA. A recent study of meiosis in lily and tulip has revealed a unique histone fraction detected by polyacrylamide gel electrophoresis; it is not found in mitotic cells. It appears during interphase, probably in S, and persists through the maturation of pollen grains, diminishing thereafter. These observations, along with those from cultured tobacco and ascites tumor cells, support the view that the synthesis of histone is independent of DNA synthesis. The possible function of a meiotic histone is not known. RNA polymerase, a protein with enzyme activity, apparently persists throughout meiosis in association with the chromosomes of lily and tulip. Since there is strong evidence that condensed chromosomes cannot function in RNA synthesis, some factor must inhibit the activity of RNA polymerase when the chromosomes are in this condition. During premeiotic interphase, the chromosomes are not highly condensed, but are characterized by the same relic coils seen in premitotic interphase.

Prophase I

During prophase I the chromosomes move in several ways. Another event marking meiotic prophase is a decided increase in the volume of the nucleus. This increase is greater than any observed during the mitotic cycle and is due in part to an increase in hydration, which also is several times as great as any observed during mitosis. Prophase I of meiosis is of extremely long duration compared with mitotic prophase and comprises several substages in which particular events occur (Figure 12–1). It must be remembered that these substages, too, are somewhat artificial but that they provide a means for a systematic study of prophase.

Leptotene

The increase in the volume of the nucleus begins in early prophase, or *leptotene* (Figure 12–2). Prior to the onset of meiosis, chromosomes may undergo a brief cycle of coiling and uncoiling. By the beginning of leptotene they are quite long and uncoiled. Then they develop a number of small coils, which vary in their degree of condensation. The tightest coils are recognized as chromomeres because of their greater density. These meiotic coils are *major* coils, which grow in diameter as prophase proceeds. Since the chromosomes remain rather elongate, individual chromosomes are not identifiable. Moreover, the chromatids remain associated since the kinetochore is still functionally single in each chromosome. The nucleolus is apparent during leptotene but in some cells is relatively small at first, increasing in size during leptotene and zygotene. Cytochemical studies have shown an increased synthesis of RNA in early prophase I, which accounts for this increase in nucleolar size.

In many meiotic cells of plants and animals, RNA and protein synthesis persist during leptotene, usually declining thereafter. The decline in RNA content observed in zygotene through late prophase I in *Lilium henryi* and *Trillium erectum* is associated with a decrease in ribosome content. However, there may be an increase in RNA content in metaphase I that can persist as long as the second half of meiosis. With this increase comes an increase in the number of ribosomes. The origin of the new ribosomes at this time is rather puzzling, since there is neither protein nor RNA synthesis during metaphase I or anaphase I. It is possible that they are assembled from RNA and protein subunits already available from previous synthetic activity. Inhibition of protein synthesis during early prophase tends to reduce the contraction of the chromosomes. It is clear that several of the biochemical events of meiosis are ambiguous and remain unsolved.

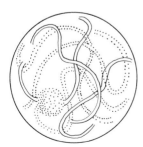   

Figure 12–2. Leptotene.   *Figure 12–3.* Zygotene.

Zygotene

The most striking and significant event of the *zygotene* substage (Figure 12–3) is the pairing, or *synapsis*, of homologous chromosomes. Since each chromosome already consists of two chromatids, each pair of homologues consists of four chromatids and is referred to as a *tetrad*. However, the four strands are not distinguishable with light microscopy until *pachytene*. The pairing of the homologues occurs part by part. That is, it is exact, with each genetic segment of one chromosome pairing with the identical segment of its homologue. This pairing may begin at the ends of the chromosomes (*proterminal*) and progress toward the kinetochore region, or it may begin near the kinetochore (*procentric*) and progress to the ends, or it may be random, with separated segments of the chromosomes undergoing synapsis in a scattered pattern. When the chromosomes are very long, there may not be complete pairing of all segments. For example, if pairing is procentric, the ends may not be paired, and if pairing is proterminal, the kinetochore regions may remain unpaired. The completion of pairing is also a function of the time during which pairing is possible. In the majority of meiotic cells, however, all of the chromosomes become almost entirely synapsed by the end of zygotene.

There are two major theories that attempt to explain the pairing phenomenon, which does not occur during mitosis. The *precocity theory* of Darlington states that leptotene chromosomes are not divided into chromatids and that therefore homologous chromosomes pair because of their singleness. In the light of evidence that DNA synthesis and chromosome duplication take place during the premeiotic interphase, this theory is not substantiated. A second theory of meiotic pairing was proposed by Sax and others and is based upon a thesis of retardation of cellular metabolism during meiotic prophase. Prophase I, as indicated, is of relatively long duration. According to the *retardation theory*, this extended time period allows the uncoiling of the relic spirals of the preceding interphase and telophase so that there is complete uncoiling of the chromosomes. As a result, the part-by-part pairing of homologues in zygotene is greatly enhanced. This theory is not entirely satisfactory, but may have some physical support.

Stern has recently provided evidence for the synthesis of a small quantity of DNA during zygotene and pachytene in *Trillium*. From 0.3 to 0.4% of the total DNA is synthesized during these meiotic stages. The results of these studies suggest that the DNA produced is structural and that chromosome pairing depends upon that portion made during zygotene. One possible difference between meiotic and mitotic cells is that the synthesis of this DNA fraction is suppressed in mitotic cells but not in meiotic cells. The delay of synthesis until zygotene may be essential to the regulation of the major meiotic characteristics (pairing and crossing over). Related to this DNA is the synthesis of at least one nuclear protein that complexes with it. Whether this protein is the meiotic histone discussed earlier remains a matter of conjecture. However, it has been suggested that DNA and histone must be in the correct proportion to allow normal meiotic pairing.

The physical basis of chromosome synapsis has been somewhat elucidated by the observations of a *synaptinemal complex*. This zygotene configuration of paired homologues is seen with the electron microscope as a linear complex of three parallel strands (Figure 12–4). Synaptinemal com-

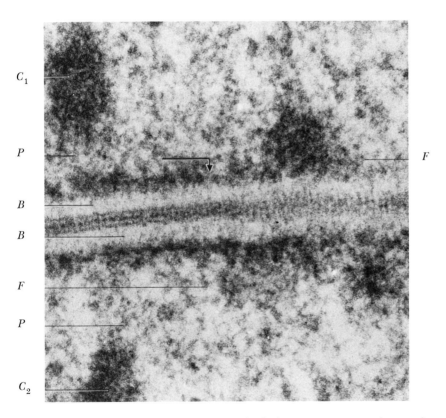

Figure 12–4. Synaptinemal complex in paired chromosomes at pachytene in *Gryllus argentinus* (×169,000). Note the three-layered structure of the central element at left and the several fibril connections. *B,* bridges between compact bars and main axis of synaptinemal complex; C_1 and C_2, homologous chromomeres; *F,* fibrils; *P,* connections between chromomeres and compact fibrils of chromosome; arrow marks location of axis around which synaptinemal complex turns. FROM J. R. Sotelo and R. Wettstein, *Chromosoma,* **20,** 234 (1966), by permission of the authors and Springer-Verlag.

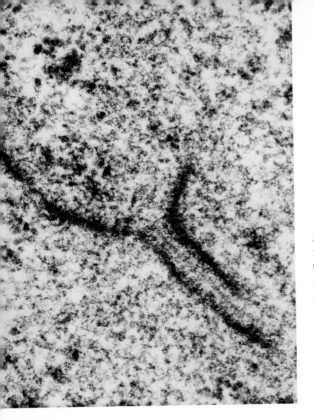

Figure 12–5. Zygotene pairing in mouse primary spermatocyte ($\times 60,000$). The lower portion of the photograph shows complete pairing in the synaptinemal complex. The upper portion shows diverging chromosomes, not yet paired, but in the process of pairing ("zipper mechanism"). COURTESY Miguel Mota, Department of Genetics, Estação Agronómica Nacional, Oeiras, Portugal.

plexes have been found in a number of organisms, including the crayfish, locust, pigeon, rat, *Tradescantia, Coprinus,* and other plants. The complex is disrupted when pairing is disrupted in late prophase I. Each of the two outermost elements represents an axial component of a homologue, and the central element the synaptic center. The central element varies in size and density among different species, and may even be absent. When present it evidently forms as a consequence of pairing (Figure 12–5). The axial elements sometimes twist about the central one, and chromosomal fibrils may link them to one another. In fact, the basic structural unit of the chromosome (as observed in these configurations) is an irregular, kinked fibril 70 to 150 Å thick. Such fibrils often emerge radially from axial elements, and are continuous with the main body of the chromosome. The central element may represent sites where ends of lateral loops from both homologues meet and pair. Although the complex may not run the entire length of a *bivalent* (a pair of homologous chromosomes), it is axial to the bivalent rather than to a homologue.

The absence of a synaptinemal complex in *Drosophila* males, where crossing over does not occur, suggests that it may be more closely allied to the process of crossing over than to synapsis. Crossing over may occur initially through exchanges in the central element. One possibility is that the synaptinemal complex is responsible for maintaining chromosome pairing long enough to allow crossing over to occur. Both DNA and protein, including histone, are principal components of the axial elements and are necessary for the integrity of the complex. The significance of DNA synthesis in crossing over is presented in the next section.

The coiling of the chromosomes continues during zygotene to produce a marked condensation. The chromosomes become shorter and thicker as the major coils increase in diameter. These coils are considerably larger than their mitotic conterparts, the somatic coils. In addition to the major coils, there is a relational coiling of the chromatids, and perhaps also of the two homologues, described as paranemic coiling in Chapter 11.

Figure 12–6. Pachytene.

Pachytene

Pachytene (Figure 12–6) commences when the pairing of the chromosomes is completed. It is one of the longer substages of prophase I and is characterized by several important events. The chromosomes grow still shorter and thicker as a result of the increase in coil diameter and the appearance of another level of coiling. Within the major coils and at right angles to them, smaller, minor coils arise. The relational coiling of the homologues persists, and the direction of this coiling is usually opposite that of the internal major coiling. Individual pairs of homologous chromosomes (bivalents) are readily identifiable now, and the staining properties of the chromosomes permit recognition of heterochromatic and euchromatic regions, the former particularly around the kinetochores.

Although the time at which genetic *crossing over* occurs is not absolutely established, this event is normally attributed to pachytene. It is possible to detect areas within each bivalent in which there is a physical exchange between adjacent chromatids. An exchange of this type is called a *chiasma,* and it is due in most cases to an exchange of genetic material, or crossing over, although in some organisms chiasmata have been ob-

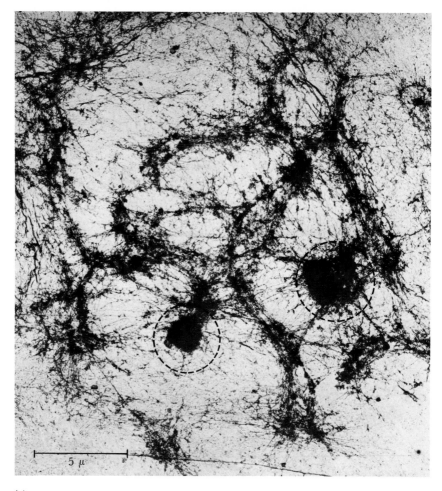

(a)

Figure 12–7. Appearance of pachytene chromosomes of *Oncopeltus
faciatus.* Delineation of fine structure: (a) with the electron microscope (×5000); (b) with the light
microscope (×2000). Note the
highly condensed sex chromosomes,
ringed in (a) and at arrows in (b).
FROM S. L. Wolfe and B. John,
Chromosoma, **17,** 85 (1965), with
permission of Springer-Verlag.

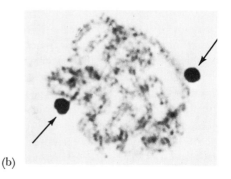

(b)

served without a correlated crossing over. The genetic significance of these events will be presented later.

The number of chiasmata in a bivalent depends on the lengths of the chromosomes: the presence of more than one chiasma is less likely in a short segment of a chromosome than in a long segment. In fact, one chiasma may interfere with the formation of another in a closely adjacent region, although the evidence for such interference is rather ambiguous. There is generally no interference by a chiasma on one side of the kineto-chore with one on the other. Evidence for a correspondence of chromatid interference with crossing-over interference is also ambiguous.

The synthesis of DNA, reported by Stern and others to occur during pachytene, may be related to the process of crossing over. If so, it may be required for the repair of the broken ends of chromatids involved in the exchange that results in genetic recombination. There is also some evidence that protein synthesis is necessary for the process of crossing over. A rather unusual type of DNA synthesis occurs in certain amphibian oocytes during pachytene. In these cells, as many as 1000 copies of the DNA from the nucleolus-organizing regions of the chromosomes may become free of the chromosomes themselves, and appear to be part of the many small nucleoli found in these cells. The question of DNA synthesis during this phase of meiosis is still unresolved. Another difficult problem is that of chromosome substructure. Although no definitive answer is available, examination of a number of organisms reveals considerable subunit organization. An example is shown in Figure 12–7.

Diplotene

The chiasmata are very easily discernible in *diplotene* (Figure 12–8). There are a continued condensation of the chromosomes through increased coiling, an apparent repulsion between homologous chromosomes in regions devoid of chiasmata, and a beginning *terminalization* of the chiasmata. As the chromosomes repel each other, the bivalent assumes a

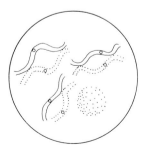

Figure 12–8. Diplotene.

configuration that is consistent with the number and positions of its chiasmata. These factors govern the configuration throughout *diakinesis* and metaphase I. The sites of the chiasmata are the only places at which the members of a bivalent remain associated. The chiasmata are most distinct during diplotene, and at the end of this substage they begin to move toward the ends of the chromosomes in the process of terminalization. Because of the increase in coiling and the resultant shortening of the chromosomes, the chiasmata appear to slide off the ends of the chromosomes through diplotene and the next two stages of meiosis. In effect, the shortening produces a kind of unraveling of the paired chromosomes.

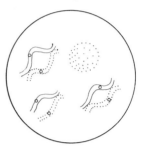

Figure 12–9.   Diakinesis.

Diakinesis

During *diakinesis* the bivalents migrate to the periphery of the nucleus and are well separated from each other (Figures 12–9 and 12–10). Although the coils tighten within the chromosomes, making them shorter still, and terminalization continues, the shapes or configurations of the bivalents are very similar to those assumed in diplotene. Often the chromosomes in this last substage of prophase I exhibit a higher degree of staining than before, as a function of the increased density of the coils. The nucleolus begins to disappear and is no longer visible at the end of diakinesis. The last event of prophase I is the disruption and dispersal of the nuclear envelope, releasing the chromosomes into the cytoplasm of the cell. By this time the spindle fibers have organized to establish the poles of the cell, and they will determine the axis of orientation of the chromosomes in metaphase I.

Metaphase I

In meiosis, as in mitosis, the chromosomes move to the equatorial region of the cell after the disruption of the nuclear envelope of the cell. The

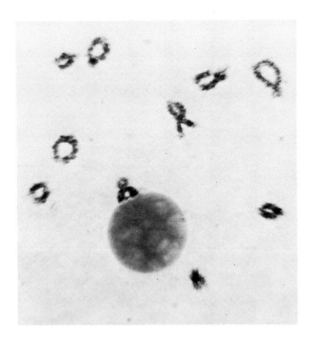

Figure 12–10. Diakinesis in corn. FROM M. M. Rhoades in J. Brachet and A. E. Mirsky, eds., *The Cell,* Vol. 3, Academic Press, New York, 1961, p. 21.

orientation of the chromosomes in meiotic metaphase (Figure 12–11a) is quite different from that in mitotic metaphase. In metaphase I the chromosomes lie near the equator with their kinetochores toward the poles and their arms toward the equator. The kinetochore regions of the homologues appear to repel each other to create this arrangement. Moreover, the kinetochore of each chromosome behaves as an individual unit. The position of each member of a bivalent with respect to the poles is strictly random. This point will be emphasized later in connection with the genetic consequences of the orientation. The areas of association between the chromosomes of each bivalent are still determined by the number and positions of the chiasmata. The effective difference between meiotic and mitotic orientations is that the chromosomes are *not* lined up along the equator in meiosis. Therefore, the number of chromosomes dividing in anaphase I will not be the same as the number of chromosomes present in the original cell. Although the kinetochore of each chromosome remains functionally single in metaphase, it is structurally double. Spindle fibers extend between the poles and are attached only to the kinetochores of the chromosomes as chromosome fibers (Chapter 11). Meiotic coils are apparent (Figure 12–12).

Anaphase I

The two chromosomes comprising a bivalent move to opposite poles of the cell during anaphase. The kinetochores move first, carrying with them the arms of the chromosomes and effecting the complete terminalization of the chiasmata. In contrast to mitotic chromosomes, the arms of the chromatids in each chromosome then diverge, apparently repelling each other (Figure 12–11b). The consequence of this stage of meiosis is a reduction of the chromosome number by one half, from the diploid to the haploid number. This is the essential difference between the first meiotic division and mitosis.

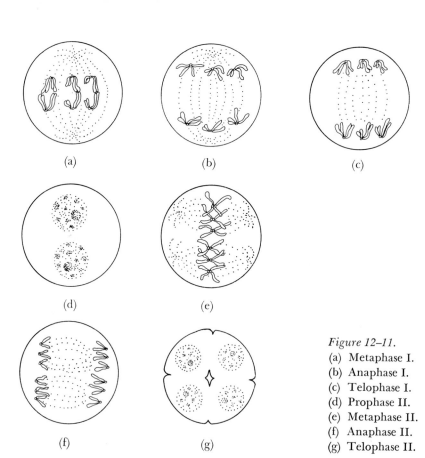

(a)   (b)   (c)

(d)   (e)

(f)   (g)

Figure 12–11.
(a) Metaphase I.
(b) Anaphase I.
(c) Telophase I.
(d) Prophase II.
(e) Metaphase II.
(f) Anaphase II.
(g) Telophase II.

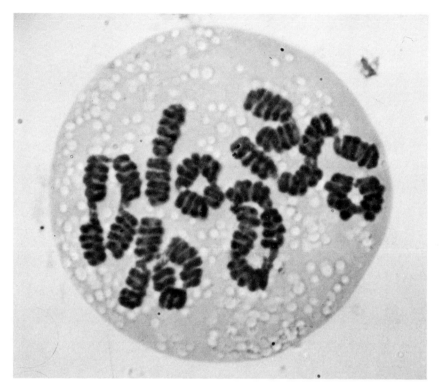

Figure 12–12. Metaphase I in a pollen mother cell of *Tradescantia virginiana* (×2000). FROM C. D. Darlington and C. G. Vosa, *Chromosoma,* **13,** 609 (1963).

Telophase I

The events of telophase are practically the same in meiosis and mitosis (Figure 12–11c). The chromosomes elongate through a loosening of their coils, the nucleolus reappears, and a nuclear envelope forms around each polar group of chromosomes. Cytokinesis may or may not occur, and so the products of the first meiotic division may be two cells or two nuclei with a common cytoplasm. In the latter case the nuclei will be separated by a plasma membrane at the end of the second meiotic division.

Some meiotic cells, such as in *Trillium* and certain members of the *Odonata,* pass immediately from anaphase I to prophase II, omitting telophase I and interphase. These cells show very little change in the behavior or coiling of the chromosomes. The most important difference between interphase at this time and other interphases is the absence of DNA synthesis.

Prophase II

The nucleus in prophase II (Figure 12–11d) resembles the nucleus in mitotic prophase with the following exceptions: the arms of the chromatids are widely separated, and there is no relational coiling; the chromosomes are still coiled but somewhat longer than in the previous anaphase I. If any uncoiling has occurred during telophase I and interphase, coiling resumes during prophase II so that the chromosomes are shortened. Prophase II ends with the disruption of the nuclear envelope and the appearance of spindle fibers in the cytoplasm.

Metaphase II

The orientation of the chromosomes on the equator in metaphase II is the same as in mitotic metaphase (Figure 12–11e). The kinetochores lie along the equator, and the arms extend outward. Metaphase II is a short stage, and the chromosomes begin moving to opposite poles as soon as each kinetochore is functionally double. Each chromatid now has its own kinetochore.

Anaphase II and Telophase II

The daughter chromosomes (the chromatids of the preceding stage) move to opposite poles in anaphase II (Figure 12–11f) and uncoil in telophase II (Figure 12–11g). The nucleolus reappears, and a nuclear envelope forms around each group. Finally the four meiotic products are separated by cytokinesis. The result of the two meiotic divisions is therefore a quartet of cells, each of which contains the haploid number of chromosomes. The first meiotic division is *reductional* with respect to the number of chromosomes, and the second meiotic division *equational*.

Genetic Significance of Meiosis

Although Gregor Mendel was not aware of the mechanisms involved, his two laws of inheritance are based upon the behavior of the chromosomes during meiosis. The relationship between these two laws and the meiotic events is shown schematically in Figure 12–13. The first law states that *the paired factors responsible for a given characteristic segregate into the gametes and are recombined at fertilization.* The second law states

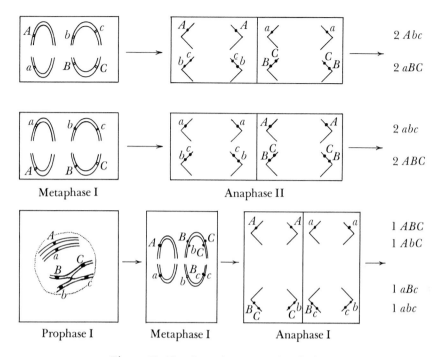

2 *Abc*

2 *aBC*

2 *abc*

2 *ABC*

Metaphase I · Anaphase II

1 *ABC*
1 *AbC*

1 *aBc*
1 *abc*

Prophase I · Metaphase I · Anaphase I

Figure 12–13. Genetic aspects of meiosis.

that *the segregation of one pair of factors occurs independently of the segregation of a second pair of factors.* The second law rests on the assumption that the two pairs of factors are located on different pairs of chromosomes. After Mendel's time, additional aspects of the patterns of inheritance were revealed by the observation of *linkage groups,* or genes located on the same chromosome, and the detection of crossing over between these linked genes. These aspects are also represented in Figure 12–13.

Law of Segregation

The behavior of the chromosomes during meiosis that is of significance here occurs in prophase I, when the synapsis of homologues takes place, and in metaphase I, when the chromosomes are oriented as bivalents at the equator of the cell. The segregation of the pair of factors *Aa* is immediately apparent at that time.

Law of Independent Assortment

This law is also illustrated by the prophase I and metaphase I events, but in this case two pairs of factors (genes) are involved. One pair, *Aa,* is on one pair of chromosomes, and the other pair, *Bb,* is on another pair of chromosomes. The possible meiotic products of varying metaphase I orientations are shown in Figure 12–13. That the chromosomes are oriented in a random fashion is critical to the operation of Mendel's second law.

Linkage

One pair of chromosomes is shown as carrying two pairs of genes or factors, *Bb* and *Cc.* The result of linkage is that these genes stay together as the chromosomes are distributed to the daughter cells or nuclei. In one case, no crossing over occurs between *B* and *C,* so that only two kinds of meiotic products result.

Crossing Over

If crossing over occurs between *B* and *C,* then four kinds of meiotic products or gametes are possible. The likelihood of crossing over between any two genetic loci is related to their linear distance from each other; the farther apart they are, the greater the frequency of crossing over. Even when crossing over occurs in all meiotic cells, however, only half of the products are crossover or recombinant types. Thus the maximum crossing-over frequency possible is 50%. This fact proves that in most organisms crossing over occurs when four chromatids are present as two pairs.

Problems in Meiotic Behavior

Synapsis of Chromosomes

There is no adequate explanation of the mechanism by which homologous chromosomes in meiotic prophase undergo pairing. In early prophase, homologues are at relatively large distances from each other, and yet they manage to come to lie side by side for their entire lengths by the end of zygotene. Their pairing is very exact in that identical genetic segments pair with each other in the part-by-part association. A number of theories have been propounded to describe the possible forces drawing together the two members of a homologous pair, particularly from diverse regions of the nucleus. All of these theories are primarily speculative, with little or no evidence to substantiate them. One of the more logical proposals presupposes the existence of specific attractive forces between the homologous chromosomes. These attractive forces are due to inherent vibrational frequencies in the chromosomes, with different regions having perhaps different frequencies. Similar vibrational frequencies in homologous segments of the two chromosomes attract each other to effect their pairing. These frequencies may be analogous to van der Waals (intermolecular) forces between the chemical components of the chromosomes. It is presumed that such forces are of sufficient magnitudes to account for attractions over the distances traveled by chromosomes undergoing synapsis.

Formation of Chiasmata

Chiasmata are observed during prophase I of meiosis in most organisms, including some that do not exhibit genetic crossing over, such as *Drosophila* males and silkworm females. The most widely accepted theory of chiasma formation and behavior is the *partial chiasmatype* theory proposed by Janssens in 1909 and Darlington in 1932. This theory states that each chiasma is derived from the breakage and reunion of two homologous chromatids. Genetic crossing over occurs during pachytene or earlier in the meiotic cycle. Crossing over occurs between only two of the four chromatids at any one locus, but it can occur between any two of the four. According to this theory, a nearly 1 : 1 ratio between chiasmata and crossovers would be expected. This, in fact, has been found in some organisms. The *classical* theory proposed by Sax in 1932 states that chiasma formation leads to crossing over through breakage of the chromatids when they spread out or repel each other. In this case, crossing over fol-

(a)   (b)

Figure 12–14.   Pairing and chiasma formation in a bivalent: (a) classical theory; (b) partial chiasmatype theory.

lows chiasma formation. Here the ratio between the number of chiasmata and the number of crossovers would not necessarily be unity (1 : 1). Subsequent studies have tended to refute the classical theory. Both the partial chiasmatype theory and the classical theory are illustrated in Figure 12–14.

Mechanism of Crossing Over

The origin of crossing over, or its cause, is another complex cytogenetic problem. The precocity theory of Darlington incorporates a mechanism to explain this phenomenon. The theory is based upon the idea that prophase I is precocious because it begins before the chromosomes are duplicated. As stated previously, the available information contradicts this assumption. Nevertheless, Darlington's hypothesis is worth reviewing for its possibilities. Basically, it indicates that crossing over is a result of the breakage of the chromosomes and their subsequent recombination. The paired but undivided chromosomes are coiled relationally about each other in a direction opposite to that of their internal coiling. Thus the two types of coils are in physical equilibrium, with a minimum of stress being imposed upon the chromosomes. When the chromosomes undergo duplication, this equilibrium is destroyed, and a torsional stress hits each strand. Because of this physical stress, a break occurs in one chromatid, and a second break in an adjacent nonsister chromatid at the same locus. The broken ends separate, the positions shift, the nonsister chromatids recombine to produce exchange chromatids, and a chiasma appears. The principal objection to Darlington's theory is that the chromosomes are duplicated before synapsis.

Modern genetic studies have suggested that there may be at least two mechanisms involved in crossing over. In addition to the reciprocal exchange of chromatids during or just prior to pachytene, when four chromatids are present, there may be some recombination during the period of DNA synthesis, affecting short, unpaired segments of the chromosomes. A small part of a new DNA helix being synthesized may copy a nonsister helix rather than a sister helix, to produce a recombination in a very short segment. This mechanism is known as *copy choice*. For clarification it may be described as the copying of a short segment of a nonsister chromatid. In summary, then, there is evidence for two types of genetic recombination, and both are compatible with the partial chiasmatype theory.

Another problem not yet completely resolved concerns the frequency of crossing over in limited segments of the chromosomes. Conflicting results have been obtained; some investigators have reported that one crossover interferes with the formation of another in an adjacent region, and others have reported no interference. In addition, there may be negative interference, so that a greater number of crossovers occur in closely linked regions than are expected. The latter type may be related to copy choice crossing over.

S E L E C T E D   R E A D I N G

General

Darlington, C. D., *Recent Advances in Cytology*, Blakiston, Philadelphia, 1932.
Darlington, C. D., "The Chromosomes and the Theory of Heredity," *Roy. Soc. (London), notes and records,* **16**(1), 44 (1961).
Lima-de-Faria, A., "Matrix and Kinetochore in Living Material," *Hereditas,* **45** (3), 463 (1959).
McLeish, J., and B. Snoad, *Looking at Chromosomes*, St. Martin's Press, New York, 1958.
Rhoades, M. M., "Meiosis," in J. Brachet and A. E. Mirsky, eds., *The Cell*, Vol. 3, Academic Press, New York, 1961, pp. 1–76.
Sager, R., and F. J. Ryan, *Cell Heredity*, Wiley, New York, 1961.
Swanson, C. P., T. Merz, and W. J. Young, *Cytogenetics,* Prentice-Hall, Englewood Cliffs, N.J., 1967.

Meiotic Coiling

Darlington, C. D., "The Internal Mechanics of the Chromosomes," *Proc. Roy. Soc. (London), Ser. B,* **118**, 35 (1935).
Darlington, C. D., and C. G. Vosa, "Bias in the Internal Coiling Direction of Chromosomes," *Chromosoma,* **13**(6), 609 (1963).
Kaufmann, B. P., "Chromosome Structure in Relation to the Chromosome Cycle," *Botan. Rev.,* **14**, 57 (1948).
Sax, H. J., and K. Sax, "Chromosome Structure and Behavior in Mitosis and Meiosis," *J. Arnold Arboretum* (Harvard Univ.), **16**, 423 (1935).
Sparrow, A. H., C. L. Huskins, and G. B. Wilson, "Studies on the Chromosome Spiralization Cycle in *Trillium*," *Can. J. Res., Sec. C,* **19**, 323 (1941).
Wilson, G. B., and P. G. Coleman, "The Ontogeny of Chromosome and Chromonema Spirals. A Re-evaluation," *Cytologia (Tokyo),* **17**, 270 (1952).

Synapsis and Crossing Over

Moens, P. B., "The Structure and Function of the Synaptinemal Complex in *Lilium longiflorum* sporocytes," *Chromosoma,* **23**(4), 418 (1968).

Moses, M. J., and J. R. Coleman, "Structural Patterns and the Functional Organization of Chromosomes," in M. Locke, ed., *The Role of Chromosomes in Development,* Academic Press, New York, 1964, pp. 11–49.

Sax, K., "The Cytological Mechanisms of Crossing Over," *J. Arnold Arboretum (Harvard Univ.),* **13,** 180 (1932).

Sax, K., "Chromosome Coiling in Relation to Meiosis and Crossing Over," *Genetics,* **21**(4), 324 (1936).

Sotelo, J. R., and R. Wettstein, "Fine Structure of Meiotic Chromosomes. Comparative Study of Nine Species of Insects," *Chromosoma,* **20**(2), 234 (1966).

Swanson, C. P., "Some Considerations of the Phenomenon of Chiasma Terminalization," *Am. Naturalist,* **76,** 593 (1942).

Wolstenholme, D. R., and G. F. Meyer, "Some Facts Concerning the Nature and Formation of Axial Core Structures in Spermatids of *Gryllus domesticus,*" *Chromosoma,* **18**(2), 272 (1966).

Synthetic Events

Bogdanov, Yu. F., et al., "Uncoupling of DNA and Histone Synthesis Prior to Prophase I of Meiosis in the Cricket *Grillus (Acheta) domesticus* L.," *Exptl. Cell Res.,* **52**(1), 59 (1968).

Henderson, S. A., "RNA Synthesis During Male Meiosis and Spermiogenesis," *Chromosoma,* **15**(4), 345 (1964).

Kemp, C. L., "The Effects of Inhibitors of RNA and Protein Synthesis on Cytological Development During Meiosis," *Chromosoma,* **15**(5), 652 (1964).

MacKenzie, A., J. Heslop-Harrison, and H. G. Dickinson, "Elimination of Ribosomes During Meiotic Prophase," *Nature,* **215**(5104), 997 (1967).

Sheridan, W. F., and H. Stern, "Histones of Meiosis," *Exptl. Cell Res.,* **45**(2), 323 (1967).

13

Gametogenesis

The process by which an organism produces gametes or other cells necessary for sexual reproduction is a complicated one. In plants it involves specific relationships between the gametophyte and sporophyte generations, and specific events during these stages in the life histories. The events are sometimes more complex in the so-called primitive plants, such as the algae, than in the advanced plants, such as the angiosperms. In most animals the sequence of cell divisions resulting in the gametes is relatively straightforward.

Gametogenesis, or the development of gametes, has as its basis both meiotic and mitotic cell divisions. The divisions of utmost importance are meiotic, for they reduce the chromosome count to the haploid number. When fertilization occurs, the diploid number is restored. The meiotic divisions give rise almost directly to gametes in animals, but not in plants. A comparison of the schemes of cell divisions leading to the formation of eggs and sperm in representative plants and animals will make clear the major differences between the two groups.

Because of their particular pertinence to meiotic and mitotic divisions, the cytological aspects of the sexual process, as outlined in Chapters 11 and 12, will be emphasized in this discussion. The formation of eggs (*oogenesis*) and sperm (*spermatogenesis*) in metazoa, such as the grasshopper and man; the formation of female gametophytes and eggs (*megasporogenesis*) and male gametophytes and sperm (*microsporogenesis*) in two types of angiosperms; and the sexual cycle of the haploid microorganism *Neurospora,* a fungus belonging to the class Ascomycetes, will be described. The closing section of the chapter will be devoted to several organisms in which the meiotic events are atypical.

Gametogenesis in Animals

Spermatogenesis

The formation of sperm in animals depends upon the completion of the meiotic divisions (Figure 13–1) and the subsequent metamorphosis of the meiotic products into active and functional sperm (Figure 13–2). This metamorphosis, which involves specific morphological and cytological changes in the meiotic products, is called *spermiogenesis*. Sperm are pro-

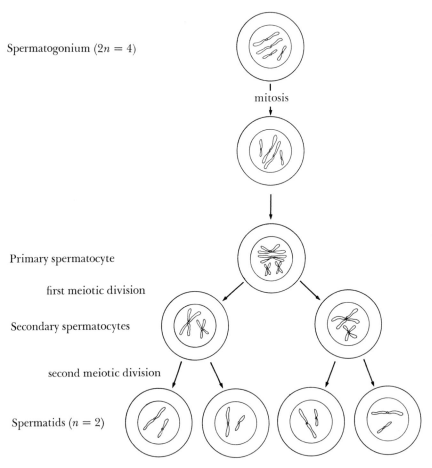

Spermatogonium ($2n = 4$)

mitosis

Primary spermatocyte

first meiotic division

Secondary spermatocytes

second meiotic division

Spermatids ($n = 2$)

Figure 13–1. Spermatogenesis.

duced in the seminiferous tubules of the testes of the male animal. In the sexually mature male the primitive germ cells, or *spermatogonia,* undergo several mitotic divisions prior to meiosis. The products of the mitotic divisions, the *primary spermatocytes,* then undergo meiosis. *Secondary spermatocytes* result from the first meiotic division, and the final meiotic products, each of which is a haploid cell, are the *spermatids.* Spermio-genesis, the process of spermatid maturation, results in the functional *spermatozoa* or sperm. In Chapter 3 cytoplasmic bridges between the

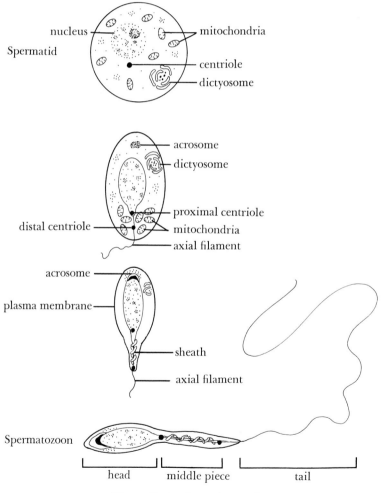

Figure 13–2. Spermiogenesis.

developing spermatocytes were described, but, for simplicity, are not included in the description here.

Spermiogenesis

Each haploid product of spermatogenesis, a spermatid, is initially a rather typical cell consisting of a nucleus in cytoplasm. The cytoplasm contains several of the organelles ordinarily found in cytoplasm, including mitochondria, centrioles, and a dictyosome (Chapter 5). The behavior of these three kinds of organelles is fundamental to the development of the spermatid into a mature spermatozoon.

The most significant changes in gross morphology during spermiogenesis are a reduction in the mass of cytoplasm and an elongation of the nucleus. Cytological events play a major role in these changes in gross morphology. (Spermiogenesis as described here and illustrated in Figure 13–2 applies primarily to mammals; it differs somewhat in other animals.) The centriole divides before the cytological changes begin, and one of the resultant centrioles, the *distal* centriole, gives rise to the main axis of the tail of the sperm. This axis, termed the *axial filament,* is made up of a complex of fibrils throughout its length. The submicroscopic organization of these fibrils was discussed in Chapter 8 in connection with the organization of cilia and flagella. In effect, the distal centriole becomes the basal body of the tail, or flagellum, of the mature sperm. The *proximal* centriole becomes closely appressed to the nuclear envelope, but a funnel-shaped connecting piece may obscure the details of this arrangement.

Mitochondria usually become oriented at the sides of the filament as two densely packed hemispheres. These ultimately form a spiral *sheath* around the filament. Although it looks like a continuous spiral, the sheath is actually an end-to-end association of elongated mitochondria. The number of turns in the sheath is a function of the number of mitochondria and their arrangements, and varies according to species. For example, there are 12 turns in human spermatozoa and as many as 115 in the bat. One function of the sheath may be to provide energy derived from mitochondrial ATP for the movement of the sperm to the egg prior to fertilization.

While the aforementioned changes are taking place, the dictyosome gives rise to another element, the acrosome (Chapter 5), which moves to the nucleus and covers it. Following formation of the acrosome, the dictyosome eventually degenerates. Association of the acrosome with the nucleus varies with different animals. In the starfish *Asterias amurensis,* for example, the acrosome appears to fit into a depression of the nucleus (Figure 13–3). Moreover, the acrosomal vesicle is absent in contrast to

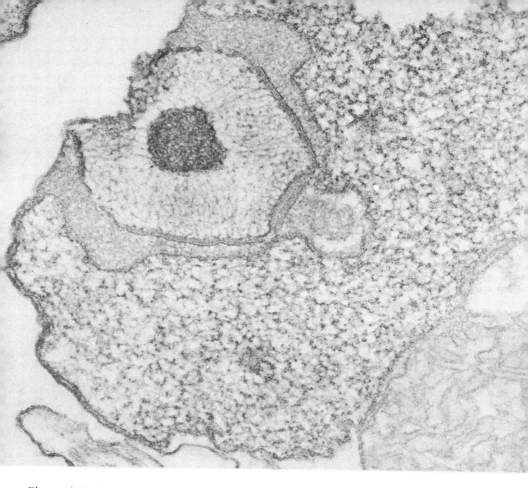

Figure 13–3. Intact acrosome of *Asterias amurensis*. Note the dense acrosomal granule. FROM Y. Hagiwara, J. C. Dan, and A. Saito, *J. Ultrastruct. Res.*, **18**, 551 (1967).

other invertebrate phyla. When the sperm comes into contact with the jelly coat surrounding the egg, the acrosome reacts rapidly (within 1 second) to form a slender process that extends beyond the anterior end of the sperm head. The process develops from the innermost part of the acrosomal depression and is covered by the plasma membrane. In other animals, fusion of the plasma membrane of the projection with the egg plasma membrane has been observed. These events, resulting in the confluence of the two cells, are necessary for the ultimate fusion of egg and sperm nuclei.

Cytochemical studies of the acrosomes of a marine echiuroid worm, *Urechis caupo,* have demonstrated the presence of basic proteins that differ from those found in the nucleus. The acrosomal protein contains about one-half as much arginine and the same amount of lysine as does the nuclear basic protein, and it is not bound to either DNA or RNA.

Polysaccharides are also present in the acrosome, and the protein may be associated with either the carbohydrate or a lipid fraction. Similar observations of basic protein and polysaccharide contents have been made on insect sperm acrosomes. Changes in the nuclear basic proteins (histones) during spermatogenesis are described later.

The developing sperm lengthens and loses most of its cytoplasm. However, the plasma membrane remains as an envelope around the entire mature sperm, including the tail. Just behind the region of the sheath, the axial filament is surrounded by a fibrous coat, with the plasma membrane outside it, but near the end of the tail it is surrounded only by the membrane. In some mammals, for example, the Chinese hamster, the proximal centriole elongates as the flagellum grows. The distal centriole disappears, leaving the flagellum without a basal body (kinetosome). Electron microscopy of developing sperm in several animals, including grasshoppers and chickens, implicates microtubules in the process of nuclear elongation. During early spermiogenesis, the microtubules are arranged helically around the nucleus. By the end of elongation the helical arrangement is replaced by nearly straight microtubules parallel to the long axis of the nucleus. In addition to effecting nuclear elongation, the microtubules may also function in sperm motility, and may provide support for the flagellar filaments, since they persist in the midpiece and tail. Persisting straight microtubules adjacent to the nucleus in chicken sperm appear to determine the final curvature of the sperm head. The mature sperm thus consists of a relatively large *head,* composed of an elongated nucleus covered by acrosomal material; a *middle piece,* composed of one or two centrioles, an axial filament, and a sheath; and a *tail,* considerably longer than either the head or the middle piece and composed primarily of the filament.

Oogenesis

Oogenesis (Figure 13–4) occurs in the ovary of the female animal. The diploid *oogonium* enlarges to become the *primary oocyte.* The primary oocyte undergoes the first meiotic division to produce one large cell, the *secondary oocyte,* and one small cell, the *first polar body (polocyte).* The secondary oocyte undergoes a second meiotic division producing one large cell, the *ootid,* and a small *second polar body.* The first polar body may or may not divide to form yet a third polar body. In most animals the polar bodies eventually disintegrate. The ootid, which is the functional product of meiosis in the female, matures as the egg or *ovum.* Thus the products of oogenesis are a single large haploid egg and two or three polar

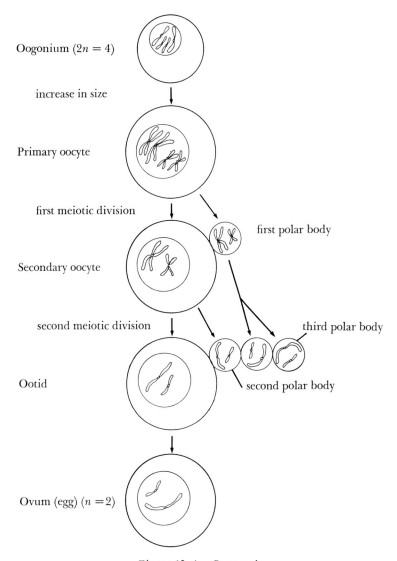

Oogonium (2*n* = 4)

increase in size

Primary oocyte

first meiotic division

first polar body

Secondary oocyte

second meiotic division

third polar body

Ootid

second polar body

Ovum (egg) (*n* = 2)

Figure 13–4. Oogenesis.

bodies, which are usually found at the periphery or on the surface of the egg. In comparison with spermatogenesis, which results in four functional sperm, oogenesis results in only one functional egg.

In a number of animals, penetration of the oocyte by the sperm is necessary for the completion of oogenesis. When the sperm enters the oocyte cytoplasm of certain mammals, amphibians, and insects, the oocyte nucleus is still in the first prophase of meiosis. Division has temporarily ceased, and does not resume until after the sperm enters. Following diplotene, during which the chromosomes have condensed, there is a reversal of the coiling process and the chromosomes decondense, taking on an interphase-like appearance. This condition is identified as the *dictyotene* stage, during which the oocyte grows and accumulates nutrients for later use by the young embryo. In humans, the immature egg may remain in this condition from 12 to 45 years! The interpretation of these events is that the decondensed chromatin is synthetically active in contrast to the inactive, condensed chromatin. That is, the DNA of the chromosomes can function in the production of RNA that is utilized in protein synthesis. Details of these activities are discussed in Chapters 14 and 19. This type of behavior is exemplified by the *lampbrush* chromosomes of amphibian oocytes; the chromosomes are so highly decondensed that loops appear along their axes (Chapter 14). After the sperm entry meiosis continues with a recondensing of the chromosomes in diakinesis, and at the end of meiosis, the sperm and egg nuclei unite. Thus fertilization (*syngamy*) must occur if a mature, functional egg is to be produced. In many other animals, however, the meiotic process is completed and the egg matured prior to fertilization. (In plants, only certain mosses exhibit a dictyotene condition; there is no growth of spore mother cells at this time, and it is a short-lived period.)

Fertilization involves first a fusion of the plasma membranes of the gametes. The portion of the sperm that first touches the egg, just before the membrane fusion, is determined by the position of the acrosome material in the sperm. The acrosome, which consists of polysaccharides, lipids, enzymes, and other proteins, changes form on contact with the egg membrane, and the sperm nucleus then enters the egg cytoplasm. The zygote results when the sperm nucleus and the egg nucleus unite to form a diploid nucleus. In contrast to the sperm, the egg contributes not only the genetic material of its nucleus but also a large amount of its cytoplasm to the zygote. This cytoplasm contains various storage materials that provide some nutrition for the young embryo.

The diploid zygote divides mitotically, and mitosis continues during the development of the embryo. In most cases the nuclear fusion of fertilization initiates the earliest mitotic divisions. The roundworm *Ascaris* illustrates this phenomenon. When fertilization occurs, the sperm nucleus and the centriole of the sperm both enter the egg, and the centriole aids in the formation of the spindle apparatus of the first mitotic division (first *cleavage*).

Gametogenesis in Plants

In the evolution of the plant kingdom, there is a significant shift in dominance from the gametophyte generation to the sporophyte generation. In the lower plants the gametophyte generation, during which gametes are formed, is the dominant phase, and the sporophyte generation may consist of only a single cell. The gametophyte tissue is haploid, and the gametes are produced by mitosis. Syngamy results in a diploid zygote, which represents the first cell of the sporophyte generation. In many of the algae and fungi, the diploid zygote then undergoes meiosis to produce haploid spores or other cells, each of which is capable of developing into a mature gametophyte. In the angiosperms, those plants that bear flowers and seeds, the sporophyte generation is the dominant phase, and the gametophyte generation is quite reduced, usually microscopic in size, and dependent upon the sporophyte for its whole existence. In a typical angiosperm flower female gametophytes (*megagametophytes*) are produced in the ovary, and male gametophytes (*microgametophytes*) in the anther, by meiosis; the meiotic products then undergo one or more mitotic divisions to give rise to the gametes. The sporophyte generation begins with the formation of the zygote.

Microsporogenesis

The chambers of the anther contain numerous diploid *pollen mother cells.* A pollen mother cell undergoes meiosis to produce a quartet of *microspores,* each of which has a single haploid nucleus (Figure 13–5). The microspore is the first cell of the male gametophyte generation. Each microspore nucleus divides by mitosis so that the cell contains two haploid nuclei. In this case there is a division of the nucleus (*karyokinesis*) but no division of the cytoplasm (cytokinesis). Morphologically the cell increases in size and develops a pattern of sculpturing in its wall, as it matures into a *pollen grain.*

One of the haploid nuclei in the pollen grain is the *tube* nucleus, and the other is the *generative* nucleus. They may or may not differ in size and shape. When the pollen grain lands on the stigma of the female reproductive organ, or *pistil,* of a flower (*pollination*), a pollen tube grows down into the *style* of the pistil. The tube and generative nuclei travel into this pollen tube, where another mitotic division occurs. The generative nucleus divides into two sperm nuclei, without accompanying cyto-

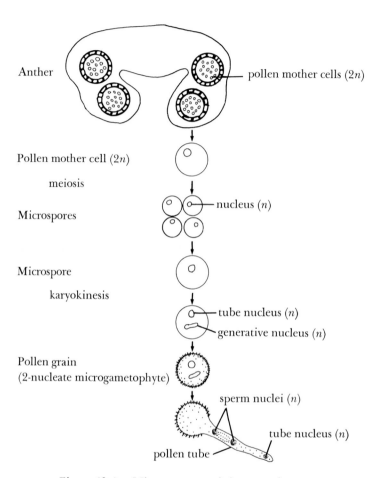

Anther

pollen mother cells (2n)

Pollen mother cell (2n)

meiosis

Microspores

nucleus (n)

Microspore

karyokinesis

tube nucleus (n)

generative nucleus (n)

Pollen grain
(2-nucleate microgametophyte)

sperm nuclei (n)

tube nucleus (n)

pollen tube

Figure 13–5.   Microsporogenesis in an angiosperm.

kinesis. The tube nucleus does not divide and ultimately degenerates. The time interval between the beginning of meiosis in the pollen mother cell and the formation of the sperm nuclei varies from one type of plant to another. In the monocotyledonous *Tradescantia* (spiderwort), for example, the entire process lasts approximately 2 weeks. The sperm nuclei are then released into the female gametophyte, where fertilization takes place.

Sexual reproduction in the flowering plants is an important illustration of a significant step in the evolution of the plant kingdom. In evolutionary history the invasion of dry land by plants was greatly facilitated by the development of pollen, since this provided a means of dissemination of gametes without the need for water.

Megasporogenesis

The ovary of a flower contains one or more *ovules*, each of which is a potential seed. In an ovule is a single diploid cell, the *megaspore mother cell*, surrounded by sterile protective tissue. The megaspore mother cell enlarges and undergoes meiosis to produce four *megaspores* (Figure 13–6). In many instances these are merely nuclei, with no cell walls about them. In a typical angiosperm three of the megaspores degenerate, and the fourth becomes the haploid female gametophyte. The female gametophyte is considerably larger than the male gametophyte.

The nucleus of the female gametophyte undergoes three successive mitotic divisions, which result in an *embryo sac* containing eight haploid nuclei. Three of the nuclei are located at one pole of the embryo sac, the *micropylar* end, three at the opposite pole, or *antipodal* end, and two in the center. The last two are the *polar* nuclei (one from each pole). They fuse to form a diploid nucleus. The three antipodal nuclei may develop cell walls but eventually degenerate. Two of the nuclei at the micropylar end are *synergids* and serve no known function. Between the two synergids is the egg nucleus. When the sperm enter the embryo sac through the *micropyle,* one sperm nucleus fuses with the egg, and the other fuses with the diploid polar nucleus. Thus double fertilization is effected. The fertilized egg is the zygote, which develops by mitotic divisions into the embryo. The fertilized polar nucleus is now a triploid nucleus, called the *endosperm* nucleus. It also develops by mitotic divisions, into endosperm tissue, which is a source of nutrition for the embryo. In some plants, such as corn, the endosperm tissue comprises a substantial portion of the mature seed, whereas in others it is digested by the embryo before the seed is mature.

Megasporogenesis does not follow the same pattern in the lily as in other angiosperms (Figure 13–6). The four haploid products of meiosis persist in the lily and take part in the ensuing mitotic divisions. One of the haploid nuclei is located at the micropylar end of the ovule, and the other three are located at the antipodal end. The latter three fuse to form a *triploid* nucleus. Hence the megagametophyte consists of one haploid nucleus and one triploid nucleus. Each of these two nuclei divides by mitosis twice, the result being four haploid nuclei and four triploid nuclei in the embryo sac. Three of the triploid nuclei lie at the antipodal

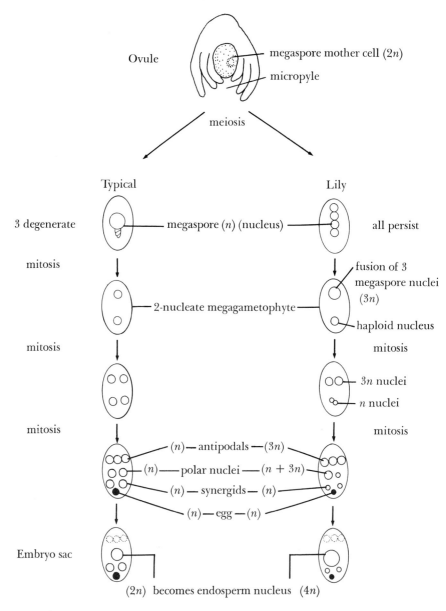

Figure 13–6. Megasporogenesis in a typical angiosperm and in the lily.

end of the sac, and three of the haploid nuclei at the micropylar end. Two of the latter three are synergids, and one is the egg. The remaining haploid nucleus and triploid nucleus migrate to the center of the sac, where they fuse to form a *tetraploid* nucleus (four sets of chromosomes). When double fertilization occurs, a diploid zygote and a *pentaploid* endosperm nucleus (five sets of chromosomes) are produced.

Biochemical Events

Variations in nuclear protein content of cells undergoing spermatogenesis have been observed at several phylogenetic levels in animals. The spermatocyte chromosomes of the snail *Helix* contain a histone rich in lysine. As sperm maturation proceeds, the lysine-rich histone is replaced by one rich in arginine, and finally by protamine, which is very arginine-rich. After fertilization, protamine disappears and is replaced during blastulation by faintly basic histones that differ from adult histone. During gastrulation the adult type of histone (lysine-rich) is restored. A similar pattern of histone change occurs during spermiogenesis in *Drosophila melanogaster,* but the arginine-rich histone is not replaced by protamine. In *Urechis caupo,* on the other hand, the transition of histone protein culminates in late spermiogenesis in a protamine-like protein. Studies of basic protein labeled with sulfur-35 in the pollen of *Lilium longiflorum* demonstrated that little of the sperm protein is actually present at the time of fertilization. Most of the protein, presumably histone, is replaced, destroyed, or left behind before gamete fusion, and new protein is synthesized just before zygote formation.

Changes in RNA content have also been observed through variations in RNA synthesis during gametogenesis. Increases in RNA content have been found in *Necturus* (newt) oogenesis in connection with the production of yolk material. In *Trillium* microspores, however, there is a long postmeiotic G_1 period that exhibits a low level of RNA synthesis. Whatever RNA synthesis does occur takes place in only 20% of the DNA that corresponds to the relatively uncondensed chromatin.

All of these facts taken together support the view that synthetically active, and therefore genetically active, cells have a relatively high proportion of uncondensed chromatin that presides over the synthesis of RNA. Moreover, cells producing RNA are also active in protein synthesis. The chemical state of basic protein as well as the degree to which these proteins are complexed with DNA may be the basis for a regulation of genetic activity. To illustrate, grasshopper spermatocytes having diffuse chromatin at prophase are active in RNA synthesis, and at the same time, exhibit relatively low concentrations of lysine-rich histone. As chromatin becomes more condensed with sperm maturation, RNA synthesis decreases and the proportion of lysine-rich histone increases. Thus, histone with a high lysine content may be the material that serves to regulate gene action. There are other features of these phenomena, some of which are inconsistent and controversial, that will be discussed in Chapters 14 and 19; the significance of histone in these respects is not yet fully resolved.

Life Cycle of *Neurospora*

Several microorganisms, including algae, fungi, and protozoa, have been used in studies of the mechanisms of heredity. These organisms have at least two advantages over more highly developed plants and animals. One advantage is that they rapidly produce large numbers of offspring. A second advantage is that some of them are primarily haploid; that is, the major phases in their life histories consist of haploid cells. The significance of this phenomenon is that an investigator can identify all of the products of a meiotic division. Thus the recovery of specific genetic types from a cross of two organisms is not left to chance. Since the investigator can obtain all of the possible genetic combinations in a multitude of individuals within a relatively short period of time, he can predict the behavior of the chromosomes during meiosis and the meiotic products in a given instance of sexual reproduction. Many of the recent discoveries about the behavior of genes and the patterns of inheritance have come from work with these microorganisms. For this reason, as an example of the sexual process in a primitive organism, the life cycle of *Neurospora,* a pink bread mold, is presented here (Figure 13–7).

True gametes are not produced in *Neurospora.* However, the cells that fuse to form the zygote behave similarly to the gametes in syngamy. Sexual reproduction takes place only when cells from two different mating types (for example, *A* and *a*) fuse. The gametic cells are derived by mitosis, and after the formation of the zygote, meiosis occurs. Each of the four haploid products of meiosis then divides mitotically. The result is an *ascus,* or spore case, containing eight haploid *ascospores.* Each ascospore is capable of giving rise to a new mycelium. Thus all of the meiotic products persist. By studying the arrangement of the ascospores in the ascus, an investigator can determine the behavior of the chromosomes during the divisions that produce the spores. The meiotic events are shown in Figure 13–8, where the letters represent genetic loci in the chromosomes and the consequences of crossing over can be detected in the pattern of the ascospores.

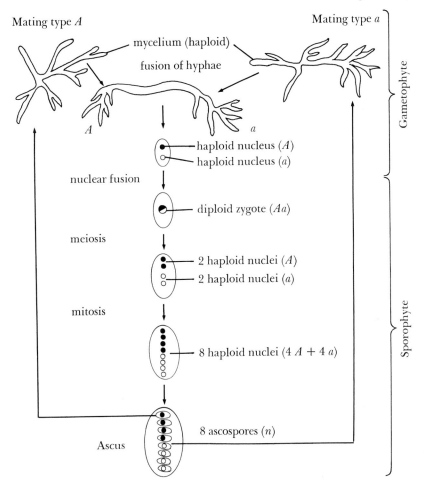

Mating type *A*

Mating type *a*

mycelium (haploid)

fusion of hyphae

Gametophyte

A

a

haploid nucleus (*A*)
haploid nucleus (*a*)

nuclear fusion

diploid zygote (*Aa*)

meiosis

2 haploid nuclei (*A*)
2 haploid nuclei (*a*)

mitosis

8 haploid nuclei (4 *A* + 4 *a*)

8 ascospores (*n*)

Ascus

Sporophyte

Figure 13–7. Life cycle of *Neurospora.*

Variations in Meiotic Phenomena

A number of animals, particularly among the arthropods, such as the wasp *Habrobracon* and the honeybee, reproduce principally by *partheno-genesis.* That is, a haploid egg develops into an embryo without fertilization by a sperm. Those eggs that develop parthenogenetically result in male offspring, whereas fertilized eggs result in diploid females. In some instances in the plant kingdom, a diploid egg rather than a haploid egg is produced. This diploid egg is capable of developing without the usual fertilization stimulus. Compensating mechanisms exist in these plants and

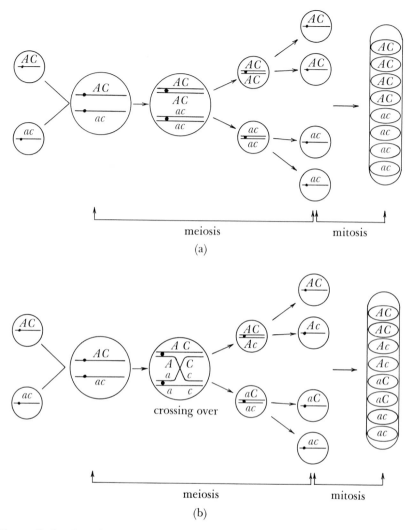

Figure 13–8. Genetic patterns in *Neurospora:* (a) with no crossing over between two genes during meiosis; (b) with crossing over between two genes during meiosis. *A* and *a* represent genes for mating type; *C* and *c* represent genes for pink and albino mycelia, respectively. Note the difference in order of the ascospores with respect to the gene pairs.

animals to maintain a continuity of chromosome number as well as a genetic continuity. These mechanisms are found in anomalous events occurring during meiosis. A few examples will be cited. It should be noted that most of the anomalies occur during spermatogenesis and that oogenesis is essentially normal.

In the order Hymenoptera, which includes the wasps, the meiotic behavior in the haploid males (products of parthenogenesis) accounts for the preservation of the species chromosome number and also permits normal fertilization and embryonic development. During spermatogenesis all the chromosomes remain unpaired. They are oriented as univalents on the spindle in metaphase I. However, since there is no anaphase I, they are all contained in a single nucleus at the end of the first meiotic division. In anaphase II this nucleus undergoes the second meiotic division, which is equational. Therefore, each of the two (instead of four) products of meiosis contains the haploid number of chromosomes. There is evidence that this type of meiosis is under genetic control.

Another type of meiotic variation concerns the segregation of the chromosomes to the poles. Typically this segregation is random, but instances have been observed in both the plant and the animal kingdoms of segregation of a specific chromosome to the same pole in every meiotic division. In other words, the chromosome does not go to one pole or the other with a probability of 50%, but always to the same pole. Such preferential segregation of a particular chromosome into the gametes is known as *meiotic drive* and is probably the result of a gene mutation.

Two families of the order Diptera, the family Sciaridae (fungus gnats) and the family Cecidomyidae (gall midges), exhibit rather striking meiotic anomalies. In the first meiotic division of spermatogenesis in *Sciara*, there is no pairing of the chromosomes and consequently no crossing over. The chromosomes of maternal origin are segregated from those of paternal origin, which separate into a bud that later disintegrates. Thus at fertilization the male contributes only the maternal chromosomes and never the paternal chromosomes. The second meiotic division is equational for all of the chromosomes except the sex chromosome. Instead of one of the two chromatids of the X (sex) chromosome going to each of the two poles, both chromatids go to the same pole prior to the movement of the other chromosomes. The result is two nuclei, one containing a full complement of chromosomes including the X chromosome and the other lacking an X chromosome. The latter nucleus degenerates, and the nucleus with the X chromosome becomes the functional sperm. Therefore, the meiotic divisions produce only a single functional spermatid instead of the usual four. There are other anomalies of meiosis in *Sciara*, but these will be discussed in connection with sex determination in a later chapter.

The gall midges, which are related to *Sciara*, show still other peculiarities in their meiotic behavior. The number of chromosomes in the somatic cells of the gall midges is quite different from the number of chromosomes in their germ cells. In the gall fly *Miastor* there are 48 chromosomes in a germ cell but only 12 in a somatic cell of the female and 6 in a somatic cell of the male. Six of the chromosomes are referred to as S (somatic) chromosomes and are larger than the rest, which are called *E* (eliminated) chromosomes, since they are eliminated at some time during the developmental cycle. There are from 16 to 56 *E* chromosomes in gall midges, depending upon the species. In prophase I of spermatogenesis, the *E* chromosomes do not pair. One haploid set of *S* chromosomes (six) and all the *E* chromosomes move to one pole; the other haploid set of *S* chromosomes moves to the opposite pole. Thus the secondary spermatocytes are unequal in size. The larger of the two, which contains the *E* chromosomes, eventually degenerates. The smaller of the two, which contains a single haploid set of *S* chromosomes, undergoes the second meiotic division, which is equational, to produce two spermatids, each with the haploid number of chromosomes. In oogenesis six of the *S* chromosomes, or a haploid set, are lost in the first meiotic division, so that the functional egg contains a haploid set of *S* chromosomes plus all of the *E* chromosomes. The chromosome number of the *Miastor* egg is 42. When the egg and sperm unite at fertilization, the chromosome number becomes 48. In the subsequent division of the embryo, all but 12 chromosomes are lost from each female somatic cell, and all but 6 from each male somatic cell. Each germ cell retains the 48 chromosomes derived at fertilization. In summary, then, the sexual cycle of a gall midge produces only two sperm, and each has a typical haploid number of chromosomes. On the other hand, the single egg produced contains many additional chromosomes, most of which are eliminated during early cleavages.

SELECTED   READING

General

Pontecorvo, G., *Trends in Genetic Analysis,* Columbia Univ. Press, New York, 1958.
Swanson, C. P., *Cytology and Cytogenetics,* Prentice-Hall, Englewood Cliffs, N.J., 1957.
White, M. J. D., *Animal Cytology and Evolution,* 2nd ed., Cambridge Univ. Press, Cambridge, 1954.

Gametogenesis

Colwin, A. L., and L. H. Colwin, "Behavior of the Spermatozoon During Sperm-Blastomere Fusion and Its Significance for Fertilization (*Saccoglossus kowalevskii:* Hemichordata)," *Z. Zellforsch.,* **78,** 208 (1967).
Dan, J. C., and Y. Hagiwara, "Studies on the Acrosome. IX. Course of Acrosome Reaction in the Starfish," *J. Ultrastruct. Res.,* **18**(5–6), 562 (1967).

Das, N. K., J. Micou-Eastwood, and M. Alfert, "Cytochemical and Biochemical Properties of Basic Proteins of *Urechis* Acrosomes," *J. Cell Biol.,* 35(2), 455 (1967).

Dill, F. J., "Dictyotene Stage of Meiosis in Mosses," *Science,* 144(3618), 541 (1964).

Friedmann, I., "Cell Membrane Fusion and the Fertilization Mechanism in Plants and Animals," *Science,* 136(3517), 711 (1962).

Kessel, R. G., "An Electron Microscope Study of Spermiogenesis in the Grasshopper with Particular Reference to the Development of Microtubular Systems During Differentiation," *J. Ultrastruct. Res.,* 18(5–6), 677 (1967).

Maheshwari, P., *An Introduction to the Embryology of Angiosperms,* McGraw-Hill, New York, 1950.

McIntosh, J. R., and K. R. Porter, "Microtubules in the Spermatids of the Domestic Fowl," *J. Cell Biol.,* 35(1), 153 (1967).

Runnstrom, J., B. E. Hagstrom, and P. Perlmann, "Fertilization," in J. Brachet and A. E. Mirsky, eds., *The Cell,* Vol. 1, Academic Press, New York, 1959, pp. 327–97.

Singleton, J. R., "Chromosome Morphology and the Chromosome Cycle in the Ascus of *Neurospora crassa,*" *Am. J. Botany,* 40(3), 124 (1953).

Biochemical Events

Bloch, D. P., "Histone Synthesis in Nonreplicating Chromosomes," *J. Histochem. Cytochem.,* 10(2), 137 (1962).

Claypool, C., and D. P. Bloch, "Synthesis of Ribonucleic Acid and Histone Change During Spermatogenesis in the Grasshopper *Chortophaga viridifasciata,*" *Nature,* 215(5104), 966 (1967).

Das, C. C., B. P. Kaufmann, and H. Gay, "Autoradiographic Evidence of Synthesis of an Arginine-Rich Histone During Spermiogenesis in *Drosophila melanogaster,*" *Nature,* 204(4962), 1008 (1964).

Kemp, C. L., "Electron Microscope Autoradiographic Studies of RNA Metabolism in *Trillium erectum* Microspores," *Chromosoma,* 19(2), 137 (1966).

Steffensen, D. M., "Proteins of Sperm Nuclei Examined by Autoradiography at Fertilization and Subsequent Nuclear Division in *Lilium,*" *Genetics,* 52(8), 631 (1965).

Anomalies

Crouse, H. V., "The Controlling Element in Sex Chromosome Behavior in *Sciara,*" *Genetics,* 45(10), 1429 (1960).

Nicklas, R. B., "An Experimental and Descriptive Study of Chromosome Elimination in *Miastor* Species *(Cecidomyidae),*" *Chromosoma,* 10(3), 301 (1959).

Rhoades, M. M., "Meiosis," in J. Brachet and A. E. Mirsky, eds., *The Cell,* Vol. 3, Academic Press, New York, 1961, pp. 31–36.

White, M. J. D., "Cytological Studies on Gall Midges *(Cecidomyidae),*" *Texas Univ. Publ.,* No. 5007, 1 (1950).

14

Chromosomes

In the preceding chapters the behavior and some of the functions of the chromosomes have been described. It has been demonstrated that the chromosomes contribute to the division of cells and that they are of prime importance as carriers of the genes. Although they have been discussed in some detail in these contexts, little has been said of their specific physical or chemical nature. Of all the components of cells, the chromosomes have been studied the most exhaustively, and perhaps more is known about them than about any other organelles. Much remains to be determined, however, concerning the correlation of their physical and chemical organization with their genetic properties.

In many ways the chromosome has greater constancy than any other cell component, and it maintains its special qualities from cell generation to cell generation. Even more remarkable is the fact that the chromosomes found in all the organisms studied have basically the same physical and chemical organization. Cells of all plants and animals contain one or more chromosomes in their nuclei. The morphology and chemistry of chromosomes have been delineated by several of the methods given in Chapter 10. In this chapter the organization of typical chromosomes will be presented, as well as several variations. Additional anomalies in meiosis and mitosis, related to variations in chromosome structure and behavior, will also be treated.

Number

The number of chromosomes in a given species is generally constant, all members of that species ordinarily having the same diploid number of chromosomes in their somatic cells and the same haploid number in their gametes. However, in some organisms certain types of tissues are likely to show some intercellular variation. In mammalian liver, for example, there are often cells with multiples of the normal diploid number of chromosomes.

The number of chromosomes varies greatly from one species to another. The lowest chromosome number found in animals occurs in the roundworm *Ascaris megalocephala,* which has a haploid number of 1. In plants a composite, *Haplopappus gracilis,* has a haploid number of 2. The chromosome number may be as high as several hundred in a diploid cell. For example, in the phylum Protozoa, the Agregata have over 300 chromosomes, and the Aulacantha, which include the Radiolaria, have as many as 1600. Particular types of cells in some organisms may have an unusually large number as a result of the duplication of chromosomes without cell division. That is, although the chromosomes divide, they do not separate into daughter nuclei but accumulate within a single nucleus. This process is known as *endomitosis.* There are instances in which the number of chromosomes exceeds 1000 in some cells of the body of the organism, while it remains the normal diploid number in all other cells.

Among the more advanced plants and animals, such as the angiosperms and primates, the members of a taxonomic group often have chromosome numbers within a limited range. In the angiosperms the most frequent haploid number is 12, and members of this group have, on the average, a haploid number of 8 to 16. Similarly, there is a definite range of chromosome numbers in the fungi, the haploid number most often falling between 3 and 8. In the primates the haploid chromosome number ranges from about 16 to 30, with man having 23. Despite several exceptions to or deviations from the expected ranges, it is frequently possible to predict the basic haploid number of a member of one of these groups. This question will be examined in some detail in Chapter 16, which deals with variations in chromosome number.

The so-called basic haploid number of chromosomes in an organism or group of organisms is the lowest number containing a complete set of genes. A specific term for the haploid set of chromosomes is *genome.* In a diploid cell there are two haploid sets, and each chromosome of each haploid set has a partner, or homologue, in the other set. Homologous chromosomes are identical in size and carry similar or identical genes in corresponding positions. The behavior of homologous chromosomes during cell division has been discussed and is particularly important in the distribution of the genes during meiosis.

Several different species of plants and animals are listed with their respective chromosome numbers in Table 14–1. It can be seen that the variation is wide and that it is difficult to classify an organism taxonomically by its chromosome number alone.

**Table 14–1   Representative Chromosome Numbers in Some
Plants and Animals**

Plant	Haploid Chromosome Number	Animal	Haploid Chromosome Number
Agave americana (century plant)	30, 60, 90	*Ascaris lumbricoides* (roundworm)	24*
Allium cepa (onion)	8	*Ascaris megalocephala univalens* (roundworm)	1
Allomyces javanicus macrogynus (water mold)	28–50	*Bombyx mori* (silkworm)	28
Fragaria vesca (strawberry)	7	*Bufo viridis* (toad)	11
Fragaria virginiana (strawberry)	28	*Cambaroides japonicus* (crayfish)	98
Iris versicolor	36, 42, 52	*Canis familiaris* (dog)	39
Magnolia grandiflora	57	*Drosophila melanogaster* (fruit fly)	4
Neurospora crassa (bread mold)	7	*Equus caballus* (horse)	32
Piper nigrum (pepper)	64	*Eupagurus ochotensis* (hermit crab)	127
Secale cereale (rye)	7	*Gallus gallus domesticus* (chicken)	39*
Spinacia oleracea (spinach)	6	*Habrobracon pectinophorae* (wasp)	10
Trillium grandiflorum (wake-robin)	5	*Homo sapiens* (man)	23
Triticum aestivum (wheat)	21	*Icerya purchasi* (scale insect)	2
Triticum durum (wheat)	14	*Macaca mulatta* (monkey)	24
Zea mays (corn)	10		

* Male

Morphology

Chromosomes range, on the average, from 0.5 to about 30 μ in length and from 0.2 to 3 μ in diameter. Major exceptions include several insects, whose giant chromosomes may reach a length of nearly 300 μ and a width of 10 μ. The stage of the cell cycle in which the chromosomes are most easily measured is during mitotic metaphase when they are usually most condensed or coiled. The giant chromosomes of insects and some other organisms, however, exist only in a premetaphase stage. In any case, the measurements are somewhat inexact, since the degree of coiling varies with individuals, with cells, and of course, with organisms. Nevertheless, such measurements provide information on the *relative* sizes of the chromosomes in quantitative terms.

The smallest chromosome is approximately 1/80,000 the size of the largest found among living organisms. Although both the plant and animal kingdoms contain individuals having these smallest known chromosomes, plants are recognized as having, on the average, larger chromosomes than animals. *Trillium* species have among the largest known chromosomes, which often reach a length at metaphase of 32 μ. With certain exceptions, plants with few chromosomes have larger chromosomes than plants with many. For example, the monocotyledons *generally* have larger chromosomes than the dicotyledons, which often contain a greater number of chromosomes. In a single set of chromosomes, the largest may be as much as 50 times as long as the shortest. On the other hand, there are many organisms in which all the chromosomes are about the same length. The evolutionary significance of size relationships among chromosomes of different species but related genera will be covered in Chapter 16, with particular emphasis on studies of primate chromosomes.

Since the chromosome is most easily observed during the metaphase of mitosis, the following description of chromosome structure is based upon the metaphase chromosome. As explained in Chapter 11, the general morphology of the chromosome is in part a function of its state of coiling. During metaphase the chromosome exhibits maximum coiling and is therefore shorter and thicker looking than at any other time. It consists of two chromatids "held together" at a point along their lengths, in the region of the kinetochore. The kinetochore appears as a constriction in the chromosome, the primary constriction, and during metaphase it stains lighter than most other portions of the chromosome. The adjacent regions are usually heterochromatic, which accounts for the apparent constriction and lighter stain reaction, especially in metaphase and anaphase.

The kinetochore can also be identified as that part of the chromosome to which the spindle fibers are connected during cell division. In fact, its role in the movement of the chromosomes during cell division can be considered its principal function. Some investigators have suggested that the chromosome movement is at least partly autonomous and that the kinetochore simply provides force for the movement. Such movements were considered in Chapter 11.

The kinetochore may occupy any position along the chromosome. According to the nomenclature recommended by Levan et al., a *median* kinetochore is at or near the midpoint of the chromosome, so that the arm ratio is 1 : 1 or nearly so, and the chromosome is described as *metacentric*. If the kinetochore is to either side of the midpoint, its position is *submedian,* and the chromosome *submetacentric.* A kinetochore located close to the end of a chromosome is *subterminal* in a subtelocentric or *acrocentric* chromosome. A *terminal* kinetochore is located at the end of a chromosome, which is called *telocentric.* Whatever its location, the kinetochore has a fixed position in each chromosome, and maintains this position throughout the lifetime of the chromosome and from generation to generation. Thus, a chromosome can be identified in any member of a species partly by its kinetochore position.

Chromosomes with truly terminal kinetochores (telocentric) are sometimes unstable. Occasionally one arm of a telocentric chromosome swings around the kinetochore to produce an isochromosome (Figure 14–1a), which has two genetically identical arms. Normally the kinetochore in a metacentric chromosome divides in a plane parallel to the axis of the chromosome. In some instances, however, the division occurs at right angles to the chromosome axis (misdivision). Misdivision of the kinetochore may result in the formation of telocentric chromosomes (Figure 14–1b) each of which is relatively stable and functional because of its kinetochore construction. Plants in which misdivision has been observed include *Pisum, Fritillaria,* and *Triticum.* At least one animal, the grasshopper *Mecostethus,* also demonstrates it.

The ends of a chromosome act differently from the interstitial portions. If an end, or *telomere,* is broken off, either spontaneously or by induction (for example, with X rays), it is usually lost from the nucleus in subsequent cell divisions because it has no kinetochore. The broken end of the remaining piece of chromosome is unstable and may unite with another broken end in its vicinity. However, a broken end will not unite with a normal end. This is the principal distinction between a telomere and any other part of a chromosome.

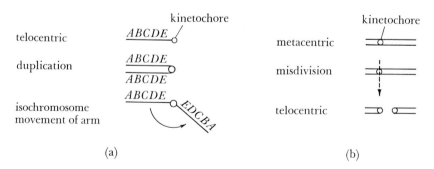

Figure 14-1. (a) Formation of an isochromosome. (b) Origin of telocentric chromosomes by misdivision.

Structure of the Kinetochore

In general, the morphology of a kinetochore resembles that of the rest of the chromosome, but there are notable differences. For example, the kinetochore is a constriction in the chromosome that is lighter-staining than the other parts of the chromosome, especially during metaphase and anaphase. This stain reaction is not due to an absence of DNA, since DNA has been demonstrated in the kinetochores of many organisms, although there may be less DNA in the kinetochores than elsewhere. Another significant difference is that the fibrils in the kinetochore remain uncoiled or less coiled than those in the rest of the chromosome. This in itself may account for the less intensive stain reaction.

The fine structure of the kinetochore has been difficult to resolve because of limitations in preparative techniques. However, recent studies with electron microscopy have begun to reveal some structural features. At the same time, there may be no common pattern of structure for both plants and animals. Some of the possible modes of kinetochore organization are described in the following paragraphs, but do not necessarily represent a universal scheme.

In many plants and some animals, the kinetochore includes one or more chromomeres of varying sizes and interchromomeral *fibrillae,* at least when studied with the light microscope. The fibrillae are strands or fibrils of the chromosome otherwise known as *chromonemata.* The number of fibrillae in a kinetochore varies somewhat, but usually only a few are visible. Not all kinetochores contain visible chromomeres; some of them show only the thin, barely perceptible fibrillae. Different patterns of kinetochore construction are illustrated in Figure 14–2. In most cases

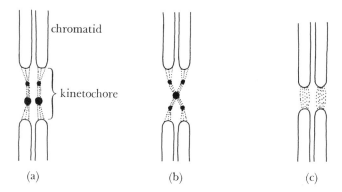

chromatid

kinetochore

(a)   (b)   (c)

Figure 14–2.   Kinetochore structure. AFTER Lima-de-Faria.

there is a symmetry in the distribution of the chromomeres and fibrillae. More precisely, their arrangement from the center of the kinetochore (*interior zone*) to either side is a "reversed repeat." That is, the kinetochore structure is the same on both sides of its central component, which is usually one or two chromomeres. This organization explains any stability of telocentric chromosomes and the formation of isochromosomes. Since the kinetochores of telocentric chromosomes produced by breakage or misdivision contain identical basic components, they are stable and functional and can reproduce themselves when the chromosome undergoes replication (Figure 14–3).

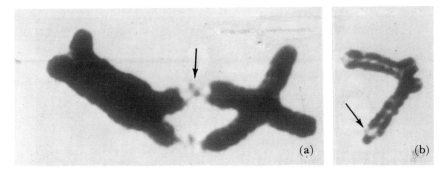

Figure 14–3. Kinetochore structure in *Chorthippus brunneus* (×2700): (a) metacentric bivalent in meiosis; (b) telocentric bivalent in meiosis. Arrows indicate kinetochore chromomeres. FROM B. John and G. M. Hewitt, *Chromosoma,* **20,** 155 (1966), with permission of Springer-Verlag.

Examination of kinetochores in mammalian chromosomes by electron microscopy has revealed a tripartite region on the outer (poleward) surface of each chromatid at metaphase. Although some differences have been noted among different species, or by different investigators, it is clear that the sister kinetochores are physically separate. The kinetochore is actually already divided before metaphase of mitosis and anaphase I of meiosis in most organisms. The chromosome is held together not by a single kinetochore but by an adhesion of the chromatids. In Chinese hamster chromosomes, the kinetochore consists of a dense core surrounded by a wider, less dense zone. The core is made up of axial fibrils, 50 to 80 Å in diameter, and the fibrils may be cohelically coiled. In the less dense zone, several microfibrils appear to loop out at right angles to the core, and resemble the loops of lampbrush chromosomes (Figure 14–4). It is possible that this represents a functional state of the kinetochore during cell division, and that the loop form is lost after the chromosomes have migrated to the poles of the cell. In effect, the kinetochore is a site of localized metabolic activity at specific times in the cell cycle. The suggestion has been made, for example, that the kinetochore participates in the organization of microtubule units into spindle filaments. It is clear that the kinetochore is more than just an anchor point for spindle fibers.

Chromosomes with Nonlocalized Kinetochores

The foregoing discussion of chromosome morphology is applicable particularly to a chromosome with a single, localized kinetochore. In some instances, however, there is no single, localized kinetochore. Instead the chromosome is *polycentric,* with more than one kinetochore, or the kinetochore, at least from a functional standpoint, is *diffuse.* According to Levan's system, a diffuse kinetochore is called a *lateral* one.

Figure 14–4. Highly magnified kinetochore of a Chinese hamster chromosome (Ch) (×86,000). Arrows indicate extended fibrils forming loops. FROM B. R. Brinkley and E. Stubblefield, *Chromosoma,* **19,** 28 (1966), with permission of Springer-Verlag.

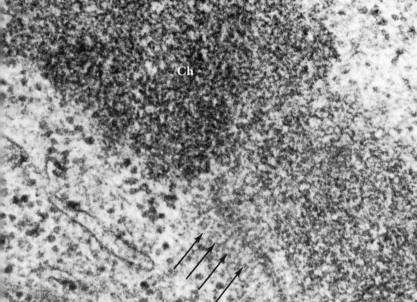

Diffuse Kinetochores

Chromosomes with the diffuse type of nonlocalized kinetochore are some-what more common than polycentric chromosomes, and are found in most homopterans and hemipterans. A chromosome with a diffuse kinetochore behaves, in effect, as if the entire chromosome were a kinetochore. During cell division spindle fibers form along the length of the chromosome, and each member chromatid moves to its respective pole in a plane per-pendicular to the axis of the poles (Figure 14–5). Since the chromatids are not specifically associated at a single kinetochore point, they freely sep-arate from each other for their entire lengths at once. Thus each chromatid acts autonomously. The basic behavior of chromosomes with diffuse kine-tochores is seen in the *coccids* (Homoptera), and other, related species exhibit variations on this theme. The bivalents form in prophase I of meiosis, and the chiasmata are completely terminalized by the beginning of metaphase I. Consequently, the two chromosomes, each consisting of two chromatids, lie in tandem on the equator in metaphase I. The first meiotic division is equational rather than reductional as in typical meiosis. Before the second division, or during interphase, the two homologous chromatids in each of the two daughter nuclei undergo secondary pairing

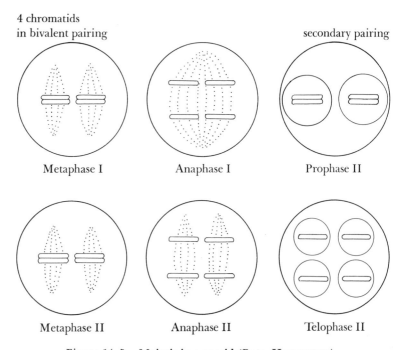

Figure 14–5. Meiosis in a coccid *(Puto,* Homoptera).

so that they are oriented together in metaphase II. This arrangement leads to the reductional second division and permits the normal segregation of the chromosomes by the end of meiosis. Therefore, each meiotic product contains the haploid number of chromosomes, and the genes are distributed normally.

Certain aspects of the meiotic divisions, primarily during spermatogenesis, are different in other coccids.

Iceryine Coccids   Males are relatively rare in this population and are not actually required for the continuation of the species, since the females are hermaphroditic and internal fertilization occurs. Such males as do appear are haploid, arising from unfertilized eggs, and their meiosis is peculiar. It consists only of one equational division. In these forms the spindle has an intranuclear origin.

Llaveiine Coccids   In *Protortonia primitiva* males there are two pairs of autosomes and one X chromosome, which separate from each other in diakinesis of prophase I of meiosis. Each chromosome consists of two chromatids, which also become dissociated from each other. The prophase nucleus develops four vesicles. The largest vesicle contains the four chromatids of one pair of autosomes, the two medium-sized vesicles each contain two chromatids, or one member of a pair of autosomes, and the smallest vesicle contains the two chromatids of the X chromosome. In metaphase I the chromatids act independently, since there is no pairing of the chromosomes. The first division is equational, with five chromatids going to each pole. Secondary pairing of the chromatids occurs during interphase, and in metaphase II there is often a linear chain of chromosomes along the polar axis (Figure 14–6). In anaphase II two of the five

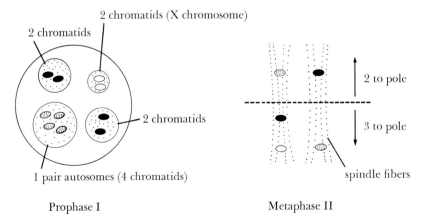

Prophase I   Metaphase II

Figure 14–6.   Meiosis in *Protortonia* (a llaveiine coccid).

chromatids go to one pole, and the remaining three go to the opposite
pole. Thus two of the resulting spermatids have X chromosomes, whereas
two do not.

Lecanoid Coccids   In male lecanoid coccids there are two haploid sets
of chromosomes. However, there is no pairing of the chromosomes during
prophase I of meiosis, nor is there secondary pairing of the chromosomes
during interphase between the two meiotic divisions. The two haploid sets
of chromosomes, identified as the heterochromatic (paternal) set and the
euchromatic (maternal) set, differ from each other in their coiling, the
heterochromatic set being permanently condensed, and in their behavior.
The condensed nature of the paternal chromosomes is illustrated in
Planococcus citri, in which the paternal set appears as a group of 10
chromosomes near the center of the cell in Figure 14–7. Division is
equational in anaphase I, so that each new nucleus contains both paternal
and maternal chromosomes. In the second meiotic division the heterochromatic and euchromatic sets segregate completely into opposite daugh-

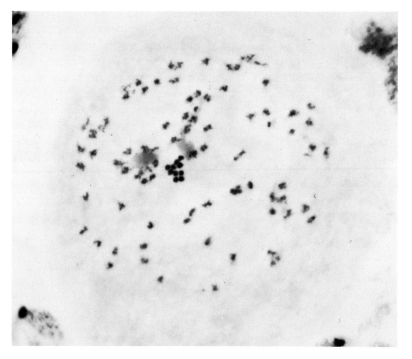

Figure 14–7.   A cell from a mealy bug showing 10 heterochromatic chromosomes
in a single group (×1500). FROM U. Nur, *Chromosoma,* **19,** 439 (1966), with permission of Springer-Verlag.

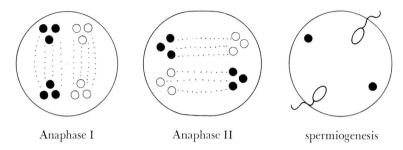

Anaphase I   Anaphase II   spermiogenesis

Figure 14–8. Distribution of maternal and paternal chromosomes during spermatogenesis in a lecanoid coccid.

ter nuclei (Figure 14–8). Of the four meiotic products, only two develop into spermatids, each with a haploid set of euchromatic chromosomes. The other two nuclei, containing the heterochromatic chromosomes, degenerate.

Although the role of the eliminated paternal set of chromosomes in these and other animals is not completely understood, cytochemical studies are beginning to reveal some of their properties. Quantitative determinations based on microspectrophotometric measurements of chromosomes stained with alkaline Fast Green have been made in the mealy bug *Pseudococcus obscurus* Essig. The relative proportions of lysine and arginine in the histones of maternal and paternal chromosomes are the same, but the total amount of histone is greater in the paternal chromosomes. Since the paternal chromosomes are highly condensed in comparison with the other chromosomes, the observation is consistent with the hypothesis of genetic inactivation expressed earlier, and implies that the paternal chromosomes are inactive or less active genetically.

Polycentric Chromosomes

The behavior of polycentric chromosomes often resembles that of chromosomes with diffuse kinetochores, as in the coccids. One outstanding difference is that polycentric chromosomes can, and regularly do, fragment into smaller chromosomal units, each of which is stable and functional. Among the organisms with polycentric chromosomes is *Ascaris megalocephala univalens*. Although the basic haploid number of chromosomes in this species is 1, the somatic tissues frequently have as many as 42 chromosomes per cell. After fertilization, in which a haploid sperm containing one chromosome fuses with a haploid egg containing one chromosome, mitotic divisions give rise to the embryo. Early in embryonic life the chromosomes of the cells that are not developing into reproductive cells fragment, and the subsequent mitotic products become the somatic cells of the body. They contain many chromosomes originating in the two chromosomes of the zygote. Another animal exhibiting similar chromosomal behavior is the hemipteran *Thyanta*. At least one species, *T. calceata,* is a false polyploid, with exactly twice the number of chromosomes, but with the same total DNA content, as the diploid. Apparently this form arises through longitudinal fragmentation of the chromosomes derived from the diploid species *(agmatoploidy)*. John has referred to this type of condition as *differential polynemy*. The behavior of the chromosomes can also be described as chromatid autonomy.

Luzula (wood rush) species also have chromosomes with polycentric kinetochores. *Luzula purpurea* has a diploid chromosome number of six. For the most part, the behavior of its chromosomes during meiosis is like that of *Puto,* the coccid. There are a few cytological distinctions, however. In anaphase I, and in subsequent meiotic stages, the chromosomes assume a U shape and effect an end-to-end association comparable to the interphasic secondary pairing of the coccids. Although there are several species with polyploid chromosome numbers, at least some are false polyploids, having origins similar to that described for *Thyanta*. The true polyploids have expected higher DNA contents, but the false ones do not. Apparently there have been at least two lines of chromosomal evolution in the genus *Luzula,* one through polyploidy and a second by agmatoploidy (as in *Thyanta*).

Secondary Constrictions

In addition to the kinetochore, the most obvious features of the chromosome visible with the light microscope are secondary constrictions and *satellite bodies*. A secondary constriction in the chromosome is a constriction other than the kinetochore. It is often associated with the nucleolus during interphase and may take part in the reorganization of the nucleolus at the end of cell division. For this reason a secondary constriction may also be called a *nucleolus-organizing* region. It appears as a heterochromatic (light-staining) region with an additional segment of the chromosome extending beyond it. This extension is the satellite body, and varies in size according to the position of the secondary constriction. If the latter is very close to an end of the chromosome, the satellite may be a barely perceptible dot. An example of a large satellite beyond a nucleolus-organizing region is illustrated in Figure 14–9. It is often seen to be connected to the main body of the chromosome by very light-staining strands.

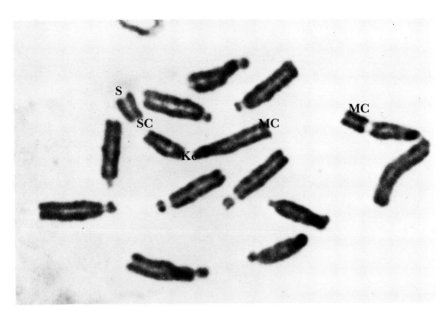

Figure 14–9. Normal *Vicia faba* chromosomes at mitotic metaphase (×2200). The satellite (S), secondary constriction (SC), and kinetochore (Kc) are visible in the two long M chromosomes (MC). COURTESY J. E. Trosko, from J. E. Trosko and S. Wolff, *J. Cell Biol.,* **26**, 125 (1965).

Ordinarily at least one chromosome in a given genome has a secondary constriction and satellite. In a few cases a single chromosome has two. If a terminal or subterminal secondary constriction is present, it is always found in the same chromosome or chromosomes and is a diagnostic characteristic of the particular genome.

Studies with several mammalian species have indicated that the nucleolus-organizing region is not actually a constriction during metaphase. Moreover, it is quite different in its fine structure from the kinetochore, exhibiting filaments with diameters of 50 to 70 Å. These observations have also suggested that terminal nucleolus organizers may be present in some chromosomes, but go undetected cytologically because of their small size.

The general morphology of a set of chromosomes, or *karyotype,* of an individual depends upon the dimensions of the chromosomes, the positions of the kinetochores, and the presence of secondary constrictions and satellite bodies. A diagrammatic representation of a karyotype showing all of the morphological features of the chromosomes is called an *idio-*

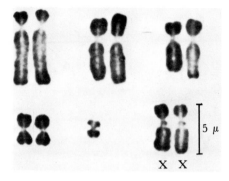

Figure 14–10. Karyotype of a mono-somic cell line of the female rat kan-garoo. Note the kinetochores and secondary constrictions on the X chromosomes. FROM T. C. Hsu, B. R. Brinkley, and F. E. Arrighi, *Chromo-soma*, **23**, 137 (1967), with permission of Springer-Verlag.

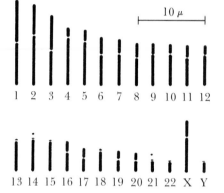

Figure 14–11. Idiogram of the hu-man haploid chromosome comple-ment. The autosomes are arranged in order of decreasing total length and of relative kinetochore positions. The sex chromosomes appear at the end. FROM E. H. Y. Chu and N. H. Giles, *Am. J. Human. Genet.*, **11**, 63 (1959).

gram. A karyotype of the rat kangaroo is shown in Figure 14–10, and an idiogram of the human is presented in Figure 14–11.

Observations of human chromosomes have revealed that five pairs, numbered 13, 14, 15, 21, and 22, have nucleolus-organizing regions. All five pairs of acrocentric chromosomes have satellites, but most of them are not easily seen with the light microscope nor together in any one cell at the same time. The use of computer-produced images of chromosomes, a relatively new technique, may allow for more feasible analyses of chromo-some detail.

Fine Structure

The gap between the molecular organization of chromosomal nucleopro-tein (DNA and protein) and the appearance of a chromosome at the light microscope level has been a major obstacle in resolving chromosomal fine structure. This section is concerned with organisms other than bacteria and viruses, which will be considered in Chapter 17. For higher organisms, there are at least two possible models of chromosomal fine structure. One views the chromosome as a multistranded body, and the other interprets it it as an enormously long, but highly coiled, arrangement of nucleoprotein fibrils. Each of these models will be described in detail.

A chromonema in *Tradescantia,* for example, may represent a quarter chromatid, so that four chromonemata comprise a chromatid and eight a chromosome. Studies of human lymphocyte chromosomes at metaphase suggest that 16 strands, each a double helix of DNA and its associated protein, make up a chromatid. Thus, four such strands comprise a quarter chromatid with a diameter of 2000 Å. Moreover, at each level of organization, there is coiling. The coiling, at least at the lowest levels of organization, appears to depend upon the specific arrangement of protein and the presence of divalent cations such as Ca^{++} and Mg^{++}. That is, the DNA helixes and protein are held together by the cations, and the coiling of the DNA helixes depends upon the protein and its binding to DNA. In support of this interpretation, the length of the DNA fibril decreases when associated with histone protein, particularly of the arginine-rich type. Two DNA molecules held together by histone in association with divalent cations result in the formation of supercoiled chromatin, in which the basic fibril is 100 to 200 Å thick. An extension of these considerations may lead to the following model of chromosomal organization.

Starting at the lowest level of organization, the DNA molecule consists of a double helix 20 Å in diameter. Upon addition of the associated protein, the diameter of the basic molecular unit becomes 35 to 40 Å. The smallest visible unit of the chromosome (by electron microscopy) is the fibril, which is 100 Å thick. This fibril contains two DNA double helixes, separated by a space about 25 Å across, and the associated protein. All of this accounts for the total thickness of the fibril, which can be called the basic cytological unit as a point of reference. Continuing up the scale from the macromolecular level, the next largest unit of the chromosome is the quarter chromatid, which has been observed in several organisms. The quarter chromatid consists of four 100 Å fibrils, so that it is about 400 Å thick, with eight double helixes of DNA and the associated protein. Two quarter chromatids comprise a half chromatid, which therefore contains 16 double helixes of DNA. A chromatid contains two half chromatids, bringing the total number of helixes in a chromatid to 32 and the diameter to about 1600 Å before DNA synthesis or replication. After replication the chromosome contains 64 double helixes of DNA with an approximate diameter of 3200 Å. The thickness is quite variable from cell to cell and from organism to organism owing to differences in the coiling of the chromosomes, which contributes to the thickness. The evidence that a

DNA molecule consists of one old helix and one new helix, the studies utilizing the incorporation of radioactive thymidine during DNA synthesis, and the model of Watson, Crick, and Wilkins are compatible with this description of the chromosome and permit a relatively straightforward scheme relating chromosome replication to DNA synthesis (see "Chemistry" section). The number of DNA helixes in each unit above fibril level varies according to species; that is, the chromosome of a higher organism may contain eight or more double helixes, depending upon its degree of subdivision. This model of chromosome structure is illustrated in Figure 14–12. Although the model is supported by studies in the plants *Tradescantia, Scilla, Haemanthus,* and *Vicia,* and in the animals *Drosophila,* Chinese hamster, and human, there is equally good support in some of these same organisms for the following model of fine structure.

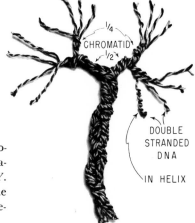

Figure 14–12. Model of a metaphase chromosome based on a multistranded organization. FROM E. E. Osgood et al., *Ann. N.Y. Acad. Sci.,* **113,** 717 (1964). Copyright, The New York Academy of Sciences, 1964. Reprinted by permission.

A model based upon a single, continuous fiber of nucleoprotein is illustrated in Figure 14–13. Because of differences in preparative methods, the diameter of the so-called basic structural unit seems somewhat variable, ranging from 100 to 400 Å. However, on the basis of X-ray diffraction and other studies, it is likely that the basic unit is about 100 to 150 Å in diameter. This unit consists of one double helix of DNA with its associated protein, arranged as a superhelix. It is possible that the protein, although mainly of the histone type, also includes acidic protein, DNA polymerase, and RNA polymerase. Fibers isolated from unfixed cells generally have diameters of about 250 Å, and may represent two parallel double helixes

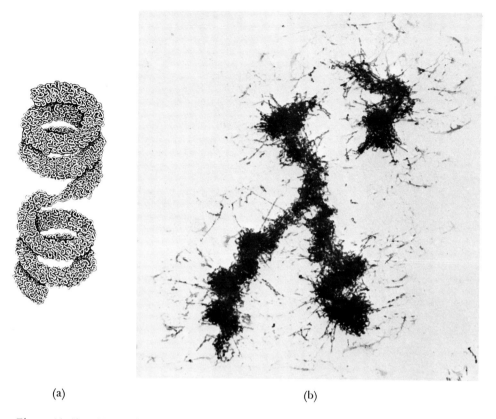

(a)   (b)

Figure 14–13. (a) Model of a metaphase chromatid based on a folded-fiber organization. Each fiber has a diameter of 250 Å. (b) Electron micrograph of un-sectioned human chromosome from which the model was developed (×18,000). FROM E. J. DuPraw, *Nature*, **209,** 577 (1966).

of DNA and protein. Such fibers in a human chromosome are apparent in Figure 14–14. Similar fibers have been observed in some plant chromo-somes. According to the model, a chromosome consists of single long chains of DNA and protein, up to several hundred microns long. The total length of the DNA–protein making up the 46 chromosomes of man, for example, has been estimated at 50 cm! The fiber is extremely coiled, the lowest level represented by the 100 Å superhelix. This helical fiber is then folded many times and irregularly entwined to form the body of a chromatid, and there is no subchromatid-strand structure. In this inter-pretation, the packing of the fibers may depend upon the divalent cations discussed above.

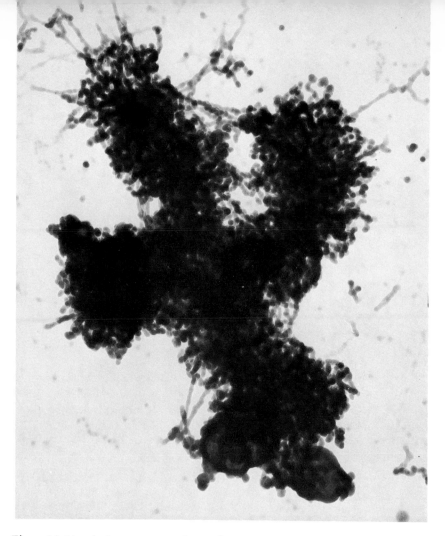

Figure 14-14. A human metaphase chromosome consisting of 250 Å fibers (×55,500). COURTESY Joseph G. Gall, Yale University, from *Chromosoma*, **20**, 221 (1966), with permission of Springer-Verlag.

As yet the question of whether a chromosome is made of many parallel strands of nucleoprotein or of a single, extremely long, continuous, and highly folded fiber has not been resolved. Moreover, it is possible that the fine structure of chromosomes varies among species of organisms, so that no one model has universal application. It is relatively certain, however, that the basic unit of structure is a DNA–protein superhelix having a diameter of about 100 Å and that these units make up the 250 Å fibers seen with the electron microscope. In addition, the presence of histone protein and divalent cations is essential for the coiling of such fibers.

Lampbrush Chromosomes

In the discussion of nucleolar function in Chapter 9, reference was made to the numerous copies of nucleolus-organizing-region cistrons responsible for the synthesis of ribosomal RNA. The many copies are represented in amphibian oocytes by the unusually large number of nucleoli during the dictyotene stage of meiotic prophase I. Paralleling this synthetic activity in amphibian oocytes is the production of messenger RNA by enormously decondensed chromosomes. As a consequence of extensive uncoiling at this time the chromosomes are large enough to be seen with the naked eye. The oocyte chromosomes of *Triturus viridescens*, for example, have a combined length of 5900 μ, each chromosome having a length of 350 to 800 μ. Even more impressive is the estimate of the total length of chromosomal material if it were completely uncoiled: 10 meters! However, this estimate is based on the assumption that a chromatid consists of only one double helix of DNA. From the foregoing discussion of fine structure, it is evident that such measurements may reflect considerable error.

More characteristic of the amphibian oocyte chromosomes is the presence of fine lateral loops extending from their main axes, except in the kinetochore regions. The loops confer a brushlike appearance to the chromosomes, which accordingly are called *lampbrush chromosomes*. By first meiotic metaphase the loops are no longer visible, and the chromosomes assume the more conventional appearance (Chapter 12). Prior to the development of specialized techniques of microscopy and cytochemistry, it was thought that the loops dropped off at the end of prophase I. We now know that they become reincorporated into the main axis of the chromosome by coiling up. Lampbrush chromosomes have been observed in many invertebrates and in all classes of nonmammalian vertebrates. Recent studies have also indicated their presence in human and rodent oocytes during the extended dictyotene stage. In spite of their relatively wide occurrence in other animals, the lampbrush chromosomes of amphibians have been studied in the greatest detail.

The main axis of a lampbrush chromosome consists of the paired homologues, each composed of two chromatids. Thus there are at least four strands present in the main axis, and several investigations indicate that each is one double helix of DNA with its associated protein. Paired loops of different sizes extend laterally from the main axis with which the loop axes are continuous (Figure 14–15). Although the loop axes are made of DNA and protein, the bulk of material present on them is the newly synthesized RNA, which gives the chromosomes a fuzzy appearance. It is also possible to demonstrate a matrix-like protein on the loops in association with the RNA. At the base of each loop are chromomeres,

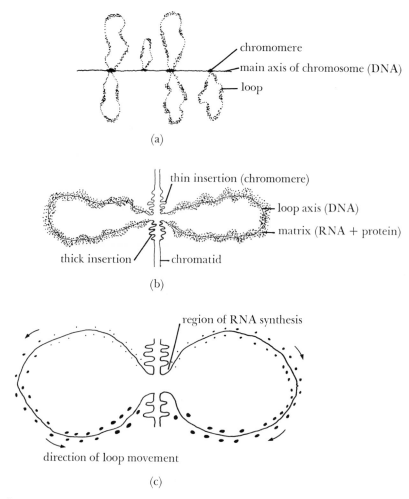

Figure 14–15. Lampbrush chromosome: (a) gross structure; (b) fine structure; (c) RNA synthesis in a loop. AFTER Gall and Callan.

which stain darker than the extended axes, and which represent tightly coiled sections of the main axis. At the base of a loop, or the position of the chromomeres, the matrix is thicker at one end, the thick insertion, than it is at the other end, the thin insertion. Experiments on the synthesis of RNA and protein by the loops have been performed with radioactively labeled precursor substances. When tritium-labeled uridine is injected into the body of the newt *Triturus cristatus cristatus,* most of the loops are uniformly labeled with the isotope after 1 day. Certain loops, including the "giant granular" loops on chromosome 12, do not show the same pattern of incorporation. One day after the injection of the labeled precursor, only a section of the loop near its thin insertion is labeled, while the rest of the loop is unlabeled. For a period of 10 days following injection, the loop is progressively labeled until the radioactive isotope is present in the entire loop. This progressive labeling points to a moving loop. That is, the loop axis is spun out at the thin insertion and wound up at the thick insertion. RNA is synthesized only at the thin insertion and then carried around the loop to the thick insertion (Figure 14–15c). There it may either be destroyed or released into the nucleus. When tritium-labeled phenylalanine is injected into the body of the animal, all of the loops are uniformly labeled after 1 day. Therefore, the pattern of protein synthesis is relatively synchronous and quite different from that of RNA synthesis. The phenomenon of loop RNA synthesis has also been observed in *T. viridescens*.

The functions of the lampbrush chromosomes in producing RNA and protein are related to the formation of yolk in the growing egg. Such activity is comparable to that occurring in the giant dipteran chromosomes during larval development, which will be discussed in the following section. The loops are presumed to correspond to genetic loci in an active state; condensed chromosomal regions (nonloop regions) are genetically inactive.

Polytene Chromosomes

Except for the lampbrush chromosomes, the giant chromosomes of the larval stages of certain Diptera are the largest chromosomes, although they are not visible without the aid of the microscope. These large chromosomes were discovered by Balbiani in 1881, but were not studied extensively until after 1930. They are found only in certain tissues, including the salivary glands, the Malphigian tubules, the epithelial lining of the gut, and some fat bodies. The organisms in which they occur include *Drosophila, Chironomus, Sciara,* and *Rhynchosciara*. The size of the giant chromosomes is a function of the large number of chromosome strands in each chromosome, many more than are present in the chromosomes of other somatic cells. Because of their numerous chromonemata the giant chromosomes have been named *polytene* chromosomes.

Figure 14–16 shows the typical polytene chromosomes of a dipteran. Several duplications of the chromosomes have taken place without the usual accompanying cell divisions. Thus all of the chromosomes remain together in the same cell. However, homologous chromosomes have not separated from each other but also remain together, in what is known as *somatic pairing*. Therefore, a cell that had eight chromosomes originally still contains eight chromosomes, but each of these consists of paired homologous chromosomes, which are responsible for the polytene structure. The process of chromosome duplication without cell division, endomitosis, has been mentioned earlier. The number of chromonemata in a single giant chromosome varies from 1024 in *Drosophila* to 4096 in *Chironomus;* the degree of ploidy has not been resolved in all cases. In contrast to normal somatic chromosomes, which have a total length of 7.5 μ, the polytene chromosomes of *Drosophila melanogaster* have a total length of 2000 μ. The cells are in G_1, S, or G_2 of interphase or undergoing endomitosis, but the chromosomes do not separate from each other after duplication and no division of the cytoplasm or nucleus occurs.

In the nuclei of *Drosophila* larval salivary glands, as an adjunct to the somatic pairing of the chromosomes, the kinetochore regions of all of the chromosomes are in association. This situation produces a chromocenter that is quite heteropycnotic during interphase and mitotic pro-

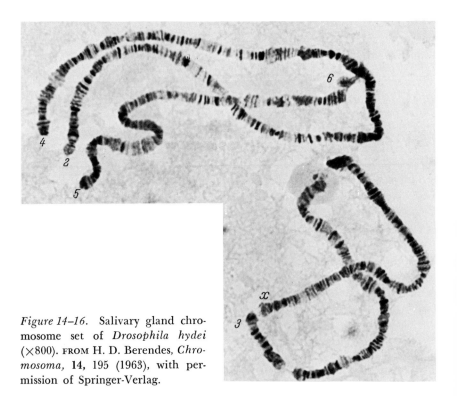

Figure 14–16. Salivary gland chromosome set of *Drosophila hydei* (×800). FROM H. D. Berendes, *Chromosoma,* 14, 195 (1963), with permission of Springer-Verlag.

phase. Chromocenters are absent, however, in *Chironomus* and *Sciara*. All of the cells destined to become the salivary gland cells are designated in the early stages of embryonic development, and no further division of these cells takes place.

When a polytene chromosome is treated with a chromosomal stain, a characteristic staining pattern results. Some regions appear as dark *bands* of varying widths, while other regions, called *interbands,* are often so light as to resemble spaces between the bands. The bands are composed of chromomeres of individual chromonemata in a linear array perpendicular to the axis of the chromosome. Thus the bands are most likely due to a tighter coiling of the chromonemata in certain regions than in others. Observations of interband regions with the electron microscope bear this out (Figure 14–17). In the interbands there is little or no coiling, and the

Figure 14–17. Interband fibrils in a salivary gland chromosome of *Drosophila melanogaster* (×141,000). Electron micrograph by Drs. Marja and Veikko Sorsa, Department of Genetics, University of Helsinki, Finland, from *Chromosoma,* **22,** 32 (1967), with permission of Springer-Verlag.

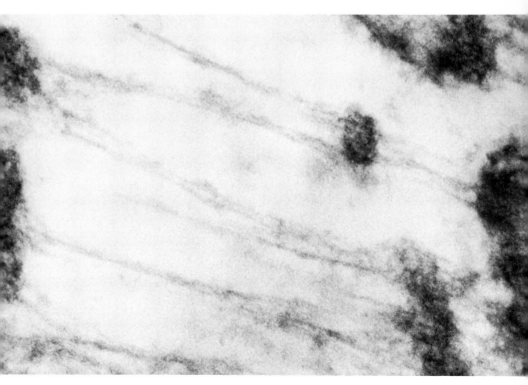

chromonemata are arranged parallel to the chromosomal axis. These and other similar observations also support the fact that the DNA–protein-containing chromonemata are continuous throughout the length of the chromosome and are not interrupted in the interbands. Moreover, there is little doubt that the chromosomes are multistranded, making the possibility of circular DNA molecules unlikely (see Chapter 17). In addition to coiling differences, there are chemical and functional differences between the bands and interbands. As will be described later, the bands undergo morphological and biochemical changes related to their genetic activity. The interbands, however, represent largely structural nucleoprotein, and are less active genetically; they are not involved in RNA synthesis. As a result of the greater concentration of coiled chromonemal strands in the bands, the ratio of DNA content between bands and interbands may be as high as 60 : 1. The magnitude of DNA content can be illustrated by estimations in *Chironomus tentans,* where the average DNA content of a chromomere (tight coil in a band) is 10^{-16} g. This corresponds to 100,000 nucleotide pairs, suggesting that a chromomere is a very large complex gene or more than one gene. In *Drosophila,* the smallest bands contain 5000 nucleotide pairs per chromatid. Variations in RNA contents have also been observed between as well as within chromosomes. The synthetic activities discussed below, however, may resolve such differences on a metabolic rather than a structural basis. Differences in protein content also indicate that interbands have a relatively high content of non-histone proteins, and bands a higher content of histone protein.

The banding patterns of polytene chromosomes have been of particular value in genetic studies. Even though direct observations to the effect have not been made, some genetic loci can be associated with specific bands. This is not to imply that a band represents a gene. However, cytological and genetic maps have been prepared of all of the chromosomes of several *Drosophila* species, and it is possible to identify the sites of genetic activity in a chromosome from the band pattern. Radiation studies have substantiated these findings. For example, the absence of a specific band or set of bands, removed from a chromosome by induced breakage of the chromosome, can be correlated with changes in the genetic behavior of an organism. Other types of abnormalities in the configuration of the chromosome can also be examined in this way.

During the development of the larvae of several dipterans, some of the band and interband regions of the chromosomes exhibit swellings or puffs. The appearance of the puffs depends on the stage of larval development. That is, the formation of a puff corresponds to a specific genetic activity at a specific time. The metabolic activities associated with chromosome puffing are related to the secretory functions of the salivary glands, for the

larvae of these organisms feed constantly and the salivary glands are therefore particularly active. Moreover, the larvae undergo changes as they
proceed to the pupal stage, and require specific proteins for their morphogenetic activities. Thus the chromosomal puffing leads ultimately to the
synthesis of proteins in the cytoplasm. Directing protein synthesis is the
messenger RNA produced at the puffs, the RNA having been transported
to the cytoplasm. The change from a nonpuffed to a puffing condition is
illustrated in Figure 14–18. Note the increase in size at the puff regions
following the addition of the molting hormone, ecdysone. Structurally,

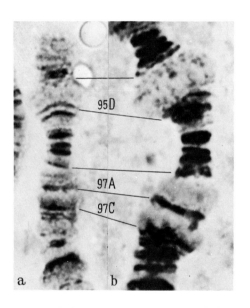

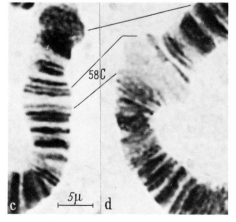

Figure 14–18. Some puffs showing increased activity after injection of ecdysone: (a) and (c), untreated controls; (b) and (d), puffs after injection of the hormone. Each region is identified by number and letter (e.g., 95D). FROM H. D. Berendes, *Chromosoma*, **22**, 274 (1967), with permission of Springer-Verlag.

the first step in puffing is a localized separation of the chromonemata from one another. This is followed by an uncoiling of the chromomeres in this region, thereby significantly altering the architecture of the band. That the puff represents a site of RNA synthesis is supported by autoradiographic studies with [³H]uridine (Figure 14–19). The large puff in Figure 14–19(a) incorporates the radioactive precursor to RNA, and its uptake is demonstrated in (b) by the presence in the autoradiogram of numerous silver grains over the puff.

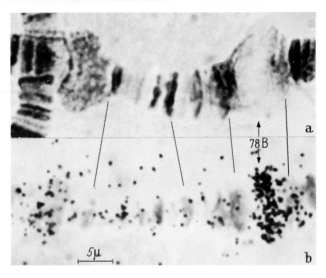

Figure 14–19. Incorporation of [³H]uridine into a chromosomal puff after injection of ecdysone. FROM H. D. Berendes, *Chromosoma,* **22,** 274 (1967), with permission of Springer-Verlag.

Some regions display larger puffs than others. These large puffing regions are called *Balbiani rings* (Figure 14–20). The chromonemata in a band extend laterally in a series of adjacent loops, which seem to stretch the chromosome to a wide diameter. The loops make up the Balbiani ring and give the chromosome a fuzzy look. In some respects a Balbiani ring resembles the lampbrush chromosome configuration, except that there are several hundred loops at a given locus in the polytene chromosome compared with as few as one in a lampbrush chromosome.

Although most puffs represent sites of RNA synthesis, some show a disproportionate synthesis of DNA, as measured by the incorporation of [³H]thymidine. DNA puffs have been found in certain chironomids, including *Sciara* and *Rhyncosciara.* Heavily labeled DNA puffs in *Sciara*

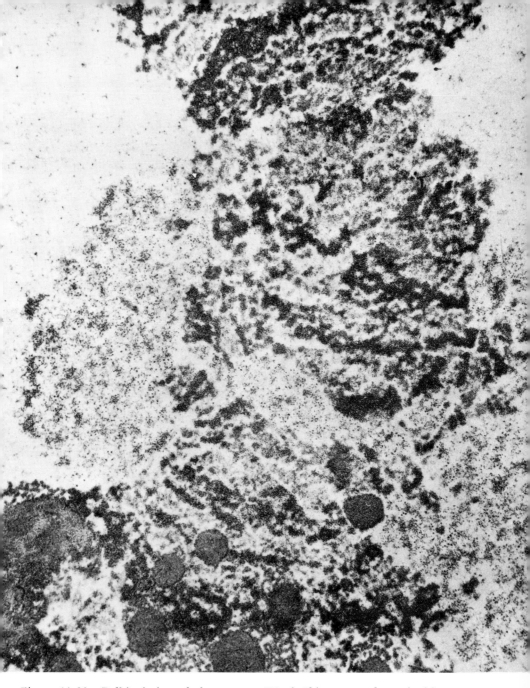

Figure 14-20. Balbiani ring of chromosome IV of *Chironomus thummi* with ribonucleoprotein particles within the large puff and in the nucleoplasm (×8000). FROM H. Swift in C. J. Dawe, ed., *The Chromosome,* Vol. 1, *In Vitro,* Williams and Wilkins, Baltimore, 1967. Reproduced with the permission of H. Swift and of the Tissue Culture Association, Inc.

coprophila appear in the fourth instar larva, but the synthetic activity drops to zero by the time of pupal molting. As DNA synthesis decreases, however, RNA synthesis continues. There have also been reports of some protein synthesis in puffs of *Chironomus* chromosomes. Presumably part of the ribosomal protein is produced here, and the ribosomes become attached to the growing mRNA molecules for transport to the cytoplasm. Ribonucleoprotein particles have been observed in a Balbiani ring of *Chironomus,* but do not represent ribosomes, and only the RNA portion has been synthesized at the puff (Figure 14–20).

The control of puffing is perhaps the most intriguing of all these activities. It has been known for some time that puffing is a cyclic as well as reversible process. That is, certain puffs appear at one developmental stage, only to regress at a later one. Still other puff regions may appear in two or more stages, but develop in different sequences at different times. In *Rhyncosciara,* for example, certain puffs appear on only two of the chromosomes in early larval stages, whereas major puffs appear on all four chromosomes in the last larval stage in preparation for the spinning of the cocoon. Changes in the patterns of puffing can be induced by temperature shock (4°C), changes in ionic strength of the growth medium, injection of heavy metals, or application of molting and juvenile hormones. Ecdysone, a molting hormone, is the only substance known to be normally involved in the control of puffing, however. Postembryonic development of insects is under hormonal control: ecdysone induces molting, while juvenile hormone determines the nature of a given molt. Thus the puffing pattern is in response to changes in the relative amounts of the two hormones. This is especially evident since juvenile hormone blocks the action of ecdysone. Although the mechanism of ecdysone stimulation is not known for certain, this hormone may act by inducing a localized uncoiling of the chromonemata, thereby increasing the rates of puffing and pupation. On the other hand, its action may be indirect, by controlling the ionic composition of the cell.

Actinomycin D, which inhibits DNA-dependent RNA synthesis by binding to the guanine residues of DNA, causes a reduction in RNA synthesis at puff sites and a regression of the puffs, although not all puff regions respond in the same way. The interpretation of this effect is that actinomycin D inhibits puff formation by reducing the rate of RNA synthesis. In fact, cytochemical observations tend to support the view that RNA synthesis is necessary for puff formation. Moreover, it appears that some early puffs are dependent on RNA synthesis more or less directly induced by ecdysone, but later puffs may be dependent on an unstable protein resulting from earlier puff activity. Inhibition of puffing may actually involve both the rate of RNA synthesis and the rate of its removal from the chromosomes. In the latter case, acidic protein may serve to capture the synthesized RNA and facilitate its removal. Acidic protein has been found to parallel the distribution of RNA, whereas basic protein parallels the distribution of DNA in the polytene chromosomes. As suggested in previous chapters, the regression of puffing (and therefore of gene activity) may be due to the presence of histone protein. This question of genetic regulation will be examined in more detail in Chapter 19.

In summary, the giant chromosomes of many dipterans are well suited to studies of nucleic acid synthesis, gene action, and the correlation of cytological changes with biochemical and genetic changes.

Chemistry

Nucleic acid and protein are the major chemical components of the chromosomes. The structures of these substances were given in Chapter 1. Quantitatively, the chromosomes of most organisms are composed primarily of DNA and basic (histone) protein, but also contain varying amounts of RNA and nonhistone protein (Tables 9–2 and 14–2). On the average, the ratio of DNA to histone is about 1 : 1, but this varies among species and according to the state of cell development or metabolism. The DNA–histone complex, however, comprises as much as 96% of a chromosome or as little as 60%. Although a very small proportion of the chromosomal DNA may not be fully complexed with histone, the distributions of the two substances along the chromosome closely parallel one another. A recent study by Caspersson and his co-workers has demonstrated that there is little quantitative variation in DNA distribution along the chromosome, with the exception of the kinetochore and nucleolus-organizing regions.

Table 14–2   Chemical Composition of Pea Embryo Chromatin*

	Purified Chromatin	*Nucleohistone from Purified Chromatin*
DNA, % of mass	36.5	41.5
histone, % of mass	37.5	55.0
histone/DNA ratio	1.03	1.32
RNA, % of total nucleic acids	28.0	5.4
nonhistone protein, % of total protein	20.0	0

* From J. Bonner, *The Molecular Biology of Development,* Oxford Univ. Press, New York, 1965.

By means of high resolution, rapid-scanning spectrophotometry and a fluorescent alklyating agent, their observations were made on the chromosomes of *Vicia, Trillium,* and Chinese hamster. Although the alkylating agent was more heavily bound in heterochromatic regions, these regions did not reflect significant differences in DNA content. Therefore, some other component may be responsible for the preferential uptake, or the agent may be especially bound in regions having high numbers of guanine–cytosine base pairs. Additional support for a lack of difference in DNA content between euchromatin and heterochromatin derives from studies of cold-treated chromosomes. When chromosomes are subjected to low temperature, certain heterochromatin regions stain less intensely with Schiff's reagent. Darlington had earlier interpreted the effect as a loss of DNA, but his view has more recently been disproved. The principal effect of cold is a localized uncoiling of the heterochromatin, accounting for its reduced stainability.

Like the DNA, histone protein appears to have both structural and functional roles in the chromosomes. It is linked to the DNA phosphate groups by ionic bonds, and according to X-ray diffraction analysis, lies on the outside of the DNA molecule but in the large grooves of the double helix (Figure 14–21a). In fact, there is strong evidence that histone may bind several DNA molecules together by linking them through their large grooves (Figure 14–21b.) Such linkage appears to confer stability on the nucleohistone complex, and may also be responsible for its supercoiling. In the absence of histone, for example, the length of the DNA molecules is much greater. It is possible that the lysine-rich histones may bind the DNA molecules in this manner. There are, in fact, as many as 12 major fractions of histones, and perhaps 10 minor ones. Some bind more readily to DNA than others, but there is little conclusive evidence for any real specificity of such binding to particular regions of the chromosome. However, there may be a relatively close relation between guanine–cytosine-rich segments of DNA with very lysine-rich histone fractions. Quantitative differences are more likely than qualitative ones in histone distribution along the chromosomes, as suggested by cytochemical observations of coccid chromosomes. Nevertheless, even this type of variation has not been found in several other organisms. Differential stainability of hetero- and euchromatin may depend more on the manner of histone binding than on qualitative or quantitative differences in histone content. Finally, as a functional parameter of histone characterization, several lines of investigation point to this protein as a regulator of genetic activity by allowing or preventing DNA-dependent RNA synthesis (Chapter 19).

If the DNA and histone are removed from a chromosome, its structure is not entirely disrupted, but some RNA and other proteins remain.

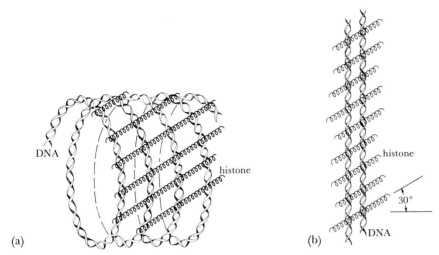

Figure 14–21. Models of histone–DNA orientation, with histone bridges in the large grooves of DNA: (a) histone bridges hold together the adjacent coils of supercoiled DNA; (b) parallel arrangements of histone bridges with DNA. FROM G. Zubay in J. Bonner and P. Ts'o, eds., *The Nucleohistones,* Holden-Day, San Francisco, 1964.

This residue, called the *residual chromosome,* consists largely of acidic (residual) protein, which contains large amounts of the amino acids aspartic acid, glutamic acid, leucine, and glycine and, in contrast to histones, also contains tryptophan. One hypothesis regarding its role in the chromosome is that it provides a link between DNA–histone segments, and another is that it may be the backbone material of the chromosome. Neither model has been experimentally substantiated. The remaining protein (nonhistone, nonresidual) includes the enzymes for DNA and RNA synthesis, namely DNA polymerase and RNA polymerase. RNA, in fact, makes up a very insignificant proportion of the permanent structure of a chromosome; most of it, when present, is the product of gene activity. Bonner has reported a chromosomal RNA bound covalently to the acidic protein, which in turn may be bound to histone by hydrogen bonds. The RNA may be bound in such a way as to be resistant to ribonuclease, and may be involved somehow in genetic regulation. A relatively short molecule, this RNA is made of from 40 to 60 nucleotides.

Investigations on the presence of specific metallic ions in cells have suggested additional linkages in the chromosomes. Divalent ions such as calcium, magnesium, and iron have been found in the nucleus, and research on chromosome breakage and selective incorporation of these ions into the chromosome has indicated that they too are essential to the structure. The metallic ions may occur between the DNA and the protein or between DNA groups. In the latter case they provide linkages through the phosphate end groups of the DNA molecules.

Chromosomal DNA

Constancy

The amount of DNA in the diploid cells is constant for a given organism, but varies considerably among different organisms. For example, the DNA content of liver cells of a frog is about seven times as great as that of liver cells of a chicken. The quantity of nuclear DNA is directly proportional to the number of chromosomes in the nucleus. The gametes of an organism have exactly half the DNA content of its somatic cells, since the gametes are haploid and the somatic cells are diploid. It follows that a triploid nucleus contains three times as much DNA as a haploid nucleus and that for each additional set of chromosomes there is a regular increase in the amount of DNA present in the nucleus.

Deviations from expected DNA values are usually accounted for by changes at the time of DNA synthesis. That is, in G_1, the nuclear DNA content has the $2C$ value, corresponding to the presynthetic amount. During G_2, when DNA synthesis has ended, the nucleus contains the $4C$ value. DNA synthesis occurs in S, and the amount of DNA present in the nucleus during this period will vary between the $2C$ and $4C$ values, depending upon the state of progress of synthesis. Although there have been several reports of a "metabolic" DNA in certain kinds of cells, there are as many that deny its presence. "Metabolic" DNA is defined as a nonpermanent, nonstructural DNA that varies in its occurrence according to the metabolic state of the cell at a given time. The concept of such a DNA remains equivocal at best.

Synthesis and Chromosomal Replication

The synthesis of DNA is important in the replication of the chromosomes and in preparation for cell division. In the majority of mitotic and meiotic cells, DNA synthesis occurs in interphase. There is no change in DNA content during cell division, except that resulting from the distribution of daughter groups of chromosomes to daughter nuclei. Each daughter group receives half the DNA ($2C$ amount) present in the parent nucleus ($4C$ amount) immediately following DNA synthesis.

The replication of the chromosomes has been studied in conjunction with the synthesis of DNA in both plant and animal tissues. Experimental findings confirm the model for DNA and its replication proposed by Watson and Crick. By using a radioactive precursor to thymine ([³H]thymidine) in an autoradiographic method (as described in Chapter 2), an investigator can observe cytologically the time and mode of DNA synthesis and chromosome replication. According to Taylor, the original DNA helix of a chromosome serves as a template for the new helix, and the new helix contains only new DNA and none of the DNA from the original helix. His conclusion is supported by the appearance of the radioactive label only in the new chromatid. The sequence of events outlined by Taylor is depicted in Figure 14–22, and the model for the replication

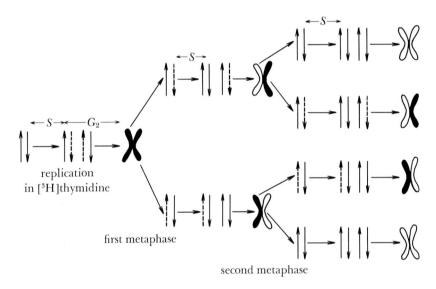

Figure 14–22. Semiconservative replication and segregation of labeled and unlabeled chromatids. During the first replication, the cells are grown in [³H]thymidine, and the first metaphase chromosomes are completely labeled (black). If the cells are allowed to replicate a second time, but in the absence of radioactive precursor, second metaphase chromosomes are only half labeled (one black chromatid). After a third replication, only half the chromosome set is labeled, and the labeled ones have one labeled chromatid. The dashed lines represent the newly replicated chromosomal strands. By treating the cells with colchicine, the products of all three replications can be accumulated in the same cell. Moreover, colchicine causes a divergence of the arms, allowing easier identification of labeled and unlabeled chromatids. Reproduced from *Thymidine Metabolism and Cell Kinetics,* by J. E. Cleaver, North-Holland Publishing Co., Amsterdam, 1967.

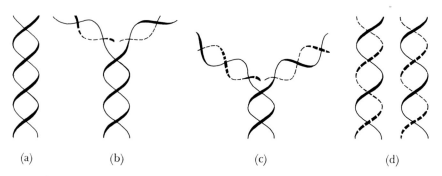

(a)   (b)   (c)   (d)

Figure 14–23. Model of DNA replication: (a) double helix of DNA; (b) and (c), separation of the helixes and synthesis of new complementary helixes (each helix serves as a template for a new one); (d) products of synthesis, two double helixes.

of DNA is given in Figure 14–23. The model shows that the two helixes separate and that each acts as a template for a new helix. The new helix is complementary to the original helix to the extent that thymine in the old one provides a template for adenine in the new one and guanine in the old one provides a template for cytosine in the new one. The separation of the two helixes is due to the disruption of hydrogen bonds between their bases.

Since each new DNA molecule consists of one old and one new nucleotide chain, the pattern of synthesis is described as *semiconservative;* half of the original molecule is conserved, the other half is new. Moreover, this same pattern is reflected in the chromosomes themselves (Figure 14–24), where labeled and unlabeled chromatids can be seen. Thus chromosome replication is also semiconservative. Experimental evidence for the semiconservative replication of DNA was provided by studies of *Escherichia coli* by Meselson and Stahl (Chapter 19), and evidence for the same pattern in the chromosomes by the work of Taylor with plant cells. Assuming a multistranded chromosome, during replication several DNA molecules would be held together so that new chains form a unit that separates from the old ones as a unit. With regard to chromosomal protein, there is considerable evidence that histone is produced in the nucleus at the same time that DNA synthesis occurs. In a few cases, some of the histone may have cytoplasmic origin and migrate into the nucleus.

Replication is not completely synchronous in all of the chromosomes of a genome, nor is its pattern the same in chromosomes of different species. A simple type is illustrated by the chromosomes of *Crepis* and *Scilla,* in which replication starts at the ends and progresses toward the kineto-

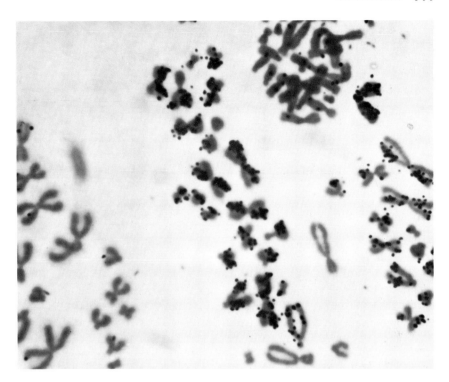

Figure 14–24. Autoradiograph of Chinese hamster chromosomes labeled with [³H]thymidine. The chromosomes are from the second metaphase after labeling and show semiconservative segregation. Note the chromosomes in which only one chromatid is labeled. With the permission of D. M. Prescott, from *Methods in Cell Physiology,* Vol. 1, Academic Press, New York, 1964, p. 367.

chores. However, in the root tips of *Tradescantia paludosa,* the terminal portions of a chromosome continue to synthesize DNA after the rest of the chromosome has stopped. Asynchronous replication is fairly common in plants and animals. In *Melanoplus* and *Vicia* the times of DNA synthesis differ between euchromatic and heterochromatic segments of a chromosome; the synthesis of DNA occurs later in heterochromatin than in euchromatin. In these organisms all of the euchromatic segments synthesize DNA at about the same time, and all of the heterochromatic segments at a later time. In other organisms, such as rye, all of the chromosomes may have different cycles of replication and yet still show a time lapse between synthesis in euchromatin and synthesis in heterochromatin. DNA synthesis in the heterochromatin of the X and Y chromosomes of the Chinese hamster is also later than that in the euchromatin of the other chromosomes of the complement, and in humans the course of DNA synthesis is extremely variable from chromosome to chromosome. A striking departure from the later-replicating heterochromatin is seen in the orchid *Spiranthes sinensis,* in which the euchromatin is late-replicating. Nevertheless, in general, synthesis may start simultaneously at several sites in the chromosomes, begin later at others, and end at different times. With certain exceptions (Chapter 16), both homologues of a chromosomal pair tend to replicate synchronously, although possibly at different rates. The observation of asynchronous replication within and among the chromosomes of a genome will be more fully considered in the discussion of mammals in Chapter 16.

Function

Several kinds of evidence support the theory that DNA is the primary genetic material. First, DNA content and chromosome number are related. Second, DNA is located in the nucleus and transmitted to daughter cells during cell division. Genetic studies on bacteria in which the DNA of one bacterium is transferred to another bacterium as heritable genetic material (*transforming principle*) contribute very strong substantiation. Finally, the wavelength of ultraviolet light (2600 Å) that induces mutation is the same wavelength that is absorbed by DNA. The most remarkable feature of DNA is that it has the same chemical constituents and physical organization in all organisms and yet allows and even provides for great diversity among organisms. The basis for this diversity is the almost infinite number of possible combinations of the four purine and pyrimidine bases in the DNA molecule.

SELECTED   READING

General

Alfert, M., "Composition and Structure of Giant Chromosomes," *Intern. Rev. Cytol.,* **3,** 131 (1954).
Beermann, W., and U. Clever, "Chromosome Puffs," *Sci. Am.,* **210**(4), 50 (1964).
Taylor, J. H., "The Duplication of Chromosomes," *Sci. Am.,* **198**(6), 36 (1958).
Taylor, J. H., "Chromosome Reproduction," *Intern. Rev. Cytol.,* **13,** 39 (1962).
White, M. J. D., *Animal Cytology and Evolution,* 2nd ed., Cambridge Univ. Press, Cambridge, 1954.

Number

Darlington, D. C., and A. Wylie, *Chromosome Atlas of Flowering Plants,* Allen and Unwin, London, 1955.

Jackson, R. C., "A New Low Chromosome Number for Plants," *Science,* **126** (3283), 115 (1957).

Makino, S., *An Atlas of the Chromosome Numbers in Animals,* Iowa State Coll. Press, Ames, Iowa, 1951.

Morphology

Brown, S. W., "Lecanoid Chromosome Behavior in Three More Families of the Coccoidea (Homoptera), *Chromosoma,* **10**(3), 278 (1959).

Brown, S. W., "Heterochromatin," *Science,* **151**(3709), 417 (1966).

Brown, S. W., and U. Nur, "Heterochromatic Chromosomes in the Coccids," *Science,* **145**(3628), 130 (1964).

Cooper, H. L., and K. Hirschhorn, "Enlarged Satellites as a Familial Chromosome Marker," *Am. J. Human Genet.,* **14**(2), 107 (1962).

Halkka, O., "A Photometric Study of the *Luzula* Problem," *Hereditas,* **52**(1), 81 (1964).

Hsu, T. C., B. R. Brinkley, and F. E. Arrighi, "The Structure and Behavior of the Nucleolus Organizers in Mammalian Cells," *Chromosoma,* **23**(2), 137 (1967).

Hughes-Schrader, S., and F. Schrader, "The Kinetochore of the Hemiptera," *Chromosoma,* **12**(3), 327 (1961).

Jokelainen, P. T., "The Ultrastructure and Spatial Organization of the Metaphase Kinetochore in Mitotic Rat Cells," *J. Ultrastruct. Res.,* **19**(1), 19 (1967).

Kaufmann, B. P., H. Gay, and M. R. McDonald, "Organizational Patterns Within Chromosomes," *Intern. Rev. Cytol.,* **9,** 77 (1960).

Ledley, R. S., and F. H. Ruddle, "Chromosome Analysis by Computer," *Sci. Am.,* **214**(4), 40 (1966).

Levan, A., K. Fredga, and A. A. Sandberg, "Nomenclature for Centromeric Position on Chromosomes," *Hereditas,* **52**(2), 201 (1964).

Lima-de-Faria, A., "The Role of the Kinetochore in Chromosome Organization," *Hereditas,* **42**(1), 85 (1956).

Lima-de-Faria, A., "Kinetochore in Living Material," *Hereditas,* **45**(4), 463 (1959).

Nelson-Rees, W. A., "New Observations on Lecanoid Spermatogenesis in the Mealy Bug, *Planococcus citri,*" *Chromosoma,* **14**(1), 1 (1963).

Nordenskiold, H., "Cytotaxonomical Studies in the Genus *Luzula.* II. Hybridization Experiments in the *Campestris–Multiflora* Complex," *Hereditas,* **42**(1), 7 (1956).

Nordenskiold, H., "Studies of Meiosis in *Luzula purpurea,*" *Hereditas,* **48**(4), 503 (1962).

Stern, H., "Function and Reproduction of Chromosomes," *Physiol. Rev.,* **42**(2), 271 (1962).

Wilson, H. J., "The Fine Structure of the Kinetochore in Meiotic Cells of *Tradescantia,*" *Planta,* **78**(4), 379 (1968).

Fine Structure

Bajer, A., "Subchromatid Structure of Chromosomes in the Living State," *Chromosoma,* **17**(4), 291 (1965).

Davies, H. G., and J. V. Small, "Structural Units in Chromatin and Their Orientation on Membranes," *Nature,* **217**(5134), 1122 (1968).

DuPraw, E. J., "The Organization of Nuclei and Chromosomes in Honeybee Embryonic Cells," *Proc. Natl. Acad. Sci. U.S.,* **53**(1), 161 (1965).

DuPraw, E. J., "Evidence for a 'Folded-Fibre' Organization in Human Chromosomes," *Nature,* **209**(5023), 577 (1966).

Gimenez-Martin, G., and J. F. Lopez-Saez, "Chromosome Structure in the Course of Mitosis," *Cytologia (Tokyo),* **30**(1), 14 (1965).

Kihlman, B. A., and B. Hartley, "Sub-chromatid Exchanges and the 'Folded-Fibre' Model of Chromosome Structure," *Hereditas, 57*(2), 289 (1967).

Osgood, E. E., D. P. Jenkins, R. Brooks, and R. K. Lawson, "Electron Micrographic Studies of the Expanded and Uncoiled Chromosomes from Human Leukocytes," *Ann. N.Y. Acad. Sci.,* **113**, 717 (1964).

Pardon, J. F., M. H. F. Wilkins, and B. M. Richards, "Super-helical Model for Nucleohistone," *Nature, 215*(5100), 508 (1967).

Peacock, W. J., "Subchromatid Structure and Chromosome Duplication in *Vicia faba,*" *Nature,* **191**(4790), 832 (1961).

Ris, H., "Ultrastructure of the Animal Chromosome," in V. V. Konigsberger and L. Bosch, eds., *Regulation of Nucleic Acid and Protein Biosynthesis,* American Elsevier, New York, 1967, pp. 11–21.

Solari, A. J., "Structure of the Chromatin in Sea Urchin Sperm," *Proc. Natl. Acad. Sci. U.S.,* **53**(3), 503 (1965).

Sparvoli, E., H. Gay, and B. P. Kaufmann, "Number and Pattern of Association of Chromonemata in the Chromosomes of *Tradescantia,*" *Chromosoma,* **16** (4), 415 (1965).

Steffensen, D., "A Comparative View of the Chromosome," *Brookhaven Symp. Biol.,* No. 12, 103 (1959).

Wolfe, S. L., and N. J. Grim, "The Relationship of Isolated Chromosome Fibers to the Fibers of the Embedded Nucleus," *J. Ultrastruct. Res.* **19**(3–4), 382 (1967).

Lampbrush Chromosomes

Baker, T. G., and L. L. Franchi, "The Structure of the Chromosomes in Human Primordial Oocytes," *Chromosoma,* **22**(3), 358 (1967).

Callan, H. G., and H. C. MacGregor, "Action of Deoxyribonuclease on Lampbrush Chromosomes," *Nature,* **181**(4621), 1479 (1958).

Davidson, E. H., V. G. Allfrey, and A. E. Mirsky, "On the RNA Synthesized During the Lampbrush Phase of Amphibian Oogenesis," *Proc. Natl. Acad. Sci. U.S.,* **52**(2), 501 (1964).

Gall, J. G., "The Lampbrush Chromosomes of *Triturus viridescens,*" *Exptl. Cell Res.,* Suppl. 2, 95 (1952).

Gall, J. G., and H. G. Callan, "H³-Uridine Incorporation in Lampbrush Chromosomes," *Proc. Natl. Acad. Sci. U.S.*, **48**(4), 562 (1962).

Lafontaine, J. G., and H. Ris, "An Electron Microscope Study of Lampbrush Chromosomes," *J. Biophys. Biochem. Cytol.*, **4**(1), 99 (1958).

Polytene Chromosomes

Beermann, W., "Chromosomal Differentiation in Insects," in D. Rudnick, ed., *Developmental Cytology*, Ronald Press, New York, 1959, pp. 83–103.

Berendes, H. D., "The Hormone Ecdysone as Effector of Specific Changes in the Pattern of Gene Activities of *Drosophila hydei*," *Chromosoma*, **22**(3), 274 (1967).

Bridges, C. B., "Salivary Chromosome Maps," *J. Heredity*, **26**, 60 (1935).

Clever, U., "Actinomycin and Puromycin: Effects on Sequential Gene Activation by Ecdysone," *Science*, **146**(3645), 794 (1964).

Clever, U., "Control of Chromosome Puffing," in L. Goldstein, ed., *The Control of Nuclear Activity*, Prentice-Hall, Englewood Cliffs, N.J., 1967, pp. 161–86.

Dawe, C. J., ed., *The Chromosome*, Vol. 1, *In Vitro*, Williams and Wilkins, Baltimore, 1967.

Ficq, A., and C. Pavan, "Autoradiography of Polytene Chromosomes of *Rhynchosciara angelae* at Different Stages of Larval Development," *Nature*, **180**(4593), 983 (1957).

MacInnes, J. W., and R. B. Uretz, "Organization of DNA in Dipteran Polytene Chromosomes as Indicated by Polarized Fluorescence Microscopy," *Science*, **151**(3711), 689 (1966).

Mattingly, E., and C. Parker, "Sequence of Puff Formation in *Rhynchosciara* Polytene Chromosomes," *Chromosoma*, **23**(3), 255 (1968).

Painter, T. S., "The Structure of Salivary Gland Chromosomes," *Am. Naturalist*, **73**(747), 315 (1939).

Pavan, C., and M. E. Breuer, "Polytene Chromosomes in Different Tissues of *Rhynchosciara*," *J. Heredity*, **43**, 151 (1952).

Rudkin, G. T., and S. L. Corlette, "Disproportionate Synthesis of DNA in a Polytene Chromosome Region," *Proc. Natl. Acad. Sci. U.S.*, **43**(11), 964 (1957).

Rudkin, G. T., and P. S. Woods, "Incorporation of Tritiated Cytidine and Tritiated Thymidine into the Giant Chromosomes of *Drosophila* During Puff Formation," *Proc. Natl. Acad. Sci. U.S.*, **45**(7), 997 (1959).

Sorsa, M., and V. Sorsa, "Electron Microscopic Observations on Interband Fibrils in *Drosophila* Salivary Chromosomes," *Chromosoma*, **22**(1), 32 (1967).

Wolstenholme, D. R., "Direct Evidence for the Presence of DNA in Interbands of *Drosophila* Salivary Gland Chromosomes," *Genetics*, **53**(2), 357 (1966).

Chemistry

Berlowitz, L., "Analysis of Histone *in situ* in Developmentally Inactivated Chromatin," *Proc. Natl. Acad. Sci. U.S.*, **54**(2), 476 (1965).

Berlowitz, L., and M. L. Birnstiel, "Histone in the Wild Type and the Anucleolate Mutant of *Xenopus laevis*," *Science*, **156**(3771), 78 (1967).

Bernardini, J. V., and A. Lima-de-Faria, "Asynchrony of DNA Replication in the Chromosomes of *Luzula*," *Chromosoma*, **22**(1), 91 (1967).

Bonner, J., et al., "The Biology of Isolated Chromatin," *Science*, **159**(3810), 47 (1968).

Caspersson, T., et al., "Chemical Differentiation Along Metaphase Chromosomes," *Exptl. Cell Res.*, **49**(1), 219 (1968).

Das, N. K., and M. Alfert, "Cytochemical Studies on the Concurrent Synthesis of DNA and Histone in Primary Spermatocytes of *Urechis caupo*," *Exptl. Cell Res.*, **49**(1), 51 (1968).

Dounce, A. L., and C. A. Hillgartner, "A Study of DNA Nucleoprotein Gels and the Residual Protein of Isolated Cell Nuclei," *Exptl. Cell Res.*, **36**(2), 228 (1964).

Hotta, Y., and H. Stern, "Ribonucleic Acid Polymerase Activity in Extended and Contracted Chromosomes," *Nature*, **210**(5040), 1043 (1966).

Huang, R. C., and J. Bonner, "Histone-Bound RNA, a Component of Native Nucleohistone," *Proc. Natl. Acad. Sci. U.S.*, **54**(3), 960 (1965).

Kirby, K. S. "Evidence for Metallic Bonds Linking DNA to Proteins in Mammalian Tissues," *Biochem. J.*, **62**, 31 (1956).

Marmur, J., and P. Doty, "Heterogeneity in Deoxyribonucleic Acids. I. Dependence on Composition of the Configurational Stability of Deoxyribonucleic Acids," *Nature*, **183**(4673), 1427 (1959).

Mazia, D., "The Particulate Organization of the Chromosome," *Proc. Natl. Acad. Sci. U.S.*, **40**(6), 521 (1954).

Meek, E. S., "A Quantitative Cytochemical Study of Chromosomal Basic Protein in Static and Proliferative Cell Populations," *Exptl. Cell Res.*, **33**(1–2), 355 (1964).

Robbins, E., and T. W. Borum, "The Cytoplasmic Synthesis of Histones in HeLa Cells and Its Temporal Relationship to DNA Replication," *Proc. Natl. Acad. Sci. U.S.*, **57**(2), 409 (1967).

Steffensen, D., and J. A. Bergeron, "Autoradiographs of Pollen Tube Nuclei with Calcium-45," *J. Biophys. Biochem. Cytol.*, **6**(3), 339 (1959).

Chromosomal DNA

Evans, H. J., "Uptake of ^{3}H-Thymidine and Patterns of DNA Replication in Nuclei and Chromosomes of *Vicia faba*," *Exptl. Cell Res.*, **35**(2), 381 (1964).

Gilbert, C. W., L. G. Lajtha, S. Muldal, and C. H. Ockey, "Synchrony of Chromosome Duplication," *Nature*, **209**(5022), 537 (1966).

Lima-de-Faria, A., "Differential Uptake of Tritiated Thymidine into Hetero- and Euchromatin in *Melanoplus* and *Secale*," *J. Biophys. Biochem. Cytol.*, **6**(3), 457 (1959).

Lima-de-Faria, A., "Bibliography on Autoradiography with Special Reference to Tritium-Labelled DNA Precursors," *Hereditas*, **45**(4), 632 (1959).

Lima-de-Faria, A., J. Reitalu, and S. Bergman, "The Pattern of DNA Synthesis in the Chromosomes of Man," *Hereditas,* 47(4), 695 (1961).

Nicklas, R. B., and R. A. Jaqua, "X Chromosome DNA Replication: Developmental Shift from Synchrony to Asynchrony," *Science,* 147(3661), 1041 (1965).

Roels, H., "Metabolic DNA: A Cytochemical Study," *Intern. Rev. Cytol.,* 19, 1 (1966).

Sofuni, T., and A. A. Sandberg, "Chronology and Pattern of Human Chromosome Replication," *Cytogenetics,* 6, 357 (1967).

Taylor, J. H., "Sister Chromatid Exchanges in Tritium-Labelled Chromosomes," *Genetics,* 43(4), 515 (1958).

Taylor, J. H., "Asynchronous Duplication of Chromosomes in Cultured Cells of Chinese Hamster," *J. Biophys. Biochem. Cytol.,* 7(3), 455 (1960).

Taylor, J. H., P. S. Woods, and W. L. Hughes, "The Organization and Duplication of Chromosomes as Revealed by Autoradiographic Studies Using Tritium-Labelled Thymidine," *Proc. Natl. Acad. Sci. U.S.,* 43(1), 122 (1957).

Wake, K., H. Ochiai, and S. Tanifuji, "DNA and Histones from Ovular Tissue Cells of Cold-Treated *Trillium,*" *Japan. J. Genet.,* 43, 15 (1968).

Wimber, D. E., "Asynchronous Replication of DNA in Root Tip Chromosomes of *Tradescantia paludosa,*" *Exptl. Cell Res.,* 23(2), 402 (1961).

Woodard, J., M. Gorovsky, and H. Swift, "DNA Content of a Chromosome of *Trillium erectum:* Effect of Cold Treatment," *Science,* 151(3707), 215 (1966).

15

Chromosomal Aberrations

The word *mutation* is used to define a genetic change in an organism, this change being expressed as a modification of form or function. A genetic change results in a new genetic pattern, which is passed from one generation to the next; it is a permanent change in the genome of the organism. There are two types of mutations. One is a gene or *point* mutation, which is described as a physical or chemical change in the organization of the gene at the molecular level (Chapter 19). The other is described as a gross morphological change in the structure of the chromosome. Since many of the latter type are self-destructive, may cause cell death, and involve several genetic loci in a chromosome, it is desirable to restrict the word mutation to a change in the molecular organization of the gene and to apply the term *chromosomal aberration* to a gross change in the chromosome.

Chromosomal aberrations have been found in a variety of plants and animals and have influenced the evolution of a number of organisms. In this chapter the kinds and origins of aberrations, and their behavior and fate in the organisms in which they occur, will be discussed. The chromosomes of cancer cells, which frequently show chromosomal abnormalities, will be briefly described.

Spontaneous Aberrations

Spontaneous chromosomal aberrations are naturally occurring rearrangements of the chromosomes. Their origin is not known. Several possible causes have been suggested, but none has been substantiated. Cosmic radiations, nutritional insufficiencies, and environmental conditions (for example, temperature) may contribute to the production of these abnormalities. It has been demonstrated that in a few cases a gene or genes promote the breakage of chromosomes, as in the *dissociator-activator* system of corn. This peculiar genetic system was discovered during a study of the bridge-breakage-fusion cycle of chromosome 9 in corn. The bridge-breakage-fusion cycle is a series of events beginning with chromosome breakage and proceeding to the formation of a chromatid bridge in anaphase of mitosis (Figure 15–1). The breakage can be induced by X rays. In anaphase of the next mitotic division of the cell containing the aberration, another bridge forms, which breaks at some point when the chromosomes move to the poles of the cell. The broken end of the chromosome fuses with its sister chromatid at the next replication of the chromosomes, and a new bridge forms during the subsequent division of the cell. The cycle continues in this manner only in the endosperm tissue in the seed.

This particular cycle of abnormal behavior illustrates several important aspects of the origin and behavior of a chromosomal aberration. First, the chromosome is broken either by physical means, such as X rays, or naturally, and the broken end is unstable. If two broken ends are in adjacent positions, they can fuse with one another, to produce a chromosome with two kinetochores, a *dicentric* chromosome. Since the chromosomes normally separate from each other at anaphase, their respective kinetochores going to opposite poles, the dicentric chromosome forms a bridge across the equator of the cell. The bridge can break at any point along its length, depending upon where the greatest stress is imposed. Alternatively, both kinetochores of the dicentric chromosome may move to the same pole, thus obviating the formation of a bridge.

The dissociator gene of corn has the ability to cause breakage at the site it occupies in the chromosome, although the mechanism of this action is not known. The behavior of the gene itself is unusual. The dissociator gene is not stationary as are other genes; it apparently can move from

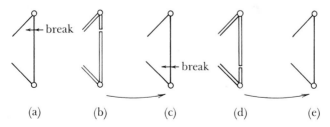

(a)   (b)   (c)   (d)   (e)

Figure 15–1. Bridge-breakage-fusion cycle in corn: (a) bridge at meiotic anaphase (the result of crossing over within an inversion); (b) fusion of sister chromatids following duplication; (c) bridge at subsequent mitotic anaphase; (d) fusion of sister chromatids at next division; (e) bridge.

place to place in the chromosome, and wherever it settles for an extended period of time, breakage can take place. When the dissociator gene and the activator gene are both present in a nucleus, the frequency of gene mutation increases in chromosome sectors adjacent to the dissociator gene.

The kinds of aberrations occurring in nature are the same as those induced by X rays or other agents. More will be said about induced aberrations later. The four principal types of spontaneous aberrations—*deficiencies, duplications, translocations,* and *inversions*—are presented in the following sections. Most of them involve one or more breaks in the chromosome.

Spontaneous aberrations are very infrequent, and in most organisms they are rare. Yet, as will be seen in the sections on translocations and inversions, they have played an important part in the evolution of some species and occur regularly in their populations. In most plants and animals, aberrations are found in fewer than 1% of the cells of a given tissue. However, there are several modifying factors that can increase this figure. Age is often significant in determining the frequency of aberrations; the older the organism or tissue, the higher the rate of spontaneous breakage of the chromosomes. This relationship is illustrated by the seeds of many plants. The older the seed, the greater the likelihood of chromosomal aberrations in the seedling roots. Other factors that influence chromosome breakage include temperature, oxygen availability, and the metabolic state of the cell. These will be discussed in detail in connection with the production of aberrations by physical and chemical agents.

Deficiencies

A deficiency results from the loss of part of a chromosome. The loss may affect the end of the chromosome, as a *terminal* deficiency, or the body of the chromosome, as an *interstitial* deficiency. A terminal deficiency is produced by a single break near the end of the chromosome, giving rise to a small acentric fragment, whereas an interstitial deficiency is produced by two breaks in an acentric region of the chromosome, also giving rise to an acentric fragment. The chromosome lacking a segment is deficient for the genes present in the segment, and the loss of the genes may have a phenotypic (observable) effect upon the organism. The fragment is lost because it lacks a kinetochore and is unstable. It may move to one pole or the other during the first mitotic (or meiotic) division following its production, or it may remain in the cytoplasm, eventually to disintegrate. If the fragment is included in a daughter nucleus, it is lost from the cell in a later division. Chromosome fragments persisting in daughter cells can often be recognized as more or less rounded bodies in the cytoplasm of Feulgen-

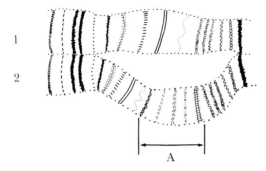

Figure 15–2. Heterozygous deficiency, shown by the pairing of homologous chromosomes in a dipteran salivary gland cell. Note the differences in the patterns of bands; segment A is absent from homologue 1, and loop occurs in homologue 2.

stained preparations. Such bodies, called *micronuclei,* are sometimes utilized in quantitative determinations of chromosomal damage.

A deficiency (or micronucleus) can vary in size from a minute, submicroscopic segment to a major portion of the chromosome. The larger the loss or deficiency, the greater the likelihood of a genetic effect, which is usually injurious to the organism. Because of their genetic effects, deficiencies have been the basis of studies of some gene mutations. If a very large segment is lost, the effect can be lethal to the cell, if not the organism. If the deficiency is sublethal, it may cause some functional or morphological change in the organism, which is passed to future generations as a gene mutation. In many cases a deficiency is so small as to have no effect upon the organism, and some organisms are able to withstand the loss of an entire chromosome without significant damage. A deficiency occurring in only one of a pair of chromosomes would be, in effect, a heterozygous deficiency and would probably act like a recessive mutation.

In the polytene chromosomes of the dipterans, heterozygous deficiencies are readily identifiable, since there is an observable alteration in the pattern of the bands, with one or more bands missing from a deficient chromosome (Figure 15–2). If a deficiency is homozygous (both members of a homologous pair of chromosomes lacking the same gene or genes), it may not be cytologically detectable, but the effect is often lethal.

Duplications

One type of duplication results from the addition of a segment of a chromosome to a chromosome. Segments vary in size and therefore in genetic constitution. Another type results from the addition of a small centric piece of chromosome to a genome. Duplication by the addition of a segment to a chromosome depends upon breakage in the chromosome, since a new segment cannot fuse with a normal chromosome end (telomere, Chapter 14). Duplications can be detected cytologically in a polytene chromosome as an extra band or bands. In the bridge-breakage-fusion cycle referred to earlier, a duplication-deficiency situation is produced. Since the anaphase bridge breaks unevenly, one daughter nucleus has an extra segment of chromosome and thus a duplication of one or more genes, while the other daughter nucleus lacks that particular set of genes, at least as a heterozygous deficiency.

Drosophila offers an excellent example of the genetic effect of a duplication in the chromosomes. A gene for eye shape and development is located in the X chromosome. The normal eye of the fly has 780 facets and is generally round in shape. Two other kinds of eyes have been found, which were originally thought to be developed from gene mutations but which actually arise from duplications. A *Bar* eye has only 325 to 358 facets, and the shape of the faceted area is irregular, whereas a *Bar-double* eye has only about 200 facets, in an area quite reduced in size (Figure 15–3). Bar and Bar-double eyes are caused by unequal crossing over during meiosis (Figure 15–4). The Bar eye is a duplication: the genetic locus

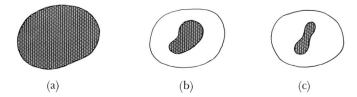

(a)   (b)   (c)

Figure 15–3. Drosophila eyes: (a) normal; (b) Bar; (c) Bar-double.

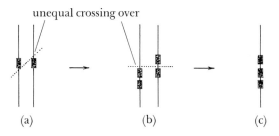

Figure 15–4. Crossing over in Drosophila, resulting in a Bar eye and a Bar-double eye: (a) normal; (b) Bar; (c) Bar-double.

| *A B C* | *A B C* | *D E F* |

(a)

| *A B C* | *C B A* | *D E F* |

(b)

| *A* | *B* | *C* | *D* | *E* | *F* |

| *L M N* | *A B C* | *O P Q R* |

(c)

Figure 15–5. Basic types of duplications: (a) tandem; (b) reverse tandem; (c) displaced. A segment of a chromosome is represented by letters for the genes it carries.

responsible for the normal eye occurs twice in adjacent segments of the chromosome. The Bar-double eye is a triplication of the genetic locus for the normal eye and is observed especially well in salivary gland polytene chromosomes. This example of duplication in chromosomes also demonstrates a position effect and is evidence for a correlation of genetic behavior with specific cytological events.

The three basic types of segment duplications are shown in Figure 15–5. In *tandem* duplication the added segment has the same genetic order as the original segment and is adjacent to the original segment in the same chromosome. In *reverse-tandem* duplication the segment is adjacent to the original segment in the same chromosome, but its genes are in the reverse order. In the third type of duplication, *displaced* duplication, a segment is inserted into a different chromosome.

Translocations

A translocation results from the transfer of a segment of a chromosome to a different part of the same chromosome or to a different chromosome. In the latter instance the transfer may take place between homologous chromosomes or between nonhomologous chromosomes. If there is an exchange of segments between nonhomologous chromosomes, the translocation is termed *reciprocal*, and the subsequent meiotic behavior of the chromosomes is altered (Figure 15–6), for a potential genetic effect. In a *simple* translocation a small terminal segment of a chromosome is added to the end of a homologous chromosome or to a nonhomologous chromosome. Simple translocation rarely occurs, primarily because of the inability of a normal chromosome end to fuse with any other chromosome end. A third type of translocation, the *shift,* involves the insertion of an inter-

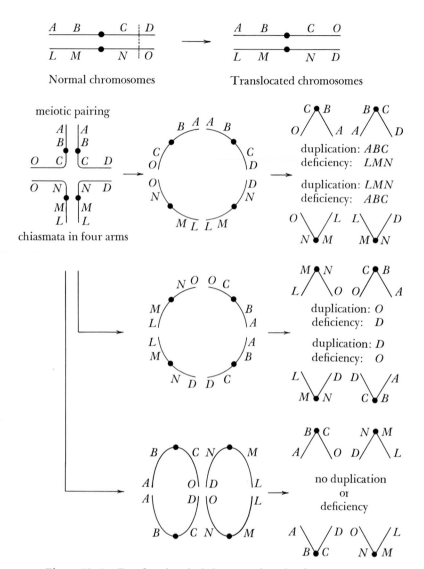

Figure 15–6. Results of meiosis in a translocation heterozygote.

stitial piece of a chromosome into a different portion of the same chromosome or into an interstitial portion of a nonhomologous chromosome. Shift translocation requires a minimum of three breaks in the chromosomes (Figure 15–7). Reciprocal and shift translocations are the most common types of translocations.

As is true for deficiencies and duplications, translocations may be either homozygous or heterozygous and are usually nonlethal in their

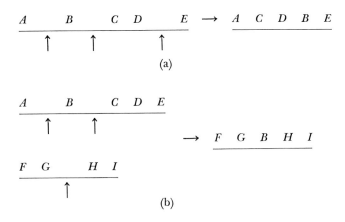

(b)

Figure 15–7. Shift translocation: (a) shift within a chromosome; (b) shift into a nonhomologous chromosome. Vertical arrows indicate breaks.

effects. A homozygous translocation exhibits normal meiotic behavior, but a heterozygous translocation shows variations in the pattern of chromosome pairing during meiosis. Figure 15–8 illustrates the pairing in the reciprocal translocation between chromosomes II and IV of *Sciara coprophila*. This particular translocation, called "Stop," acts like a *recessive lethal* and results in a characteristic wing design in the heterozygous condition.

In Figure 15–6 meiosis in a translocation heterozygote is depicted. Three possible arrangements of the chromosomes in metaphase I and their gametic products are shown. The positions of the chromosomes during meiosis are dependent upon several factors, including the lengths of

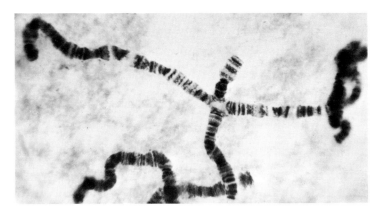

Figure 15–8. Stop translocation. FROM H. V. Crouse, *Chromosoma,* 11, 146 (1960), with permission of Springer-Verlag.

the chromosomes, the positions of the breaks giving rise to the translocation, the number and positions of the chiasmata, and the degrees of terminalization of the chiasmata.

Translocations occur regularly in the genomes of many plants. A wide
spectrum of reciprocal translocations is seen in several races of *Oenothera
lamarkiana* (evening primrose), one or more translocations being peculiar
to each race. There may be only one translocation per cell, producing a ring
of two chromosomes during meiotic metaphase, or there may be translocations in all of the chromosomes, producing a ring of all 14. These translocations are heterozygous and are maintained in the population by a
system of genes known as *balanced lethals*. That is, each organism contains two or more genetic loci carrying recessive lethals. Thus only heterozygous individuals survive, since they are heterozygous for the lethal genes
as well as the reciprocal translocations. Translocations are a stagnating
influence in these organisms: because the genomes are maintained in such
a stable condition from generation to generation, there is little chance for
any additional change that would lead to evolutionary advancement. In
other words, they have reached an evolutionary dead end.

Another plant with regular translocations is *Rhoeo discolor,* in which
a ring of 12 chromosomes often forms. The formation of a ring, whether
of two chromosomes or more, occurs if there are chiasmata in all four arms
of the paired chromosomes. When the chiasmata terminalize, the arms
open out into a ring as the kinetochores of the chromosomes move toward
opposite poles of the cell. Some species of *Datura* (Jimson weed) exhibit
translocations, but there is no evidence of a direct relation between specific translocations and speciation.

Although translocations generally have been of greater importance in
the plant kingdom than in the animal kingdom, one type of translocation
has had some evolutionary significance in animals. This aberration, described as a *centric fusion,* is actually a translocation between two chromosomes. It has been found in *Drosophila,* arthropods, certain birds, and
mammals. Studies with *Drosophila* have indicated that translocations, particularly centric fusions, have caused evolutionary changes of chromosome
numbers in various species. Their principal effect has been to reduce the
chromosome numbers. Examples of centric fusions are given in Figure
15–9, which presents the possible evolutionary patterns in two subgenera,
Drosophila and *Sophophora*. Each fusion involves a translocation of almost the entire arm of a rod chromosome to produce a V-shaped chromosome. Translocations of small portions of an arm are rare in *Drosophila*.
There are other differences besides the translocations in the chromosomes
of the species represented, including inversions, and the genetics of these
organisms is rather complex, especially since hybridization is possible
among many of the species.

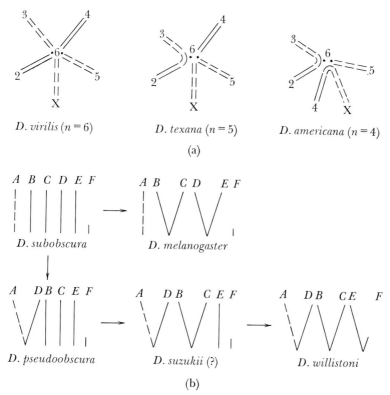

Figure 15–9. Centric fusions in two subgenera of *Drosophila:* (a) subgenus *Drosophila;* (b) subgenus *Sophophora,* proposed evolutionary scheme. —— and — — —, Acrocentric rod chromosome; V, metacentric V-chromosome.

A similar reduction in chromosome number is exhibited by the plant *Crepis*. The more primitive species of *Crepis* have a basic chromosome number of six $(n = 6)$, whereas the more advanced species have basic numbers of three, four, and five. Reciprocal translocations have contributed greatly to this evolutionary trend toward reduction in chromosome number. In those cases where centric fusions lead to a decrease in chromosome number, little genetic material is lost from the genome, since most of the translocated chromosome is retained. Thus there is little loss in viability or fertility of the offspring of later generations.

Inversions

The most complex type of chromosomal aberration is that which results from the realignment of an interstitial segment of a chromosome. An in-

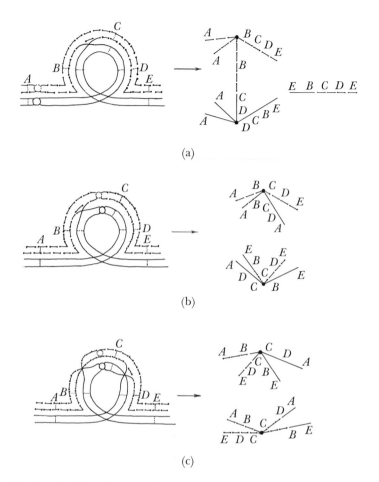

Figure 15–10. Configurations and meiotic results of crossing over in heterozygous inversions: (a) paracentric inversion with crossing over, resulting in an anaphase bridge and fragment and duplication-deficiency products; (b) pericentric inversion with crossing over, resulting in anaphase (no bridge) and duplication-deficiency products; (c) pericentric inversion with double crossing over, resulting in anaphase (no bridge) and duplication-deficiency products.

version requires two breaks within the chromosome and the reinsertion of the segment between the breaks in a direction opposite to its original position in the chromosome. The linear order of the genes is thereby reversed in the particular section of the chromosome. For example, if the arrangement of the genes on the chromosome were originally *ABCDEFG-HIJK,* and an inversion occurred between *D* and *H,* the inverted chromosome would have a gene sequence of *ABCDGFEHIJK.* The length of an inversion varies according to the locations of the two breaks in the chromosome and can affect any part of the chromosome. If the inverted segment does not include the kinetochore, the inversion is *paracentric;* if it does include the kinetochore, the inversion is *pericentric.* Homologous chromosomes with identical inversions undergo normal meiotic pairing and distribution, but if only one homologue has an inversion, the pairing relations are disrupted, and the chromosomes take on a characteristic appearance. Heterozygous inversions are obvious in the polytene dipteran chromosomes because specific segments are so clearly identifiable by their banding patterns.

The consequences of a heterozygous inversion are varied, depending upon the position of the inversion (paracentric or pericentric), the presence and the number of chiasmata within the inversion, and the distribution of the meiotic products in the gametes. Figure 15–10 illustrates the genetic consequences of chiasma formation in the inverted segment. In the case of a paracentric inversion with crossing over, a bridge is produced in anaphase I of meiosis, and an acentric fragment is lost. The bridge may break at any point, giving rise to duplications and deficiencies in the meiotic products. The fragment associated with the bridge has the effect of a deficiency, and the size of the deficiency determines the reduction in fertility imposed. That is, a meiotic product or gamete lacking one or more genes because of the loss of a portion of the chromosome is likely to be nonviable and thus sterile. The products of pericentric heterozygous inversions, as well as variations due to the chromatids exchanged during crossing over and to the number of chiasmata within the inversion, are also shown.

The simplest type of inversion is that just described. A single chromosome, however, may have two *independent* inversions of this type (Figure 15–11). More complex still is the case in which one inversion is included within another, or overlaps another, in the same chromosome. In predicting the meiotic products of any particular inversion, it is necessary to include all four chromatids of a bivalent pair of chromosomes. Observations of inversions have added to the information on the phenomenon of crossing over; there is further proof that crossing over occurs when four chromatids are present and that it occurs between only two of the four chromatids at any one locus.

Inversions have been instrumental in establishing a number of species relationships in *Drosophila* and may have as much evolutionary significance as translocations. The major effect of inversions may be to restrict the recombination of genetic loci by crossing over and thereby to maintain in the population a specific segment of a chromosome. In several instances a particular segment or group of segments confers on individuals a selective advantage; that is, they seem to survive well under the influ-

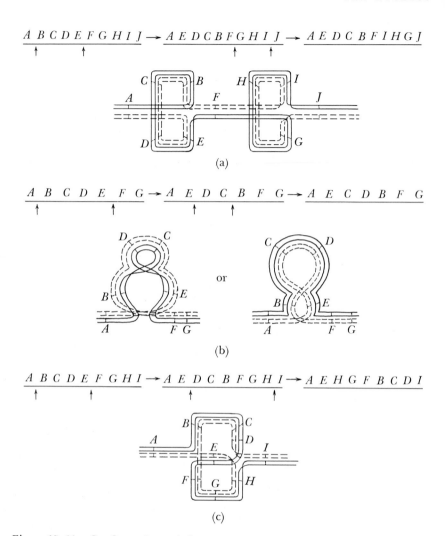

Figure 15–11. Configurations of three types of heterozygous inversions: (a) two independent inversions; (b) one inversion included in another inversion; (c) two overlapping inversions.

ences operating in natural selection. Consequently, the maintenance of a particular set of genes has real value for the survival and reproductive capacity of the species. Inversions have been found in plants as well as animals, and appear more often in natural populations than other types of spontaneous aberrations. Although the actual frequencies have not been determined for many organisms, the most common natural inversions are paracentric ones.

Induced Aberrations

The difference between spontaneous and induced aberrations lies in the frequency with which they occur. The use of a physical or chemical agent simply increases the frequency of chromosomal aberrations; it does not create new types. Most of the agents inducing mutations also induce breakage in the chromosomes. Radiations have been utilized for many years to cause mutations and chromosomal damage for experimental purposes. With ionizing radiations the number of mutations is directly proportional to the dose, but such a ratio does not hold for chromosomal aberrations. This is one way in which point mutations can be distinguished from chromosomal aberrations.

Radiation

In 1927 Muller presented experimental data which established that radiation could induce mutations in living organisms. Shortly thereafter, Riley, Sax, and others began to study radiation-induced chromosomal aberrations. Various kinds of radiations cause mutations, chromosomal aberrations, and other cellular effects. X rays and gamma rays are *nonparticulate* radiations, described as quanta or photons of energy producing a series of *ionizations* in the material exposed. Upon exposure to ionizing radiations, electrons are raised to a higher level of energy and are ejected from the atoms of which they are a part. The initial ejection of electrons is called *primary* ionization. In turn, these energetic electrons bring about the ejection of other electrons from adjacent atoms, in *secondary* ionizations. Thus radiation can induce a change in the molecular organization of protoplasm. The change may be expressed as a mutation, a break in a chromosome, or an alteration in the physiological activity of the cell. Other types of (*particulate*) ionizing radiations include alpha particles, beta rays, protons, and neutrons, all of which have been used as tools for biological studies.

There are important physical differences among these ionizing radiations, expressed, in one way, as densities of ionization. The nonparticulate radiations, X and gamma rays, are less densely ionizing than the others, in that they produce fewer ionizations per path of radiation and that their ionizations are produced near the tail of the energy path as it travels through the cell. On the other hand, these same radiations are much more penetrating than many other types of radiation. They are able to move through layers of tissue deep into the interior of an organism. Once radiation has passed through an organism, there is no longer

any radiation energy in its tissues; the energy is dissipated almost instan-
taneously.

Particulate radiations are more densely ionizing than nonparticulate
ones, alpha rays being the most densely ionizing. Alpha particles are
atomic nuclei of helium atoms and produce a cluster of ionizations of
high density in tissue. A beta ray is an electron, and protons and neutrons
are also components of atoms with high energies. Because of their greater
densities of ionization, these radiations are much more damaging than
nonparticulate types. However, they are generally less penetrating, alpha
rays being stopped by the skin, and beta rays by a layer of clothing. Differences in biological response accompany variations in ionization density.
These will be discussed later. The similarities and differences among
radiations and the applications of radioactive isotopes should now be
clear, in view of this discussion and that in Chapter 2.

The disruption of biological molecules can also be induced by ultraviolet radiation, but this is non-ionizing radiation, and its mechanism is
somewhat different from that of ionizing radiation. Ultraviolet radiation
produces *excitation* rather than ionization in the molecules. In this case
electrons are raised to a higher energy state but are not ejected from
the atoms. The principal effect is an instability in molecular structure
that can ultimately lead to changes similar to those produced by ionizing
radiations.

Figure 15–12 is a pictorial representation of the densities of different
ionizing radiations. Table 15–1 lists the principal types of radiations and
their characteristics. The ionization density of a radiation is calculated by
dividing the total number of ion pairs formed by the total length of the
radiation track or path. On the basis of this formula, the relative biological
efficiencies of various radiations can be determined.

One of the standard units of measure of ionizing radiation is the *roentgen* (R), but it does not represent the same amount of ionization or
energy dissipation for all types of radiations on living cells. A roentgen is

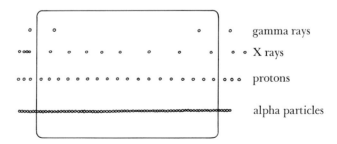

Figure 15–12.   Relative ionization densities of various radiations.

Table 15–1 Principal Types of Ionizing Radiations*

Radiation	Description	Origin
20 MeV beta ray	high-speed electrons, particulate	high-voltage generator, radioactive isotopes
gamma ray†	electromagnetic wave, nonparticulate	radioactive isotopes (cobalt-60, radium)
1 MeV X ray†	electromagnetic wave, nonparticulate	high-voltage generator (bombardment of metals by electrons)
100–200 keV X ray	electromagnetic wave, nonparticulate	high-voltage generator (bombardment of metals by electrons)
10 keV electrons	high-speed electrons, particulate	high-voltage generator, radioactive isotopes
neutrons‡	particulate; very energetic, most penetrating	atomic pile or reactor
alpha particles	nuclei of helium atoms, particulate; most densely ionizing	radioactive isotopes

* Listed in the order of increasing ionization density and increasing biological efficiency. Note that 1 keV = 1 thousand electron volts and 1 MeV = 1 million electron volts.
† Gamma and X rays have very short wavelengths (less than 1 Å) and very high energies.
‡ Neutrons cause the production of protons, which cause ionizations.

the dose of radiation producing 1 electrostatic unit of charge in 1 square centimeter (cm^2) of air at standard temperature and pressure. From a biological standpoint, 1 R produces approximately two ionizations in 1 μ^3 of tissue. Other units of measure can be used for ionizing radiation and translated to roentgens for convenience. Ultraviolet radiation is designated in terms of wavelengths or Ångström units, and the dose is measured in *ergs* per unit of exposed area. The most efficient wavelengths fall within the range 2200 to 3000 Å.

A distinction can be made between direct and indirect effects of radiation on biological molecules. A direct effect results from primary ionizations occuring in a limited volume of the exposed cell, the dimensions being measured in microns or fractions thereof. Thus a direct effect depends on the physical events initiated by the radiation. An indirect effect results from the production in protoplasm of active radicals or other substances having the power to damage the molecules of the cell. Water, the most abundant component of protoplasm, is split by radiation into such active radicals as [H] and [OH]. In the presence of oxygen, the hydroperoxyl radical ($[HO_2]$), hydrogen peroxide, and several organic peroxides may be formed. It has been suggested that these peroxides are capable of doing secondary damage to the molecules. The significance of direct and indirect effects of radiation will be summarized later in connection with the development of chromosomal aberrations under diverse environmental conditions.

In the following discussion of radiation cytology, reference is made primarily to those organisms that have been studied most extensively, namely, the grasshopper, *Drosophila, Tradescantia, Vicia faba,* and *Allium.* Different types of tissues in these organisms have been compared with respect to their radiation responses, and, consequently, general conclusions have been reached about the radiation syndrome. However, these are not always applicable to all organisms or all tissues. The organisms emphasized here are not the only ones that have been used experimentally in radiation research, but they are especially valuable because of the relative ease with which chromosomal effects in them can be observed.

General Effects of Radiation

There is considerable variation in sensitivity to radiation at all levels of biological organization. Simple individuals such as bacteria, viruses, and protozoa are much more radioresistant than the more elaborate plants and animals. The most sensitive organisms belong to the primate group, which includes man. Space exploration has led to renewed interest in radiation effects on humans. Plants and animals of several kinds, as well as cells growing in culture, have been sent into space on some of the manned flights. For example, the effect of extraterrestrial radiations on human blood cells in culture has been examined in such experiments.

Dividing cells, mitotic and meiotic, are more sensitive than non-dividing cells, expressing their sensitivity as lethality, mutations or chromosomal aberrations, or changes in cellular metabolism, such as the disruption of DNA synthesis or protein synthesis. The sensitivity to radiation of a cell undergoing mitosis depends upon the time during cell division at which exposure occurs. From the standpoint of a tendency to mutation or chromosome breakage, late prophase and metaphase are more sensitive than other stages, and the synthetic stages of interphase are almost as sensitive. If a cell is irradiated while in interphase or early prophase, mitosis can be inhibited, even by an extremely small dose. According to the quality of the radiation, the intensity, and the dose, a cell may be prevented from dividing either permanently or temporarily. Once a certain stage has been reached (usually in late prophase), the interference of radiation with mitotic activity diminishes. Meiotic cells are more sensitive to radiation than are mitotic cells. Moreover, according to the work of Sparrow and others, chromosome volume is an important factor in radiosensitivity.

One of the more readily discernible effects of radiation on a dividing cell takes place during metaphase. The chromosomes become sticky, so that they are not easily separated in the ensuing anaphase. Instead, chromosome bridges form between the poles of the cell. If a cell in metaphase is examined immediately following exposure to radiation, the surfaces of the chromosomes show this stickiness or fuzziness, which is described rather ambiguously as the *physiological effect*. Although the molecular basis for it has not been demonstrated, possibly the bonds between the protein and nucleic acid constituents of the chromosomes are disrupted, or DNA depolymerizes.

The inhibition of cell division by another means was referred to in Chapter 9. Exposing one of the two nucleoli of a grasshopper neuroblast to ultraviolet radiation during certain mitotic stages results in the complete cessation of mitosis. This reaction is not a general one in all organisms, however.

Many types of radiation effects have been studied, but those of greatest cytological interest are the breaks induced in chromosomes, which lead to alterations in chromosome morphology. Changes in morphology, or aberrations, can have grave consequences for the cell and even for the organism; they may bring about the production of new phenotypes, the development of new chromosomal races, the production of abnormal cells (that is, cancer), death of the cell, or death of the organism. On the other hand, they may have no visible or significant biological effect. Within the framework of the ecological and evolutionary ramifications of radiation effects, 99% of the effects are harmful in some way, in the sense that they reduce the viability of an organism in a population or reduce the reproductive capacities of an organism or population.

Radiation-Induced Chromosomal Aberrations

Radiation-induced chromosomal aberrations can be divided into two main categories, the chromosome type and the chromatid type. The difference between the two lies in the time during the cell cycle at which the breaks occur in the chromosomes. If the chromosome is irradiated before duplication, the aberrations observed in the subsequent metaphase and anaphase are of the chromosome type, and if the chromosome is effectively double

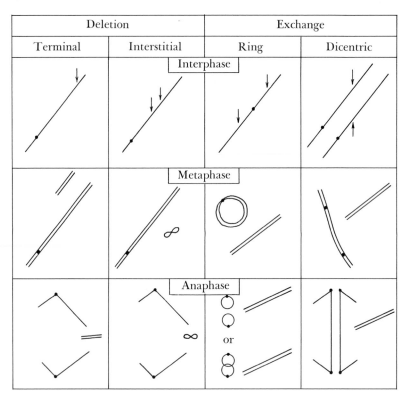

Figure 15–13. Radiation-induced chromosomal aberrations: the chromosome type.

at the time of irradiation, the aberrations observed during the ensuing division are of the chromatid type. The principal chromosome and chromatid aberrations are diagrammed in Figures 15–13 and 15–14.

Chromosome Aberrations

Chromosome aberrations can be classified further as *terminal deletions, interstitial deletions,* and *exchanges.* Inversions can also be induced by radiation or other treatment. An induced inversion in a meiotic cell is detected in the same manner as a spontaneous inversion. It cannot be detected in a somatic cell.

A terminal deletion is the result of a single break in the chromosome at a terminal position and is represented by a rodlike fragment without a kinetochore, consisting of two chromatid arms. After the break occurs in the single chromosome during interphase, the chromosome duplicates,

Deletion		Asymmetrical exchange	
Chromatid	Isochromatid	Interchange	Intrachange

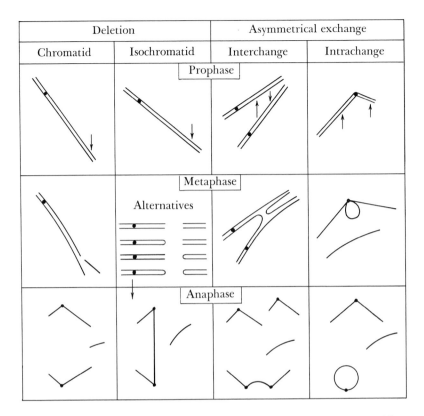

Figure 15–14. Radiation-induced chromosomal aberrations: the chromatid type.

and the fragment also duplicates. If the chromosome and the fragment do not undergo *restitution* (which restores the normal morphology of the chromosome) within a certain period of time, the fragment becomes separated from the main body of the chromosome and is eventually lost because of its lack of a kinetochore. Depending upon the size of the fragment, a terminal deletion can cause the loss or deficiency of one or more genetic loci. Thus it is comparable to the deficiency type of spontaneous aberration. Terminal deletions are the least common induced aberrations in most organisms.

An interstitial deletion is the result of two breaks in the chromosome, both occurring at the same side of the kinetochore. Barring restitution, the small segment between the breaks is displaced from the chromosome arm, and the remaining parts of the arm undergo *reunion*. At the same time the ends of the fragment usually undergo reunion to produce an *acentric ring,* which varies in size according to the distance between the two breaks in the chromosome. An interstitial deletion is also basically a deficiency type of aberration. Interstitial deletions are the most common induced aberrations in many organisms.

A chromosome exchange involves two breaks, either in a single chromosome or in two adjacent chromosomes. If a break occurs on each side of the kinetochore of one chromosome, the behavior of the segments closely parallels that in an interstitial deletion. In this case the kinetochore is included in the displaced fragment, which forms a *centric ring*. The remaining arms of the chromosome undergo reunion to give rise to an acentric fragment, which is eventually lost from the nucleus; the result is therefore a deficiency aberration. The centric ring is an exchange aberration that acts in different ways depending upon the configuration it takes during duplication of the chromosomes and the subsequent stages of division. The alternative fates of a ring are shown in Figure 15–13.

If a break occurs in each arm of two adjacent chromosomes, and if the broken ends lie close to each other—not more than 0.2 μ apart—reunion can produce a dicentric chromosome and an acentric fragment (Figure 15–15). An exchange between two chromosomes that does not produce a dicentric chromosome is equivalent to a reciprocal translocation and is not apparent unless the chromosomes have different lengths. The behavior of a dicentric chromosome of corn has been outlined in the bridge-breakage-fusion cycle (Figure 15–1). Dicentric chromosomes in other types of cells do not usually persist by such fusion. Chromosomes with more than two kinetochores (tricentric, quadricentric, etc.) have been observed occasionally but appear very seldom. These multiple-kinetochore chromosomes arise from breaks in more than two chromosomes.

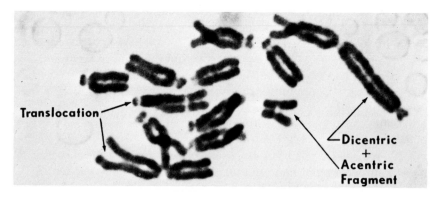

Figure 15–15. Induced translocation and dicentric chromosomes in a metaphase cell of *Vicia faba*. Both aberrations are of the exchange type. Photo by Sheldon Wolff and H. E. Luippold, from J. A. Heddle, *Genetics,* **52,** 1329 (1965).

Chromatid Aberrations

The differences between chromosome and chromatid aberrations are demonstrated in Figures 15–13 and 15–14. The three main types of chromatid aberrations are *chromatid deletions,* of a terminal nature, *isochromatid deletions,* and *chromatid exchanges.* The simplest, and usually the least frequent, are the chromatid deletions. Since the chromosome consists of two chromatids at the time of irradiation, breakage is possible in either one chromatid or both chromatids. A broken end may undergo (1) restitution, which retstores the chromosome to normal morphology; (2) displacement, which leaves a terminal deletion; or (3) reunion with the broken end of another chromatid in the vicinity. In the last instance a chromatid exchange takes place. Although only one chromatid may be broken, breakage of both chromatids in corresponding positions is more likely. This situation produces four broken ends, which may recombine (by restitution or reunion) in several ways. If restitution does not occur, an isochromatid deletion, the most common type of chromatid aberration, results.

Exchanges are the most complex chromatid aberrations. They are designated as *interchanges* or *intrachanges,* according to origin, and most of them can also be classified as translocations. An interchange is an exchange of chromatid arms between two chromosomes. If the interchange produces four normal-looking chromatids by anaphase, it is *symmetrical* and is difficult to detect unless the sizes of the two interchanging chromosomes differ. An *asymmetrical* interchange results in the formation of a dicentric chromatid, with an associated acentric fragment, and two normal chromatids. It is recognized easily during metaphase and anaphase. Two breaks within the same chromosome may lead to symmetrical or asymmetrical intrachange. In the latter event a chromatid ring (centric or acentric) and a fragment are produced.

Chromosomal Breakage Patterns and Modifying Factors

Examination of the positions of chromosomal breaks induced by ionizing radiations reveals that breaks can occur at any point along the chromosome; they are distributed at random. The pattern of breakage, as expressed in chromosomal aberrations, is due to this random distribution of breaks and to the nonrandom restitution and reunion of the broken ends. The last two processes are influenced by one or more factors inherent in the cell or by external changes in the cell environment. Determinations of the behavior of broken chromosomes are complicated by the fact that most of the breaks initiated by radiation undergo immediate restitution and therefore are never recovered for cytological observation. With X rays and neutrons, for example, only about 10% of the breaks undergo reunion to produce aberrations. Thus relatively high doses of radiation are required to cause sufficient numbers of aberrations for quantitative analyses.

According to the work with metabolic inhibitors, such as carbon monoxide and potassium cyanide, the restitution or reunion of broken chromosomes is dependent upon a source of energy, perhaps ATP. It has also been suggested that protein synthesis is somehow associated with the process.

Time and space are also important factors in the activities of broken chromosomes. The time that a break remains open varies with the tissue and the organism, but most breaks undergo restitution very rapidly or undergo reunion to form rearrangements within a matter of minutes. Some, as in *Allium* root tip cells and *Drosophila* spermatozoa, remain open for several hours. In those *Drosophila* cells the broken ends do not rejoin until fertilization. Most of the broken microspore chromosomes of *Tradescantia paludosa* undergo restitution within an hour. As far as space is concerned, two breaks must be close to each other to permit their reunion, as mentioned earlier.

The relation between radiation dose (and intensity) and the yield of aberrations depends in part upon the time and space factors. With an increase in the dose of radiation, there is an increase in the frequency of aberrations arising from one break in the chromosome. The proportion is linear. It holds for terminal deletions, chromatid deletions, and isochromatid deletions and for all types of ionizing radiations. If two breaks provide the basis for an aberration, the relation between dose and aberration frequency is not always linear. With X rays and gamma rays, which are less densely ionizing than other radiations, the frequency of aberrations increases with nearly the square of the dose, so that the proportion is geometric rather than linear, when the intensity (number of roentgens per unit time) is high. If the dose is administered over a long period of time, the increase is less, but the proportion is still not linear. In other words, a decrease in the intensity of a dose of radiation results in a decrease in the frequency of aberrations. This relationship is explained by the fact that the breaks remain open and available for reunion for only a limited time and some of the breaks induced at the beginning of radiation exposure undergo restitution before other breaks are induced. Since not all of the breaks are present at the same time, the formation of a certain percentage of exchange aberrations is precluded. In brief, the dosage-squared relation is applicable only to exchange-type aberrations induced by the less densely ionizing radiations, and if a given dose of radiation is extended over a long period of time, the frequency of the exchanges is reduced.

With neutrons the frequency of aberrations is linearly rather than geometrically proportional to the dosage because of the efficiency of neutrons in breaking chromosomes. According to the classical interpretation, a single path of neutron radiation can produce two breaks in a chromosome, whereas a single path of X radiation can produce only one. Thus the relation between neutron dose and aberration frequency is independent of the intensity of the radiation. The linear proportion holds for aberrations induced by all the more densely ionizing radiations, such as neutrons and alpha rays.

Relatively recent investigations of chromosomal breakage have led to some new interpretations of the mechanisms of induced-aberration production. Although the studies and the hypotheses derived from them are rather complex, they can be summarized as follows. According to Evans, for example, radiation does not produce direct breakage in chromosomes, but initiates a lesion requiring DNA synthesis for repair. An exchange would arise as a consequence of *misrepair* of the lesions. Revell and others, in fact, have stated that *all* aberrations are a consequence of exchange following a process of misrepair of primary lesions. Variations in radiosensitivity at different stages of the cell cycle are then explained as being due to differences in the time available for repair and to changes in chromatid structure during chromosomal replication.

The effects of ionizing radiations are influenced by a variety of environmental factors, such as temperature, oxygen concentration, centrifugation, cell nutrition, chemical agents, and other types of radiation. These modifying factors have the consequences summarized in Table 15–2. The factors are discussed with regard to their influence on the effects of the less densely ionizing radiations, since the actions of neutrons and alpha rays are immune to most of them.

Not all of the modifying effects can be explained. The low frequency of aberrations in the absence of, or at low concentrations of, oxygen may be due to a low yield of active products of the irradiation of water. In the presence of oxygen, peroxides form, and these may account for what has been called the indirect effect of radiation. The reactions of calcium-, magnesium-, and iron-deficient cells to radiation have brought forth the hypothesis that divalent metallic ions are important for the structural maintenance of the chromosome, as pointed out in Chapter 14.

Ultraviolet irradiation of the generative nuclei in pollen tubes of *Tradescantia* before or after their exposure to X rays reduced the aberration frequency below that for X rays alone. In contrast to this result, other data indicate that dry pollen of *Tradescantia* treated with ultraviolet and X rays exhibits a frequency of chromatid aberrations higher than the additive effect of the two radiations. The amount of hydration of the pollen

Table 15–2   Effects of Environmental Factors on Frequency of X Ray–Induced Chromosomal Aberrations

Factor	Application	Effect
temperature	0–10°C	increase
oxygen concentration	0–21%	gradual increase
	21–100%	threshold, slight increase
centrifugation	2080 rpm	increase
sonic vibrations	9100 cycles/second	increase
calcium, magnesium, or iron deficiency	roots grown in deficient medium	increase
—SH compounds	pretreatment or treatment during irradiation	decrease
ultraviolet radiation	pretreatment, posttreatment, or treatment during irradiation	decrease or increase
far red radiation	pretreatment or posttreatment (at 12°C)	increase (primarily exchanges)

and the time intervals between radiation exposures affect the degree of synergistic action. Whether protection from or intensification of X-ray damage occurs with ultraviolet treatment, restitution rather than breakage of the chromosomes appears to be involved.

Although ultraviolet light has been used more extensively for mutation induction, it has also been effective in the production of chromosomal damage in plant and animal cells. Moreover, ultraviolet light produces mitotic inhibition, inhibition of DNA synthesis, and cell death. For the induction of chromosomal aberrations in mammalian cells, the most effective wavelength is 2650 Å, and a dose of 100 ergs/mm² induces about one chromatid break per cell. The mechanism by which ultraviolet produces chromosomal breakage is not known, but it appears to be quite different from that for ionizing radiation. For example, most ultraviolet-induced breaks do not undergo restitution. Mutation and lethality are most effectively induced by ultraviolet light at a wavelength of 2537 Å. The mechanism of cell killing is much better understood than that for chromosomal aberrations, and because of its importance to an understanding of certain aspects of cell metabolism, it is presented here. When the chromosomal (genetic) material, DNA, is exposed to ultraviolet light, crosslinks may be formed between the two helixes of the molecule, or bonds may develop between adjacent thymine moieties in one of the helixes. In the latter event, normal DNA replication is impaired. Ultimately, if no repair occurs, this will lead to cell death, and the use of ultraviolet light in germicidal lamps utilizes this effect. The bonded thymines (dimers of thymine) may undergo repair in the dark if the appropriate repair enzymes are present, as they are in certain bacterial cells. The repair process involves the removal of the defective bases (dimer excision) and their replacement by the normal base sequence. In some studies with microorganisms, such as bacteria, exposure of the cells to visible light after treatment with ultraviolet light results in the recovery of the cells instead of their dying. This process is called *photoreactivation,* and is due to the activation of an enzyme by visible light, the enzyme causing a splitting of the thymine dimers so that normal replication of DNA can then occur. Photoreactivation has recently been observed in *Paramecium aurelia,* and is thus not restricted to bacteria. Such repair processes, however, are not involved in the production of chromosomal aberrations.

Radiomimesis

With the discovery in 1947 that mustard gas and similar compounds could induce mutations and chromosomal aberrations, there began a series of experiments with a variety of chemicals in an attempt to induce specific changes. Because the properties of these chemicals were known, it was thought that they might provide a key to the exact nature of mutation and breakage. It is apparent from most of the results that the basis for chemical effects differs from that for radiation effects. Still, chemical agents produce the same kinds of effects that X rays produce, and so the name *radiomimetic* agents has been given them, to denote that their effects mimic those of radiations. These effects include breakage of chromosomes, stickiness, and mitotic inhibition. Moreover, radiomimetic agents may cause or destroy cancer cells. Chemical and radiation effects do not always coincide in time. Some radiomimetic agents are most effective in interphase (when the cells are most sensitive to them), whereas others are most effective during stages of the mitotic cycle.

The most widely used radiomimetic agents are alkylating agents (including the mustards and their derivatives), diepoxides, purine and pyrimidine analogues, and phenols. The effects of some of them are influenced by such environmental factors as temperature, pH, metabolic inhibitors, and oxygen concentration. At this juncture, it is of interest to note that oxygen alone, in high concentrations and at high pressures, can induce chromosome breakage, although it is not generally considered to be a *mutagenic* or radiomimetic agent. It has been reported as breaking chromosomes in cells of *Tradescantia.*

The mechanism of action is not the same for all radiomimetic agents and, in fact, is not known for many of them. Certain agents, such as mustards and related alkylating compounds, may react with biological molecules, such as DNA, by alkylation of the guanine bases. Since alkylated guanine has a tendency to pair erroneously with thymine instead of cytosine, the replication following its production may result in the substitution of an adenine-thymine base pair for the óriginal guanine–cytosine base pair in the DNA molecule, at that particular site. Such substitution may lead to a mutation, but a different, rather obscure, mechanism leads to chromosomal breakage.

The most interesting feature of many radiomimetic agents is their localized effect upon the chromosomes. This effect is usually demonstrated as a higher frequency of breaks in the heterochromatic regions of the chromosomes than in the euchromatic regions. The breakage pattern is nonrandom, in contrast to that induced by ionizing radiations. Some of the agents exhibiting this specificity of action are maleic hydrazide, 8-ethoxycaffeine, diepoxybutane, and β-propiolactone. Alkylating agents may cause chromosomal breakage by binding to DNA regions rich in guanine–cytosine base pairs, causing these regions to become unstable. On the other hand, most of the evidence points to a disruption of the main chain of DNA, perhaps in regions where protein is bound. Thus, it remains unclear why certain agents tend to affect heterochromatic regions of the chromosomes more frequently than euchromatic regions.

Cancer

Cancer can be induced by radiation and treated by radiation. In either case, at least part of the effect is due to the production of chromosomal aberrations and/or mutations. Changes involving the chromosomes in cancer cells are primarily associated with an increase in chromosome number, many cells having three or more times the haploid number of chromosomes. This phase of the cancer syndrome will be discussed in more detail in the next chapter. Some instances have been found in which chromosomal aberrations characterized some of the cells in a cancer in vivo. However, they are not necessarily a diagnostic feature of all cancers or even of any given cancer. Nevertheless, almost all types of chromosomal aberrations have been identified in cancer cells grown in vitro. In addition, cancer cells may exhibit multipolar spindle formation, nuclear fragmentation, multinucleate cells, or abnormal distribution of the chromosomes to the poles during division. Since some normal cells grown in vitro may also exhibit certain of these phenomena after long-term culturing, it is difficult to conclude how close the relationship is between cancer and abnormal chromosome conditions. At least two possibilities exist. The abnormalities may aid in the formation of a cancer, or they may be by-products of a cancer already formed. Most of the evidence indicates that the latter alternative is more probable. The abnormalities may arise from somatic mutations, which may also be responsible for the development of cancer cells. Such a source has been postulated because the types of abnormalities observed with these mutations are seen in cancers caused by various mutagenic or *carcinogenic* (cancer-inducing) agents.

Cancer cells may also be induced by hormones or viruses. For example, RNA-containing viruses have been shown to produce leukemias and solid tumors in chickens and rodents, and DNA viruses produce tumors in rodents and in man. The Rous-sarcoma virus not only produces tumors when tested in *Drosophila* larvae, but also may induce lethal mutations or chromosomal aberrations. The presence of chromosomal damage has been noted after infection by several other viruses, including measles, polio, and *Herpes simplex* virus. These effects are found in vivo as well as in vitro in human cells. Although not all such cells infected with one of these viruses and having chromosomal damage develop into cancer cells, there is now strong evidence for the hypothesis that some cancers may be initiated by certain viruses. The relation between viruses and diseases other than cancer is well established. In addition to measles and polio, for example, chromosomal damage has also been found in the cells of individuals infected with chicken pox virus. The damaged cells, however, usually are replaced by normal ones after the infection has run its course. Whether the chromosomal damage is the primary event or only secondary to the infection is not yet certain.

SELECTED READING

General

Darlington, C. D., *Recent Advances in Cytology,* Blakiston, Philadelphia, 1937.

Darlington, C. D., ed., "Symposium on Chromosome Breakage," *Heredity,* **6,** Suppl. (1952).

Dobzhansky, T., *Genetics and the Origin of Species,* 3rd ed., Columbia Univ. Press, New York, 1958.

Elkind, M. M., and G. F. Whitmore, *The Radiobiology of Cultured Mammalian Cells,* Gordon and Breach, New York, 1967.

Evans, H. J., "Chromosome Aberrations Induced by Ionizing Radiations," *Intern. Rev. Cytol.,* **13,** 221 (1962).

Hanawalt, P. C., and R. H. Haynes, "The Repair of DNA," *Sci. Am.,* **216**(2), 36 (1967).

Hollaender, A., *Radiation Biology,* Vols. I–III, McGraw-Hill, New York, 1954–56.

Kihlman, B. A., *Actions of Chemicals on Dividing Cells,* Prentice-Hall, Englewood Cliffs, N.J., 1966.

Lea, D. E., *Actions of Radiations on Living Cells,* 2nd ed., Cambridge Univ. Press, Cambridge, 1955.

Loveless, A., *Genetic and Allied Effects of Alkylating Agents,* Pennsylvania State Univ. Press, University Park, Pa., 1966.

Stebbins, G. L., *Variation and Evolution in Plants,* Columbia Univ. Press, New York, 1950.

Spontaneous Aberrations

Babcock, E. B., "The Genus *Crepis,*" *Univ. Calif. (Berkeley) Publ. Botany,* **21**, 22 (1947).

Cleland, R. E., ed., "Studies in *Oenothera* Cytogenetics and Phylogeny," *Indiana Univ. Publ., Sci. Ser.,* No. 16 (1950).

John, B., and K. R. Lewis, "Chromosome Variability and Geographic Distribution in Insects," *Science,* **152**(3723), 711 (1966).

Lewis, K. R., and B. John, "The Meiotic Consequences of Spontaneous Chromosome Breakage," *Chromosoma,* **18**(2), 287 (1966).

Lubs, H. A., and J. Samuelson, "Chromosome Abnormalities in Lymphocytes from Normal Human Subjects," *Cytogenetics,* **6**, 402 (1967).

McClintock, B., "Spontaneous Alterations in Chromosome Size and Form in *Zea mays,*" *Cold Spring Harbor Symp. Quant. Biol.,* **9**, 72 (1941).

Novitski, E., and G. Braver, "An Analysis of Crossing Over Within a Heterozygous Inversion in *Drosophila melanogaster,*" *Genetics,* **39**(3), 197 (1954).

Rhoades, M. M., and E. Dempsey, "Cytogenetic Studies of Deficient-Duplicate Chromosomes Derived from Inversion Heterozygotes in Maize," *Am. J. Botany,* **40**(6), 405 (1953).

Riley, H. P., "Chromosome Aberrations in Natural Populations of *Tradescantia paludosa,*" *Nucleus (Calcutta),* **1**(1), 11 (1958).

Sax, H. J., and K. Passano, "Spontaneous Chromosome Aberrations in Human Tissue Culture Cells," *Am. Naturalist,* **95**(881), 97 (1961).

Induced Aberrations

Brewen, J. G., "Cell Cycle and Radiosensitivity of the Chromosomes of Human Leukocytes," *Intern. J. Radiation Biol.,* **9**, 391 (1965).

Chu, E. H. Y., N. H. Giles, and K. Passano, "Types and Frequencies of Human Chromosome Aberrations Induced by X Rays," *Proc. Natl. Acad. Sci. U.S.,* **47**(6), 830 (1961).

Dewey, W. C., and R. M. Humphrey, "Restitution of Radiation-Induced Chromosomal Damage in Chinese Hamster Cells Related to the Cell's Life Cycle," *Exptl. Cell Res.,* **35**(2), 262 (1964).

Evans, H. J., and J. R. K. Savage, "The Relation Between DNA Synthesis and Chromosome Structure as Resolved by X-Ray Damage," *J. Cell Biol.,* **18**(3), 525 (1963).

Giles, N. H., "The Oxygen Effect on Radiation-Induced Chromosome Aberrations: Breakage-Versus-Recombination Hypotheses," *J. Cellular Comp. Physiol.,* **45,** Suppl. 2, 271 (1955).

Heddle, J. A., and S. Wolff, "Estimation of the Rejoining Distance for Chromosome Exchanges Induced in *Drosophila* Sperm by Combined Doses of X Rays and Neutrons," *Intern. J. Radiation Biol.,* **10**, 207 (1966).

Hutchinson, F., "Molecular Basis for Action of Ionizing Radiations," *Science,* **134** (3478), 533 (1961).

Kubitschek, H. E., "Mutagenesis by Near-Visible Light," *Science,* **155**(3769), 1545 (1967).

Moh, C. C., and R. B. Withrow, "Non-ionizing Radiant Energy as an Agent in Altering the Incidence of X-Ray-Induced Chromatid Aberrations. II. Reversal of the Far-Red Potentiating Effect in *Vicia* by Red Radiant Energy," *Radiation Res.,* **10**(1), 13 (1959).

Revell, S. H., "The Accurate Estimation of Chromatid Breakage and Its Relevance to a New Interpretation of Chromatid Aberrations Induced by Ionizing Radiations," *Proc. Roy. Soc. (London), Ser. B,* **150**, 563 (1959).

Savage, J. R. K., R. J. Preston, and G. J. Neary, "Chromatid Aberrations in *Tradescantia bracteata* and a Further Test of Revell's Hypothesis," *Mutation Res.,* **5,** 47 (1968).

Scott, D., "The Additive Effect of X Rays and Maleic Hydrazide in Inducing Chromosomal Aberrations at Different Stages of the Mitotic Cycle in *Vicia faba,*" *Mutation Res.,* **5,** 65 (1968).

Scott, D., and H. J. Evans, "X-Ray-Induced Chromosomal Aberrations in *Vicia faba:* Changes in Response During the Cell Cycle," *Mutation Res.,* **4,** 579 (1967).

Sparrow, A. H., A. G. Underbrink, and R. C. Sparrow, "Chromosomes and Cellular Radiosensitivity. I. The Relationship of D_0 to Chromosome Volume and Complexity in Seventy-nine Different Organisms," *Radiation Res.,* **32**(4), 915 (1967).

Sutherland, B. M., W. L. Carrier, and R. B. Setlow, "Photoreactivation in Vivo of Pyrimidine Dimers in *Paramecium* DNA," *Science,* **153**(3809), 1699 (1967).

Trosko, J. E., E. H. Y. Chu, and W. L. Carrier, "The Induction of Thymine Dimers in Ultraviolet-Irradiated Mammalian Cells, *Radiation Res.,* **24**(4), 667 (1965).

Radiomimesis

Alexander, P., "Radiation-Imitating Chemicals," *Sci. Am.,* **202**(1), 99 (1960).

Auerbach, C., "The Chemical Production of Mutations," *Science,* 158(3805), 1141 (1967).

Cohen, M. M., M. J. Marinello, and N. Back, "Chromosomal Damage in Human Leukocytes Induced by Lysergic Acid Diethylamide," *Science,* 155(3768), 1417 (1967).

Kihlman, B. A., and B. Hartley, "Hydroxyurea: Effect on *Vicia* Chromosomes Previously Exposed to X Rays or to Radiomimetic Chemicals," *Exptl. Cell Res.,* 48(3), 629 (1967).

Merz, T., C. P. Swanson, and N. S. Cohn, "Interaction of Chromatid Breaks Produced by X Rays and Radiomimetic Compounds," *Science,* 133(3454), 703 (1961).

Steffensen, D., "Chromosome Structure with Special Reference to the Role of Metal Ions," *Intern. Rev. Cytol.,* 12, 163 (1961).

Cancer

Bartsch, H. D., K.-O. Habermehl, and W. Diefenthal, "Chromosomal Damage After Infection with Poliomyelitis Virus," *Exptl. Cell Res.,* 48(3), 671 (1967).

Bayreuther, K., "Chromosomes in Primary Neoplastic Growth," *Nature,* 186 (4718), 6 (1960).

Burdette, W. J., and J. S. Yoon, "Mutations, Chromosomal Aberrations, and Tumors in Insects Treated with Oncogenic Virus," *Science,* 155(3760), 340 (1967).

Dulbecco, R., "Transformation of Cells in Vitro by Viruses," *Science,* 142(3594), 932 (1963).

Hampar, B., and S. A. Ellison, "Chromosomal Aberrations Induced by an Animal Virus," *Nature,* 192(4798), 145 (1961).

Hsu, T. C., "Mammalian Chromosomes in Vitro. IV. Some Human Neoplasms," *J. Natl. Cancer Inst.,* 14(4), 905 (1954).

Levan, A., and J. J. Biesele, "The Role of Chromosomes in Cancerogenesis as Studied in Serial Tissue Culture of Mammalian Cells," *Ann. N.Y. Acad. Sci.,* 71, 1022 (1958).

Nichols, W. W., "The Role of Viruses in the Etiology of Chromosomal Abnormalities," *Am. J. Human Genet.,* 18(1), 81 (1966).

Nichols, W. W., A. Levan, P. Aula, and E. Norrby, "Extreme Chromosome Breakage Induced by Measles Virus in Different in Vitro Systems," *Hereditas,* 51 (3), 380 (1964).

16

Chromosome Number

Somatic cells, with the exception of those of male hymenopterans and the vegetative stages of many algae and fungi, contain a diploid number of chromosomes, while germinal, or gametic, cells are haploid. The constancy of this ratio within a given species was emphasized earlier. It has also been noted that chromosome numbers vary from species to species and occasionally within certain tissues of an organism. As may be expected with any biological phenomenon, there is, in addition, a significant incidence of variation from the diploid or haploid condition in some organisms or in specific cell types. Several aspects of these variations will be presented, although they are not all related with respect to origins or biological influence.

Aneuploidy

A classification of the basic types of variations in chromosome number is given in Table 16–1. An addition or loss of less than an entire set of chromosomes (haploid) is called *aneuploidy,* and it subsumes two classes, *hypoploidy* and *hyperploidy.* Both arise from an abnormal distribution of the chromosomes to the poles during anaphase of meiosis. Whereas one daughter cell receives an extra chromosome (or chromosomes), the other lacks a chromosome (or chromosomes). Abnormal distribution of the chromosomes during division of the cell is known as *nondisjunction.* Thus a gamete containing one extra chromosome unites at fertilization with a normal gamete to produce a zygote *trisomic* for that chromosome, and a gamete lacking one chromosome unites at fertilization with a normal

Table 16–1   Types of Variations in Chromosome Number

Type	Number	Description
aneuploidy		loss or addition of less than a set
hypoploidy	$2n - x$	loss of one or more chromosomes
nullisomic	$2n - 2$	loss of a homologous pair
monosomic	$2n - 1$	loss of one member of a pair
double monosomic	$2n - 1 - 1$	loss of two nonhomologous chromosomes
hyperploidy	$2n + x$	addition of one or more chromosomes
trisomic	$2n + 1$	addition of a third homologue to a pair
tetrasomic	$2n + 2$	addition of two homologues to a pair
double tetrasomic	$2n + 2 + 2$	addition of two homologues to one pair and two homologues to a second pair
euploidy		loss or addition of one or more sets
monoploidy (haploid)	n	genetically hemizygous
diploidy	$2n(n + n)$	two homologous sets
polyploidy		
triploidy	$3n(2n + n)$	three homologous sets
tetraploidy	$4n(2n + 2n)$	four homologous sets
pentaploidy	$5n$	five homologous sets
hexaploidy	$6n$	six homologous sets
heptaploidy	$7n$	seven homologous sets
octoploidy	$8n$	eight homologous sets

gamete to produce a *monosomic* zygote. The result of nondisjunction on an organismal level is an individual with all its cells having an atypical number of chromosomes. Nondisjunction can also occur in somatic cells, producing patches of cells in the body with atypical chromosome numbers. If the differences in chromosome number are important as far as the genetic loci are concerned, cells in these patches may be morphologically distinct from the cells having normal chromosome numbers. Individuals with such cell patches are *mosaics*.

Extreme decreases in chromosome number often cause cell death, with a consequent reduction in the viability of the gametes if the decreases have taken place in meiotic cells. The sensitivity of the organism or cell to chromosome loss varies with the species and perhaps with the individual. Some individuals can survive the loss of several chromosomes, some can survive the loss of only one chromosome, and many cannot withstand the loss of even a single chromosome. Increases in chromosome number are less likely to reduce cell viability than decreases, although the particular genetic loci associated with the additions are a limiting factor.

Of the aneuploid types listed in Table 16–1, the most common are the trisomics and monosomics; yet the probability of their continuation in cell lineage is relatively low. Monosomics, rare in normally diploid organisms, are very likely of polyploid origin and may persist in polyploid individuals through several cell generations. In a cell with more than the diploid number of chromosomes, the loss of a single chromosome would be expected to have little or no effect on viability. Monosomics have been found in species of wheat and tobacco identified as polyploid. The deleterious effect of the loss of a single chromosome from a diploid cell is evident upon observation of meiosis in a monosomic individual that is normally diploid. Since the remaining member of a bivalent no longer has a homologue with which to pair, it behaves as a univalent chromosome, moving to either pole of the cell during division. The gametes developing with a deficiency for this chromosome are usually nonviable.

Nullisomics can arise from the union of two monosomic gametes or from nondisjunction. If the individuals survive, they usually exhibit decreased vigor and altered phenotypes as compared with normal individuals. The pairing relationships of the chromosomes in cells showing variations in chromosome number are important in determining the cells' persistence as well as their genetic potential. As an illustration, the meiotic behavior of representative aneuploids is depicted in Figure 16–1.

Trisomic individuals have been found in a number of species, including *Drosophila, Datura,* and *Zea mays.* The presence of a third homologous chromosome in a cell undergoing meiosis interferes with the pairing process. Under normal circumstances two homologous chromosomes pair over their entire lengths, giving rise to a bivalent in late prophase and metaphase of the first meiotic division. Since only two homologues can pair at any one position, three homologues assume several arrangements. A *trivalent* configuration results from an association of all three chromosomes. On the other hand, two of the chromosomes may join to produce a bivalent, leaving the third as a univalent. The longer the chromosomes, the more likely the formation of chiasmata and therefore of a trivalent. An example of a trisomic individual is *triplo-IV* of *Drosophila,* in which chromosome IV is present three times. The phenotype includes narrow pointed wings, coarse bristles, and smooth eyes. Genetic ratios obtained in the offspring of such trisomic individuals mated to normal individuals are consistent with the expected patterns of segregation and are different from the ratios obtained when two diploid individuals are mated. The

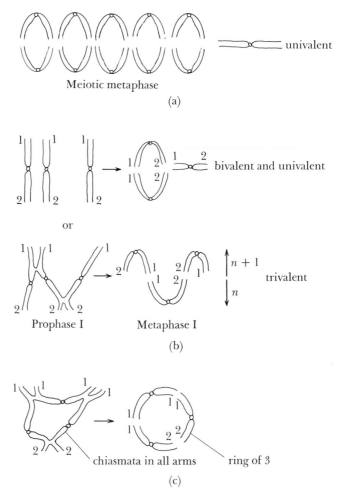

Figure 16–1. Meiotic behavior in aneuploids: (a) monosomic $(2n − 1)$ (in *Tradescantia* $2n = 12$, diploid, and $2n = 11$, monosomic); (b) primary trisomic $(2n + 1)$; (c) secondary trisomic $(2n + 1)$.

genetic schemes of crosses between normal and atypical individuals are shown in Figure 16–2. Whereas the normal ratio is 1 : 1, the ratio in offspring of crosses between normal and atypical individuals is 2 : 1 or 5 : 1, depending upon the viability of the gametes.

The foregoing discussion deals with *primary trisomics,* in which all three chromosomes have the same genetic constitution. Individuals in which the third chromosome is not identical to the other two are called *secondary trisomics.* These arise from primary trisomics when a bivalent

Normal: $Aa \times aa \rightarrow$

	a	*a*	$\rightarrow 1A:1a$
A	*Aa*	*Aa*	
a	*aa*	*aa*	

Trisomic: $AAa \times aa \rightarrow$

	a	$\rightarrow 5A:1a$ if all gametes survive
2*A*	2*Aa*	or $2A:1a$ if encircled
(2*Aa*)	2*Aaa*	gametes do not survive
(1*AA*)	1*AAa*	
1*a*	1*aa*	

Figure 16–2. Gene segregation in a normal diploid cross and in a cross between a diploid and a trisomic.

and a univalent form and the univalent later acts abnormally. The kineto-chore of the univalent chromosome undergoes misdivision to produce isochromosomes. Thus the third member of the group in a secondary triso-mic is a chromosome with two identical arms. The pairing in a secondary trisomic is indicated in Figure 16–1. In contrast to primary trisomics, secondary trisomics result in a ring of three chromosomes during meiosis. In *Datura* the haploid number of chromosomes is 12, and there are 24 possible secondary trisomics. Many of these have been observed, and each has a characteristically different phenotype. More complex trisomics are known, including some in *Datura,* such as *tertiary trisomics,* in which translocations take place between nonhomologous chromosomes, and in which the pairing is disrupted in a fashion similar to that in other tri-somics.

Euploidy

Monoploidy

The behavior of normally haploid organisms has been described in pre-vious chapters. There are cases, particularly in plants, in which individ-uals that would normally be diploid are haploid (*monoploid*), but they are very infrequent, since haploids of this type have a high incidence of sterility and are often rather weak. From a genetic standpoint, monoploid individuals are *hemizygous,* for they contain only a single genome or set of genes.

Although the origins of all spontaneous monoploids have not been determined, there are several ways in which they may arise. In plants an unfertilized egg may be stimulated to develop into an embryo by the growth of the pollen tube or by some other physical, environmental stimulus. Extremely rarely, synergids develop into twin embryos after environmental stimulation. Plant eggs as well as some animal eggs can be stimulated to develop by exposure to electrical shock, chemical treatment, or other experimental procedures. When a haploid individual survives, it is often less viable than its diploid counterpart, it may be smaller, and it is less likely to produce viable gametes. *If* meiosis occurs, the chromosomes have no homologues with which to pair, and their distribution is quite irregular; they move to the poles of the dividing cell at random. Thus a gamete may contain no chromosomes, an entire haploid set of chromosomes, or an irregular number of chromosomes. Only the gametes with a full set of chromosomes are viable, and the percentage of sterile gametes depends upon the total number of chromosomes in the monoploid and the probability of their all going to the same pole. The number of gametes containing a particular chromosome is $(\frac{1}{2})^n$, where n equals the haploid number of chromosomes, and the probability of any one chromosome's moving to a pole is $\frac{1}{2}$.

Polyploidy

Cells containing more than two haploid sets of chromosomes, from *triploids* on up, are *polyploids.* There are two major types, according to the origins of the chromosomes. Polyploids having chromosomes derived from parents with similar genomes are *autopolyploids,* whereas those having chromosomes derived from parents with different genomes are *allopolyploids.* For example, if the chromosomes of one parent are designated as *AA* and the chromosomes of the other parent as *AA,* the pairing of the chromosomes in the resulting autopolyploid is consistent with their similar genetic constitutions. On the other hand, if the chromosomes of the second parent are designated as *BB,* the pairing is indicative of significant differences in genetic make-up. An autotriploid's chromosomal content may be designated as *AAA,* an autotetraploid's as *AAAA,* and an allotetraploid's as *AABB,* where each letter represents a haploid set of chromosomes of specific genetic composition. A triploid organism may arise from the union of a tetraploid individual (the gametes are diploid) and a diploid individual (the gametes are haploid). An autotetraploid may arise naturally from a doubling of the diploid number in somatic cells or from the union of two diploid gametes. However, autotetraploids are not common in nature and have apparently been of little evolutionary consequence. As noted in Chapter 10, colchicine, or a similar drug, can induce autopolyploidy experimentally.

Although polyploidy appears very seldom in animal populations, it is found in a number of species in the plant kingdom. It has been estimated that half of the species of seed plants are polyploid. Examples include wheat and blueberries, in which the range of chromosome numbers is from the diploid to the hexaploid condition. The few well-established cases of polyploidy in animals include some of the annelids, the axolotl, and the golden hamster. The most widely accepted explanation of the general absence of polyploidy in animals is based upon their chromosomal mechanisms of sex determination. As will be shown later, in many bisexual animals a definite ratio of sex chromosomes to somatic chromosomes must be maintained for continued fertility. Any upset in this genetic balance, such as that caused by polyploidy, reduces fertility and decreases the chances of the individuals to survive and reproduce. Therefore, polyploids would rapidly disappear from the populations. They could persist, however, in some organisms that reproduce parthenogenetically, as certain lepidopterans and crustaceans. Another aspect of this problem is related to the differences in the reproductive processes of plants and animals. Most higher animals can reproduce by sexual means only, whereas plants can also reproduce by vegetative means. Thus the likelihood of establishing a polyploid through somatic orgins is considerably greater in plants than in animals.

Autopolyploid plants are often larger than their diploid counterparts, partly because of large cell sizes. *Salix aurita* ($4n = 76$) and *Crepis bungei* ($4n = 16$) demonstrate this size difference. Other morphological characteristics of autopolyploids as compared with diploids include larger pollen grains and more chloroplasts. On the other hand, chromosome numbers higher than the tetraploid may result in plants that are smaller and less viable than their diploid relatives. These phenotypic variations are dependent upon the specific genetic make-ups of the organisms in question and can only be considered as generalities to which there are exceptions.

The cytological behavior of autopolyploids during meiosis is illustrated in Figure 16–3. Since a triploid individual is trisomic for each chromosome, the pairing of the chromosomes parallels that in a trisomic. Fertility is decreased in triploid individuals because of the lowered probability that a gamete will receive a complete set of chromosomes. Autotetraploids have a somewhat higher fertility because the chances of normal pairing are increased. For the most part, those polyploids with an

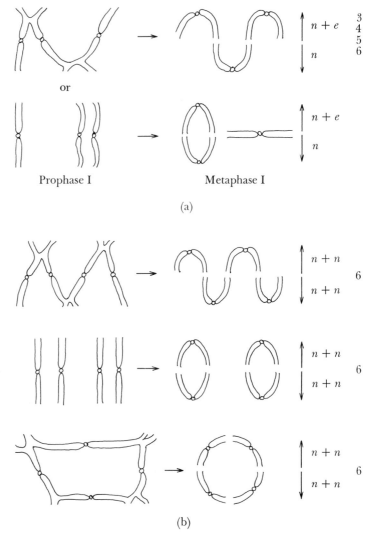

Figure 16–3. Meiotic behavior in autopolyploids (e = one or more extra chromosomes): (a) autotriploid ($n = 3$; $3n = 9$); (b) autotetraploid ($n = 3$; $4n = 12$). The gametic chromosome number appears at right.

even number of haploid sets are more fertile than those with an odd number of sets. In all cases, however, no polyploid exhibits the degree of fertility of a diploid organism.

Allopolyploids have been of much more evolutionary importance than autopolyploids, and their chromosomes may behave in several ways during meiosis (Figure 16–4). The basic pattern of allopolyploid formation consists in a doubling of the chromosome number in a hybrid offspring of two genetically different parents. If hybridization occurs without doubling of the chromosome number, the offspring acts as a monoploid and is quite sterile. Allopolyploids arise, as do autopolyploids, from doubling in the somatic tissues or from the union of diploid gametes. The genetic composition of an allotetraploid was given earlier as *AABB*, where *AA* represents the chromosomes from one parent (or species) and *BB* the chromosomes from the other parent (or species). In this particular instance, pairing during meiosis would be normal, *A* chromosomes with *A* chromosomes and *B* with *B*, and the individual would be fertile and viable. A classic example of an allotetraploid hybrid is the result (*Raphanobrassica*) of a cross between the radish (*Raphanus sativa*) and the cabbage (*Brassica oleracea*). Each parent has a haploid number of 9, and the allotetraploid hybrid has 36 chromosomes. Only identical chromosomes, or homologues, pair, but since each chromosome is present twice, pairing is complete, and the hybrid is fertile and viable, although not commercially valuable. The type of pairing observed in this and similar hybrids is called *autosyndesis*. Thus pairing in an allotetraploid is usually normal, with the chromosomes behaving as they do in a diploid organism. For this reason an allotetraploid with complete pairing (autosyndesis) is also called an *amphidiploid* (double diploid).

Pairing between two or more nonhomologous chromosomes, whether it be complete or partial, is called *allosyndesis*. The term describes pairing of any kind between an *A* chromosome and a *B* chromosome, which are nonhomologous, in the allotetraploid *AABB*. This type of pairing can result if nonhomologous chromosomes have one or more small segments that are homologous owing to a prior translocation or some other similar structural change. Allopolyploids with such chromosomes are *segmental allopolyploids*.

In the plant kingdom, several allopolyploids of taxonomic and evolutionary significance have been studied. They are as follows:

Primula kewensis: An allotetraploid hybrid resulting from a cross between *P. verticillata* ($2n = 18$) and *P. floribunda* ($2n = 18$). *P. kewensis* ($4n = 36$) is fertile, since pairing is normal and usually complete.

Spartina townsendii: An amphidiploid that is not an allotetraploid. *S. alterniflora* ($2n = 70$) and *S. stricta* ($2n = 56$) are probably of polyploid origin themselves, and their hybrid, *S. townsendii*, has 126 chromosomes, which pair normally.

Rosa: A genus with a basic haploid number of 7 and many poly-

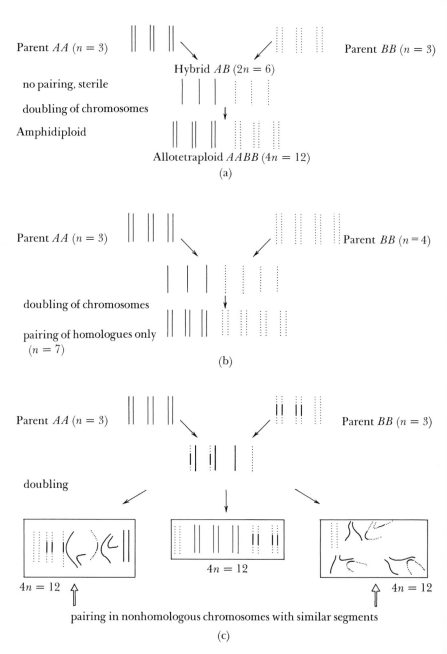

Parent AA ($n = 3$)   Parent BB ($n = 3$)

Hybrid AB ($2n = 6$)

no pairing, sterile

doubling of chromosomes

Amphidiploid

Allotetraploid $AABB$ ($4n = 12$)

(a)

Parent AA ($n = 3$)   Parent BB ($n = 4$)

doubling of chromosomes

pairing of homologues only
($n = 7$)

(b)

Parent AA ($n = 3$)   Parent BB ($n = 3$)

doubling

$4n = 12$

$4n = 12$

$4n = 12$

pairing in nonhomologous chromosomes with similar segments

(c)

Figure 16–4. Meiotic origins of and behavior in allopolyploids: (a) origin;
(b) autosyndesis; (c) allosyndesis.

ploid species. Pentaploid ($5n$) individuals have 35 chromosomes. However, pairing is not complete, since the chromosomes are not entirely homologous. In the $5n$ plant there are 7 pairs of chromosomes (7 bivalents) and 21 univalents.

Papaver: A hybrid offspring of *P. nudicaule* ($n = 7$) and *P. striatocarpum* ($n = 35$) with 42 chromosomes, all of which undergo normal pairing, demonstrating the occurrence of allosyndesis and autosyndesis in the same plant. There are 21 bivalents produced; 7 nudicaule chromosomes pair with 7 striatocarpum chromosomes in allosyndesis, and 14 striatocarpum chromosomes pair with 14 striatocarpum chromosomes in autosyndesis. This is not an amphidiploid, even though pairing is complete, since the chromosomes are not of similar genetic constitutions.

Iris versicolor: A hybrid offspring of *I. setosa* ($n = 19$) and *I. virginica* ($n = 35$) with 108 chromosomes. It is an amphidiploid, since the chromosomes are similar and pairing is complete. This particular case is a very good example of the role of polyploidy in plant speciation; certain polyploids differ enough from their parents to be given new species names. The problem of speciation is rather ticklish, for a number of factors must be considered, including morphogenetic differences and the viability and fertility of hybrids. If a polyploid is morphologically identical to a diploid, it is not recognized as a different species. In most instances such similarity indicates autopolyploidy. If a tetraploid is quite distinct from a diploid, and if the two forms do not produce fertile hybrids, then it is reasonable to relegate the tetraploid to a different species. An autotetraploid may give rise to an allotetraploid through an accumulation of genetic changes (mutations) that clearly distinguish the polyploid from the diploid species.

Crepis: A genus containing American species in which polyploidy has been of considerable importance. All 10 American species exhibit autopolyploidy and allopolyploidy, with chromosome numbers ranging from 33 to 88 ($n = 11$), but there are diploid forms of these species as well. The Old World species include few polyploids (tetraploids and octoploids) and, in general, tend to have lower haploid chromosome numbers ($n = 3$ to 7).

Still more complex polyploids than those mentioned may occur, their frequency in the population depending upon the several conditions, including homologies of chromosomes, just discussed. Autoallopolyploids have been found in several species of plants, most of them hexaploid. According to the designations used heretofore, the formula would be *AAAABB*, resulting from the union of an *AA* gamete with a *B* gamete, followed by a doubling of the chromosome number. An autoallooctoploid, *AAAABBBB,* could result from the union of two autotetraploids, *AAAA* and *BBBB,* with subsequent doubling of the chromosomes, or from the doubling of the chromosomes in an allotetraploid, *AABB.*

Heteroploidy in Tissues

Although most organisms have diploid chromosome numbers, many show variations in chromosome number within the body tissues. Numerous examples of variations in germ tissue have been cited, but variations in somatic cells have also been observed. Certain tissues in both plants and animals have been found to contain more or less than the usual diploid number of chromosomes, with the differences being sporadic or regular according to the nature of the tissue and the nature of the change in chromosome number. For example, aneuploidy appears to be a normal occurrence in human endometrium; in one study of 28 women, chromosome numbers ranged from 17 to 103, where 46 is the normal diploid number. Tetraploid cells have been found in mammalian liver, and in certain brain cells, including the Purkinje cells of the cerebellum. Somatic differences arise in several ways, including the mechanisms of *somatic reduction, somatic segregation,* and *endomitosis.* They appear in otherwise normal tissue as well as in abnormal tissue.

Somatic Reduction

In Chapter 13 the behavior of the chromosomes in the gall fly *Miastor* was discussed in connection with anomalous aspects of development. During the early stages of embryogenesis, certain chromosomes are lost from many of the cells. In *Sciara* and in *Icerya purchasi,* the cottony cushion scale (Chapter 14), similar phenomena occur. In a hermaphrodite, chromosome loss from the male cells of the developing organism produces a sector of haploid tissue. Each haploid cell later undergoes an equational meiotic division resulting in the formation of two sperm, the process resembling that described in Chapter 14 for the normal haploid male. During development of the larva of the mosquito *Culex pipiens,* there is an increase in chromosome number in the epithelial cells lining the ileum. These cells are quite large, a function of their level of ploidy, and contain what have been called *multiple complexes,* or groups of chromosomes in close association. As metamorphosis proceeds, the number of chromosomes in these cells decreases, and by the end of metamorphosis the chromosome number is appreciably lessened, and there are very few large cells. The mechanism of reduction is similar in some ways to meiotic division; the chromosomes pair and separate to the poles. Several divisions of this type take place, gradually lowering the chromosome number. The haploid number for the species is 3, and the first reductional division is character- ized by a pairing of homologous chromosomes, with each group consisting of up to 64 strands. In anaphase the homologous strands separate from each other without any longitudinal division, so that the daughter cells have reduced numbers of chromosomes. At the end of several divisions, the chromosome number is cut from $64n$ to $4n$.

Somatic Segregation

Normally the division of a cell results in two daughter cells that are ge- netically and cytologically identical. Occasionally there is a genetic or mechanical disturbance that leads to two unlike daughter cells. For ex- ample, nondisjunction causes the production of daughter cells with differ- ent chromosome numbers. Here there is a cytological dissimilarity and usually a genetic one. Such a difference in somatic tissue is an instance of somatic segregation, which defines any process in which somatic divisions give rise to cells differing genetically and/or cytologically. Somatic gene mutation and somatic reduction may also produce tissue variants. n plants a sector of cells lying adjacent to normal cells, but varying from them in genetic composition, is known as a *chimaera*. The term *mosaic,* introduced earlier, is generally applied to a similar phenomenon in ani- mals. However, it refers specifically to genetic differences, whereas chi- maera indicates that morphological differences are evident in a single plant and that patches of cells with different morphologies (color, size, etc.) can be observed. Both chimaeras and mosaics may occur sponta- neously or be induced by radiation or chemical treatment. In plants sec- tors of morphologically different cells can be utilized to establish new forms, since propagation by vegetative means is possible. In both plants and animals these sectors are valuable as a rapid means of recognizing genetic or cytological changes.

Endomitosis

Increases in chromosome number, or polyploidization, have received some attention in an earlier discussion of polytene chromosomes. Polyteny is one of the principal results of endomitosis, and is a form of *endopoly- ploidy*. Endomitosis involves repeated duplications of the chromosomes without nuclear divisions. In polyteny the chromosomes remain in association as multistranded, giant chromosomes. In another form of endopolyploidy, *polysomaty,* the chromosomes separate from each other within the nucleus; each chromosome is normal in appearance, and the total polyploid number of chromosomes is distinguishable. One of the earliest well-documented cases of polysomaty is in the pond skater, *Gerris lateralis.* The diploid number of chromosomes in the male is 21, one of which is the heteropycnotic X (sex) chromosome. By counting the number of heteropycnotic bodies in the nucleus, one can determine the number of sets of chromosomes present. This correlation is comparable to that which usually exists between the number of nucleoli and the number of chromosome sets in other organisms. In *Gerris,* chromosome numbers as high as $1024n$ have been found in several somatic tissues.

Polysomaty occurs also in certain lepidopterans, specific cells of the grasshopper, and some plant tissues. The root cells of spinach often exhibit varying degrees of polysomaty, as do those of *Rhoeo discolor.* At least one organism is known in which particular cells exhibit polyteny and polysomaty simultaneously. The salivary gland cells of *Lestodiplosis,* a gall midge, contain the conventional polytene chromosomes of dipterans. One of the cells, however, has a polyploid number of chromosomes—32 sets. The origin of this combination has not been established; either polyteny or polyploidy may have come first. Studies on *Culex* suggest that polyteny arose first and that a longitudinal separation of the chromosomes followed, increasing the ploidy of the cell without affecting the polyteny (endomitosis of polytene chromosomes).

Polysomaty may result from some mechanism other than endomitosis. Most liver cells in female rats are diploid at birth, but the number of polyploid cells increases with age (especially during the first 3 months). Concurrently cells with two diploid nuclei and others with two tetraploid nuclei appear. Such binucleate cells arise through karyokinesis without cytokinesis, the nuclei fusing to form single polyploid nuclei in subsequent divisions.

Much emphasis has been placed upon the significance of changes in chromosome number during differentiation. The secretory cells of many animals have been useful for research on this subject. The possible bases for relationships between chromosome number and activity and differentiation are embodied in Beermann's statement: "In synthetically active cells, growth is simply a means to increase productivity, which, of course, would be impossible without a corresponding increase in the number of enzymatically active sites in the nucleus, i.e., multiplication of the chromosome strands."

Neoplasms

The variations in chromosome number covered in the preceding sections are found in normal tissues. They occur regularly in all cells of an organism or irregularly as in the production of chimaeras. However, they do not seriously impair the viability of either the tissue or the organism in question. Although the cells involved are atypical for one reason or another, they cannot truly be called abnormal.

Abnormal tissues usually exhibit a variety of changes, both morphological and physiological, and often genetic. In recent years techniques have been devised by which cells and tissues of many organisms can be grown in culture in the laboratory for cytological analyses. Mammalian cells grown in culture, especially long-term culture, sometimes show changes in chromosome number, which affect initially normal cells and tissues as well as abnormal cells and tissues. As an illustration of the effect in normal cells, a culture of the embryonic cells of a Swiss strain of mice provided a cell undergoing endomitosis. The chromosome number in this cell was increased to 320 ($16n$), with the chromosomes associated in bundles of 8. Similar cases of polyploidy have been seen in several strains of neoplasms grown in culture, in plant cells as well as animal cells.

Variations in chromosome number have been noted in the tumors (crown gall) of *Picea glauca,* the range being 3 to 70 chromosomes, with a relatively high incidence of aneuploidy. The normal diploid number in this species is 24. Repeatedly the callus tissue developing on a cut stem has been observed to contain polyploid cells. These are but two examples of heteroploidy from the many that have been investigated in plant and animal cell populations, in vitro and in vivo, including a number of different tissues from humans. Aneuploidy and polyploidy have been detected in sarcomas and carcinomas of several strains in man and other mammals. Recent findings support the interpretation that polyploidy or aneuploidy in a cell culture is a consequence or characteristic of neoplastic growth. A culture of normal cells, however, may be influenced by the artificial conditions of growth. A report of the spontaneous occurrence of a polyploid in a normal mouse cell culture stresses this possibility. When mouse cells of two different strains were grown in a mixed culture, polyploid hybrid cells formed. The "hybridization" took place in the absence of any artificial treatment. Hybrid cells have also been derived in mixed cultures of mouse and human cells. Often the fusion of the two very different cell types is effected by the addition of virus particles, such as the influenza-type Sendai virus.

In spite of the variations in chromosome number in cultured cells, significant numbers of cells in many cultured populations have normal genomes. Therefore, changes imposed by culture methods and long-term growth are not the explanation for changes in normal cell lines. As indicated earlier, certain tissues are consistent in producing at least a few heteroploid cells in vivo. Cited were mammalian liver cells, which undergo mitosis almost continuously and which often are polyploid.

The concept of the *stem line* has been of considerable help in attempts to determine the sources of heteroploidy in some tumor tissues, particularly in culture. In the early stages of development of such tumors as ascites tumors, cells with chromosome numbers (and sometimes morphologies) differing from the normal appear. As the tissues are continued in culture, through subculturing and serial transfers, these cells increase in number and become characteristic of the tumor. These stem line cells promote the growth of the tumor as they become dominant in the population and may give rise to additional cells with other chromosome numbers. In human tumors, for example, the variation in stem line number is from about 40 to 100 or more. Yet, according to Levan, each stem line in a tumor represents the "survival of the fittest," since the same stem line karyotype often persists for very long periods. Differences in chromosome number are only one feature of *some* cancer cells, which display other cytological and biochemical anomalies.

Efforts have been made for many years to elucidate the causes, characteristics, and developmental histories of cancers. Currently, emphasis is being placed upon the secondary roles of chromosome anomalies, for several reasons. Not all types of cancer cells exhibit consistent changes in their chromosome constitutions, and many tissues are cancerous before changes in the genomes begin. Some virus-induced cancers of a number of organisms and the cancers apparently related to hormonal imbalance have normal chromosome complements. In fact, when chromosomal abnormalities are found, they tend to follow no consistent pattern. Even in the well-documented chronic granulocytic leukemia, not all patients with the cancer have the small chromosome usually associated with it. The chromosome is called the Philadelphia chromosome (Ph[1]), and is identified as one of the group G chromosomes (see Figure 16–7) with a deletion of part of the long arm. The loss of genetic material is illustrated by differences in DNA contents; the Ph[1] chromosome has 61% as much DNA as the normal chromosome (number 21 or number 22). Although the evidence is not entirely established, the presence of two Ph[1] chromosomes in some cases of acute granulocytic leukemia has suggested a chromosomal basis for the transition of one type of cancer to another. Compared with tumors in general, in which there may be a tendency to losses in the G group of chromosomes, in some types of leukemias there may be a tendency to gains in this group. Such losses or gains in one particular chromosome group do not preclude similar changes in other chromosomes.

Attempts to understand the nature and origin of cancer cells have led to several hypotheses, not all of which relate directly to chromosome number. Some studies, for example, suggest that cancer cell DNA has a more rigid configuration and a smaller mean molecular weight than normal cell DNA. These differences may be correlated with an alteration of the bases in DNA, leading to the process of transformation from normal cell to cancer cell. In effect, a genetic change occurs. Changes in chromosome number may, for that matter, be due to a gene mutation that increases the incidence of nondisjunction. Clearly, it is not possible to draw general conclusions about all cancer cells, since their origins vary. At best, it can be stated that often there is a definite association between cancer cells and chromosomal abnormalities and that the consequent genetic upset favors the progression of the cancer.

Sex Chromosomes

Sex determination in a variety of organisms is based upon differences in the chromosomal constitutions of the male and female. In certain animals, including humans, the male carries one X chromosome, and the female two X chromosomes. The remainder of the chromosomes (autosomes) are paired normally. In addition to the single X, the male has a Y chromosome, which is largely heterochromatic but which, in some mammals, plays a significant part in the development of male characteristics. Contrary to earlier descriptions, the Y chromosome is not genetically inert but carries genes necessary for the normal expression of maleness. A subsequent consideration of human "diseases" related to changes in chromosome number will clarify the role of the Y chromosome.

Several mechanisms exist for the determination of sex, but only those involving chromosome number and chromosomal interaction will be discussed here. The case just mentioned, in which the male is the *heterogametic* sex (XY), relies on the maintenance of a genetic equilibrium between the sex chromosomes and the autosomes. Man, the other mammals, and certain dipterans have this type of determination, whereas the lepidopterans, some fish, some reptiles, and all birds have heterogametic females. In these cases the female may be XY or XO, the latter term representing a single X chromosome and no Y chromosome.

In some organisms there are sufficient homologies between the X and Y chromosomes to permit at least partial pairing and some crossing over.

In others there are no homologies between the X and Y chromosomes. The elimination of the Y chromosome in certain organisms (for example, birds) seems to be the most recent sign of the evolution of sex determination with respect to chromosome number. The fact that such species develop males and females without Y chromosomes and the fact that sex determination in *Drosophila* occurs independently of the behavior of the Y chromosomes stress the superfluity of the Y chromosome in these species. Although this conclusion is justified, for the most part, the Y chromosome may still contribute to the developmental aspects of sex.

The ratio of sex chromosomes to autosomes is of prime importance in the determination of sex in *Drosophila,* as is seen in Table 16–2. The ratio of the number of X chromosomes to the number of sets of autosomes is 1.0 for the normal female and 0.5 for the normal male. Variations from these ratios produce sexual anomalies—supermales, superfemales, and intersexes—which are sterile. An intersex usually begins as a male but then tends toward the female.

The role of the Y chromosome becomes ambiguous again when other organisms are examined. Although it is apparently of relatively little value in *Drosophila,* it has great significance in the plant *Silene.* (This plant was known formerly as *Melandrium* or *Lychnis;* its common name is red or white campion.) Here there is an interaction between the X and Y chromosomes, as indicated in Table 16–3. The genetic constitutions of these chromosomes in terms of sex development are shown in Figure 16–5. Other plants with sex chromosomes include mosses, some liverworts, and the higher plants *Humulus* (hop), *Rumex* (sorrel), and *Cannabis* (hemp). Another organism in which the Y chromosome is important is the axolotl. Females with two Y chromosomes have been obtained, and sex determina-

Table 16–2   Sex Determination in *Drosophila*

Sex	Chromosome Constitution*	X/A Ratio
superfemale	$3X + 2A$	1.5
superfemale	$4X + 3A$	1.33
diploid female	$2X + 2A$	1.0
intersex	$3X + 4A$	0.75
intersex	$2X + 3A$	0.67
diploid male	$1X + 2A$	0.5
tetraploid male	$2X + 4A$	0.5
supermale	$1X + 3A$	0.33

* X = sex chromosome; A = haploid set of autosomes.

Table 16–3   Sex Determination in *Silene* (Caryophyllaceae)

Sex	*Chromosome Constitution*	*X/Y Ratio*
female	$2X + 2A$	0.00
male	$XYY + 2A$	0.50
male	$XY + 2A$	1.00
male	$XY + 3A$	1.00
male	$XY + 4A$	1.00
male	$XXYY + 4A$	1.00
male	$XXXYY + 4A$	1.50
male (occasional flower with both sexes)	$XXY + 2A$	2.00
	$XXXXYY + 4A$	2.00
male (occasional flower with both sexes)	$XXXY + 4A$	3.00
hermaphrodite (occasional male flower)	$XXXXY + 4A$	4.00

tion appears to depend upon the presence or absence of the Y. Mechanisms of sex determination involving large numbers of chromosomes have also been observed. In some species of mantids the male has two kinds of X chromosomes and a Y chromosome (X_1X_2Y), and the female has four X chromosomes $(X_1X_1X_2X_2)$. Among the most extreme cases, the beetle *Blaps polychresta* has the following chromosome constitutions: male, $18A + 12X + 6Y$; female, $18A + 24X$.

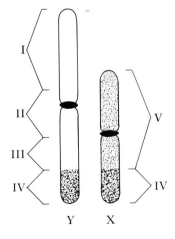

Figure 16–5. Sex chromosomes in *Silene*. I, Female suppressor region; when absent, complete flowers occur. II, Male-promoting region; when absent, the plant is female. III, Male fertility region. IV, Pairing region. V, Differential region; basic sex genes for femaleness. Only regions IV are homologous in X and Y.

A number of species of Hymenoptera (bees, wasps, ants) have haploid and diploid males and diploid females. The haploid males develop from unfertilized eggs (parthenogenesis), and the females and diploid males from fertilized eggs. Sex is determined genetically by a series of multiple alleles (X_1, X_2, etc., are genes) in the chromosomes, represented as follows:

Heterozygotes (females): X_1X_2; X_2X_3; X_1X_3
Homozygotes (diploid males): X_1X_1; X_2X_2; X_3X_3
Hemizygotes (haploid males): X_1; X_2; X_3

Thus a fertilized egg with a heterozygous genetic constitution becomes a female, whereas a fertilized egg that is homozygous becomes a male. All unfertilized eggs develop into males.

The development of an individual having tissues of both sexes is a rather curious process. In *Drosophila*, silkworms, and bees, mosaics arise if one of the X chromosomes is lost from an XX embryo. If an X chromosome is eliminated from one of the daughter cells of the first zygotic division, half of the individual will be female (XX cells), and the other half male (XO). The genes of the X chromosome (sex-linked genes) can easily be identified if the XX zygote is heterozygous for one or more genes. If an X chromosome is eliminated later in the development of the embryo, only certain parts of the individual will have male tissue. Organisms developing in this manner are *gynandromorphs*.

Human Cytogenetics

For many years the diploid number of chromosomes in the human was believed to be 48. In 1956 several workers announced that the correct number is 46, and subsequent studies have verified this figure. The change from 48 to 46 resulted from improvements in technique that permitted an accurate cytological analysis of mammalian tissue. It is now possible to maintain living cultures of human cells of almost all types and to prepare the cells for microscopic examination from fresh material. Although there have been a few reports of 47 or 48 chromosomes in normal human cells, there is universal acceptance of the diploid number 46.

According to their lengths, seven groups of chromosomes have been designated in the human karyotype. Each member of a group may be distinguished from the others by its length and kinetochore position. Group A (chromosomes 1, 2, and 3) consists of the longest chromosomes, which have median kinetochores. Group B (chromosomes 4 and 5) consists of the next longest chromosomes, with submedian kinetochores. There are seven chromosomes in group C, all of medium size and with submedian kinetochores. Group D (chromosomes 13, 14, and 15) is characterized by somewhat shorter chromosomes than group C and almost terminal kineto-chores (acrocentric). In group E (chromosomes 16, 17, and 18) the chromosomes are quite short, and the kinetochores are median or submedian. Group F (chromosomes 19 and 20) consists of still shorter chromosomes with median or submedian kinetochores. The shortest chromosomes (21 and 22) comprise group G and are acrocentric. The sex chromosomes (X and Y) differ in size and are assigned to two of the seven groups on the basis of their lengths. Although the X chromosome is almost identical to group C chromosomes, the Y chromosome (group G) is easily recognized.

Chromosome number and morphology are quite constant in most tissues of an individual as well as within a species (Figures 16–6 and 16–7).

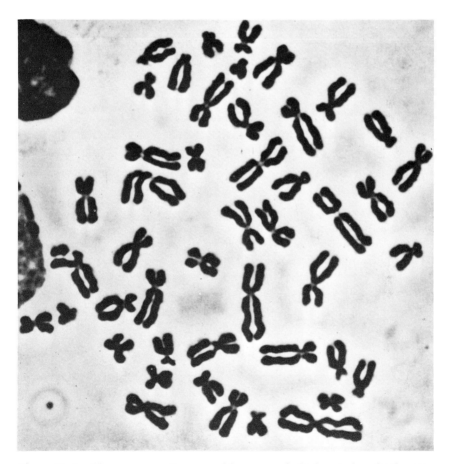

Figure 16–6. Chromosomes of a normal human male leukocyte in mitotic meta-phase (×3200). FROM J. L. Hamerton, *Intern. Rev. Cytol.,* 12, 1 (1961).

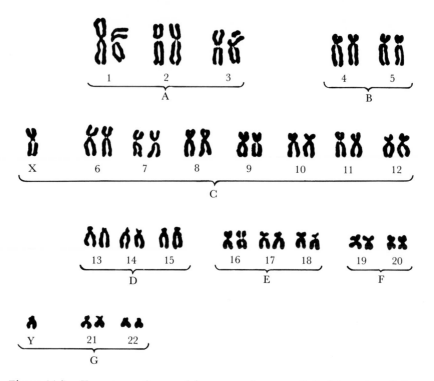

Figure 16–7.   Karyotype of normal human male. FROM J. L. Hamerton, *Intern. Rev. Cytol.,* **12,** 1 (1961).

Then why is the human karyotype discussed in a chapter on variations in chromosome number? Among the several reasons for its inclusion here are (1) human abnormalities associated with changes in chromosome number, (2) the significance of these changes in sex determination, and (3) modifications in the concept of the genetic roles of the X and Y chromosomes. These three aspects are interrelated, and the cases to be presented provide striking proof of the importance of changes in the karyotype for human heredity.

The human X chromosome has some interesting genetic and cytological characteristics that set it apart from the rest of the chromosomes. Previous chapters have dealt with the pattern of DNA synthesis in the chromosomes and the nature of the sex chromatin bodies in the nuclei of female cells. The X chromosome of humans exhibits behavior connected with both of these phenomena; the synthesis of DNA is later in one of the X chromosomes. In mammalian females the two X chromosomes differ from each other in the times of DNA synthesis. Since late DNA synthesis is associated with the formation of sex chromatin bodies, and since these bodies are relatively infrequent in the male, which has only one X chromosome, a late-replicating X chromosome must be responsible for the production of the sex chromatin bodies in female nuclei.

An explanation of the differences between the two X chromosomes states that the X chromosomes are identical in very early stages of embryonic development but that one later becomes heteropycnotic. This heteropycnotic X chromosome is genetically active in the male but inactive in the female. Either X chromosome may become heteropycnotic. The presence of one active and one inactive X chromosome leads to the formation of mosaics, or patches of cells with varying properties. This idea of somatic differentiation was first suggested by Mary Lyon. In diploid cells the number of sex chromatin bodies is always one less than the number of X chromosomes. There is now considerable substantiation of the inactivation theory in humans and other mammals. The type of hemolytic anemia found in 11% of American Negroes offers support for the Lyon hypothesis. An individual with this disorder is sensitive to primaquine, which causes a block of glutathione metabolism. This condition is linked genetically to the color-blindness locus, which is on the X chromosome. In some cases the female is not affected by the mutation, whereas in others she is. A possible explanation of the mechanism invokes a difference in genetic activity between the two X chromosomes. The genetic basis for the synthesis of glucose 6-phosphate dehydrogenase provides still more striking support for the inactivation theory. Individuals with the mutant form of the gene in the homozygous state (on both X chromosomes) exhibit a deficiency of the enzyme in all erythrocytes. Females heterozygous for the mutant gene have an enzyme level intermediate between that of normal and deficient subjects. Examination of their erythrocytes shows that there are two classes of erythrocytes; one has normal levels, and the other very low levels of the enzyme. Thus one X chromosome carrying the normal allele is inactivated in some cells, and the other X chromosome carrying the mutant allele is inactivated in the remaining cells. Further involvement of the X chromosome in human disease will be mentioned later.

The Y chromosome is among the smallest of the human chromosomes, but it has been identified, and its morphology described. There are two constrictions in the Y chromosome, a kinetochore and a secondary constriction. In some cells the distal arm from the secondary constriction to the end of the chromosome is missing, but apparently this deficiency has no phenotypic effect. In other individuals part of the long arm of the chromosome may be missing, and its absence has no effect on the development of male sexual characteristics. These missing portions are largely heterochromatic and genetically inert. The male-determining genes thus appear to be located on the short arm of the Y chromosome. Although the size of the Y chromosome varies among different families, it is usually inherited at a constant length in any one family. Since a relatively large proportion of the Y chromosome is heterochromatic, late DNA synthesis, as found in the X chromosome, is expected, and it has been observed. The chromatids of the Y chromosome tend to remain associated, even when treated with colchicine, while those of the other chromosomes exhibit normal spreading. However, this peculiarity likely has little to do with genetic activity. Even though the Y chromosome is highly heterochromatic, the human sexual anomalies to be discussed here emphasize its genetic function.

Cases of abnormal sexual development in humans have been clarified on the basis of chromosome constitution. In many instances the chromosome number deviates from the normal, and so does the sex chromatin body content. As a matter of fact, the latter irregularity first aroused the speculation that sexual abnormality was related to variations in chromosome number. Certain individuals with essentially male phenotypes had sex chromatin bodies in the nuclei of the buccal mucosa or skin, whereas others, essentially female, were sex chromatin negative. This is the reverse of the normal situation. Examination of the chromosomes of the abnormal persons disclosed discrepancies in chromosome numbers, specifically, in the numbers of X and/or Y chromosomes. Some examples of abnormal sexual conditions in humans and their chromosome constitutions are given in Table 16–4. The obvious conclusion is that the addition of a Y chromosome to a complement of X chromosomes converts a potential female into a male (the X chromosome provides for the development of female characteristics, and the Y chromosome for the development of male characteristics). The Y chromosome tends to mask the expression of the genes on the X chromosome. This phenomenon has also been seen in the mouse and possibly occurs in all mammals. For the most part, deviations from the normal number of X or Y chromosomes result from nondisjunction during oogenesis or spermatogenesis, when all or most of the body cells have the same chromosome number.

The Y chromosome alone is not responsible for all the sexual phenotypic variations. If more than two X chromosomes are present, upsets in sexual and mental development are increased. The specimens XXXY and XXXXY exhibit severe malformations of the sex organs and are mentally retarded, as are their female counterparts with XXX and XXXX chromosome constitutions. Similar effects, such as the Klinefelter and Turner syndromes, are apparent in individuals that are mosaics for the sex chromosomes. For example, persons with XY in some cells and XXY in other cells exhibit the Klinefelter syndrome to varying degrees, as do individuals

Table 16–4   Chromosomal Abnormalities in Humans

Sex Chromo- somes	Chromo- some Number	Condition	Sex Chromatin Test
XXY	47	Klinefelter syndrome: underdeveloped	positive
XXYY	48	testes; sterility; weak secondary sexual characteristics; retarded growth; some mental retardation	positive
XO	45	Turner syndrome: underdeveloped gonads; sterility; some neck webbing; short stature; some skeletal anomaly	negative
XXXY	48	severe testicular atrophy; mental retardation. Similar to Klinefelter syndrome	positive
XXXXY	49	malformed genitalia; congenital heart defect; mental retardation	positive
XXX	47	triplo-X female: phenotypically normal females; some menstrual upset; some fertility; lack of development of secondary sexual characteristics	positive
XXXX	48	phenotypically normal females; mental retardation	positive

with an XXY/XXXXY constitution. The Turner syndrome is evident in individuals with the following mosaic patterns: XO/XY, XO/XX, and XO/XYY. Mosaics of this type arise during the early mitotic divisions following fertilization, when the distribution of the chromosomes parallels that in meiotic nondisjunction. The presence of additional X chromosomes can often be diagnosed by counting the number of sex chromatin bodies at interphase, according to the formula

$$S.C. = X - \frac{h}{2}$$

The number of X chromosomes minus the number of haploid sets of autosomes divided by 2 is equal to the number of sex chromatin bodies.

Variations in sex chromosome number are not the only causes of sexual abnormalities. True or pseudo hermaphroditism and testicular feminization are due to the action of one or more genes. Deletions or duplications in the X chromosome usually arrest sex organ development and may prevent the development of secondary sexual characteristics. Although complete statistical surveys have not been conducted, sexual

Table 16-5 Chromosome Numbers in Primates

Major Group	Family	Scientific Name	Common Name	Chromosome Number
prosimians	Tupaiidae	*Urogale everetti*	Philippine tree shrew	26, 44*
	Lemuridae	*Lemur macaco*	black lemur	44
		Lemur catta	ring-tailed lemur	56
		Lemur mongoz	mongoose	60
simians				
Old World monkeys: infraorder Catarrhina	Cercopithecidae	*Macaca mulatta*	rhesus monkey	42
		Papio papio	guinea baboon	42
		Erythrocebus patas	military red-grass monkey	54
		Cercopithecus aethiops sabaeus	African green monkey	60
		Cercopithecus nictitans buttikoferi	white-nosed or spot-nosed monkey	66
		Cercopithecus mitis	diadem guenon	72
	Hylobatidae	*Hylobates hoolock*	hoolock gibbon	44
	Pongidae	*Pan troglodytes*	northern chimpanzee	48
	Hominidae	*Homo sapiens*	man	46
New World monkeys: infraorder Platyrrhina	Cebidae	*Cebus capucinus*	capuchin ringtail	54
		Callicebus cupreus	red titi	46
		Saimiri sciureus	squirrel monkey	44
		Ateles geoffroyi cucullatus	hooded spider monkey	34
	Callithricidae	*Callithrix chrysoleucos*	golden marmoset	46
		Leontocebus illigeri	red-mantled tamarin	46

* Uncertain.

anomalies resulting from changes in chromosome number, changes in chromosome morphology, and gene action affect less than 2% of the general population, with the figure probably slightly higher in mentally retarded individuals. This does not imply that mental retardation or some other atypical mental condition always accompanies a change in chromosome number.

The aneuploidy associated with mental retardation is not confined to the sex chromosomes. The best-known type of mental retardation related to an autosomal change is mongolism. In the majority of mongoloids the chromosome number is 47, and chromosome 21 is trisomic. Since this trisomic condition has been found in several races of man, there is little doubt that it is diagnostic. The extra chromosome originates through nondisjunction during the first meiotic division in oogenesis. An interesting feature of this event is its connection with maternal age; the incidence of mongoloid births is greatest in women between the ages of 35 and 45. Mongolism also occurs through translocations between chromosome 21 and another 21 and between chromosomes 13 and 21, 14 and 21, 15 and 21, and 22 and 21. In most of these cases the loss of chromosomal material is slight, so that the individual has, in effect, the same amount of chromosome 21 substance as in the trisomic condition. In contrast to mongoloids with trisomics, however, mongoloids with translocated chromosomes arise independently of the age of the mother.

There are several characteristics in the phenotype of a mongoloid in addition to mental retardation. There may be a third fontanelle or white spots on the iris at birth, and the patterns of the ridges on the palms of the hands and the soles of the feet are quite different from those in a normal human. The mongoloid is generally more susceptible to infection than a normal individual, owing partly to abnormal cell and tissue development, and its life span is somewhat shorter than normal, although this has been much improved in recent years by the use of antibiotics. Leukemia strikes at least three times as often in mongoloids as in the normal population and may be due to abnormal development of the blood cells, although this possibility has not been unequivocally established. Other physiological differences have been observed, including low blood calcium and abnormal tryptophan metabolism.

Primate Chromosomes

By means of tissue culture techniques, the numbers and morphologies of the chromosomes in several members of the primate order have been determined (Table 16–5). Taken at face value, the chromosome numbers

imply that polyploidy leads to variations in these species, but more detailed analysis of the karyotypes discounts this possibility. In all of the
primates examined, the mechanism of sex determination is the same, and
there is no evidence of multiple sex chromosomes (which would indicate
polyploidy); each male has an X chromosome and a Y chromosome, and
each female has two X chromosomes. Since the sums of the chromosome
lengths are the same in several species, the differences in chromosome
number in these species can be interpreted as due to translocations that reduce the chromosome number. Sums of chromosome lengths have been
compared in Old World monkeys and New World monkeys. Measurements of the chromosomes in each infraorder suggest that centric fusions,
and perhaps pericentric inversions, have contributed most to the variations in chromosome number. There seems to be some correlation between chromosome number and the evolutionary appearance of species,
with the trend toward reduction in chromosome number in more recent
species. In the Platyrrhina, or New World monkeys, for example, the
genus *Cebus* would be more primitive (or older) than the genus *Ateles,*
which has fewer chromosomes. However, *Cebus* is not necessarily an
ancestor of *Ateles,* nor is it the most primitive of the Platyrrhina.

Other primates, such as the gorilla and the orangutan, each of which
has a diploid number of 48, have been investigated, but more thorough
work on more species is necessary to resolve the current problems concerning primate evolution. The evolutionary scheme, not yet clear, is certain
to be elucidated eventually by cytological research. Consideration of the
primate chromosomes produces additional evidence for the significance
of changes in chromosome number and morphology. Other illustrations
of the importance of chromosomal aberrations and aneuploidy have been
presented earlier; now, with new cytological methods, karyotype changes
can be detected in organisms that previously have been difficult to study.

SELECTED   READING

General

Darlington, C. D., *The Evolution of Genetic Systems,* 2nd ed., Cambridge Univ.
Press, Cambridge, 1958.
Hamerton, J. L., "Sex Chromatin and Human Chromosomes," *Intern. Rev.
Cytol.,* **12,** 1 (1961).
Hsu, T. C., "Chromosomal Evolution in Cell Populations," *Intern. Rev. Cytol.,*
12, 69 (1961).

Lederberg, J., "Genetic Approaches to Somatic Cell Variation," *J. Cellular Comp. Physiol.,* **52**(3), Suppl. 1, 383 (1958).

Mittwoch, U., *Sex Chromosomes,* Academic Press, New York, 1967.

Stebbins, G. L., *Variation and Evolution in Plants,* Columbia Univ. Press, New York, 1950.

Suomalainen, E., "Parthenogenesis in Animals," *Advan. Genet.,* **3,** 193 (1950).

White, M. J. D., *Animal Cytology and Evolution,* 2nd ed., Cambridge Univ. Press, Cambridge, 1954.

Aneuploidy and Euploidy

Fankhauser, G., "The Effect of Changes in Chromosome Number on Amphibian Development," *Quart. Rev. Biol.,* **20,** 20 (1945).

Giles, N. H., "Spontaneous Chromosome Aberrations in Triploid *Tradescantia* Hybrids," *Genetics,* **26**(10), 632 (1941).

Gustafson, A., "Polyploidy, Life-Form, and Vegetative Reproduction," *Hereditas,* **34**(1–2), 1 (1948).

Karpechenko, G. D., "Polyploid Hybrids of *Raphanus sativa* L. × *Brassica oleracea* L.," *Z. Induktive Abstammungs- und Vererbungslehre,* **39,** 1 (1928).

Stebbins, G. L., and E. B. Babcock, "The Effect of Polyploidy and Apomixis on the Evolution of Species in *Crepis,*" *J. Heredity,* **30,** 519 (1939).

White, M. J. D., "The Evidence Against Polyploidy in Sexually Reproducing Animals," *Am. Naturalist,* **80**(795), 610 (1946).

Somatic Segregation and Endomitosis

Alfert, M., and I. I. Geschwind, "The Development of Polysomaty in Rat Liver," *Exptl. Cell Res.,* **15**(1), 230 (1958).

Berger, C. A., "Multiple Chromosome Complexes in Animals and Polysomaty in Plants," *Cold Spring Harbor Symp. Quant. Biol.,* **9,** 19 (1941).

Grell, S. M., "Cytological Studies in *Culex*. I. Somatic Reduction Divisions. II. Diploid and Meiotic Divisions," *Genetics,* **31**(1), 60 (1946).

Hakansson, A., and A. Levan, "Endoduplicational Meiosis in *Allium odorum,*" *Hereditas,* **43**(2), 179 (1957).

Herman, C. J., and L. W. Lapham, "DNA Content of Neurons in the Cat Hippocampus," *Science,* **160**(3827), 537 (1968).

Hughes, E. C., and T. V. Csermely, "Chromosomal Constitution of Human Endometrium," *Nature,* **209**(5020), 326 (1966).

Huskins, C. L., "Segregation and Reduction in Somatic Tissues," *J. Heredity,* **39,** 310 (1948).

Jones, D. F., "Somatic Segregation and Its Relation to Atypical Growth," *Genetics,* **22**(5), 484 (1937).

Satina, S., A. F. Blakeslee, and A. G. Avery, "Demonstration of the Three Germ Layers in the Shoot Apex of *Datura* by Means of Induced Polyploidy in Periclinal Chimeras," *Am. J. Botany,* **27**(10), 895 (1940).

Neoplasms

Atkins, N. B., and A. J. Ross, "Polyploidy in Human Tumors, *Nature,* **187**(4737), 579 (1960).

De Torok, D., "The Cytologic and Growth Characteristics of Tumor and Normal Clones of *Picea glauca*," *Cancer Res.,* **28**, 608 (1968).

Dumars, K. W., Jr., "Cancer, Chromosomes and Congenital Abnormalities," *Cancer,* **20**(6), 1006 (1967).

Ford, C. E., J. L. Hamerton, and R. H. Mole, "Chromosomal Changes in Primary and Transplanted Reticular Neoplasms of the Mouse," *J. Cellular Comp. Physiol.,* **52**, Suppl. 1, 235 (1958).

Harris, H., and J. F. Watkins, "Hybrid Cells Derived from Mouse and Man: Artificial Heterokaryons of Mammalian Cells from Different Species," *Nature,* **205**(4972), 640 (1965).

Hsu, T. C., "Numerical Variation in Chromosomes in Higher Animals," in D. Rudnick, ed., *Developmental Cytology,* Ronald Press, New York, 1959, pp. 47–62.

Kiossoglu, K. A., W. J. Mitus, and W. Dameshek, "Two Ph[1] Chromosomes in Acute Granulocytic Leukemia," *The Lancet,* **7414**, 665 (1965).

Levan, A., "Repeated Endoreduplication in a Mouse Cell," *Hereditas,* **47**(1), 69 (1961).

Levan, A., "Some Current Problems of Cancer Cytogenetics," *Hereditas,* **57**(3), 343 (1967).

Levan, A., and T. C. Hsu, "The Chromosomes of Two Cell Strains from Mammary Carcinomas of the Mouse," *Hereditas,* **46**(1), 231 (1960).

Partanen, C. R., "Quantitative Chromosomal Changes and Differentiation in Plants," in D. Rudnick, ed., *Developmental Cytology,* Ronald Press, New York, 1959, pp. 21–46.

Rudkin, G. T., D. A. Hungerford, and P. C. Nowell, "DNA Contents of Chromosome 21 in Human Chronic Granulocytic Leukemia," *Science,* **144**(3623), 1229 (1964).

Sorieul, S., and B. Ephrussi, "Karyological Demonstration of Hybridization of Mammalian Cells in Vitro," *Nature,* **190**(4776), 653 (1961).

Sex Chromosomes

Chandra, H. S., and D. A. Hungerford, "Identification of the Human X Chromosome: A Reconciliation Between Results Obtained from Morphological and from Radioautographic Studies," *Ann. Genet.,* **10**, 13 (1967).

Gallien, L., "Sex Determination," in J. Brachet and A. E. Mirsky, eds., *The Cell,* Vol. 1, Academic Press, New York, 1959, pp. 399–436.

Hill, R., and J. J. Yunis, "Mammalian X Chromosomes: Change in Patterns of DNA Replication During Embryogenesis," *Science,* **155**(3766), 1120 (1967).

Jacobs, P. A., and A. Ross, "Structural Abnormalities of the Y Chromosome in Man," *Nature,* **210**(5034), 352 (1966).

Warmke, H. E., "Sex Determination and Sex Balance in *Melandrium*," *Am. J. Botany,* **33**(8), 648 (1946).

Westergaard, M., "The Mechanism of Sex Determination in Dioecious Flowering Plants," *Advan. Genet.,* **9**, 217 (1958).

White, M. J. D., "The Evolution of the Sex Chromosomes. I. The XO and X_1X_2Y Mechanisms in Praying Mantids," *J. Genet.,* **42**, 143 (1941).

Whiting, P. W., "The Evolution of Male Haploidy," *Quart. Rev. Biol.,* **20**, 231 (1945).

Witschi, E., "Sex Reversal in Animals and Man," *Am. Scientist,* **48**(3), 399 (1960).

Human Cytogenetics

Chu, E. H. Y., and N. H. Giles, "Human Chromosome Complements in Normal Somatic Cells in Culture," *Am. J. Human Genet.,* **11**(1), 63 (1959).

Davidson, R. G., H. M. Nitowsky, and B. Childs, "Demonstration of Two Populations of Cells in the Human Female Heterozygous for Glucose 6-Phosphate Dehydrogenase Variants," *Proc. Natl. Acad. Sci. U.S.,* **50**(3), 481 (1963).

Evans, H. J., "The Nucleolus, Virus Infection, and Trisomy in Man," *Nature,* **214**(5086), 361 (1967).

Ford, C. E., P. E. Polani, J. H. Briggs, and P. M. F. Bishop, "A Presumptive Human XXY/XX Mosaic," *Nature,* **183**(4667), 1030 (1959).

German, J. L. III, A. P. De Mayo, and A. G. Bearn, "Inheritance of an Abnormal Chromosome in Down's Syndrome (Mongolism) with Leukemia," *Am. J. Human Genet.,* **14**(1), 31 (1962).

Harnden, D. G., and P. A. Jacobs, "Cytogenetics of Abnormal Sexual Development in Man," *Brit. Med. Bull.,* **17**(3), 206 (1961).

Lyon, M. F., "Sex Chromatin and Gene Action in the Mammalian X Chromosome," *Am. J. Human Genet.* **14**(2), 125 (1962).

Morishima, A., M. M. Grumbach, and J. H. Taylor, "Asynchronous Duplication of Human Chromosomes and the Origin of Sex Chromatin," *Proc. Natl. Acad. Sci. U.S.,* **48**(5), 756 (1962).

Muldal, S., C. H. Ockey, M. Thompson, and L. R. White, " 'Double Male.' A New Chromosome Constitution in the Klinefelter Syndrome," *Acta Endocrinol.,* **39**(2), 183 (1962).

Nowell, P. C., and D. A. Hungerford, "A Minute Chromosome in Human Chronic Granulocytic Leukemia," *Science,* **132**(3438), 1497 (1960).

Penrose, L. S., "Mongolism," *Brit. Med. Bull.,* **17**(3), 184 (1961).

Polani, P. E., "Turner's Syndrome and Allied Conditions," *Brit. Med. Bull.,* **17**(3), 200 (1961).

Sofuni, T., and A. A. Sandberg, "Chronology and Pattern of Human Chromosome Replication," *Cytogenetics,* **6**, 357 (1967).

Tjio, J. H., T. T. Puck, and A. Robinson, "The Somatic Chromosome Constitution of Some Human Subjects with Genetic Defects," *Proc. Natl. Acad. Sci. U.S.,* **45**(7), 1008 (1959).

Yunis, J. J., ed., *Human Chromosome Methodology*, Academic Press, New York, 1965.

Primate Chromosomes

Bender, M. A., and L. E. Mettler, "Chromosome Studies of Primates," *Science*, **128**(3317), 186 (1958).

Bender, M. A., and L. E. Mettler, "Chromosome Studies of Primates. II. Callithrix, Leontocebus, and Callimico," *Cytologia (Tokyo)*, **25**, 400 (1960).

Borgaonkar, D. S., "A List of Chromosome Numbers in Primates," *J. Heredity*, **57**, 60 (1966).

Chiarelli, B., "Chromosomes of the Orangutan (*Pongo pygmaeus*)," *Nature*, **192**(4799), 285 (1961).

Chiarelli, B., "Some New Data on the Chromosomes of Catarrhina," *Experientia*, **18**(9), 405 (1962).

Chu, E. H. Y., and M. A. Bender, "Chromosome Cytology and Evolution in Primates," *Science*, **133**(3462), 1399 (1961).

Chu, E. H. Y., and N. H. Giles, "A Study of Primate Chromosome Complements," *Am. Naturalist*, **91**(860), 273 (1957).

Chu, E. H. Y., and B. Swomley, "Chromosomes of Lemurine Lemurs," *Science*, **133**(3468), 1925 (1961).

part three

Nucleocytoplasmic Relations

17

Prokaryotes: Their
Structure and Behavior

Since the 1940's progress in the fields of genetics and biochemistry has been unprecedented. One reason for the rapid growth of these areas of study and the vast increase in our knowledge of biological mechanisms derived from them has been the utilization of microorganisms for experimental assays. Among the advantages of their use are the facility with which large numbers of individuals may be handled, the recovery of numerous progeny for genetic analysis, and the possibility of performing metabolic investigations on a large-scale in vivo and in vitro. As a result, it has been possible to achieve a better understanding of the behavior and properties of the genetic material and, by extrapolation, to obtain more information regarding pathways of biosynthesis.

This last part has been entitled "Nucleocytoplasmic Relations," which is to some degree a misnomer for several of the discussions contained in it. Many of the microorganisms that have proved of great experimental value are not structurally organized in the typical patterns of cells described in Parts One and Two. On the other hand, they lend themselves so readily to certain kinds of genetic and biochemical studies that they must be included in any relatively comprehensive consideration of cellular activities. In addition, it has been through the extensive use of these atypical cells or organisms that much of the latest information has come.

The organisms to be dealt with here are not cellular according to the accepted definition of the word. For this reason they are called *prokaryotes* as contrasted with more typical cells or *eukaryotes*. Among the prokaryotes are the blue-green algae, bacteria, and viruses. These individuals exhibit no organization into nucleus and cytoplasm. Their chromosomes do not have the elaborate structure of those in eukaryotes, and are not confined to a membrane-enclosed nucleus. Moreover, cell division is not typically mitotic nor does meiosis occur in the conventional sense. Prokaryotes may make DNA over a large fraction of their life cycle, and the lifetime of messenger RNA molecules is considerably shorter than in eukaryotes. In many prokaryotes, several of the cytoplasmic organelles are absent.

The terms prokaryote and eukaryote are desirable in view of the difficulty in classifying the individuals in question as unicellular or acellular. Each of the organisms mentioned exists as a single functional unit rather than as a group of cells arranged in tissues or more complicated structures. This same condition characterizes other, more complex organisms, such as the protozoa and many algae, but the problem is more acute with bacteria and viruses, which are less typical structurally. Unfortunately there has been little agreement on terminology, since each term proposed has limitations. Often all of the atypical organisms, including the protozoa, some of the algae, and some fungi, are merely designated as exceptions to the cell theory. From an operational standpoint, or the position of a biologist experimenting with these individuals, all but the viruses can be considered cells.

Blue-Green Algae

The blue-green algae are generally considered to be the most primitive organisms in the plant kingdom. They arose rather early in evolutionary time and possess quite primitive characteristics. Most are filamentous, living as colonies of cells, although a few live as single cells. In either case, each cell is surrounded by a gelatinous sheath covering a cell wall, which consists of polysaccharides and mucopeptides. The plasma membrane lies inside the cell wall enclosing the living contents. Often the *nucleoplasm,* or DNA-containing material, is centrally located, and shows a fibrillar structure (Figure 17–1). The nucleoplasm is Feulgen-positive, but is not organized within a nucleus. The colors of these algae, which range from red to emerald to near black, are due to pigments located in lamellae located peripherally in the cytoplasm. These lamellae are membranes derived from the plasma membrane, and are presumed to be unit membranes (Chapter 3). The pigments in them include chlorophyll, carotene, and xanthophyll, and c-phycoerythrin and c-phycocyanin; the last two are found in blue-green algae only. The principal function of the pigments is in photosynthesis. In addition to the lamellae, which are sometimes stacked in layers, membrane-bound vesicles are also observed in the cyto-

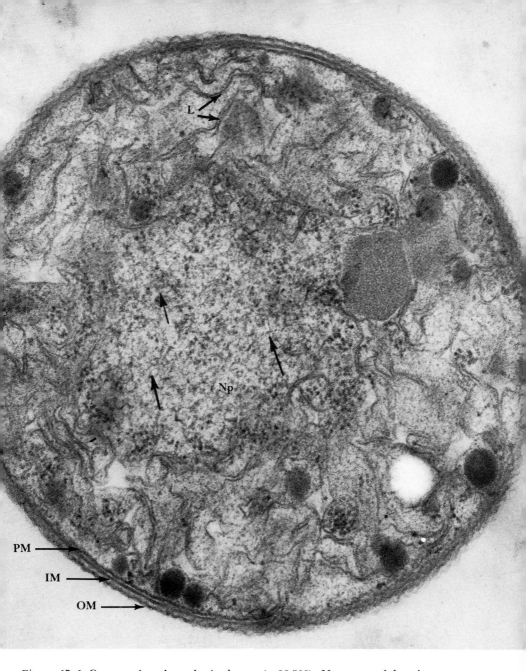

Figure 17–1. Cross section through *Anabaena* (×66,500). Note central location of the nucleoplasm (Np) and its fibrillar structure (arrows). The cell wall consists of an outer convoluted membrane (OM) and an inner membrane (IM). The inner membrane is separated by spaces from the outer membrane and the plasma membrane (PM). Note the numerous photosynthetic lamellae (L). FROM L. V. Leak, *J. Ultrastruct. Res.,* **20,** 190 (1967).

plasm. Scattered throughout the cytoplasm more or less freely are ribosomes, comparable to those in eukaryotes.

The blue-green algae are valuable both phylogenetically and as examples of prokaryotes, although their use as experimental organisms has only recently become feasible through improvements in preparative techniques and microscopy. Electron microscopy, for example, has revealed a relatively complex structure for the outer layers of the cell. The cell wall that lies within a gelatinous sheath is often two or three layers thick. An *inner vestment* may be shared by adjacent cells in a colony; it lies between the outer wall layer and the plasma membrane. Cell division and nuclear structure have also been more clearly delineated through the use of electron microscopy. Although sexual reproduction has never been observed in blue-green algae, some species may produce asexual spores in addition to undergoing asexual division. Studies of *Anabaena variabilis* cells stained with the Feulgen method have indicated that mitosis-like divisions occur in this filamentous form. Several vacuoles in the cell are surrounded by the Feulgen-positive material. During division the vacuoles break down and the nucleoplasm material is dispersed throughout the cell. Before final division of the cell, the nucleoplasm divides in two; no spindle apparatus participates in this division. Fine structure studies have also made clear that the photosynthetic lamellae are not organized into discrete plastid bodies, further emphasizing a difference between prokaryotes and eukaryotes. Although important steps have been taken, further studies are needed to delineate morphology and biochemical activities in the blue-green algae.

Bacteria

On the basis of its internal organization, there is little justification for calling a bacterium a cell. Nevertheless, for purposes of discussion and convenience, the terms cell, nuclear material, and cytoplasm will be used here. Very few conventional organelles are found in a bacterium. Yet a bacterial cell is capable of most of the biochemical reactions necessary for viability and reproduction.

Usually a bacterium is surrounded by a mucoid sheath or capsule (composed of a protein or polysaccharide complex), which is closely related to the underlying cell wall. The wall itself consists of polysaccharide, lipid, protein, and a mucopeptide complex, varying according to the type of bacterium. Within the wall is a very thin plasma membrane enclosing the cytoplasmic substance of the bacterium. The plasma membrane is quite difficult to see since it has a thickness of only 50 to 100 Å. Its lipoprotein content is similar to that of the plasma membrane of a eukaryote. Enzymes are variously distributed in the plasma membrane, and include some of those responsible for cell wall synthesis.

In a typical cell the mitochondria and other membrane-constructed organelles are responsible for much of the enzymatic activity concerned with respiration and synthesis. In a bacterium the burden of activity is on the plasma membrane and derivative membranes. Several enzymes have been detected in the bacterial membranes that attest to this function. Included are the cytochromes of the electron transport system and the enzymes of the Krebs cycle. In addition, reduced NAD (NADH), acid phosphatase, and enzymes for ATP production have been found. Several bacteria contain membranous bodies (*mesosomes*) apparently derived from invaginations of the plasma membrane. A mesosome is bounded by a single unit membrane that is often continuous with the plasma membrane. Internally the mesosome consists of a convoluted arrangement of two unit membranes lying in apposition, similar to the double arrangement in eukaryotic endoplasmic reticulum (Figure 17–2). The cavities resulting from this arrangement resemble the cavity system of eukaryotic mitochondria. In fact, the mesosome is the principal location of the bacterial respiratory enzymes, including all of the cell's cytochromes, making it functionally homologous with a mitochondrion.

Enzyme activity has also been observed in several small granules located in the cytoplasm. These granules range in diameter from 100 to 200 Å and are freely dispersed rather than associated with membranes as in higher organisms. Their size and organic content strongly suggest homology to the ribosomes of other cells. An analysis of the amino acid content of ribosomes from *Escherichia coli,* for example, indicates the presence of relatively large amounts of lysine, arginine, and histidine, as well as small quantities of polyamines (putrescine, cadaverine, spermidine). The enzymes linked with the granules are succinic oxidase and cytochrome oxidase, which are also located in the plasma membrane, the principal site for their activity. The major function of bacterial ribosomes is in protein synthesis, and, in fact, much of the available information on the process has come from work with bacteria (Chapter 19).

Other particulate components of the cytoplasm are the basal bodies of flagellated bacteria and metachromatic granules. The latter, also identified as *volutin,* are quite small, usually no more than 0.6 μ in diameter. Their metachromasia is obvious in a cell stained with Toluidine Blue; the acidic constituents of the cell are blue, while the granules are red. They apparently participate in the synthesis of ATP since they contain phosphates (which are utilized in ATP production). The flagella of those bacteria having them consist of spiral filaments made of protein subunits and some carbohydrate material. The proteins (flagellins) have molecular

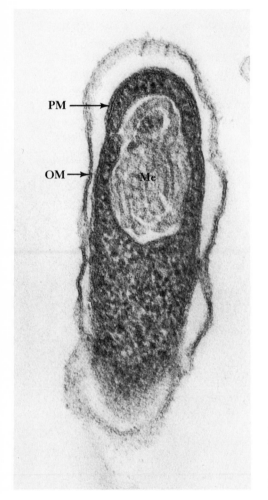

Figure 17–2. A mesosome of *Chondrococcus columnaris* (×126,000). PM, plasma membrane; Me, mesosome; OM, outer membrane. FROM J. L. Pate and E. J. Ordal, *J. Cell Biol.,* **35,** 1 (1967).

weights of 20,000 to 40,000. In *Acetobacter suboxydans,* the flagellum is 120 to 150 Å in diameter and consists of two parallel fibers. This contrasts strikingly with the more complex flagellar ultrastructure of eukaryotes (Chapter 8).

In Chapter 10 the gram-stain method for bacteria was described, its reaction being attributed to the presence of ribonucleoprotein. Evidence for the reactivity of RNA with crystal violet and iodine is somewhat ambiguous, however, especially since the RNA content of most bacterial cells is rather high. Some authorities believe that a positive reaction to gram stain is due instead to the presence of some component in or near the cell wall. Regardless of this uncertainty, some bacteria can be distinguished from others by reacting positively or negatively to the stain. Streptococci and actinomycetes, for example, are gram-positive, whereas pseudomonads and spirilla are gram-negative. Although the significance of the difference is unknown, mesosomes are absent in gram-negative bacteria but prominent in gram-positives.

Certain bacteria capable of photosynthetic activity are devoid of pigment-containing plastids. Their pigments are located in 600 Å diameter particles known as *chromatophores,* which consist mainly of protein with a trace of RNA. Other contents are phospholipid, bacteriochlorophyll, and enzymes of the electron transport system. Electron microscopic studies of the purple bacterium *Rhodospirillum* and the green bacterium *Chlorobium* have resolved in detail the structure and composition of a chromatophore, which could not be resolved with light microscopy. Relative to their photosynthetic activity, the particles can conduct a light-dependent anaerobic synthesis of ATP. The major sites of photosynthetic activity, however, are membrane-enclosed vesicles, with 500 Å diameters, that are found in many places in the cytoplasm but primarily near the periphery of the cell (Figures 17–3 and 17–4). The number of such vesicles is inversely pro-

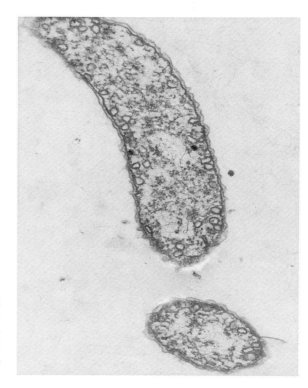

Figure 17–3. Ultrastructure of *Rhodospirillum rubrum* (×39,-000). COURTESY Dr. G. Cohen-Bazire, from G. Cohen-Bazire and R. Kunisawa, *J. Cell Biol.,* **16**, 401 (1963).

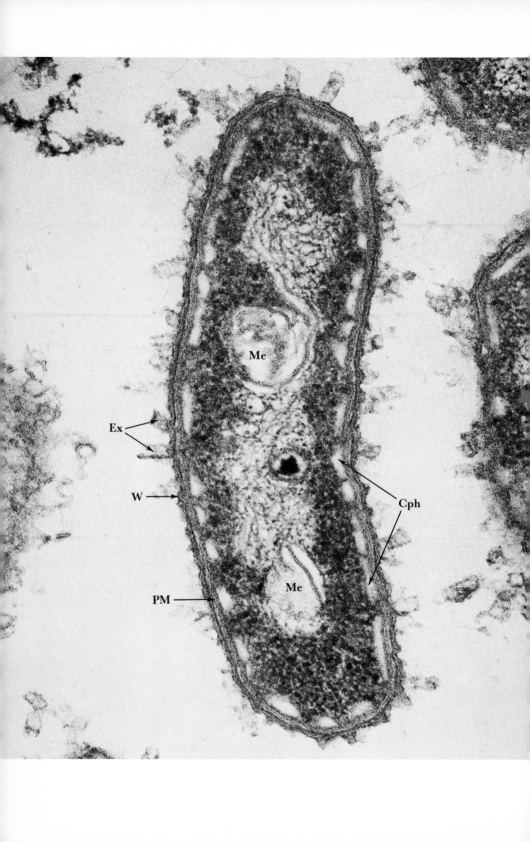

Figure 17–4. Longitudinal section of *Chlorobium thiosulfatophilum* T (×115,-000), showing the complex cell wall (W) with extensions (Ex), plasma membrane (PM), chromatophores (Cph), and two mesosomes (Me). COURTESY Dr. G. Cohen-Bazire, from G. Cohen-Bazire, N. Pfennig, and R. Kunisawa, *J. Cell Biol.,* **22,** 207 (1964).

portional to the light intensity to which the cell is exposed and directly proportional to the chlorophyll content. In some regions the membranes of the vesicles are continuous with the plasma membrane, a situation suggesting that the vesicles are derived from invaginations of the plasma membrane.

Considerable controversy has centered around the organization of the Feulgen-positive material and the mode of division of the bacterial cell. Without question, DNA is present in most bacterial cells, as is demonstrated by the Feulgen method as well as other techniques. A positive response to specific staining for DNA is facilitated by prior treatment with ribonuclease, since the amount of RNA in a bacterium is sometimes great enough to interfere with analysis. RNA may, in fact, constitute as much as 11.5% of the total dry weight of the organism.

As in the blue-green algae, there is no discrete nuclear body in a bacterium. The DNA is distributed with no visible membrane separation from the cytoplasm. It often occupies more than one position in a single cell and is completely surrounded by cytoplasm. The DNA fibrils are 30 to 60 Å in diameter, and represent the chromosomal material. Most of the DNA appears to be free rather than complexed with protein, but some may be bound to protein of the nonhistone type.

Most difficult to determine has been the mechanism by which the bacterial cell divides, including the behavior of the DNA material. In general, the DNA is equally distributed between the daughter cells during division, but details of the distribution are unclear. A cell grows by elongating and then divides by constricting and separating into two daughters, each with one chromosome. Thus there is an equal distribution of the genetic material, but the process of division is not typically mitotic. Moreover, evidence from studies with *Bacillus subtilis* indicates that the chromosome may be attached to the plasma membrane via a mesosome. It is possible that the mesosome plays an important part in the replication process by providing a mechanism (and/or energy) for the unwinding of the DNA double helix, a process necessary for the synthesis of new DNA helixes (see below). Moreover, the spatial separation of daughter chromosomes appears to depend on their connection to the bacterial membrane.

Still other data from investigations of DNA synthesis in bacteria argue against a typical division cycle. When a culture of *E. coli* or *Salmonella typhimurium* is exposed for a short time to [³H]thymidine, almost all of the cells exhibit labeled DNA. Furthermore, exposure of an asynchronous population of cells to radioactive phosphorus of high specific activity for only part of a generation leads to the death of most of the cells. These results indicate that the bacteria synthesize DNA continuously or, at most, that the period during which no DNA synthesis occurs is very short. In other organisms DNA synthesis is interrupted by the division cycle. On the other hand, in synchronous populations of *E. coli* there are short periods during which DNA synthesis does not take place. It is possible that these represent the times of "nuclear" divisions.

Some question remains, then, concerning the nature of the division of a bacterial cell. However, there seems to be little doubt that the process is atypical. For one thing, there is no sign of a spindle apparatus during the cell cycle, and for another, the division of the cytoplasm, or cytokinesis, involves an inward growth of the plasma membrane but no constriction of the cell wall—a new wall develops transversely across the cell.

Extraction of DNA from *E. coli* labeled with [³H]thymidine has established the single chromosome as one circle of two-stranded DNA with a length of 1100 μ and a molecular weight of about 2 billion. Since an *E. coli* cell is only about 3 μ long and 0.8 μ in diameter, this largest known biological molecule must be packed into a remarkably small space! Replication has been observed by means of autoradiography and electron microscopy, and it has been proposed that a fork is formed, each daughter limb of which consists of a single strand of new and a single strand of old DNA. During replication the distal ends of the two daughter molecules are joined. The method of chromosomal replication based on a circular DNA is illustrated in Figure 17–5. In this model there are two important posi-

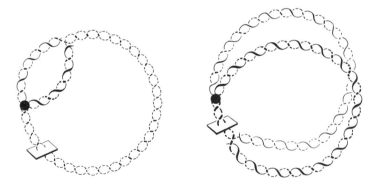

Figure 17–5. Two stages in the replication of a circular chromosome of *Escherichia coli*. The rectangle marks the breakage point. FROM J. Cairns, *J. Mol. Biol.*, **6,** 208 (1963).

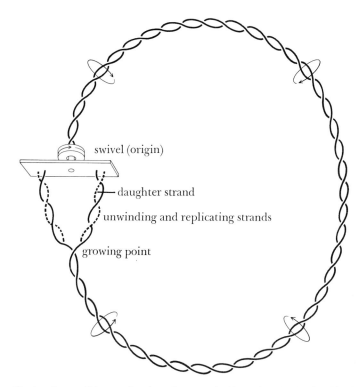

swivel (origin)

daughter strand

unwinding and replicating strands

growing point

Figure 17–6. A possible mechanism for unwinding the DNA double helix. It utilizes a "swivel" apparatus to which the parent molecule and ends of the two daughter molecules are joined. The torque imparted by the apparatus is transmitted along the double helix, resulting in unwinding at the replicating fork. FROM "The Bacterial Chromosome" by J. Cairns. Copyright © 1966 by Scientific American, Inc. All rights reserved.

tions, the growing point and the point of origin (Figure 17–6). The former is the site of DNA replicase responsible for DNA synthesis and is physically attached to the bacterial membrane. The point of origin is the site of beginning of each replication and may involve a non-DNA linker connecting the ends into a circle. This linker may also be involved in untwisting of the helixes as a "swivel" point (Figure 17–6). According to Jacob and Brenner the chromosome acts like a single unit of replication, or *replicon*. Each replicon contains a unique site, the "replicator," at which DNA synthesis is initiated by the action of a diffusible gene product, an "initiator," specific for each replicator. Each replicon may be attached to the bacterial membrane at the "replicator" site. Both *E. coli* and *B. subtilis* have a fixed point of origin of DNA replication and a fixed order of DNA replication, and the rate of synthesis may be as high as 3000 nucleotide pairs per second. This rate compares with an average RNA chain growth of 30 nucleotides per second, and protein chain growth of 10 to 15 amino acids per second per ribosome. Thus the metabolism of a bacterial cell is extraordinarily rapid.

Viruses

In 1951 Burnet stated, "There is no possible escape from the general conclusion that viruses are in no sense ultimate particles. They are complex organisms, with a genetic mechanism which has to be thought of as something other than the virus particles as a whole and which seems to be built up of units analogous to the genes of higher organisms." Viruses are certainly not cells, but they do possess some properties common to other organisms. The most compelling reasons for classifying them as organisms are their DNA or RNA content, which serves as the hereditary material; their reproduction, which gives rise to several identical progeny; and their production of genetic recombinants. On the other hand, the mechanisms by which viruses act are somewhat different from those of other organisms. Particularly striking is the fact that they cannot exist outside the living cells of another organism; they are entirely parasitic. This is not a unique biological phenomenon, however, and the burden of evidence tends to support the contention that viruses, although unusual in many ways, are organisms.

There are three kinds of viruses: animal, plant, and bacterial (*bacteriophages*). The sizes and shapes of many forms have been determined by several techniques, including electron microscopy, ultracentrifugation, and X-ray diffraction. Such methods are necessary because, as indicated in Chapter 2, a virus is smaller than the wavelength of light. Viruses range in length from 10 to 250 mμ, animal viruses generally being the largest (for example, smallpox virus), although some animal viruses (for example, polio viruses) are among the smallest. A few representative viruses are shown in Figure 17–7. They illustrate the major shape groupings—cubic, helical, and complex. Cubic viruses may be tetrahedral (4 faces), dodecahedral (12 faces), or icosahedral (20 faces). The *Herpes* virus is dodecahedral. The tobacco mosaic virus (TMV) and the T2 bacteriophage are, respectively, helical and complex.

Morphologically a virus is a core of nucleic acid (DNA or RNA) surrounded by a protein shell. The organization of the shell, or *capsid,* may be quite complicated. In many viruses it consists of *capsomeres* (protein molecules), varying in number and shape with viral type. A capsomere may

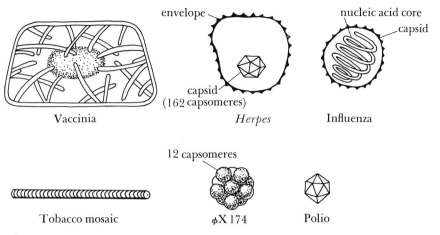

envelope

nucleic acid core

capsid

capsid
(162 capsomeres)

Vaccinia

Herpes

Influenza

12 capsomeres

Tobacco mosaic

φX 174

Polio

Figure 17–7. Shapes of representative viruses. AFTER Horne.

be a hollow prism, hexagonal or pentagonal in cross section, or, as in TMV, it may be lobular (Figure 17–8).

Although most viruses have DNA cores, several have RNA instead. The animal viruses causing polio, encephalitis, influenza, and Newcastle's disease (a respiratory condition in fowl) contain RNA, as do all plant viruses including TMV, Southern bean mosaic virus, and turnip yellow mosaic virus. Almost all bacteriophages contain DNA. Whichever nucleic acid is present acts as the genetic material of the organism. Since the most extensively studied viruses, from the standpoint of genetic and metabolic

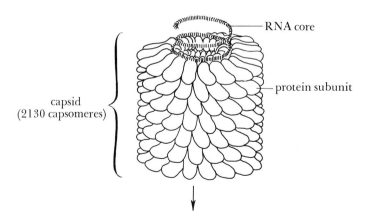

RNA core

protein subunit

capsid
(2130 capsomeres)

Figure 17–8. Structure of tobacco mosaic virus.

behavior, have been TMV and the bacteriophages, this discussion will deal primarily with them.

Tobacco Mosaic Virus

Tobacco is infected by TMV through injuries on the leaf surface, and relatively large amounts of the virus can be recovered from the tissue after infection. The virus is rod-shaped, with a length of about 3000 Å, a diameter of 180 Å, and a hollow core of 20 Å diameter. The capsomeres are helically arranged around the core in 130 turns. According to one estimate, the TMV capsid comprises 2130 to 2200 capsomeres, each containing 158 amino acids and having a molecular weight of 21,000. Another estimate fixes the number of capsomeres at 2800, each with a molecular weight of 17,000 to 18,000.

Of the total virus composition, 94.4% is protein and 5.6% is RNA. The main function of the protein is to protect, but it also confers some stability on the virus, as is obvious when the infectiousness of intact virus is compared with that of protein-free virus. The latter fraction is only about 0.1% as infectious as whole virus. However, after infection, free RNA can multiply at a much faster rate than intact virus.

The RNA in TMV has a molecular weight of about 2 million. Apparently only one molecule is present in a single virus, and it consists of a chain of approximately 6400 nucleotides. The total molecular weight of the intact virus is usually 45 to 50 million, but it may be as high as 100 million. As implied in the preceding paragraph, it is possible to remove the protein shell from the nucleic acid core by chemical treatment without damaging the RNA. Some very interesting and significant information has resulted from the application of this technique.

Fraenkel-Conrat and others have been able to separate the protein from the nucleic acid in different viral strains and effect a reconstitution of the original components as well as a production of hybrids between the nucleic acid of one strain and the protein of another. In all cases the protein synthesized in subsequent replications is characteristic of the original nucleic acid. This observation confirms the genetic role of RNA; it is the RNA alone that carries the genetic information for protein synthesis from generation to generation.

Bacteriophages

Viruses that attack bacteria are classified according to the specific bacteria affected. For example, the T phages infect *E. coli,* and they are divided into

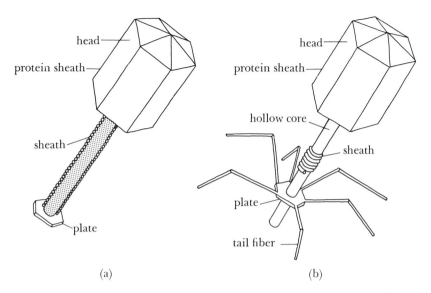

Figure 17–9. Structure of T2 bacteriophage: (a) intact; (b) triggered.

two main categories, T-even (T2, T4, T6, etc.) and T-odd (T1, T7, lambda, etc.). The T-even phages have certain distinguishing characteristics, including a capacity to destroy bacterial nuclear material, a high sensitivity to ultraviolet inactivation, and an inability to cause lysis of a bacterium.

The general structure of a T phage is depicted in Figure 17–9. The DNA-containing head is surrounded by a protein sheath, and a hollow core, enclosed by a contractile protein sheath, extends from the head to the tail region. The head is hexagonal in shape and measures 950×650 Å, whereas the tail measures 1000×250 Å. When the sheath contracts, tail fibers are extended, the end of the core penetrates the wall of the bacterium, and DNA passes through the core into the bacterial cell. Positively charged amino groups on the tail fibers provide attachment by interacting with negatively charged carboxyl groups on the bacterial surface. Then an enzymatic group on the phage surface reacts with polysaccharide material on the surface of the bacterium to effect adsorption and penetration. In addition to enzymes, two antigens can be identified on the tail of the phage, one of which is also present on the head. Structural details can be observed in electron photomicrographs of the type in Figure 17–10, which depicts a T4 phage. Recent studies of T-even phages have suggested that the base plate is star-shaped, a tail fiber emerging from each of the six points. Each fiber has at least two sites for specific attachment to the host cell. On the *E. coli* cell the attachment of

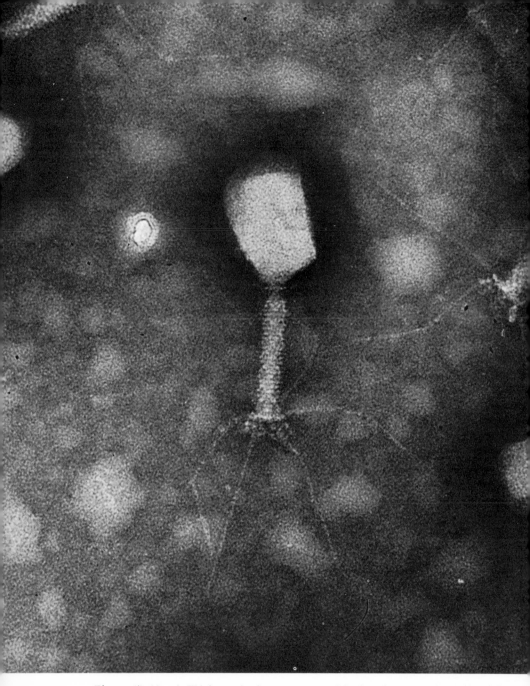

Figure 17–10. A T4 bacteriophage as seen with the electron microscope. The head, neck, collar, tail, base plate, and tail fibers can be observed. Figure 8 (p. 46) by Thomas F. Anderson, in *Molecular Organization and Biological Function,* edited by John M. Allen, Harper & Row, New York, 1967. Reprinted by permission of the publisher.

T2 or T6 phage occurs in lipoprotein of the outermost layer of the wall, whereas the site of T4 attachment may be in the underlying lipopoly-saccharide.

As with TMV, the genetically important constituent of a phage is nucleic acid, in most cases DNA. Only the DNA enters the bacterium, the sheath material and tail fibers remaining outside. The injected DNA carries all the necessary information for the construction of phage progeny.

Although the DNA is the same both structurally and chemically in most bacteriophages, some variations have been noted. Bacteriophages T2, T4, and T6, for example, have 5-hydroxymethylcytosine in place of cyto-sine among the component bases. The three phages differ from one an-other in the amount and types of sugars bound to this base. Most T phages, including lambda (λ) phage, have a linear double-stranded DNA. As is the case in bacteria, the very long phage DNA is packed into a very small space. An example of viral DNA in its intracellular form is shown in Figure 17–11.

Of particular interest are the viruses designated as φX174, M13, *fd,* and S13, which contain single-stranded rather than double-stranded DNA, that is, one helix instead of two. In φX174 and *fd,* which attack *E. coli,* there is one molecule of single-stranded DNA of molecular weight 1.5 to 2 million. The strand is in the form of a ring, having no free ends. Proof of its single stranding can be derived by several methods, among them the determination of the base ratios. In a typical double helix the base ratios are usually about 1 : 1 (Chapter 1), but in φX174 the adenine, thymine, guanine, and cytosine proportions are 1 : 1.33 : 0.98 : 0.75. Thus in some ways this DNA is more like RNA than DNA. At least part of the time during replication of the molecule, however, two strands are present.

Another unusual bacteriophage is *f2,* which contains RNA instead of DNA. In RNA-containing viruses two enzymatic events are required for replication. One event converts single strands into double strands, and the second event involves the use of the double-stranded form to synthesize new viral RNA. The multiplicity of forms in viral nucleic acid is thus quite obvious; some are linear, others are circular, and the nucleic acid may be double- or single stranded.

The replication of viruses is quite different from that of other orga-nisms. The customary sequence of events in the infection of a bacterial cell by a virus and the subsequent liberation of phage progeny (Figure 17–12) is as follows: After the tails of the viruses have been adsorbed on the surface of the bacterium, nucleic acid is passed through the viral cores into the host cell. The time during which replication of new phage takes place within the host is called the *latent* period. It lasts approximately 20 minutes. During the first half of the period, the *eclipse* period, no intact

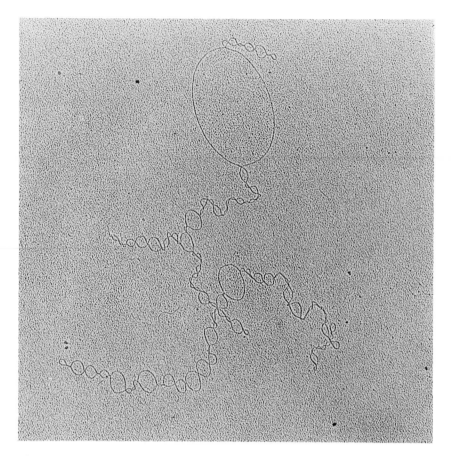

Figure 17–11. Intracellular form of P22 bacteriophage DNA. Micrograph by Marc Rhoades and C. A. Thomas, Jr., from C. A. Thomas, Jr., *J. Cellular Comp. Physiol.,* **70,** Suppl. 1, 13 (1967).

virus particles can be found in the host cell. However, new protein and nucleic acid are synthesized. Shortly after infection the synthesis of bacterial RNA ceases, to be followed by a rapid drop in bacterial DNA synthesis. About 5 minutes after infection the synthesis of phage RNA begins, and at 7 minutes phage DNA synthesis commences. Protein synthesis appears to occur independently of nucleic acid synthesis soon after its onset. During the second half of the latent period, the *rise* period, some of the newly synthesized protein sheaths contain DNA. Thus there is a constitution of intact virus progeny. Until the bacterial cell bursts (lysis), and it often does so before all the DNA present is incorporated into the phage units, there is a linear increase in the number of phage particles.

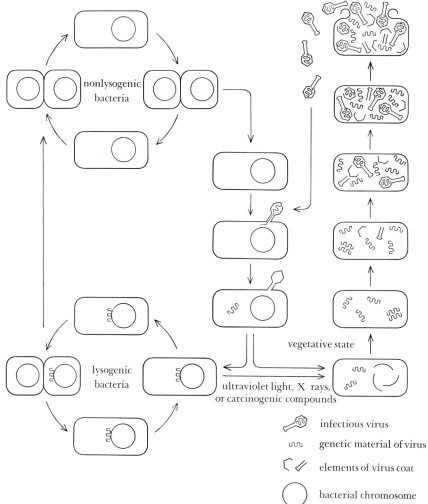

Figure 17–12. Life cycle of a bacteriophage. FROM "Viruses and Genes" by F. Jacob and E. L. Wollman. Copyright © 1961 by Scientific American, Inc. All rights reserved.

When the cell bursts, from 100 to 200 phage progeny are released, for each phage particle involved in the original infection.

Infection of *E. coli* by T-even bacteriophages has demonstrated that the first progeny virus appears 12 minutes after entry of the bacterial cell. After 21 minutes a lysozyme, produced by the phages, causes lysis of the bacterial cell, and the phage progeny are released.

In summary, the physical as well as the physiological processes of virus infection do not resemble the usual cycles of cell replication. Most viruses essentially assume direction of the activities of the host cell, controlling the synthesis of viral nucleic acid and protein through the host system.

In contrast to the virulent phages just described, *temperate* phages do not cause lysis of the host cells. Bacteria infected with them are *lysogenic*, however; that is, they carry a factor that can lead to lysis in certain circumstances. With a temperate phage there is no production of progeny. Instead the phage somehow becomes attached to the bacterial chromosome. A virus in this integrated condition is called a *prophage*, or *provirus*; it is actually the viral DNA. In a small percentage of bacterial cells (0.00001 to 0.01%), a spontaneous change may occur resulting in the formation of phage progeny and lysis of the host cell. A reversion of this type can also be induced by exposure to ultraviolet or X radiation. This procedure is useful in certain studies of bacterial genetics.

The effct of a prophage on bacterial behavior is illustrated with the prophage of diphtheria bacilli. The bacilli produce their toxin, which causes the disease, only if they carry their specific prophage. The prophage also confers on the hosts immunity to infection by other viruses of the same strain. Another important phenomenon may involve prophage activity. There is some indication that temperate phages are found in certain animal cells, particularly in some forms of cancer.

Since viruses are unable to live outside other living organisms, for laboratory work they must be grown with cultures of bacteria or other cells. The method of detecting them on a macroscopic level is relatively straightforward. When grown in a bacterial culture on an agar plate, they form clear areas or *plaques* on the culture surface. The plaques result from clarification of the culture after lysis of the cells. This technique has been utilized in genetic analyses of mutant phages. For example, among the mutants that arise spontaneously or are induced by mutagenic agents are variations in the shapes or sizes of the plaques. Other phage mutants are changes in host specificity and changes in antigenic properties. The scope of the genetic experiments performed with viruses is too wide for this discussion, but some basic aspects of phage genetics will be presented in the next section.

Genetic Mechanisms in Bacteria and Viruses

In order to emphasize the importance of DNA as the hereditary material in all organisms (with the exception of RNA-containing viruses), and to indicate that basic mechanisms of inheritance operate in bacteria and viruses as well as in other organisms, a few significant genetic phenomena of these prokaryotes are summarized here.

One of the earliest discoveries concerning bacteria was that DNA from one bacterial strain can sometimes produce a *transformation* of the characteristics of a different strain. Transformation was first demonstrated in *Diplococcus pneumoniae,* a bacterium causing a pneumonia-like disease in mice. Among the several strains of *D. pneumoniae* are smooth and rough forms. The smooth type, which is virulent, is characterized by smooth-looking colonies due to the presence of a polysaccharide capsule around each cell. The rough type, which is nonvirulent, has no capsules. Although the rough type can arise by spontaneous mutation from the smooth type, a reverse spontaneous mutation does not occur. However, transformation from the rough type to the smooth type has been observed in mice. Infection of mice with strain 3 of the smooth type (S3) results in death, whereas infection with strain 2 of the rough type (R2) has no serious effect. Heat-killed S3 cells are also ineffective. However, when mice are infected with both R2 and heat-killed S3 cells, they die. Examination of the blood of the killed mice reveals living cells of the S3 type, suggesting that some of the R2 cells are transformed into virulent S3 cells during infection.

It has been shown that an extract of S cells is capable of transforming R cells in vitro, also. The extract is identified as DNA. Thus DNA represents the *transforming principle.* Further analysis has indicated that intact DNA is necessary for transformation, since transformation does not take place after degradation of the molecule to smaller units (that is, with molecular weights less than 1 million).

The process by which transforming principle is integrated into the recipient cell is not clear. It may involve a breakage of the host chromosome and subsequent incorporation of the donor DNA, or it may involve an altered synthesis of DNA. That is, transforming principle instead of the host DNA may be copied for some part of the chromosome during replication so that it becomes part of the progeny DNA. This mechanism is known as copy choice, or *partial-replica* formation (Figure 17–13). Transformation has been reported in *Hemophilus influenzae, E. coli, B. subtilis, Salmonella,* and in about 10 other bacteria, as well as in cultured human cells.

Recombination also takes place in bacteria, offering further testimony for their relationship to other organisms. The development of recombinant types of progeny from two different bacterial strains is well demonstrated by *E. coli.* When two different strains, each unable to produce one or more different nutritional requirements, such as amino acids, are mixed and placed in a culture medium also deficient in these requirements, no

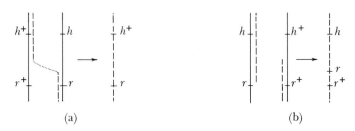

Figure 17–13. Copy choice: (a) during chromosome replication (no reciprocal is formed); (b) during the formation of a partial heterozygote (heterozygous for *r*).

bacterial colonies are expected. However, in a few instances colonies appear. They consist of progeny resulting from a recombination of the genes.

The process of recombination is somewhat complex, relatively rare, and quite unusual. *E. coli* has two sexually different strains that, when mixed, reproduce under certain conditions (Figure 17–14). One of the strains is called F^+, or donor strain, and the other F^-, or recipient strain. Usually a cross between these two strains gives rise to extremely few recombinant-type progeny. Sometimes, however, recombination occurs with a frequency 100 to 20,000 times that in the standard mixture. Such significant numbers of recombinants are due to F^+ strains known as *Hfr* (*high-frequency recombination*) strains. There is appreciable evidence that an Hfr strain contains a fertility factor, *F,* attached to the chromosome, whereas an F^- strain is devoid of the factor. The *F* factor apparently can cause a break in the circular chromosome of the donor cell, which permits the introduction of the donor chromosome, or a part of it, into the recipient cell and thereby leads to recombination. Investigators using electron microscopes have, in fact, observed small bridges between two bacterial cells in a mixed culture. Early studies showed that recombination in *E. coli* is incomplete, since the donor strain does not always contribute a full set of genes to the progeny.

The *F* factor has been a valuable tool in establishing the behavior of the circular chromosome of *E. coli*. For example, the conjugation of two bacterial cells takes approximately 60 minutes, during which, in the presence of the *F* factor, donor chromosome material is transmitted to the recipient cell. The amount of chromosome material entering depends on the time allowed for conjugation. Thus it is possible to effect a transfer of a short segment of donor chromosome by stopping conjugation after a brief interval. Analysis of the recombinant types recovered provides a measure of the amount of chromosome transferred and points up the

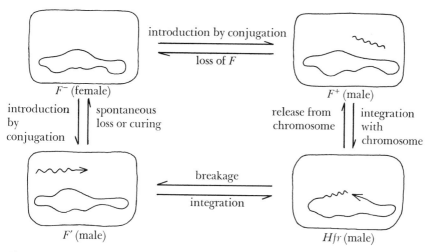

Figure 17–14. The relationship between mating types of *E. coli* in conjugation. Reprinted with permission from S. Silver in J. A. V. Butler and H. E. Huxley, eds., *Progress in Biophysics and Molecular Biology*, Vol. 16, Pergamon Press, New York, 1966.

linearity of the genetic material as well as the circularity of the chromosome.

Another means for the transmission of genetic material is the remarkable process of *transduction,* in which donor DNA is carried to a recipient cell by a prophage. On infection of the donor cell by the prophage, the host DNA is depolymerized to nucleotide units and incorporated into the phage progeny. These progeny then infect a recipient bacterium and introduce the donor DNA segment into the chromosome of the recipient cell. Usually just single characteristics are transmitted in this manner, or in other words, a single genetic locus is transduced, but the frequency of transduction is quite low (about one in 1 million cells). The incorporation of the donor segment into the recipient chromosome may occur through breakage of the recipient chromosome or through copy choice. Transduction was first noted in *Salmonella typhimurium* by Lederberg and others.

One of the reasons cited earlier for including viruses among organisms was that they produce genetic recombinants. The consideration of this aspect of virus behavior has been extended in recent years to the level of the fine structure of a gene. The property of recombination is common to all bacteriophages except the S13 type and can be demonstrated by infecting a bacterial cell with two or more different phages and recovering phage progeny. Two characteristics of phages based upon gene action are host range (h) and plaque type (r). If a strain with the genotype h^+r^+ and one with the genotype hr are introduced simultaneously into a bacterial culture, the following kinds of phage progeny may be recovered: h^+r^+, hr, h^+r, and hr^+. The latter two are recombination types and usually form in equal numbers. The proportion of recombinants to the total progeny varies from less than 1% to 40%.

It is possible, nevertheless, to find only one recombinant type or the two types present in unequal numbers in a bacterium. Such variants result from copy choice. Of the variants 2% are mottled plaques, apparently representing individuals heterozygous for only one genetic locus (Figure 17–13). Infection of *E. coli* by two strains of λ phage can result in the recovery of up to 2% recombinant phage progeny. Experimental evidence supports a crossing-over mechanism involving breakage and repair of the DNA strands, whereas the evidence for a copy-choice mechanism is weak. The cross-over regions involve 500 to 1000 nucleotide pairs, and some regions may show heterozygosity. An interesting feature of λ infection is that its DNA circularizes when the virus becomes integrated in the host cell.

Research on recombination has led to the determination of circular genetic linkage groups in the phages T2 and T4, the detection of a linear order of the genes, and the mapping of very small parts of a genetic locus. In fact, estimates have been made of the number of nucleotide units in a unit of genetic function (*cistron*), a unit of genetic recombination (*recon*), and a unit of mutation (*muton*). In T4 phage, for example, in which the DNA consists of about 80,000 nucleotides, the smallest unit of genetic activity, the muton, presumably contains at least five nucleotide pairs.

SELECTED   READING

General

Burnet, F. M., "Viruses," *Sci. Am.*, **184**(5), 43 (1951).
Burnet, F. M., and W. M. Stanley, *The Viruses*, Vols. 1–3, Academic Press, New York, 1959.
Dulbecco, R., "The Induction of Cancer by Viruses," *Sci. Am.*, **216**(4), 28 (1967).
Fraenkel-Conrat, H., *Design and Function at the Threshold of Life: The Viruses*, Academic Press, New York, 1962.
Gunsalus, I. C., and R. Y. Stanier, eds., *The Bacteria*, Vol. I, *Structure*, Academic Press, New York, 1960.

Jacob, F., and E. L. Wollman, *Sexuality and the Genetics of Bacteria,* Academic Press, New York, 1961.

Kellenberger, E., "The Genetic Control of the Shape of a Virus," *Sci. Am.,* 215(6), 32 (1966).

Sagan, L., "On the Origin of Mitosing Cells," *J. Theoret. Biol.,* 14(3), 225 (1967).

Blue-Green Algae

Echlin, P., "The Blue-Green Algae," *Sci. Am.,* 214(6), 75 (1966).

Leak, L. V., and G. B. Wilson, "Distribution of Chromatin in a Blue-Green Alga, *Anabaena variabilis* Kutz," *Can. J. Genet. Cytol.,* 2, 320 (1960).

Ris, H., and R. N. Singh, "Electron Microscope Studies on Blue-Green Algae," *J. Biophys. Biochem. Cytol.,* 9(1), 63 (1961).

Bacteria

Bisset, K. A., "The Genetical Implications of Bacterial Cytology," *Cold Spring Harbor Symp. Quant. Biol.,* 16, 381 (1951).

Cairns, J., "The Bacterial Chromosome and Its Manner of Replication as Seen by Autoradiography," *J. Mol. Biol.,* 6(3), 208 (1963).

Cairns, J., "The Bacterial Chromosome," *Sci. Am.,* 214(1), 36 (1966).

Cairns, J., "The Mechanics of DNA Replication in Bacteria," *J. Cell Physiol.,* 70(2), 65 (1967).

Cohen-Bazire, G., and R. Kunisawa, "The Fine Structure of *Rhodospirillum rubrum*," *J. Cell Biol.,* 16(2), 401 (1963).

Cohen-Bazire, G., N. Pfennig, and R. Kunisawa, "The Fine Structure of Green Bacteria," *J. Cell Biol.,* 22(1), 207 (1964).

Delamater, E. D., "A Cytological and Chemical Analysis of the Bacterial Nucleus," *Exptl. Cell Res.,* 16(3), 636 (1959).

Hopwood, D. A., and G. Sermonti, "The Genetics of *Streptomyces coelicolor*," *Advan. Genet.,* 11, 273 (1962).

van Iterson, W., "The Fine Structure of the Ribonucleoprotein in Bacterial Cytoplasm," *J. Cell Biol.,* 28(3), 563 (1966).

Jacob, F., S. Brenner, and F. Cuzin, "On the Regulation of DNA Replication in Bacteria," *Cold Spring Harbor Symp. Quant. Biol.,* 28, 329 (1963).

Spahr, P. F., "Amino Acid Composition of Ribosomes from *E. coli*," *J. Mol. Biol.,* 4(5), 395 (1962).

Viruses

Anderson, T. F., "The Molecular Organization of Virus Particles," in J. M. Allen, ed., *Molecular Organization and Biological Function,* Harper & Row, New York, 1967, pp. 37–64.

Burton, A., and R. L. Sinsheimer, "Electron Microscopy of the Replicative Form of the DNA of the Bacteriophage φX174," *Science,* 142(3594), 961 (1963).

Cohen, J. A., "Chemistry and Structure of Nucleic Acids of Bacteriophages," *Science,* **158**(3799), 343 (1967).

Fraenkel-Conrat, H., "Rebuilding a Virus," *Sci. Am.,* **194**(6), 42 (1956).

Fraenkel-Conrat, H., and B. Singer, "Reconstitution of Tobacco Mosaic Virus. III. Improved Methods and the Use of Mixed Nucleic Acids," *Biochim. Biophys. Acta,* **33**(2), 359 (1959).

Freifelder, D., A. K. Kleinschmidt, and R. L. Sinsheimer, "Electron Microscopy of Single-Stranded DNA: Circularity of DNA of Bacteriophage ϕX174," *Science,* **146**(3641), 254 (1964).

Haselkorn, R., "Physical and Chemical Properties of Plant Viruses," *Ann. Rev. Plant Physiol.,* **17**, 137 (1966).

Horne, R. W., "The Structure of Viruses," *Sci. Am.,* **208**(1), 48 (1963).

Jacob, F., and E. L. Wollman, "Viruses and Genes," *Sci. Am.,* **204**(6), 92 (1961).

Krimm, S., and T. F. Anderson, "Structure of Normal and Contracted Tail Sheaths of T4 Bacteriophage," *J. Mol. Biol.,* **27** (2), 197 (1967).

Lodish, H. F., and N. D. Zinder, "Replication of the RNA of Bacteriophage *f2*," *Science,* **152**(3720), 372 (1966).

Lwoff, A., "Principles of Classification and Nomenclature of Viruses," *Nature,* **215**(5096), 13 (1967).

Genetic Mechanisms

"Basic Mechanisms in Animal Virus Biology," *Cold Spring Harbor Symp. Quant. Biol.,* **27** (1962).

Benzer, S., "The Fine Structure of the Gene," *Sci. Am.,* **206**(1), 70 (1962).

Gross, J. D., and L. Caro, "Genetic Transfer in Bacterial Mating," *Science,* **150** (3704), 1679 (1965).

Jacob, F., "Genetics of the Bacterial Cell," *Science,* **152**(3728), 1470 (1966).

Lwoff, A., "Interaction Among Virus, Cell, and Organism," *Science,* **152**(3726), 1216 (1966).

Silver, S., "Molecular Genetics of Bacteria and Bacteriophages," in J. A. V. Butler and H. E. Huxley, eds., *Progress in Biophysics and Molecular Biology,* Vol. 16, Pergamon Press, New York, 1966, pp. 191–240.

Thomas, C. A., "The Organization of DNA in Bacteriophage and Bacteria," in J. H. Taylor, ed., *Molecular Genetics,* Part 1, Academic Press, New York, 1963, pp. 113–51.

Tsugita, A., and H. Fraenkel-Conrat, "Contributions from TMV Studies to the Problem of Genetic Information Transfer and Coding," in J. H. Taylor, ed., *Molecular Genetics,* Part 1, Academic Press, New York, 1963, pp. 477–520.

Zinder, N., and J. Lederberg, "Genetic Exchange in *Salmonella*," *J. Bacteriol.,* **64**, 679 (1952).

18

Nuclear and
Cytoplasmic Controls

Now that the structural and functional organizations of a variety of cells have been considered in some detail, it is necessary to examine some of the ways in which the activities of the two major regions of the cell—the nucleus and the cytoplasm—are integrated. Among the most important cellular functions in the whole organism are those concerned with genetic regulation and coordination. Although the activities of the nucleus and cytoplasm may appear to be separate and distinct, they are, in fact, intimately dependent upon each other. The integration of nuclear and cytoplasmic controls is also important in the process of differentiation.

The first part of this chapter deals with specialized patterns of inheritance in only a few organisms in order to demonstrate how nuclear activity may be integrated with cytoplasmic activity in the expression of genetic characteristics. It must be kept in mind, however, that most organisms and most genetic patterns are essentially under nuclear controls, in that the genes located on the chromosomes are responsible for most of the expressed characteristics of the individuals in successive generations. However, since the emphasis here is on cytological phenomena and nucleo-cytoplasmic relations, only passing reference will be made to Mendelian inheritance in the cases to be described.

Genetic Interactions

Among the several cytoplasmic organelles discussed in previous chapters, the plastids and mitochondria have been shown to have considerable autonomy in their ability to reproduce. Although there are undoubtedly specific nuclear genes that ultimately govern their existence, they have a continuity of their own. The presence of DNA in the chloroplasts and mitochondria supports this conclusion. Moreover, certain features of plastid inheritance have been observed and studied from a genetic stand-point. As noted in Chapter 7, a number of chromosomal mutants affect-ing plastid characteristics have been found in barley. Other plastid mutations arise, at least in part, from cytoplasmic factors called *NC* (non-chromosomal) genes, or sometimes "plasmagenes."

One of the earliest discoveries of a cytoplasmic involvement in plastid inheritance was the condition known as *status albomaculatus,* or striping pattern, in the four-o'clock (*Mirabilis jalapa*). If a striped female is crossed with a normal green male, three types of progeny are recovered, colorless (lethal), striped, and normal green. If the reciprocal cross, normal green female with striped male, is made, however, only normal green progeny are recovered; the striped phenotype is not transmitted by the male. Con-tinued recovery of this inheritance pattern indicates that the striping characteristic cannot be accounted for by a nuclear gene but only by some cytoplasmic factor. Typical nuclear genes segregate during the meiotic divisions, while plasmagenes do not.

In corn the *iojap gene,* which is chromosomal, gives rise to green and white striped plants when in the homozygous recessive state. (The name is derived from "Iowa," the source of the corn strain, and "japonica," the name of a striped variety.) A reciprocal cross between striped and normal green individuals exhibits a maternal pattern of inheritance as found in *status albomaculatus;* there is no effect of the male parent even in the absence of the *iojap* gene. This result has been attributed to a mutation in the plastids, making them incapable of producing chlorophyll, since even continued crossing to remove the *iojap* gene fails to eliminate progeny with the striped phenotype. Once the mutation occurs, it is stable, and its transmission is not modified by the nuclear gene. There is considerable evidence that the initial determinant is not the plastids themselves but some other cytoplasmic factor affected by the *iojap* gene. Thus this case is an example of a nucleocytoplasmic interaction leading to genetic auton-omy of the cytoplasm.

Heslop-Harrison has stated that "the plasmagene theory . . . has . . . been kept between life and death over the years by occasional mesmeric passes, but instead of showing signs of putrefaction, the cadaver appears to be coming alive." There is no better example of this resurrection than in the nonchromosomal genes in *Chlamydomonas*. Most wild type *Chlamy-domonas* individuals are killed by a 100 μg/ml streptomycin solution. That is, they are streptomycin-sensitive (*ss*). Occasionally, however, there develop in a culture colonies of cells that are resistant to streptomycin (*sr*). These represent mutants. Two classes of mutants are found, *sr*-100, which is resistant to 100 μg/ml streptomycin and appears in one out of 1 million cells, and *sr*-500, which is resistant to 500 μg/ml streptomycin

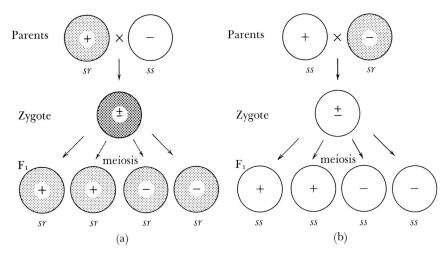

Figure 18–1. Inheritance of streptomycin resistance in *Chlamydomonas:* (a) all progeny are streptomycin resistant (*sr*), like the mating-type (+) parent; (b) all progeny are streptomycin sensitive (*ss*), like the mating-type (+) parent.

and occurs with a frequency of one in 10 million. The *sr*-100 mutants are chromosomal in origin, whereas the *sr*-500 mutants exhibit nonchromosomal patterns of inheritance, with one parent transmitting the resistance characteristic; all progeny have the resistance level of the parent of mating type (+). (Mating type, (+) or (−), is inherited as a single, chromosomal gene.) Mating type–dependent transmission of streptomycin resistance is illustrated in Figure 18–1. All of the data attest that this phenomenon is not due to an abnormality of the chromosomes or of any of the typical genetic events involving chromosomes.

Other similar mutants include streptomycin-dependent (*sd*) and *sr*-1500 (resistant to 1500 μg/ml streptomycin) mutants. Although the patterns of inheritance signify cytoplasmic mechanisms, there is some interaction with nuclear genes. A chromosomal gene *A* ("amplifier"), for example, amplifies the resistance of *sr* mutants but confers no resistance on *ss* strains. However, this gene does not affect the uniparental inheritance pattern of *sr*-500 mutants and segregates independently of the cytoplasmic factor.

It remains, of course, to explain the nature of the cytoplasmic factors and their behavior. Sager, who has studied the *sr–ss* system and a number of acetate-requiring mutants of like origins in detail, suggests that the *NC* genes are permanent constituents of the cell, well integrated into cellular metabolic activities and having stable inheritance patterns, whether or not they are expressed. Sager favors the hypothesis that the cytoplasmic units are nonchromosomal genes, for several reasons. Uniparental transmission rules out a position in the chromosomes, and the partial interaction of the A gene and sr-500 mutants indicates a separation of the units. In addition, mutation from ss to sr-500 occurs only in the presence of streptomycin, and resistance develops gradually instead of rapidly as with chromosomal mutants.

Occasionally the NC genes from both parents are transmitted through the zygotes to the progeny. Although these "exceptional" zygotes occur at low frequencies, from 0.01 to 0.1%, they can be recovered for analysis when grown on a medium that favors their survival. Also, since the zygotes contain NC genes from both male and female parents (for example, ss and sd), they will grow equally well on a minimal medium or a streptomycin-containing medium. After one or more mitotic divisions some of the NC genes will segregate and give rise to pure clones of either ss or sd cells. Thus mitotic segregation occurs instead of the usual meiotic segregation. Sager has made use of the exceptional zygotes to study the possibility that recombination occurs between NC genes, and to establish that they are made of nucleic acid. She has shown not only that recombination indeed occurs, but also that they act like allelic pairs. For example, the acetate mutants ac_1 and ac_2 segregate in an average 1 : 1 ratio, the sr and ss genes segregate from each other, and the two pairs segregate independently of each other. Treatment of female cells with low doses of ultraviolet light just prior to mating raises the frequency of exceptional zygotes to over 50%, and the effect is reversible by visible light (photoreactivation; Chapter 15). High doses of ultraviolet light lead to the loss of female NC genes. A possible explanation of these effects is that ultraviolet light affects the nucleic acid of a gene that controls the formation of a substance (enzyme?) responsible for the loss of the male NC genes. Normally the mating process would be expected to induce the formation of such a substance, but ultraviolet light prevents the gene from functioning. The fact that ultraviolet light has such effects in *Chlamydomonas* has provided additional support for the contention that the NC genes are made of nucleic acid. However, it has not yet been possible to determine whether DNA or RNA is the principal component. Moreover, there is no clear evidence to indicate whether the NC genes are confined to specific cytoplasmic organelles or lie free in the cytoplasm.

Kappa Particles

Probably the best-known cases of genetic nucleocytoplasmic interactions involve certain varieties of the protozoon *Paramecium aurelia*. The life

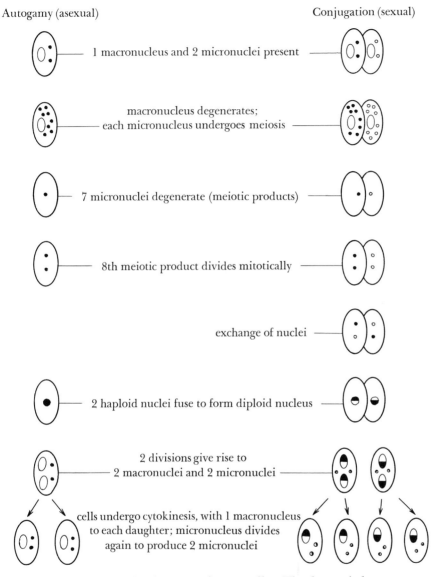

Autogamy (asexual)   Conjugation (sexual)

1 macronucleus and 2 micronuclei present

macronucleus degenerates;
each micronucleus undergoes meiosis

7 micronuclei degenerate (meiotic products)

8th meiotic product divides mitotically

exchange of nuclei

2 haploid nuclei fuse to form diploid nucleus

2 divisions give rise to
2 macronuclei and 2 micronuclei

cells undergo cytokinesis, with 1 macronucleus
to each daughter; micronucleus divides
again to produce 2 micronuclei

Figure 18–2. Life cycle of *Paramecium aurelia.* The large circles represent macronuclei, and the small circles micronuclei.

cycle of this organism is shown in Figure 18–2. Members of the species have macronuclei that function in maintenance and reproduction and micronuclei from which the macronuclei are derived. On conjugation or

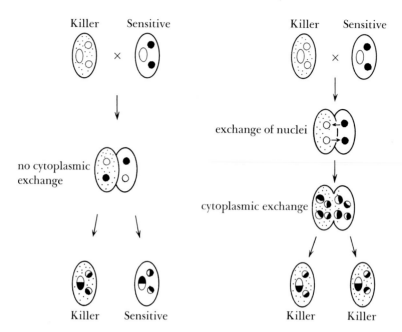

Figure 18–3. Transmission of the killer trait in *P. aurelia*. The stippling represents kappa particles in the cytoplasm.

autogamy, the macronucleus begins to degenerate, and one or more of the
micronuclei undergo meiosis. In each cell seven of the meiotic products
degenerate, and the one remaining haploid nucleus divides mitotically.
In autogamy the two resultant haploid nuclei fuse to form a diploid
micronucleus, and in conjugation there is an exchange of micronuclei,
one going from each partner to the other, followed by a fusion of the two
different nuclei in each cell. The diploid nucleus in each instance then
divides twice to produce two macronuclei and two micronuclei. During
the formation of the macronuclei, the diploid number of chromosomes
may be increased several times, so that polyploid nuclei are created.
Finally the cytoplasm divides, and thus two daughter cells develop from
each original cell, each daughter containing one macronucleus and one
micronucleus, which divides once again. Usually there is little or no cytoplasmic exchange during conjugation.

Cultures of *P. aurelia* contain individuals synthesizing a substance
(*paramecin*) toxic to other individuals in the population. The individuals
producing the effect are called *killers,* and those affected are called *sensitives.* When killer cells are mated with sensitive cells and some exchange
of cytoplasm occurs during conjugation, all the progeny are killers. If

no cytoplasmic exchange occurs, the progeny segregate into killers and sensitives (Figure 18–3). Thus cytoplasmic factors are obviously responsible for the killer trait, which is transmitted uniparentally. Under the light microscope the cytoplasmic units can be identified as 0.2μ Feulgen-positive bodies present in varying numbers. Their deoxyribonucleoprotein content is substantiated by observations that they are inactivated by deoxyribonuclease, pepsin, or chymotrypsin. It has been demonstrated that a killer cell carries enough toxic material to be lethal in only one unit, or *kappa* particle, although usually several hundred such particles appear in a cell. Two morphologically different kappa particles in stock 51 of *P. aurelia* have been investigated. A *bright* particle, which contains a refractile body, is associated with the ability to kill sensitive animals, whereas a *nonbright* particle, which lacks the refractile body, is associated with the ability to convert sensitive animals of the proper genotype to killer animals. The particles differ in the nitrogenous base compositions of their respective DNA's.

As implied, the activity of a killer animal is based on an interaction of the cytoplasmic kappa particles and a nuclear gene. A cell having the nuclear gene K maintains kappa particles and permits their self-replication, whereas a cell homozygous for k, the recessive allele of K, loses its capacity to maintain and reproduce kappa particles and thus becomes sensitive (Figure 18–4). The transmission of the killer characteristic therefore depends on a nuclear gene. In addition to K, the nuclear genes S_1 and S_2 are necessary for the maintenance of kappa particles.

Other cytoplasmic particles have been found in *P. aurelia*, some of which represent mutants of kappa particles. They include *pi* particles, which are nontoxic, and *mu* particles, or mate killers, which are toxic

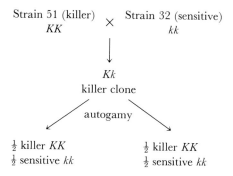

Figure 18–4. Nuclear control, through chromosomal gene K, of the replication of kappa particles in *P. aurelia*.

only at the time of conjugation; nuclear divisions cease in a sensitive mate. Gibson and Beale have proposed the "metagon" hypothesis to explain the behavior of the *mu* particles. A metagon is considered to be the product of nuclear gene *M*, is responsible for the maintenance of mu particles, and acts like a cytoplasmic gene. In this case, however, the gene is not made of DNA, since the metagon is a messenger RNA! Others have not found any evidence to support such a hypothesis for the kappa system. Of particular interest, on the other hand, is the attention that has been given to kappa particles and other cytoplasmic bodies found in certain strains of *Drosophila melanogaster*. Some workers have suggested that these particles may be nonviral microorganisms! In view of the discussion to follow, this suggestion may not be as startling as it appears.

Episomes

In Chapter 17 extrachromosomal factors were mentioned in connection with bacteria and bacteriophages, respectively: the *F* factor and temperate phage. Both of these elements participate in still another kind of nucleocytoplasmic interaction related to genetic activity. In 1958 Jacob and Wollman described them as being able to exist in two states: *integrated* with the chromosomes and *autonomous,* in that they multiply independently of and sometimes faster than the cells they occupy and, therefore, independently of the chromosomes. The term *episomes* has been coined for them. Both the *F* factor and the lambda phage, which are discussed here, consist primarily of DNA, as has been determined by spectrophotometry and the use of acridine dyes, which affect nucleic acid. The DNA of the *F* factor has a molecular weight of between 90 and 120 million, and that of the lambda phage a molecular weight of about 60 million. The dissociator-activator elements in corn (Chapter 15) may be considered as episomes according to the stated criteria; they are integrated in the chromosomes sometimes but not at other times.

   The behavior of the *F* factor in *Escherichia coli* was outlined in Chapter 17. How it is integrated is not yet clear, but the suggestion has been made that it is present as a side arm on the circular chromosome or closely paired for part of the length of the chromosome. The fact that the *F* factor is transmitted from cell to cell during conjugation faster than the genes is evidence for its episomal nature. Studies have shown that it is possible to transfer the *F* factor of the K12 strain of *E. coli* to *Salmonella* species. Either wild type *F* or mutant *F* (*F'*) of K12 with an attached piece of the host chromosome can then be transferred to other species of *Salmonella,* as well as to *E. coli.*

The *F* factor is incorporated at any point in the circular chromosome, this point marking the breakage site and the zero position in the gene sequence. In a transfer of genetic material from one bacterial cell to another (resulting in recombination), it enters the recipient cell last, after one or more genes. A bacterial strain donating most or all of its circular chromosome to a recipient cell is known as *Vhf* (very high frequency recombination) strain.

When a bacterial cell is infected by temperate phage, the DNA of the phage becomes integrated with the bacterial chromosome at a particular locus and replicates synchronously with the chromosome. If lysis occurs, the phage may carry with it certain genetic loci from the bacterial chromosome into a newly infected lysogenic bacterium, thereby effecting their transduction. Lambda phage has the ability to transduce only the galactose locus of the *E. coli* chromosome. When this transduction takes place, the resultant bacterial progeny may contain two such loci, one of which is wild type (able to metabolize galactose) and the other of which is mutant type (unable to metabolize galactose). The bacteria in this case are heterozygous for the galactose locus and are called *heterogenotes*. The attachment to the bacterial chromosome is very likely a side arm, as lambda phage, like the *F* factor, enters the recipient cell *after* the locus. A characteristic of prophage that is indicative of its genetic behavior is its capacity to replicate. Of special significance in this respect is a mutant prophage that may be infective but that cannot reproduce. Defective prophage of this type can undergo reverse mutation to the normal, replicating form.

In summary, there appear to be at least two kinds of nucleocytoplasmic interactions governing genetic behavior that is not strictly Mendelian. One kind involves discrete cytoplasmic units or particles that exhibit uniparental inheritance and that are always physically independent of the chromosomes, as in *Chlamydomonas* and *Paramecium*. The other kind involves nonchromosomal factors that exist in two different states, as part of the chromosomes and independently of the chromosomes; it is peculiar to certain systems, as, for example, bacteria. The examples given here represent only a small fraction of the inheritance patterns found in plants and animals and are in many ways atypical; they are emphasized only because of their particular cytological interest, not because they illustrate all of the nucleocytoplasmic genetic mechanisms. In any event, all genetic behavior, Mendelian and otherwise, depends on interrelations of nuclear activity and cytoplasmic activity. For instance, the elaborate biochemical pathways throughout the cell are generally initiated by and under the control of the nucleus. Attention will be focused on them in the following paragraphs.

Biochemical Interactions

Several means by which substances move into and out of cells and between the nucleus and cytoplasm were examined in Part One. An extensive system of membranes within the cell provides channels for the passage of materials and takes an active part in transport. This system is vital for the normal functioning of the cell at the metabolic level and permits the exchanges necessary for nucleocytoplasmic interactions. Although considerable data have been presented pointing to the dominance of the nucleus in cellular behavior, two outstanding questions remain: when during the cellular interactions are the nuclear and cytoplasmic activities integrated, and where do the activities of the nucleus "end" and those of the cytoplasm "begin"? It is possible, of course, that there is no clear-cut separation of these activities. Some of the present knowledge on the subject is reviewed in this discussion.

Three investigative procedures are of value in research on biochemical interactions. They are (1) observation of morphological changes in a cell during a specific metabolic activity; (2) transplantation of a nucleus from one kind of cell into the cytoplasm of another and observation of possible changes in metabolic activity; and (3) utilization of a radioactive isotope to determine the pattern of incorporation of a specific substance into the nucleus and the cytoplasm. An example of the first approach is the behavior of the nucleus in a salivary gland cell of *Drosophila* during larval development (Chapter 14).

Ribonucleic acid is considered to be of prime importance for the synthesis of proteins in the cytoplasm, and its activity depends ultimately on the genetic information resident in the DNA of the chromosomes. Support for this contention will be forthcoming in Chapter 19. In this chapter it will also be shown that most of the RNA is synthesized in the nucleus and subsequently transported to the cytoplasm. Such a scheme of RNA metabolism has been found in the salivary gland cells of the *Drosophila* larva. In these cells the heterochromatic regions of the chromosomes, associated particularly with the nucleolus, are quite active in conveying RNA from the nucleus to the cytoplasm. It has been possible to correlate this activity with developmental changes in the larva. During larval growth the cells increase in size, and then secretion granules appear in their cytoplasm. In the late stages of larval development, or the period just prior to pupation, the secretion granules disrupt, and their contents are carried to the cavity of the salivary gland. The substance so released is used to attach the pupa to a surface and contains large amounts of protein and some carbohydrate.

Just before the secretion granules arise in the cytoplasm, small pockets or *blebs* may be seen in the nuclear envelope by electron microscopy. The material in a bleb is mostly RNA. More significant is the fact that this material apparently originates in a specific heterochromatic region of the chromosome, which may lie near the nuclear envelope at the time of bleb formation. Each outpocketing separates from the nuclear envelope to become a small secretion granule, surrounded by two membranes similar to the nuclear envelope and presumably derived therefrom. The morphological changes in the nucleus and cytoplasm in this case can be closely coordinated with the production of RNA in the nucleus and the production of protein, under the direction of the RNA, in the cytoplasm.

Observations of this kind have been made in various cells. Electron microscopy has revealed large nuclear blebs containing, among other substances, material seemingly of nucleolar origin in pancreatic acinar cells of the rat. This finding is in agreement with that in *Drosophila,* since the nucleolus is high in RNA and cells active in protein synthesis have high proportions of RNA in well-developed nucleoli. The small vesicles formed from the nuclear envelope in an oocyte of *Triturus viridescens* closely parallel those in other cells. However, there is at least one difference between the vesicle of the amphibian oocyte and that of the *Drosophila* larva; in the oocyte only a single membrane encloses the extruded material. This characteristic is possibly a function of whether one or both of the membranes of the nuclear envelope participate in bleb formation (Chapter 3).

Studies with *Amoeba*

A great number of experiments involving removal of the nucleus from a cell (*merotomy*) and nuclear transplants have been performed on protozoa and a few other organisms in attempts to delineate the individual roles of the nucleus and the cytoplasm. Among the organisms most widely studied are such species of *Amoeba* as *A. proteus* and *A. sphaeronucleus.* When the nucleus of an amoeba is transferred to an anucleate cell fragment, it must be protected from the external environment, or it will degenerate rapidly, and a close association of the donor nucleus and the recipient cytoplasm must be maintained from the outset, or the transplant will not take. These precautions must also be observed with transplants in other cells, such as those of a frog embryo. Therefore, to ensure a successful transplant, some of the donor cytoplasm is invariably included with the nucleus, even though it contaminates the recipient cytoplasm and makes analysis of interaction difficult. Unfortunately no synthetic medium has yet been developed that will support a cell-free nucleus for a long period of time. Despite these limitations, careful application of transplanting techniques provides some interesting insights into nuclear and cytoplasmic activities.

When the nucleus is removed from *A. proteus,* the organism exhibits a loss of motility, as demonstrated by a cessation of pseudopod formation, and becomes spherical and incapable of feeding. However, an anucleate fragment may survive for as long as 2 weeks in this fasting condition. Nucleated fragments live 3 weeks. Similar effects are seen in *A. sphaeronucleus,* but in this case if the nucleus is reintroduced into the cytoplasm within 3 days, motility is restored. After 6 days, there is no recovery, a situation implying some irreversible change in the anucleate cytoplasm. In contrast to the findings on amoebae, the removal of the nucleus from a human HeLa cell in culture does not modify the activity of the cell for as long as 40 hours. This result suggests that the mammalian nucleus has fewer functions than the mammalian cytoplasm and that the cytoplasm retains numerous general functions.

Especially worthy of note is the production of a "hybrid" amoeba when the nucleus of one species is transplanted into the cytoplasm of another. A transplant of the nucleus of either *A. proteus* or *A. discoides* into the anucleate cytoplasm of the other can re-establish motility. The morphology of the hybrid is strongly influenced by the cytoplasmic contribution, whereas its locomotion characteristic is intermediate between that of the cell supplying the nucleus and that of the cell supplying the cytoplasm. Interspecies grafting has not been nearly so successful in other protozoa, such as *Paramecium* and *Stentor,* as in amoebae.

Several metabolic changes can be observed in the cytoplasmic fragments of amoebae immediately after enucleation, although significant changes are not evident for 2 or 3 days. Usually, there is an increase in the utilization of protein and a concurrent decrease in the utilization of glycogen. The incorporation of labeled amino acids into anucleate fragments is considerably less than into nucleate fragments, indicating a substantial reduction in protein synthesis. Since the bulk of RNA is synthesized in the nucleus, and since the nucleus is absent, there is much less controlling material (RNA) present to direct the synthesis of protein than in a normal cell. However, even after 8 days, there may be only 40% inhibition of protein synthesis. The lowered RNA level is reflected in diminishing basophilic response within 2 days following enucleation, and by 5 days there is no stain reaction for RNA. On the other hand, nucleate fragments retain their RNA contents for at least 12 days. Thus the nucleus clearly is necessary for the production of RNA and its maintenance in the cytoplasm. There have been some claims that the cytoplasm also synthesizes RNA, but the latest information refutes them. In addition to affecting protein and nucleic acid metabolism, enucleation generally upsets phosphate and carbohydrate metabolism.

A study of species and strain transplants in *A. proteus* and *A. discoides* has revealed still another facet of the relations between the nucleus and the cytoplasm. These species exhibit interstrain differences in resistance to streptomycin. The growth of sensitive strains is retarded by concentrations higher than 0.06 μg/ml. When a nuclear transplant is made between two strains of *A. proteus,* one resistant and one sensitive, the streptomycin resistance of the hybrid progeny is the same as that of the sensitive parent. Progeny of heterotransfers (resistant nucleus in sensitive cytoplasm or sensitive nucleus in resistant cytoplasm) in *A. discoides* are more resistant and absorb less streptomycin than the sensitive parent. Cole and Danielli have suggested that the interrelationships between the nucleus and the cytoplasm differ in the two species—that in *A. proteus* the mechanisms controlling level of resistance are transmitted via an interaction between nucleus and cytoplasm and that in *A. discoides* independent nuclear and cytoplasmic factors determine the level of resistance.

Additional differences have been noted in connection with nuclear size. When an *A. discoides* nucleus is transplanted to an *A. proteus* cytoplasm, the nucleus increases in size. When the reciprocal transplant is made, the *A. proteus* nucleus decreases in size. In either case the ultimate size of the nucleus is typical of the species from which the cytoplasm was derived, indicating a *cytoplasmic* controlling mechanism. There is also evidence, from transplants of nuclei of *A. proteus* during different interphase stages, that the cytoplasm influences the initiation and the termination of nuclear DNA synthesis. When a nucleus in the S stage (DNA synthesis) is placed in a cell in G_2, DNA synthesis is inhibited, but when a G_2 nucleus is placed in an S-stage cell the G_2 nucleus may begin to synthesize DNA. An "initiator" of synthesis may be present in S-stage cells and absent in G_2 cells.

Studies with *Acetabularia*

The unicellular green, marine alga *Acetabularia* (mermaid's wineglass) has been of great value in demonstrating the activities of the nucleus and cytoplasm during specific events in differentiation. Because of the relatively large size of the cell (nearly 1 inch long), and the fact that the nucleus occupies a specific position in the cytoplasm, nuclear transplants are

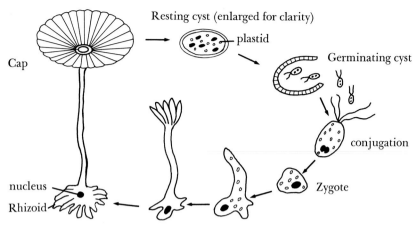

Figure 18–5. Life cycle of *Acetabularia mediterranea.*

facilitated. Two species in particular, *A. mediterranea* and *A. crenulata,* each of which has a unique morphology (Figure 18–5), have been investigated by several workers, including Brachet and Haemmerling. In the normal vegetative cell the nucleus is located in one of the *rhizoids* at the base and contains a very well-developed nucleolus, rich in RNA. During the reproductive cycle the nucleus divides several times, giving rise to daughter nuclei, which migrate throughout the cell. In the cap, cysts develop, containing several nuclei and plastids. Before germination, these nuclei divide, and their products are incorporated, along with some cytoplasm, into flagellated gametes. When the gametes are released from a cyst, two conjugate to form a zygote, which then becomes a new stalk. The entire cycle lasts approximately 1 year in nature but can be stimulated to occur in about 5 months in the laboratory.

Early research by Haemmerling showed that the division of the nucleus depends on the cytoplasm. If a large cap is removed just before nuclear division, the division is delayed until a new cap forms. Furthermore, if a young rhizoid is grafted to a cell with a large cap, nuclear division may occur within 2 weeks, whereas normally it takes 2 months. Other activities of the cell, however, especially those concerned with morphogenesis, seem to be primarily under nuclear control, according to transplant and grafting experiments. Nevertheless, observations of environmental effects on the nucleus hint at a possible involvement of the cytoplasm. For example, if *Acetabularia* is kept in the dark for several days, the volume of the nucleus decreases, and the size, shape, and basophilic nature of the nucleolus change. These effects are light-reversible. They can also be caused by an inhibition of oxidative phosphorylation, as by the addition of dinitrophenol, which uncouples oxidation from phosphorylation. Thus they are apparently due to a lowered energy production in the cytoplasm.

Some interesting grafting experiments have been carried out with *A. mediterranea* and *A. crenulata*. It should be noted that these cells are able to survive, and even produce caps, for several months following enuclea-tion. As illustrated in Figure 18–6, when a binucleate graft is made be-tween the stalks of the two species, the resulting cap has an intermediate morphology, with loose rays as in *crenulata* but rounded ends as in *medi-terranea*. As might be expected, a trinucleate graft results in a cap more like that of the species represented by two of the three nuclei. When a nucleated stalk of one species is grafted onto an anucleate fragment of another species, the cap first formed combines features of the caps of both species but more closely resembles that of the species contributing the nucleus. If this cap is removed, a new cap will form, which is typical of the species contributing the nucleus. Haemmerling has interpreted these

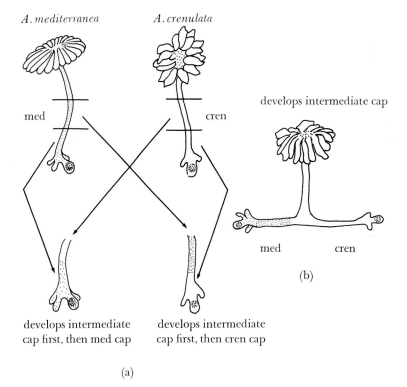

Figure 18–6. Grafting in *Acetabularia:* (a) uninucleate grafts; (b) a binucleate graft.

findings as evidence for nuclear control over the synthesis of some morphogenetic substances in the cytoplasm, which exhibit species specificity. In a binucleate graft the substances are produced by both nuclei, and an intermediate cap is formed. In a uninucleate graft the anucleate cytoplasm contains some stored substances specific for its species, and the nucleus produces substances specific for its species; if enough of the cytoplasmic substances are present, an intermediate cap is formed.

The role of RNA in the regeneration and morphogenesis of *Acetabularia* has been substantiated by data indicating that the nucleus is the main site of the synthesis of RNA, which then governs the synthesis of protein in the cytoplasm. For instance, trypaflavin, a substance that combines with nucleic acids, inhibits the regeneration of nucleate as well as anucleate pieces. Moreover, ultraviolet radiation at a wavelength of 2537 Å is inhibitory, and actinomycin D suppresses the formation of the morphogenetic substances.

The few differences in metabolic behavior of anucleate fragments between *Acetabularia* and *Amoeba* can be accounted for by the different properties of the two organisms. *Acetabularia* is photosynthetic, whereas *Amoeba* is not, and therefore the two do not have the same kinds of metabolic systems.

In enucleated *Acetabularia,* RNA synthesis continues during the week immediately following enucleation, and at a somewhat faster rate than in nucleate fragments. After 1 week, however, the rate decreases. It has also been demonstrated that there is a DNA-dependent synthesis of RNA in the chloroplasts, together with an increase in the number of chloroplasts, which may cause the initial rise in rate. Since the cytoplasmic RNA in the plastids is essentially independent of the nuclear RNA, it is not significant with respect to nuclear controls, as treatments with ultraviolet light, mentioned earlier, and ribonuclease show. These agents inhibit cap formation and growth, confirming that the controls are principally nuclear and that the RNA affected is nuclear in origin. Finally, and related to these observations, photosynthetic activity is apparently normal in anucleate fragments for as long as 4 weeks.

Studies of protein synthesis and energy-yielding reactions have provided additional intelligence on the biochemistry of morphogenesis. In anucleate cells the level of protein synthesis remains relatively constant for about 2 weeks, and then synthesis stops. Experiments with different amino acids have suggested that a sulfur-containing protein is necessary for cap formation. Thus if protein synthesis ceases and the store of sulfur-containing protein is depleted, no cap develops. Labeling techniques point to two sites of protein synthesis in these photosynthetic cells, one, requiring light, in the plastids and the other in the ribosomes. The latter site is obviously under nuclear control and is primarily responsible for morphogenesis. As will be described in Chapter 19, although the mechanisms of protein synthesis involve nucleic acids in both the cytoplasm and the nucleus, the nucleus contains the genetic information leading to the production of specific proteins and is therefore the seat of ultimate control. In essence, the genetic information in DNA is transferred to the cytoplasm by RNA synthesized in the nucleus. When RNA synthesis stops, protein synthesis stops, and regeneration does not occur. Mazia proposed a *replacement* phenomenon to explain the nucleocytoplasmic relations in *Acetabularia* and other cells in which the removal of the nucleus is not followed by immediate changes in cell metabolism. According to his theory, nuclear activity may give rise to a cytoplasmic unit that is important in synthetic activities in the cytoplasm but that requires continuous replacement by the nucleus; this unit may be comparable to the kappa particle of *Paramecium*.

RNA: A Morphogenetic Substance

RNA has been established as the key to metabolic behavior through studies on the incorporation of labeled precursors into human cells in culture, *Drosophila* salivary gland cells, *Amoeba proteus,* and *Tetrahymena* (another protozoon). In the last-named organism, as an example, labeling reveals that all RNA is produced in the nucleus and then transferred to the cytoplasm. There is no sign of RNA synthesis in anucleate fragments, since the process depends on the presence of DNA. The cessation of protein synthesis in anucleate fragments after a short time indicates that a cytoplasmic fraction of RNA has been used up. This fraction is most likely the messenger RNA molecules that are stable in the cytoplasm of enucleated cells for 2 to 3 weeks, and represents the morphogenetic substances mentioned earlier. Thus the continuation of protein synthesis after enucleation depends upon the presence of a pool of stable messenger RNA in the cytoplasm. According to Haemmerling, the RNA molecules are released from the nucleus in the light or in the dark, but are not active in protein synthesis except under suitable light conditions.

Differentiation

One of the most compelling subjects in biology is differentiation. With Briggs' and King's methods for nuclear transplants in amphibian eggs and embryos, various patterns of development can be examined, with a view to determining the functions of the nucleus and the cytoplasm. Observations of amphibian eggs into which embryonic nuclei have been transplanted show that up to the blastula stage the nucleus does not undergo any irreversible differentiation but that by the gastrula stage the endoderm nucleus has a fixed and specific destiny. Consequently, nuclear transplants from older embryos result in fewer normally developing eggs than those from young embryos. The general conclusion from such studies is that the nucleus specifies the type of tissue or organ to be developed but the cytoplasm specifies whether or not said tissue or organ will develop. Considerable gaps remain, however, in the knowledge of the nature of the cytoplasmic substances and the nuclear controls involved in differentiation. Among the anomalies seen in embryos developing from eggs into which differentiated nuclei have been transplanted are abnormal chromosome numbers, usually aneuploidy, and rearranged chromosomes. Although the source of these anomalies is not known, they apparently arise through some incompatibility between the nucleus and the cytoplasm.

SELECTED READING

General

Brachet, J., *The Biochemistry of Development,* Pergamon Press, New York, 1960.

Brachet, J., "Nucleocytoplasmic Interactions in Unicellular Organisms," in J. Brachet and A. E. Mirsky, eds., *The Cell,* Vol. 2, Academic Press, New York, 1961, pp. 771–841.

Campbell, A. M., "Episomes," *Advan .Genet.,* **11,** 101 (1962).

Ephrussi, B., "The Cytoplasm and Somatic Cell Variation," *J. Cellular Comp. Physiol.,* **52**(3), Suppl. 1, 35 (1958).

Fischberg, M., and A. W. Blackler, "How Cells Specialize," *Sci. Am.,* **205**(3), 124 (1961).

Gay, H., "Nuclear Control of the Cell," *Sci. Am.,* **202**(1), 126 (1960).

Sonneborn, T. M., "Partner of the Genes," *Sci. Am.,* **183**(5), 30 (1950).

Wilkie, D., *The Cytoplasm in Heredity,* Wiley, New York, 1964.

Wilson, E. B., *The Cell in Development and Heredity,* Macmillan, New York, 1925.

Wischnitzer, S., "The Ultrastructure of the Nucleus and Nucleocytoplasmic Relations," *Intern Rev. Cytol.,* **10,** 137 (1960).

Genetics

Balbinder, E., "The Genotypic Control of Kappa in *Paramecium aurelia,* Syngen 4, Stock 51," *Genetics,* **44**(6), 1227 (1959).

Gillham, N. W., "The Nature of Exceptions to the Pattern of Uniparental Inheritance for High Level Streptomycin Resistance in *Chlamydomonas reinhardi*," *Genetics,* 48(3), 431 (1963).

McClintock, B., "Some Parallels Between Gene Control Systems in Maize and in Bacteria," *Am. Naturalist,* 95(884), 265 (1961).

Mäkelä, P. H., J. Lederberg, and E. M. Lederberg, "Patterns of Sexual Recombination in Enteric Bacteria," *Genetics,* 47(10), 1427 (1962).

Preer, J. R., "Microscopically Visible Bodies in the Cytoplasm of the Killer Strains of *P. aurelia*," Genetics, 35(2), 344 (1950).

Sager, R., "Genetic Systems in *Chlamydomonas*," *Science,* 132(3438), 1459 (1960).

Sager, R., "Genes Outside the Chromosomes," *Sci. Am.,* 212(1), 70 (1965).

Sager, R., and Z. Ramanis, "The Particulate Nature of Nonchromosomal Genes in *Chlamydomonas*," *Proc. Natl. Acad. Sci. U.S.,* 50(2), 260 (1963).

Sager, R., and Z. Ramanis, "Biparental Inheritance of Nonchromosomal Genes Induced by Ultraviolet Irradiation," *Proc. Natl. Acad. Sci. U.S.,* 58(3), 931 (1967).

Smith-Sonneborn, J., L. Green, and J. Marmur, "Deoxyribonucleic Acid Base Composition of Kappa in *Paramecium aurelia,* Stock 51," *Nature,* 197(4865), 385 (1963).

Nuclear Transplants

Brachet, J., "Nucleic Acids in Development," *J. Cellular Comp. Physiol.,* 60(2), Suppl. 1, 1 (1962).

Briggs, R., and T. J. King, "Nuclear Transplantation Studies on Early Gastrula (*Rana pipiens*)," *Develop. Biol.,* 2, 252 (1960).

Cole, R. J., and J. F. Danielli, "Nuclear-Cytoplasmic Interactions in the Responses of *Amoeba proteus* and *Amoeba discoides* to Streptomycin," *Exptl. Cell Res.,* 29(1), 199 (1963).

Gibor, A., "*Acetabularia:* A Useful Giant Cell," *Sci. Am.,* 215(5), 118 (1966).

Goldstein, L., R. Cailleau, and T. T. Crocker, "Nuclear-Cytoplasmic Relationships in Human Cells in Tissue Culture," *Exptl. Cell. Res.,* 19(2), 332 (1960).

Haemmerling, J., "Nucleocytoplasmic Interactions in *Acetabularia* and Other Cells," *Ann. Rev. Plant Physiol.,* 14, 65 (1963).

Moore, J. A., "Nuclear Transplantation and Problems of Specificity in Developing Embryos," *J. Cellular Comp. Physiol.,* 60(2), Suppl. 1, 19 (1962).

Biochemistry

Clark, W. H., Jr., "Electron Microscope Studies of Nuclear Extrusions in Pancreatic Acinar Cells of the Rat." *J. Biophys. Biochem. Cytol.,* 7(2), 345 (1960).

Gay, H., "Nucleocytoplasmic Relations in Salivary Glands of *Drosophila,*" *Proc. Natl. Acad. Sci. U.S.,* 41(6), 370 (1955).

Goldstein, L., and J. Micou, "Nuclear-Cytoplasmic Relationships in Human Cells in Tissue Culture. III. Autoradiographic Study of Interrelation of Nuclear and Cytoplasmic RNA," *J. Biophys. Biochem. Cytol.,* 6(1), 1 (1959).

McMaster-Kaye, R., "The Metabolism of Nuclear Ribonucleic Acid in Salivary Glands of *Drosophila repleta,*" *J. Histochem. Cytochem.,* **10**(2), 154 (1962).

Prescott, D. M., "Nucleic Acid and Protein Metabolism in the Macronuclei of Two Ciliated Protozoa," *J. Histochem. Cytochem.,* **10**(2), 145 (1962).

Prescott, D. M., and L. Goldstein, "Nuclear-Cytoplasmic Interaction in DNA Synthesis," *Science,* **155**(3761), 469 (1967).

Wischnitzer, S., "Vesicle Formation from the Nuclear Envelope in Amphibian Oocytes," *Chromosoma,* **13**(5), 600 (1963).

19

Molecular Cytology

The field of molecular biology had its greatest impact upon the scientific world in the early 1960's. Yet molecular biology as a new approach in the life sciences actually began in the latter part of the 19th century with the work of Wilhelm His and Carl Ludwig. These men realized the importance of analyzing biological phenomena on the basis of physics and chemistry. In spite of this early beginning, however, the advances made in nucleic acid and protein research, especially as related to genetic mechanisms, have been most compelling in recent years. Moreover, molecular biology as an experimental approach has strongly influenced the direction of other biological disciplines. Reference has been made throughout this text to the fact that nucleocytoplasmic relations involve both physical and chemical interdependencies. Although they can hardly be considered the culmination of experimental cytology, the phenomena of cellular biosyntheses underscore the close physiological association of the nucleus and the cytoplasm. It is clear from a variety of studies that the ultimate control of cellular activities rests in the nucleus and specifically in the deoxyribonucleoprotein. Hence this final chapter treats the biochemical mechanisms directly concerned in the nuclear control of cellular behavior at the molecular level. The syntheses of DNA, RNA, and protein will be described in terms of their relations with one another and their functions in genetic regulation.

DNA Synthesis

DNA was isolated by F. Miescher about 100 years ago (1869), but it was conclusively established as the genetic material only about 25 years ago. Through the efforts of many investigators studying biological compounds at the molecular level, DNA was established to be a double helix structure containing phosphates, sugars, and nitrogenous bases (Chapter 1). Most of it is located in the cell nucleus, where, as the genetic material, it presides over numerous biochemical systems. Among its important properties is self-replication, by means of which it is duplicated and transmitted to subsequent generations in a relatively stable state. Although the nucleus is the principal site of DNA metabolism, other organelles in the cell have been shown to contain small amounts of the substance. The DNA present in chloroplasts, mitochondria, and basal bodies may be instrumental in conferring replicating ability upon them. In rare instances DNA has been found in extranuclear regions of the cell not associated with organelles. For example, small quantities of DNA have been identified in the cytoplasm of amphibian eggs, cotton embryos, fern eggs, and *Tetrahymena*. Since the significance of the nonnuclear DNA remains in doubt, except for the kappa particles in *Paramecium* and in mitochondria and chloroplasts, the discussion that follows deals exclusively with nuclear DNA synthesis.

The structural organization of the DNA molecule was outlined in Chapter 1, and Table 19–1 clarifies the compositions of some of its constituents. According to Watson and Crick, the replication of DNA requires a separation of the complementary helixes, so that each may serve as a template for a new helix. Mononucleotides available in the nucleus become aligned along the original helix and polymerize a new helix complementary to the original template helix. This is a process best described as semiconservative, since each original strand remains intact during and after replication and is paired with a new strand.

Table 19–1   Nucleic Acid Compositions

Base	Nucleoside*		Nucleotide†	
	RNA	DNA	RNA	DNA
purine				
adenine	adenosine	deoxyadenosine	adenylic acid	deoxyriboadenylic acid
guanine	guanosine	deoxyguanosine	guanylic acid	deoxyriboguanylic acid
pyrimidine				
thymine		deoxythymidine		deoxyribothymidylic acid
uracil	uridine		uridylic acid	
cytosine	cytidine	deoxycytidine	cytidylic acid	deoxyribocytidylic acid

* Base plus sugar. Deoxyribose is the sugar in DNA, ribose in RNA.
† Base plus sugar plus phosphate.

Experiments with *Escherichia coli* and with chromosomes of *Vicia faba, Chlamydomonas,* and mammals support the semiconservative mode of replication proposed by Watson and Crick. Taylor and his colleagues investigated the incorporation of labeled DNA precursors into the chromosomes of root tip cells of *Vicia faba* and other plant species (Chapter 14), and Meselson and Stahl the incorporation of heavy nitrogen into *E. coli.* Since DNA containing nitrogen-15 has a greater density than normal DNA (with nitrogen-14), it can be detected with density gradient centrifugation. When bacteria are grown in a medium containing nitrogen-15, the heavy isotope becomes uniformly distributed through all the cells in a short time. If the cells are then transferred to a normal medium (without nitrogen-15), the level of heavy DNA can be expected to diminish with subsequent cell divisions. This reaction was observed in *E. coli.* After the transfer of the "labeled" cells to normal medium and the onset of DNA synthesis, a new hybrid appeared, with its nitrogen content half nitrogen-15 and half nitrogen-14, as shown by density gradient centrifugation. With succeeding generations the hybrid population decreased, until almost all the cells contained only normal DNA. Thus the distribution of the isotopes was as shown in Figure 19–1.

These experimental procedures demonstrate the general pattern of DNA synthesis but not its biochemical events. These have not been directly observed in living cells, although Kornberg and others have reported on them in cell-free systems, and the mechanisms are apparently the same. Kornberg prepared a system capable of synthesizing DNA, for which he received the Nobel Prize. With extracts from *E. coli,* he isolated an enzyme that catalyzes the synthesis of DNA in vitro. The enzyme is not pure, for it contains some nucleases and diesterases. It is identified as *deoxyribonucleotide polymerase,* and it promotes the synthesis of DNA in several different organisms.

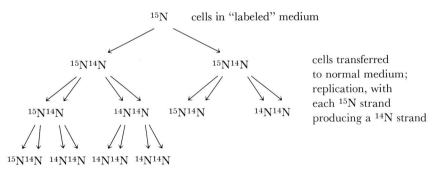

Figure 19–1. The distribution of nitrogen-15 during DNA replication in *E. coli.*

For an understanding of the stepwise manner in which new DNA is added in a cell-free system, it must be noted that the basic structural unit of a nucleic acid is an activated deoxynucleoside 5′-phosphate. This unit becomes attached by the 3′-hydroxyl group (OH) to the end of a polydeoxynucleotide chain, with the release of inorganic phosphate. The pattern of synthesis depends upon the specific base-pairing relationships in the DNA molecule; adenine pairs with thymine, and guanine with cytosine. In other words, the number of 6-amino groups of purine is equal to the number of 6-keto groups of pyrimidine, and the two bases are linked by hydrogen bonds (Chapter 1). In the Kornberg system, in addition to deoxyribonucleotide polymerase, the following substrates are required: deoxyadenosine triphosphate (dAPPP), deoxythymidine triphosphate (dTPPP), deoxyguanosine triphosphate (dGPPP), and deoxycytidine triphosphate (dCPPP). If one of these substrates is missing, the reaction is diminished by a factor of 10^4 or more, since a hydrogen-bonding mate for one of the bases is not present. No synthesis occurs in the absence of exogenous DNA. It may be obtained from any one of several organisms—animal, plant, or virus—and single-stranded DNA from ϕX174 bacteriophage is an especially good *primer* DNA. Since all of the data indicate that the added DNA is most effective when single-stranded, as in ϕX174, DNA from other sources must be degraded by heating or by treatment with deoxyribonuclease; either technique, under the proper conditions, results in strand separation. One additional substance is necessary for the successful operation of the system, namely, magnesium ions (Mg^{++}). The general equation for the reaction involved may be written

$$\left.\begin{array}{l} n\text{dAPPP} \\ n\text{dTPPP} \\ n\text{dGPPP} \\ n\text{dCPPP} \end{array}\right\} + \text{primer DNA} \xrightarrow[\text{Mg}^{++}]{\text{enzyme}} \text{DNA}-\left(\begin{array}{l} \text{dAP} \\ \text{dTP} \\ \text{dGP} \\ \text{dCP} \end{array}\right)_n + \begin{array}{c} 4n\text{PP} \\ \text{pyrophosphate} \end{array}$$

The product accumulates until one of the substrates is used up, and it has been possible to collect as much as 20 times the amount of DNA initially present. There is considerable evidence that the primer DNA serves mainly as a template for the synthesis of the new DNA. For example, the amount of adenine in the new DNA is equal to the amount of thymine in the primer, the amount of guanine in the new DNA is equal to the amount of cytosine in the primer, and the ratio of adenine–thymine pairs to guanine–cytosine pairs (AT : GC) in the new DNA resembles closely the ratio in the primer. Thus the enzyme action is directed by the primer DNA, which determines the order or sequence of the bases in synthetic DNA as well as the base composition. Of great significance is the observation that synthetic DNA has the high molecular weight and double stranding typical of natural DNA. Hence the physical and chemical properties of synthetic DNA are the same as those in naturally occurring DNA. However, this synthetic DNA is biologically inactive.

Additional studies with viral DNA have provided further information on certain aspects of DNA synthesis. If only single-stranded DNA can be used as a primer, as is the case with calf thymus polymerase, which can utilize only φX174 DNA or heat-denatured DNA, there may be an enzyme that separates the strands of DNA in a living cell. Investigations of rat liver homogenates in in vitro systems of synthesis gave no signs of such an enzyme, however. These results suggest that DNA in a living cell is never completely separated into single strands before DNA synthesis but that synthesis starts at the ends of the DNA double helix and proceeds with successive breakdowns of hydrogen bonds (Figure 14–23). This possibility is not inconsistent with the Watson-Crick theory, which presupposes a disruption of the relatively weak hydrogen bonds between the nitrogenous bases. A new enzyme, deoxyribonucleophosphatase, has been found in preparations of deoxyribonucleotide polymerase and appears to participate in readying DNA for primer function by splitting the terminal 3'-phosphoryl esters.

One of the most exciting new developments in the field of DNA synthesis was the production of a synthetic DNA with measurable biological activity. Goulian, Kornberg, and Sinsheimer used φX174 DNA as the template strand and DNA polymerase in a highly purified state to synthesize a new DNA strand capable of infecting *E. coli*. The template DNA isolated from *E. coli* after infection is identified as the (+) strand, and the product of in vitro synthesis is called the (−) strand. Since the DNA must be in a circular form to be infective(as occurs normally in φX174 infection of *E. coli,* the newly discovered polynucleotide-joining enzyme (DNA ligase) was employed to effect the covalent joining of the two opposite ends of the (−) strand of DNA. The result was a covalent duplex circle, consisting of the complementary (+) and (−) strands. The two strands were then separated by density gradient centrifugation. This was facilitated by substituting 5-bromodeoxyuridylic acid for thymidylic acid in the (+) strand; the presence of a bromine atom in place of a methyl group on the base makes the (+) strand heavier than the (−) strand. The separated synthetic (−) strands were found to be capable of infecting *E. coli,* giving rise to a new generation of normal φX174 virus. Furthermore, these workers used the synthetic (−) strands to make new synthetic (+) strands, which also were infective.

The ligase enzyme mentioned in the previous paragraph has a very important role in DNA synthesis, as demonstrated by experiments with bacteriophage T4. DNA replication occurs through the synthesis of short, single-stranded segments, which are then assembled (joined) by the action of the DNA ligase.

Although the role of DNA in other synthetic processes in the cell will be discussed later, studies on isolated nuclei have emphasized its importance as a controlling material. When as much as 75% of its DNA is removed or degraded with deoxyribonuclease, a nucleus loses its capacity to support ATP synthesis, does not incorporate amino acids into protein, and does not incorporate adenosine into nuclear RNA. If polyanions are added to the DNA-deficient nucleus, its activity is restored, but polycations are not effective. This result indicates that a negative charge may be associated with the biochemical activity of the chromosomes.

The discovery that hybridization between single-stranded DNA components from different origins can occur has been useful in attempts to determine genetic relatedness among species. Although the properties of molecular weight and nucleotide content are useful in characterizing nucleic acids in different organisms (Table 19–2), base sequences are more revealing of genetic similarities and differences. The technique of hybridization includes the following steps. High molecular weight DNA is heated to separate the individual strands, and the single strands are immobilized in agar. Small, radioactive, single-stranded fragments of DNA are prepared and incubated with the high molecular weight DNA strands in agar. This allows recombination between the fragments and the fixed DNA *if* homologies exist between them. The extent of homology is measured by the de-

Table 19–2   Quantity of Genetic Material in Several Organisms

	Molecular Weight	*Nucleotide Pairs**	*Estimated Number of Genes*
DNA			
ϕX174 phage*	1.7×10^6	5×10^3	7
T2 phage	1.3×10^8	2×10^5	270
E. coli	3.0×10^9	5×10^6	6×10^3
Drosophila	5.0×10^{10}	8×10^7	1×10^5
Zea mays	4.5×10^{12}	7×10^9	1×10^7
man	1.6×10^{12}	2.5×10^9	3×10^6
RNA			
MS2 virus*	1.0×10^6	3×10^3	4
TMV	2.0×10^6	6×10^3	8
polio virus	2.0×10^6	6×10^3	8

* Nucleotides in single-stranded DNA or RNA.

gree of hybridization (recombination) through assays for radioactivity. Several studies of this type have revealed definite homologies in polynucleotide sequences of a number of organisms. For example, substantial hybridization occurs between the DNA's of humans and Old World monkeys, and even more between the DNA's of rhesus and green monkeys. It has also been suggested that the mean guanine–cytosine percentage in DNA reflects phylogenetic relatedness among organisms; as differences in base composition increase, genetic relatedness decreases. In plants, as expected, maximum hybridization is observed when DNA is "selfed," and minimum hybridization when the DNA's are from very different species (on classical taxonomic grounds). Such studies illustrate the way in which molecular biology has influenced investigative procedures in fields formerly nonbiochemical.

RNA Synthesis

The composition of RNA is quite similar to that of DNA (Chapter 1). Generally RNA is considered to exist as a single strand, but recent work has shown that part of the molecule may have a helical organization, with base pairing of the kind found in DNA. In fact, according to the base ratios in *E. coli* and in specific transfer RNA's isolated from yeast cells, most of the RNA molecule may exhibit helical pairing. The analysis of RNA activities in a cell is somewhat complicated because not only is the RNA distributed in various places in the nucleus and cytoplasm, but it also occurs in different forms. Furthermore, although the bulk of RNA seems to be synthesized in the nucleus, chloroplasts and mitochondria also are sites for its production. These and other problems will be examined in detail after the in vitro systems utilized for the study of RNA synthesis have been dealt with.

Since it has been established that most types of RNA in the cell are synthesized under the direction of DNA, the system of RNA synthesis demonstrated by Ochoa and his collaborators, and for which he received the Nobel Prize, is of questionable biological significance. Nevertheless, because of its historical value, it should be described here. Its experimental value will be pointed out later. This synthetic system resembles in several ways Kornberg's first system for DNA synthesis. An enzyme, *ribonucleotide phosphorylase,* which can be isolated from any one of several microorganisms, including *E. coli* and *Azotobacter vinelandii*, catalyzes the synthesis of RNA under certain conditions. The system requires magnesium ions and the nucleoside diphosphates—adenosine diphosphate (ADP), uridine diphosphate (UDP), guanosine diphosphate (GDP), and cytidine diphosphate (CDP)—but all four substrates need not be present at the same time. For example, with only ADP an RNA polymer containing only adenine is produced; with adenosine and uridine diphosphates a polymer containing adenine and uracil is produced; and with all four diphosphates a polymer containing the four bases—adenine, guanine, uracil, and cytosine —is produced. There is a quantitative relation between the amount of nucleoside diphosphate used and the amount of base in the resultant RNA polymer. The order of the bases in synthetic RNA, in contrast to that in synthetic DNA, is random. This randomness is to be expected, inasmuch as the system lacks a primer, and therefore a template, to ensure sequential incorporation of the bases. However, synthetic RNA has properties like those of natural RNA.

When primer DNA is used with a *ribonucleotide polymerase* system, along with magnesium or manganese ions, all four ribonucleoside triphosphates are necessary. In fact, if any one of them is missing, synthesis is inhibited. This reaction is comparable to that for DNA synthesis (page 456) and has greater biological application than the one just reviewed. It is as follows.

$$n(\text{ATP} + \text{UTP} + \text{GTP} + \text{CTP}) \xrightarrow[\substack{\text{enzyme} \\ \text{Mg}^{++}}]{\text{primer DNA}} \begin{pmatrix} \text{AMP} \\ \text{UMP} \\ \text{GMP} \\ \text{CMP} \end{pmatrix}_n + 4n\text{PP}$$

Primer DNA obviously serves as a template for RNA synthesis, since the order of the bases in the RNA is complementary to that in the DNA. There are several sources for the primer, including T2 phage, calf thymus, and *E. coli*. Such synthetic systems have also been found in pea seedlings and mammalian reticulocytes. With ribonucleotide polymerase in vitro both strands of primer DNA are copied. However, with ribonucleotide polymerase in vivo only one strand is copied. For example, when *E. coli* is infected with ϕX174 virus, the single-stranded viral DNA replicates, and *then* only the *new* DNA helix serves as an RNA template. DNA–RNA hybridization studies confirmed this conclusion. Investigations of RNA synthesis in RNA-containing viruses have demonstrated the presence of an RNA polymerase (RNA replicase) dependent on an RNA template. Experiments performed with the MS2 and Qβ phages that infect *E. coli* have shown that an RNA replicase is specific for its own viral RNA; it will not function with the RNA from a different virus. Spiegelman and his co-workers also performed experiments resembling the more recent work on infectious viral DNA described in the preceding section. These studies showed that the synthetic viral RNA was capable of infecting *E. coli*.

The system of RNA synthesis in *E. coli*, utilizing a DNA primer, produces *messenger* RNA. Messenger RNA is of nuclear origin, comprises about 5% of cellular RNA, and conveys genetic information from DNA in the nucleus to the ribosomes in the cytoplasm, where amino acids are assembled into proteins. Another RNA important in protein synthesis appears in the cytoplasm but also originates in the nucleus. This is *transfer* RNA, which is identified in a cell homogenate after the removal of nuclei, mitochondria, and ribosomes. In bacteria such as *E. coli,* which have been widely studied, transfer RNA constitutes 10 to 20% of the total cellular RNA. It is a smaller molecule than messenger RNA, with an average molecular weight of 24,000. Although different transfer RNA's exist for the various amino acids involved in protein synthesis, all share a common characteristic. The nucleotide at one end of the molecule consists of an adenosine moiety, next to which are two cytidylic acid groups. This is the end to which an amino acid is attached as it is carried to the ribosomes for incorporation into protein. Another region of the molecule has a nucleotide sequence specific for the transfer RNA and specific for a particular amino acid. This region becomes temporarily associated with the messenger RNA in the ribosomes during protein synthesis, and is called the *anticodon* (see page 467). A third region may have an identical nucleotide sequence in all transfer RNA's, but its function is not established. The sequence is guanosine–thymidine–pseudouridine–cytidine–guanosine.

The RNA of the ribosomes comprises up to 80% of the cellular RNA in *E. coli* and can be recognized by its sedimentation rate. An intact *E. coli* ribosome has a sedimentation value of 70 S and divides into a 50 S particle and a 30 S particle. The 30 S particles of *E. coli* yield, on analysis, 16 S RNA with a molecular weight of 600,000, and the 50 S particles yield 23 S RNA with a molecular weight of 1.3 million; the ratio of 23 S RNA to 16 S RNA in the ribosome is about 1.5 : 1. The significance of the RNA fractions will be presented later. The 5 S ribosomal RNA mentioned in Chapter 4 may play a role in recognizing a specific sequence of messenger RNA.

As noted, the synthesis of all of these RNA's is contingent on the presence of a DNA template and ribonucleotide polymerase. The latest findings on the relationships between RNA synthesis and the behavior of lampbrush and polytene chromosomes support the conclusion of a DNA-dependent system. When the loops of amphibian oocyte chromosomes are exposed to actinomycin D (which combines with DNA), RNA synthesis is inhibited. This result provides some evidence that DNA is required as a primer in this cell. Since the loops are not affected by an inhibitor of protein synthesis (puromycin), it seems most likely that DNA is the key substance in chromosomal function.

The RNA's obtained from the chromosomes, nucleolus, and cytoplasm of a *Chironomus* salivary gland cell differ from each other in their base compositions. Both nucleolar and cytoplasmic RNA's are rich in adenine and uracil, but cytoplasmic RNA has a higher guanine/uracil ratio. In connection with earlier discussions of the synthetic activities of salivary gland chromosomes (Chapter 14), it has been found that the RNA/DNA ratios of the chromosome segments increase during the development of Balbiani rings and decrease during their regression. This relationship has a bearing on gene action, which will be discussed later.

At least two additional questions concern RNA metabolism, one of which has already been raised: Where is RNA synthesized? When does synthesis occur with respect to other cellular activities? Autoradiographic methods have permitted observations of the uptake and pathways of movement of materials in the cell, including labeled RNA precursors. There is little doubt that in a number of different cell types messenger RNA comes from the nucleus, and more specifically from the regions of the chromosomes. The origin of transfer RNA, on the other hand, has been more difficult to establish but is at least nuclear. Ribosomal RNA appears to derive ultimately from the nucleolus-organizing regions of the chromosomes. Much of the RNA is transported to the cytoplasm. For example, in pea seedlings tritiated cytidine is incorporated first into the chromatin and then into the nucleolus, a pattern that suggests shifting of the RNA within the nucleus itself. In other cells nucleolar RNA has been seen to pass into the cytoplasm.

In general, DNA synthesis is restricted to premitotic or premeiotic S, during interphase. In many cells, such as in *Tradescantia* root tips, the peak time of RNA synthesis is prior to DNA synthesis, and in several, such as in *Tetrahymena*, RNA synthesis does not take place at all during DNA replication. In most organisms RNA synthesis stops in mid-mitosis, when the chromosomes are most tightly coiled. In other words, RNA synthesis does not usually occur during cell division or concurrently with DNA synthesis. Experiments involving various inhibitors of protein synthesis, and labeled compounds, have shown that in *Trillium erectum*, for example, RNA synthesis occurs *after* chromosome duplication during the meiotic cycle. In roots of *Allium cepa*, RNA synthesis remains at a normal level while nucleoli are present, but synthesis near the chromosomes diminishes as condensation increases. These activities were discussed in greater detail in Chapter 11.

Protein Synthesis

Among the chemical constituents of the cell, the most important substances functionally are the proteins, mainly because about 2000 of them are enzymes. From the foregoing chapters it is clear that the metabolic properties of the cell are fundamentally dependent upon the presence and activity of these enzymes. As reported in Chapter 1, the compositions and structures of only a few enzymes have been determined. One of these is ribonuclease, a rather small protein containing 124 amino acids and having a molecular weight of about 14,000 (Figure 19–2). Ribonuclease, as well as most other proteins, consists of one or more polypeptide chains, connected in various places by hydrogen bonds or stronger linkages such as disulfide bonds. Contributing to the stability of the protein is its helical configuration, which favors hydrogen bonding. The amino acid chain, then, may be described as helical and is considered the secondary structure of the protein. If there is any folding of the chain on itself, a tertiary structure is produced, which in some proteins is quite complicated. Ribonuclease has secondary and tertiary structures and, in addition to hydrogen bonds, disulfide bonds in four specific positions. If any of these bonds are broken, enzymatic function is destroyed. Of particular interest in any enzyme are the sites conferring activity on the protein. There are at least

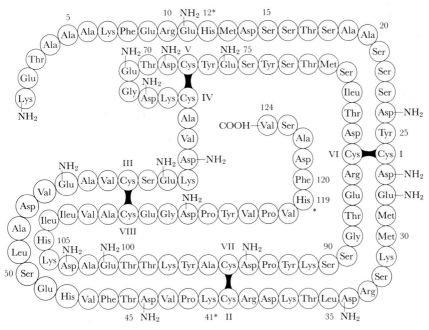

Figure 19–2. Amino acid sequence of ribonuclease. Note the four disulfide bridges at the cysteine residues. Asterisks indicate reactive sites. FROM H. P. Avey et al., *Nature,* **213,** 557 (1967).

three so-called reactive sites in ribonuclease, where the enzyme becomes associated with the substrate on which it operates. Two of these sites are the histidine residues numbers 12 and 119 in the chain of 124 amino acids. Treatment with certain agents at these sites causes complete inactivation of the enzyme. The third site is the lysine residue, amino acid number 41. Recent studies have shown that the active sites of the molecule lie in a cleft of its three-dimensional configuration. Other proteins that have been studied in detail are adrenocorticotrophic hormone (39 amino acids); insulin (51 amino acids), which consists of two polypeptide chains bonded by two disulfide bridges; and the different forms of hemoglobin, a protein with a rather complex organization including a quaternary structure of four polypeptide chains. Hemoglobin is a large molecule containing 584 amino acids and having a molecular weight of 66,000. Another well-known protein is that of the coat of tobacco mosaic virus, which contains 158 amino acids in an established sequence.

Sites

Although most protein is synthesized in the cytoplasm, some is also synthesized in the nucleus. Nuclear protein characterizes both DNA complexes and RNA complexes and appears to influence the behavior of the nucleic acids. In particular, the protein of the chromosomes has been shown to contribute to the functions as well as the structures of the chromosomes (Chapters 9, 13, and 14). Some nuclear protein, especially that of the chromosomes, is synthesized at or near the time of DNA synthesis. Nonchromosomal protein is apparently produced at various times during the cell cycle, but mostly in interphase. When the nucleus is disrupted during cell division, some of this protein may be transferred to the cytoplasm. A few studies have indicated that certain proteins have an affinity for the nucleus, even though they pass from the nucleus into the cytoplasm, and that many of the major nuclear proteins, including chromosomal protein, may be replaced by new proteins during the cell cycle. However, the fate of nuclear protein in *Lilium longiflorum* suggests that some structural protein (chromosomal) is stable and retained from one cell generation to the next (Chapter 13).

Although definite conclusions have not been reached on protein synthesis in the nucleus, considerable information is now available on protein synthesis in the cytoplasm, and it is this aspect of protein metabolism that is presented in the next part of this section. As discussed in Chapter 4, the major site of protein synthesis is in the vicinity of the rough endoplasmic reticulum, especially in the ribosomes. Some synthesis of protein may take place in the plastids, but this is of relatively minor importance in terms of the cell as a whole. In *E. coli* the ribosomal fraction directly active in protein synthesis is the 100 S fraction, which comprises less than 10% of all the ribosomes present. The 70 S fraction is also active, but in a particular manner to be outlined later. The principal role of the ribosomes in protein synthesis is to provide a substrate upon which the amino acids may be assembled. Otherwise, ribosome activity is nonspecific; the information for the construction of specific proteins is relayed by messenger RNA, which simply uses the ribosomes as if they were machinery. Although ribosomal RNA functions in the association of the ribosome with messenger RNA, the ribosome by itself is not capable of protein synthesis.

Ribosomes similar to those in the cytoplasm are present in the nucleus. They are 37 to 62% RNA, the balance being protein. In calf thymus nuclei the major ribosomal fraction consists of 78 S units, 200 Å in diameter; this is comparable to the 70 S fraction in *E. coli*. The incorporation of labeled amino acids into nuclear protein depends more on sodium ions than on potassium ions, as in some cytoplasmic systems.

Mechanism

The experiments of Hoagland in 1955 initiated a series of investigations from which most of the current knowledge of cytoplasmic protein synthesis derives. Using a cell-free system, Hoagland found that labeled amino acids were incorporated into newly synthesized protein in the presence of the following materials: ribosomes, transfer RNA, activating enzymes, ATP, and amino acids. Several researchers have since utilized cell-free systems containing extracted ribosomes, messenger RNA, and other substances. All these studies have shown that DNA serves as a template for the synthesis of messenger RNA, which moves into the cytoplasm and to the ribosomes, where it imparts its information and directs the synthesis of protein. Transfer RNA molecules gather the amino acids and carry them to the ribosomes, where they are assembled into protein according to the directions of messenger RNA. The importance of DNA in this scheme is demonstrated by the effects of treatment with deoxyribonuclease; protein synthesis declines and then stops, since the template (DNA) necessary for the production of messenger RNA is destroyed. It has also been observed that the base ratios in messenger RNA are complementary to those in the DNA template.

In view of these findings, it seemed reasonable to suppose that the addition of messenger RNA would stimulate protein synthesis in cell-free systems, as, in fact, it has. It has also been possible to stimulate protein synthesis in cell-free systems by adding RNA from tobacco mosaic virus, or by adding synthetic nucleic acids. The events of protein synthesis may now be detailed.

The first significant step in protein synthesis, at least in the cytoplasm, is the activation of amino acid, as follows:

$$\text{AA} + \text{ATP} \xrightarrow{\substack{\text{AA-activating} \\ \text{enzyme}}} \text{AMP}{\sim}\text{AA} + \text{PP}$$

$$\text{AMP}{\sim}\text{AA} + \text{tRNA} \xrightarrow{\substack{\text{AA-activating} \\ \text{enzyme}}} \text{AA}{\sim}\text{tRNA} + \text{AMP}$$

$$(\text{AA}{\sim}\text{tRNA})_n + \text{GTP} \xrightarrow{\substack{\text{ribosomes;} \\ \text{enzymes}}} \underset{\text{protein}}{\text{AA}_1{-}\text{AA}_2{-}\text{AA}_3{-}\text{AA}_n} + \text{GDP} + \text{tRNA}$$

In the first reaction, an amino acid (AA) is activated by ATP in the presence of an activating enzyme specific for the amino acid. The products are the activated amino acid (AMP~AA), called aminoacyl adenylate, and pyrophosphate (PP). This activated amino acid is capable of being attached to the 3'-OH end of a specific transfer RNA (tRNA). There may be at least two different transfer RNA's for each amino acid. In the presence of the activating enzyme, aminoacyl adenylate joins the adenylic–cytidylic–cytidylic acid end of its specific transfer RNA to produce an amino acid–tRNA complex and adenosine monophosphate (AMP). In the third reaction the amino acid is released from the transfer RNA by guanosine triphosphate (GTP) in the presence of specific enzymes in the ribosomes and is incorporated into a polypeptide chain to form a protein. As a result, the transfer RNA is liberated along with guanosine diphosphate (GDP), or guanosine monophosphate.

The synthesis of the protein chain begins at the amino end of the polypeptide and progresses to the carboxyl end at the rate of two amino acids per second.

It is presumed that there is one peptide bond–synthesizing site per ribosome. Consequently, a question arises on the nature of the association between the ribosomes and the amino acids transported to them by tranfer RNA.

As mentioned earlier, less than 10% of the ribosomes are active at any one time during protein synthesis in vitro, although the proportion may be different in vivo. The data recorded here refer primarily to *E. coli* and certain bacteriophages, but experiments with other cell types, such as *Chlamydomonas* and mammalian reticulocytes, indicate that ribosomes are species-nonspecific. It has been found in mammalian reticulocytes that ribosomes with sedimentation rates greater than 100 S are more active in hemoglobin synthesis than are 78 S ribosomes. Investigations with *E. coli* using RNA from plant viruses or from bacteriophage T2 have shown that the 70 S particles are sufficient for protein synthesis and that magnesium ions are necessary for the interaction of the viral RNA and the ribosomes. These studies and others emphasize that RNA from a variety of sources can direct protein synthesis in *E. coli*. Thus synthetic polymers of RNA have been utilized for this purpose.

The critical units in ribosomal activity are transfer RNA, messenger RNA, and the ribosomes themselves. Transfer RNA is partly helical, closed at one end, and contains some unpaired bases (Figure 1–15). These apparently are the means by which transfer RNA exhibits its specificity. The positioning of the amino acids in the polypeptide chain depends upon the complementary pairing of transfer RNA with messenger RNA through a triplet of unpaired bases that serves as a recognition site in the transfer RNA molecule. This triplet is called the anticodon, and it is complementary to a triplet of bases in messenger RNA that specifies the position of a particular amino acid in the growing polypeptide chain. A base triplet in messenger RNA is called a *codon* (see later discussion). A complication is introduced into this process by the fact that a specific transfer RNA can recognize more than one codon when the first two of the three bases in the triplet are identical. For example, in *E. coli,* lysine–tRNA recognizes the messenger RNA codons composed of adenine–adenine–adenine or adenine–adenine–guanine. The significance of the ordered triplet is discussed below.

Electron microscopy has revealed a physical relationship between the ribosomes and messenger RNA (mRNA). During protein synthesis in *E. coli,* one molecule of messenger RNA links together 5 to 11 ribosomes in a cluster known as a polysome (Chapter 4). In hemoglobin synthesis, newly synthesized hemoglobin arises from polysomes of 4 or 6 ribosomes, and in rat reticulocytes a polysome consists usually of 5 ribosomes but occasionally of 3. HeLa cell polysomes may contain as many as 40 ribosomes. In other words, a rat polysome, for example, with a sedimentation rate of about 200 S and a molecular weight of 2 million, is held together by one messenger RNA molecule attached to the 30 S subunits of each ribosome or at the junctions of the 30 S and 50 S subunits (Figure 19–3). Magnesium ions are required to maintain the stability of the mRNA–ribosome complex. This arrangement explains the importance of the RNA component of the ribosomes; it joins the ribosomes to the messenger RNA. Transfer RNA, on the other hand, is usually bound at the larger 50 S subunit. The ribosomal proteins, of which there may be as many as 50 major fractions, may also play a functional role in amino acid incorporation and in the binding of aminoacyl–tRNA's. In the latter connection, there are two major binding sites in the ribosome. One is the binding site that receives and positions the aminoacyl–tRNA, and the other is a protein binding site which holds the transfer RNA in position during peptide bond formation. There is now evidence that the smaller ribosomal subunit is the place where protein synthesis starts; the two subunits are not bound together when synthesis begins. Protein synthesis begins when a 30 S subunit combines with a strand of messenger RNA and with a molecule of transfer RNA bound to formylmethionine (see page 474). This complex *then* joins with a 50 S subunit and protein synthesis proceeds to completion.

During protein synthesis the information in the messenger RNA is "read" by the transfer RNA as the ribosome moves along the messenger RNA molecule from its 5′-OH end to its 3′-OH end. Each transfer RNA molecule deposits its amino acid in the correct position according to the tRNA–mRNA recognition described above. Consistent with the *translation* of the RNA message into protein is the *transcription* of the messenger

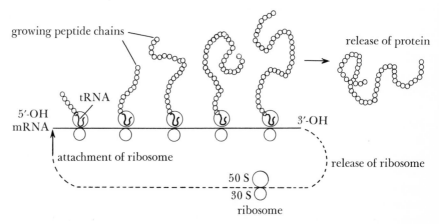

Figure 19–3.   Diagram representing the mechanics of protein synthesis.

RNA on the DNA template from the 5'-OH end to the 3'-OH end. It has been postulated that one polysome directs the synthesis of one protein subunit with a molecular weight of from 40,000 to perhaps 100,000. Thus messenger RNA conveys its information to transfer RNA, which releases the amino acids in specific sequence into the polymerizing polypeptide. In *Bacillus subtilis* messenger RNA functions in protein synthesis about 15 times, after which it is degraded by enzyme action. With the exception of hemoglobin–mRNA, however, most messenger RNA's are unstable and short-lived.

Code

A number of observations have led to the delineation of a coding mechanism for the synthesis of proteins. The code originates in the DNA molecule and is carried to the ribosomes by messenger RNA. The transcription is confirmed by the bonding of RNA and DNA when the bases in the two substances have complementary orders. In addition, it has been found that ribonucleotide polymerase catalyzes the synthesis of messenger RNA on the DNA pattern. Synthetic polynucleotides of RNA with particular base compositions have been utilized to establish the nature of the code.

It is possible to synthesize RNA containing only one or two bases by using the enzyme *polynucleotide phosphorylase* in the system developed by Ochoa. This enzyme forms polymers of RNA by linking bases at random rather than by following the DNA model as does ribonucleotide polymerase. One of the first synthetic polymers was polyuridylic acid, which contains only uracil. When this was added to a ribosomal extract along with a mixture of amino acids, the product was polyphenylalanine, a polymer of phenylalanine. If the numbers and kinds of bases in the synthetic RNA are adjusted, specific amino acid–containing polypeptides can be produced. In this way the code responsible for the incorporation of a particular amino acid into a protein has been determined. Here the synthetic polymer serves as messenger RNA, and it can be made to order without a DNA primer. Such messenger RNA is of value in investigations of ribosomal involvement in protein synthesis. Polyuridylic acid, for example, has been found to stimulate the aggregation of 70 S particles in *E. coli* into 200 S polysomes.

If polyuridylic acid, in the presence of other requirements, promotes the formation of polyphenylalanine, presumably the code for the amino acid consists specifically of the base uracil. Since at least 20 amino acids are necessary for protein synthesis in a cell, the smallest possible combination of the four bases is a triplet. A pair would allow only 16 different amino acids, whereas a triplet allows 64. A triplet of bases is called a

Table 19-3 Amino Acid Codons

5'-OH Terminal Base	Middle Base				3'-OH Terminal Base
	U	C	A	G	
U	UUU ⎱ phenylalanine UUC ⎰ UUA ⎱ leucine UUG ⎰	UCU ⎱ UCC ⎰ serine UCA ⎱ UCG ⎰	UAU ⎱ tyrosine UAC ⎰ UAA ⎱ nonsense UAG ⎰ (terminator)	UGU ⎱ cysteine UGC ⎰ UGA (terminator) UGG tryptophan	U C A G
C	CUU ⎱ CUC ⎰ leucine CUA ⎱ CUG ⎰	CCU ⎱ CCC ⎰ proline CCA ⎱ CCG ⎰	CAU ⎱ histidine CAC ⎰ CAA ⎱ glutamine CAG ⎰	CGU ⎱ CGC ⎰ arginine CGA ⎱ CGG ⎰	U C A G
A	AUU ⎱ isoleucine AUC ⎰ AUA ⎰ AUG methionine	ACU ⎱ ACC ⎰ threonine ACA ⎱ ACG ⎰	AAU ⎱ asparagine AAC ⎰ AAA ⎱ lysine AAG ⎰	AGU ⎱ serine AGC ⎰ AGA ⎱ arginine AGG ⎰	U C A G
G	GUU ⎱ GUC ⎰ valine GUA ⎱ GUG ⎰	GCU ⎱ GCC ⎰ alanine GCA ⎱ GCG ⎰	GAU ⎱ aspartic acid GAC ⎰ GAA ⎱ glutamic acid GAG ⎰	GGU ⎱ GGC ⎰ glycine GGA ⎱ GGG ⎰	U C A G

codon, coding for one amino acid. The latest data on the code, resulting from experiments with specific nucleotide mixtures, are given in Table 19–3. The important constituent of each nucleotide is obviously the base. Of the 20 amino acids listed, 18 are coded by only two different bases. However, each codon must consist of three parts. It should be remembered, in connection with the code, that polyuridylic acid, codon UUU, is a complement to DNA codon AAA (adenine triplet).

The effectiveness and directional activity of synthetic messenger RNA are illustrated in Table 19–4, in which specific polymers are shown to stimulate the production of specific amino acids. The number of counts of radioactivity incorporated into the acid-insoluble product (polypeptide) is a measure of the number of units of amino acid incorporated into protein. There is no significant incorporation in the absence of polynucleotides. A difficulty arises when one codon directs the incorporation of two or more amino acids into a protein. This situation is not critically significant, however, for it is exceptional. In the case of polyuridylic acid, some leucine is incorporated in addition to the polyphenylalanine, but the ratio is 30 molecules of phenylalanine to only 1 molecule of leucine.

Although the code appears to be universal—that is, the same for all species—most amino acids are coded by more than one codon (*degeneracy*) as indicated by Table 19–3. Thus, in different species, different codons may be used for a given amino acid. A few codon are, in effect, nonsense words, which code for no amino acid, and the code is *nonoverlapping* (Figure 19–4).

Table 19–4 Incorporation of Amino Acids into Protein of *E. coli* Through Use of Various Synthetic Polynucleotides*

Amino Acid	None	poly U	poly UA, 5:1	poly UC, 5:1	poly UAC 6:1:1	poly UCG, 6:1:1	poly UAG, 6:1:1
Synthetic Polynucleotide							
isoleucine	0.01	0.09	0.62	0.32	1.2	0.1	0.4
leucine	0.09	0.2	0.4		3.3	0.4	0.4
phenylalanine	0.06	18.0	3.4	7.0	7.5	1.0	1.1
serine	0.02	0.02		1.6	2.0	0.3	0.1
threonine	0.10		0.1	0.5	0.8	0.15	0.15

* In millimicromoles per milligram of protein; values of 0.5 and over are considered significant. From Wahba et al., *Proc. Natl. Acad. Sci. U.S.,* **49**(1), 116 (1963).

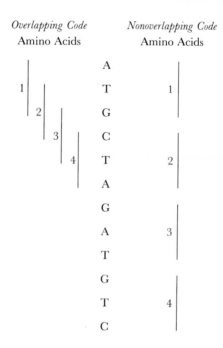

Figure 19–4. Overlapping and nonoverlapping codes based on the sequences of the nucleotides in DNA. A, T, G, and C represent nucleotides of adenine, thymine, guanine, and cytosine, respectively.

One of the major problems in clarifying the code concerned the order of the bases in a codon. According to the work by Crick on T4 phage, the code is read from one end of the messenger RNA to the other. The loss or addition of a nucleotide results in a disruption of the entire sequence. A substitution, on the other hand, has no such effect. Moreover, individuals with four closely spaced losses or additions produce only nonfunctional proteins. This type of evidence led to the conclusion that a codon can consist only of three nucleotides, and that the order of the three bases is critical to the specificity of a codon for a given amino acid. When synthetic polynucleotides with known repeating sequences were used in cell-free systems for protein synthesis, regular repeating amino acid sequences appeared in the polypeptides. For example, the sequence CUCUCUCUCU. . . resulted in the polypeptide leucine–serine–leucine–serine–leucine–serine. . . . This type of experimental approach proved not only that the codon is a triplet, but that the order of the bases in a codon is specific and can be determined. The base orders in most of the 64 codons are now known (Table 19–3).

In connection with base order, it is appropriate to return briefly to the anticodon sequence in transfer RNA molecules. The specific sequence has been recognized now in a few of the aminoacyl–tRNA's. For example, in tyrosine–tRNA the anticodon is guanosine–pseudouridine–adenosine, and in alanine–tRNA it is inosine–guanosine–cytidine. As indicated earlier, the third position of a codon may vary and still be recognized by an aminoacyl–tRNA for positioning of the amino acid in the growing polypeptide chain. Crick has proposed the hypothesis that the pairing between the codon of messenger RNA and the anticodon of transfer RNA is normal in the first two positions, but may be more complex in the third position. That is, there may be a wobble in the pairing in the last position. (Crick has named this the "wobble" hypothesis.) Certain bases do indeed have the ability to pair with more than one base partner; inosine, for example, can pair with uracil, cytosine, or adenine. This explanation allows for the variation in position three that is so common in the code system. It has been suggested, in fact, that the degeneracy in the code and the arrangement in a triplet provide a mechanism for protection of the organism against the consequences of mutation. In effect, the code has adaptive value. Similarities in phylogeny are strikingly illustrated by the universal nature of the code. Studies with microorganisms as well as such higher organisms as mammals and amphibians have firmly established the code as universal. For example, the transfer RNA's of amphibian and mammalian liver can function in a system of protein synthesis utilizing *E. coli* ribosomes. There are, however, a few differences in the relative responses of some transfer RNA's to certain codons. Such differences are illustrated by the observation that although alanine–tRNA binds to ribosomes in response to GCU, GCC, GCA, and GCG, mammalian and amphibian alanine–tRNA responds only slightly to GCG, whereas *E. coli* transfer RNA responds best to GCG. Nevertheless, the similarities far exceed these relatively minor differences.

One of the most puzzling features of the coding system has been the problem related to punctuation; is there a mechanism by which synthesis is initiated and one by which it is ended? Recently these questions have been answered through analyses of the coding system. The "period at the end of the sentence" has to be a codon that codes for no amino acid, but brings to an end the elaboration of the polypeptide chain. Current evidence points to the nonsense words UAA, UGA, and UAG as alternative chain-terminating codons. Moreover, termination also requires a release factor, R, discovered by Capecchi. The R factor contains at least one protein with a free sulfhydryl group.

Chain initiation is somewhat more complex, and in bacteria and phages it involves the following scheme. A specific transfer RNA exists in the cell that binds to a methionine that is capable of formylation. After attachment of this amino acid to the transfer RNA_F molecule, the methionine is converted to formylmethionine through the action of a specific enzyme. The presence of the formyl group prevents the normal formation of a peptide bond at the amino end of the amino acid, such that formylmethionine can occur only at the beginning of a polypeptide chain. The delivery of this formylmethionine–tRNA to the mRNA–ribosome complex signals the start of the protein chain. On the basis of the code, one would expect a specific codon for formylmethionine, but there is none. However, the codon AUG, which normally codes for methionine, serves this function. When it occurs at the beginning of the code, it provides for formylmethionine, but internally it codes for methionine. Similarly, GUG codes for valine internally, but may specify formylmethionine for chain initiation. Since formylmethionine–tRNA binds only to the 30 S ribosomal subunit, it is evident that chain initiation also depends on the reconstitution of the ribosomal subunits at about the same time. Finally, in the living cell, an enzyme removes the formylmethionine from the first position in the polypeptide chain, and the next amino acid assumes the number one position in the final protein. The initiation process is clearly quite complex, and may also require the presence of GTP (page 466) for the formation of the first peptide bond.

Perhaps the most satisfying discovery in recent years was that the polypeptide chain and the genetic map of an organism are *collinear;* it was a predictable discovery, but it had to be proved. Yanofsky and his colleagues observed that a single mutational change results in the change of one amino acid in a protein, and that the changes that are close together on a genetic map result in changes close together on the polypeptide chain. These studies were performed with the *A* gene in *E. coli* that is responsible for the synthesis of tryptophan synthetase, a protein containing 280 amino acids. Through selected crosses of mutant bacteria, Yanofsky and his co-workers found that a change from the codon GGA (for glycine) to GAA resulted in the substitution of glutamic acid in a specific position in the protein and to AGA in the substitution of arginine. Their experiments proved that the code reads from left to right, and that the order for the transcription process is the same as that for translation. Thus the order of bases in DNA is reflected in the order of the amino acids in a protein whose synthesis is controlled by that particular DNA sequence (gene).

Genetic Implications

Among the most extensively studied proteins is hemoglobin. Research on its synthesis and amino acid composition, as well as on those of other proteins, has disclosed some fundamental features of the genetic code, including its nonoverlapping nature.

Several types of anemia appear in the human population. *Sickle cell anemia,* which is found primarily among Negroes, is characterized by red blood cells that assume abnormal shapes under less than normal oxygen pressures. As a result, there may be destruction or clumping of the cells, which interferes with normal circulation. Individuals with this affliction are weak and poorly developed and exhibit varying degrees of tissue damage, usually dying at an early age. Other individuals may carry the trait but have normal phenotypes; they are heterozygous for the factor, with two kinds of hemoglobin, normal hemoglobin (designated *HbA*) and sickle cell anemia hemoglobin (designated *HbS*). Analyses of various hemoglobins, most of which are associated with anemia, have indicated that an alteration in the amino acid composition of one portion of the hemoglobin molecule is responsible for the condition (Table 19–5). In sickle cell anemia hemoglobin, the amino acid valine has replaced the amino acid glutamic acid of normal hemoglobin. This substitution can be interpreted as a single base change in the triplet genetic code of messenger RNA; the adenine member of the triplet is replaced by uracil, so that the code changes from AUG to UUG. Similar substitutions produce other abnormal hemoglobins, as shown in the table. Thus it may be argued that, in these cases at least, a point mutation involves a single base change in the DNA molecule. However, it does not necessarily follow that all point mutations are derived in this manner. At the same time, it seems likely that the mutational events most commonly retained by natural selection are those that lead to the replacement of a single amino acid in a polypeptide chain. Contemporary analyses of hemoglobins in different organisms illustrate the influence of molecular approaches to fields of biology—evolution and systematics—heretofore employing more classical methodologies. A beginning has been made in the use of molecular sequences for the derivation

Table 19–5 Amino Acid Differences in Various Hemoglobins*

Hemo-globin	Amino Acid	Code	Hemoglobin	Amino Acid	Code
normal	glutamic acid	AUG	S (sickle cell)	valine	UUG
normal	glutamic acid	AUG	C, E	lysine	AUA
normal	valine	UUG	M (Milwaukee)	glutamic acid	AUG
normal	asparagine	UAA	G (Philadelphia)	lysine	AAA
normal	lysine	AUA	I	aspartic acid	GUA

* A single base change in the code of the normal hemoglobin at the left converts it into the abnormal hemoglobin at the right.

of phylogenetic relations among several different organisms with respect to their hemoglobins.

Mutation induction has only recently reached the stage where it is possible to relate a change in the genetic material to a change in molecular organization. With agents known to affect only certain bases, it can now be demonstrated that an induced mutation arises from a change in one or more base pairs. Agents utilized in such experiments include 5-bromouracil, 5-fluorodeoxyuridine, 5-bromodeoxyuridine, and nitrous acid. Some are directly incorporated into the DNA molecule, altering the pattern of base pairing and eventually bringing about a substitution of one base pair for another, whereas others are not incorporated but in some way alter the pairing capacity of a specific base so that abnormal base pairing and, again, a substitution of one base pair for another result. These changes are, in general, compatible with the genetic code and provide another approach to the delineation of gene function. Some of the agents have also been used to induce chromosomal breaks and may be of value in detecting the chemical differences between one chromosomal region and another, especially in instances of preferential breakage of heterochromatin.

Regulation

There are more genes in a living cell than will be required for the function of that cell at any particular time. Some genes at a given time will be active in the transcription of messenger RNA, while others are inactive. What regulates the genes so that they are functioning at one time but not at another time? In 1961 Jacob and Monod proposed the theory of repression to explain the regulation of protein synthesis in a cell. Simply stated, there exist in the genome *regulator* genes capable of switching off those genes responsible for the production of specific enzymes. Through detailed analyses of specific genetic loci in *E. coli,* Jacob and Monod developed the theory of the *operon*. Three cistrons responsible for the production of the enzymes β-galactosidase, permease, and transacetylase comprise the operon, by virtue of their coordinated control by a common gene, their *operator*. The operator gene is closely linked to the operon, and can exist in an open or closed state. When open, the operon cistrons synthesize messenger RNA, and protein is produced in the form of the three enzymes. When closed, the operon cistrons cannot function in the synthesis of messenger RNA, and no protein is produced. The state of the operator depends upon the activity of another gene, the *regulator*. The regulator gene produces a *repressor substance* (a protein) that acts by closing or inactivating the operator gene. The state of the repressor substance in turn depends upon the presence or absence of a particular substrate on which the enzyme β-galactosidase acts. The enzyme catalyzes the splitting of lactose, and is produced only when lactose is present in the medium on which the bacteria are living. It is therefore called an *inducible* enzyme. In the absence of lactose, the repressor substance inactivates the operator so that no enzyme is produced by the appropriate cistron. When lactose is present, it acts as an inducer by binding to the repressor substance so that the latter cannot any longer inactivate the operator gene. Consequently, β-galactosidase is produced, since the operon is now free to code for the enzymes. Permease is required for the transport of lactose into the cell. The third enzyme, thiogalactoside transacetylase, is also produced but plays no part in lactose metabolism. In summary, when *E. coli* is grown in the presence of lactose, gene expression is induced as observed through the presence of the inducible enzymes in quantities far exceeding their normal levels. The operon scheme is illustrated in Figure 19–5.

Another type of repressor is involved in the regulation of repressible enzymes whose amount is reduced by the presence of their end products. In this case, the operator gene is closed so that no more enzyme is produced. The term "allosteric" enzyme was proposed by Jacob and Monod to explain such enzymes. An allosteric enzyme must exist in two alternative states; one is reactive when the supply of the product runs out, and the other is unreactive when the supply exceeds the demand. This means also that there must be two sites on the enzyme, an active site for binding of the substrate and an allosteric site for binding of the product thereby rendering the enzyme inactive. Such controlling mechanisms are related to the phenomenon of "feedback inhibition."

Recent studies with *E. coli* and with lambda phage have established that the repressor substance is directly bound to the genes, presumably those directly involved in enzyme production. This and other information has provided added support for the operon theory. However, relatively few specific cases are known in which the operon is in effect, and most of the evidence has come from investigations with microorganisms. One of the newer facets in the operon theory is the possibility of a *promoter* gene lying adjacent to the operator gene (Figure 19–5). The promoter may serve as an initiator site for messenger RNA synthesis, but only when its two DNA strands are separated by disruption of their hydrogen bonds. Transcription begins at the promoter site, and this process is necessary for the maximum rate of expression of the operon.

In higher organisms the earliest reported genetic situation compatible

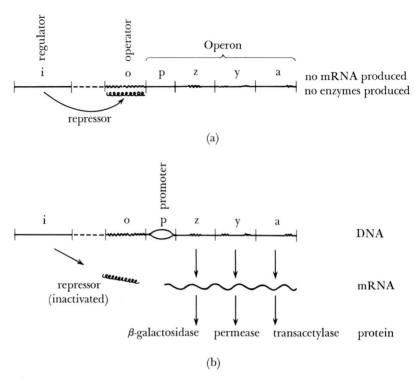

Figure 19–5. The operon theory: (a) no inducer present; (b) inducer present.

with the operon theory was by Barbara McClintock in corn. Here the *dissociator-activator* gene system is such that the dissociator gene can be considered as an operator gene, and the activator gene a regulator gene. The dissociator gene, which in some cases causes chromosomal breaks, is effective only in the presence of the activator gene. Moreover, the dissociator gene is capable of changing its position among the chromosomes! It has an episomal quality. McClintock has also studied a suppressor-mutator system of genes in corn which affects the formation of anthocyanin pigments. When the suppressor-mutator (operator) gene is absent, pigment is produced. When it is present, structural genes are sensitive to the suppressor-mutator and are repressed. Both of these systems are rather complicated compared with the "simple" system described in *E. coli.*

There are several examples of repression and derepression of genetic activity in plant and animal cells that cannot be explained unequivocally on the basis of the operon theory, but that may require a different type of regulation mechanism, or at least a modification of the operon theory. Some of the cases were discussed in Chapter 14 with descriptions of lampbrush and polytene chromosomes. That different lampbrush loops or chromosome puffs are active at different times clearly implies that different genetic loci are functional at different times. At least three additional systems of regulation are also pertinent here. One of these was cited in connection with the shift from histone protein to protamine or to an arginine-rich histone in animal sperm. The mature sperm is, until after fertilization, inactive in the synthesis of cellular materials. A similar repression of the genome is observed in the nucleated red blood cell of birds in which there is no synthesis of DNA, RNA, or protein and the cell does not divide. The third case is that of Mengo virus–infected cells. A basic protein, coded for by the virus, penetrates the host cell nucleus and blocks its metabolism. A still different type of control can be illustrated by the activity of certain plant hormones. For example, there is evidence that the growth hormone gibberellin promotes the germination of barley seeds by activating genes responsible for producing the enzyme α-amylase. The flowering hormone, which stimulates protein and messenger RNA synthesis in plant buds, lowers the ratio of histone to DNA. It has been suggested that the hormone removes the histone from the DNA, allowing the latter to serve as template in RNA synthesis. In fact, deproteinized DNA from pea chromatin in the apical bud has been shown to support the synthesis of a messenger RNA required for the production of seed globulin.

These and other studies have raised particular interest in the possibility of regulation of gene action through chromosomal protein. There are several histone fractions in the chromosome, but two have been of major concern in regulation: an arginine-rich fraction and a lysine-rich fraction. These fractions may have different effects on gene action because of differences in their binding to DNA; lysine-rich histone tends to be more tightly bound. Experiments involving the study of DNA-dependent RNA synthesis by pea chromatin and in calf thymus chromatin have shown that whole histone is quite inhibitory when it is complexed with DNA. When it is removed from the DNA, RNA synthesis can proceed. Moreover, of all the histone fractions the lysine-rich one is the most inhibitory of DNA-dependent RNA synthesis when the fraction is used at low concentration. On the basis of the binding capacity of lysine-rich histone (Chapter 14), its removal from the DNA may allow for a decondensing of the chromatin so that the chromatin can serve as a template for RNA synthesis. It is quite clear that diffuse (decondensed) chromatin is considerably more active in this respect than is condensed chromatin (heterochromatin). The state of the histone–DNA complex may be more important in regulation than the particular fraction of histone, however. Observations of the nuclei of some animal cells, among them calf thymus and human lymphocytes, have shown that phosphorylation or acetylation of histone reduces its inhibitory capacity. This results in the ability of the DNA to serve as template for RNA synthesis. Of significance in many of these studies is the demonstration that most of the DNA (up to 80%) is in the repressed state; derepression may occur by histone acetylation or phosphorylation.

The detection of an RNA complexed with histone in the chromatin may provide for the mechanism that controls which part of the genome will be repressed at any given time. An RNA that is different from messenger, transfer, and ribosomal RNA's has been found in pea bud chromatin, chick embryo cells, and rat liver cells. This RNA turns over rapidly in the nucleus but is not lost from it. Moreover, it is associated with DNA in such as way as to be immune to attack by ribonuclease. In the complex histone comprises about 92% and the RNA about 8%, and the RNA is capable of hybridizing with about 5% of the nuclear DNA. Bonner has suggested that this special chromosomal RNA may function as a sequence detector for chromosomal protein; the RNA–histone complex binds to that part of the chromatin in which the RNA is complementary to a DNA sequence. In other words, the RNA may guide the histone to those gene locations that are to be repressed at a particular time. Proof of this hypothesis of a regulating RNA has not yet come.

Extrapolation of the information about genetic regulation to the phenomena of cellular differentiation is tempting and yet logical. Chromosomal protein, either as histone or perhaps through repression of operator genes, may determine the times of genetic activity during embryogenesis. Variations in rates of protein synthesis and RNA synthesis have indeed been observed during different developmental stages. Although every cell has identical genetic potential, some cells, for example, muscle, will develop according to one pattern, while others, for example, blood, develop along different lines. The determination of which genes will function in one cell and which other ones in a different cell may be through one or more of the regulatory activities described above. At a given time in the process of development, a particular type of messenger RNA may be produced that is specific for a particular cell or tissue type. At the same time, there must be a coordination of the many events in differentiation occurring simultaneously. As yet there is relatively little information available to explain such coordination. The field of development, which encompasses all of these problems and which requires knowledge of cytology, especially at the molecular level, is the most mysterious in biology and therefore the most demanding of our attention.

Summary

According to the generally accepted theory, a great deal of which has been substantiated experimentally, several factors are involved in the regulation of cellular activities by the genetic material. They are reviewed in the following paragraphs.

1. The genetic material is *DNA*. DNA is found in the chromosomes of most organisms and has at least two main functions: to provide a code in the form of nucleotide units for imparting information to the machinery of the cell and to govern gene action, perhaps through regulator and operator genes.

2. DNA serves as a template for the production of messenger RNA. During the synthesis of messenger RNA, DNA transmits the code information through its nucleotide base composition and sequence to the complementary bases of the messenger RNA.

3. Messenger RNA carries the genetic information to the ribosomes. It uses the ribosomes only as a site for the assembling of amino acids. The ribosomes themselves do not act as a template for the synthesis of protein.

4. Transfer RNA carries the amino acids to the ribosomes. Through complementary pairing of the bases, transfer RNA recognizes the coded information present in messenger RNA and releases the amino acids in the order specified.

5. Certain characteristics of the genetic code have been confirmed by experimental methods: it is degenerate, it is read from one end in a non-overlapping sequence, and it seems to be universal in its application to living organisms.

SELECTED READING

General

Bonner, J., *The Molecular Biology of Development,* Oxford Univ. Press, New York, 1965.

Changeux, J.-P., "The Control of Biochemical Reactions," *Sci. Am.,* **212**(4), 36 (1965).

Clark, B. F. C., and K. A. Marcker, "How Proteins Start," *Sci. Am.,* **218**(1), 36 (1968).

Crick, F. H. C., "The Genetic Code III," *Sci. Am.,* **215**(4), 55 (1966).

Holley, R. W., "The Nucleotide Sequence of a Nucleic Acid," *Sci. Am.,* **214**(2), 30 (1966).

Hurwitz, J., and J. J. Furth, "Messenger RNA," *Sci. Am.,* **206**(2), 41 (1962).

Nirenberg, M. W., "The Genetic Code II," *Sci. Am.,* **208**(3), 80 (1963).

Rich, A., "Polyribosomes," *Sci. Am.,* **209**(6), 44 (1963).

Spiegelman, S., "Hybrid Nucleic Acids," *Sci. Am.,* **210**(5), 48 (1964).

Taylor, J. H., ed., *Molecular Genetics,* Part 1, Academic Press, New York, 1963.

DNA Synthesis

Allfrey, V. G., and A. E. Mirsky, "Some Effects of Substituting the DNA of Iso-lated Nuclei with Other Polyelectrolytes," *Proc. Natl. Acad. Sci. U.S.,* **44**(10), 981 (1958).

Dutta, M., S. K. Richman, N. Woodward, and V. W. Mandel, "Relatedness Among Species of Fungi and Higher Plants Measured by DNA Hybridiza-tion and Base Ratios," *Genetics,* **57**(3), 719 (1967).

Goulian, M., A. Kornberg, and R. L. Sinsheimer, "Enzymatic Synthesis of DNA. XXIV. Synthesis of Infectious Phage φX174 DNA," *Proc. Natl. Acad. Sci. U.S.,* **58**(6), 2321 (1967).

Hoyer, B. H., B. J. McCarthy, and E. T. Bolton, "A Molecular Approach in the Systematics of Higher Organisms," *Science,* **144**(3621), 959 (1964).

Kornberg, A., "Biological Synthesis of Desoxyribonucleic Acid," *Science,* **131** (3412), 1503 (1960).

Kornberg, A., "The Synthesis of DNA," *Sci. Am.,* **219**(4), 64 (1968).

Meselson, M., and F. W. Stahl, "The Replication of DNA," *Cold Spring Harbor Symp. Quant. Biol.,* **23**, 9 (1958).

Sarkar, N. K., S. Okada, and A. Devi, "Mechanism of Deoxyribonucleic Acid Synthesis in Vitro," *Exptl. Cell Res.,* **29**(1), 36 (1963).

Walker, P. M. B., "How Different Are the DNAs from Related Animals?" *Nature,* **219**(5151), 228 (1968).

RNA Synthesis

Allfrey, V. G., and A. E. Mirsky, "Evidence for the Complete DNA Dependence of RNA Synthesis in Isolated Thymus Nuclei," *Proc. Natl. Acad. Sci. U.S.,* **48**(9), 1590 (1962).

Chamberlain, M., and P. Berg, "Deoxyribonucleic Acid–Directed Synthesis of Ribonucleic Acid by an Enzyme from *Escherichia coli,*" *Proc. Natl. Acad. Sci. U.S.,* **48**(1), 81 (1962).

Das, N. K., "Chromosomal and Nucleolar RNA Synthesis in Root Tips During Mitosis," *Science,* **140**(3572), 1231 (1963).

Edstrom, J. E., and W. Beermann, "The Base Composition of Nucleic Acids in Chromosomes, Puffs, Nucleoli, and Cytoplasm of *Chironomus* Salivary Gland Cells," *J. Cell Biol.,* **14**(3), 371 (1962).

Fuller, W., "Two-Stranded Helical Configurations for RNA," *J. Mol. Biol.,* **3**(2), 175 (1961).

Fuller, W., F. Hutchinson, M. Spencer, and M. Wilkins, "Molecular and Crystal Structures of Double-Helical RNA. I. An X-ray Diffraction Study of Fragment

Yeast RNA and a Preliminary Double-Helical RNA Model," *J. Mol. Biol.,* **27** (3), 507 (1967).

Galibert, F., J. C. Lelong, C. J. Larsen, and M. Boiron, "Position of 5 S RNA Among Cellular Ribonucleic Acids," *Biochim. Biophys. Acta,* **142**(1), 89 (1966).

Haruna, J., and S. Spiegelman, "Specific Template Requirements of RNA Replicases," *Proc. Natl. Acad. Sci. U.S.,* **54**(2), 579 (1965).

Hayashi, M., M. N. Hayashi, and S. Spiegelman, "Restriction of in Vivo Genetic Transcription to One of the Complementary Strands of DNA," *Proc. Natl. Acad. Sci. U.S.,* **50**(4), 664 (1963).

Madison, J. T., and G. A. Kung, "Nucleotide Sequence of a Yeast Tyrosine Transfer RNA," *Science,* **153**(3735), 531 (1966).

Maggio, R., P. Siekevitz, and G. E. Palade, "Studies on Isolated Nuclei. II. Isolation and Chemical Characterization of Nucleolar and Nucleoplasmic Subfractions," *J. Cell Biol.,* **18**(2), 293 (1963).

Prescott, D. M., and M. A. Bender, "Synthesis of RNA and Protein During Mitosis in Mammalian Tissue Culture Cells," *Exptl. Cell Res.,* **26**(2), 260 (1962).

Sirlin, J. L., J. Jacob, and K. I. Kato, "The Relation of Messenger to Nucleolar RNA," *Exptl. Cell. Res.,* **27**(2), 355 (1962).

Sisken, J. E., "The Synthesis of Nucleic Acids and Proteins in the Nuclei of *Tradescantia* Root Tips," *Exptl. Cell Res.,* **16**(3), 602 (1959).

Spiegelman, S., et al., "The Synthesis of a Self-propagating and Infectious Nucleic Acid with a Purified Enzyme," *Proc. Natl. Acad. Sci. U.S.,* **54**(3), 919 (1965).

Protein Synthesis

Allfrey, V. G., "Nuclear Ribosomes, Messenger-RNA and Protein Synthesis," *Exptl. Cell Res.,* Suppl. 9, 183 (1963).

Barondes, S. H., and M. W. Nirenberg, "Fate of a Synthetic Polynucleotide Directing Cell-Free Protein Synthesis. I. Characteristics of Degradation. II. Association with Ribosomes," *Science,* **138**(3542), 810 (1962).

Berger, H., and C. Yanofsky, "Suppressor Selection for Amino Acid Replacements Expected on the Basis of the Genetic Code," *Science,* **156**(3773), 394 (1967).

Bernfield, M. R., and M. W. Nirenberg, "RNA Codewords and Protein Synthesis," *Science,* **147**(3657), 479 (1965).

Brimacombe, R., et al., "RNA Codewords and Protein Synthesis. VIII. Nucleotide Sequences of Synonym Codons for Arginine, Valine, Cysteine, and Alanine," *Proc. Natl. Acad. Sci. U.S.,* **54**(3), 954 (1965).

Capecchi, M. R., "Polypeptide Chain Termination in Vitro: Isolation of a Release Factor," *Proc. Natl. Acad. Sci. U.S.,* **58**(3), 1144 (1967).

Caskey, C. T., et al., "Sequential Translation of Trinucleotide Codons for the Initiation and Termination of Protein Synthesis," *Science,* **162**(3849), 135 (1968).

Eikenberry, E. F., and A. Rich, "The Direction of Reading Messenger RNA During Protein Synthesis," *Proc. Natl. Acad. Sci. U.S.,* **53**(3), 668 (1965).

Goldberg, A. L., and R. E. Wittes, "Genetic Code: Aspects of Organization," *Science,* 153(3734), 420 (1966).

Groves, W. E., and E. S. Kempner, "Amino Acid Coding in *Sarcina lutea* and *Saccharomyces cerevisiae,*" *Science,* 156(3773), 387 (1967).

Haselkorn, R., V. A. Fried, and J. E. Dahlberg, "Cell-Free Protein Synthesis: The Association of Viral RNA and *E. coli* Ribosomes," *Proc. Natl. Acad. Sci. U.S.,* 49(4), 511 (1963).

Hershey, J. W. B., and R. E. Thach, "Role of Guanosine 5'-Triphosphate in the Initiation of Peptide Synthesis. I. Synthesis of Formylmethionylpuromycin," *Proc. Natl. Acad. Sci. U.S.,* 57(3), 759 (1967).

Hoagland, M. B., "An Enzymic Mechanism for Amino Acid Activation in Animal Tissues," *Biochim. Biophys. Acta,* 16(2), 288 (1955).

Last, J. A., et al., "Translation of the Genetic Message. IV. UAA as a Chain Termination Codon," *Proc. Natl. Acad. Sci. U.S.,* 57(4), 1062 (1967).

Marshall, R. E., C. T. Caskey, and M. W. Nirenberg, "Fine Structure of RNA Codewords Recognized by Bacterial, Amphibian, and Mammalian Transfer RNA," *Science,* 155(3764), 820 (1967).

Matthaei, J. H., O. W. Jones, R. G. Martin, and M. W. Nirenberg, "Characteristics and Composition of RNA Coding Units," *Proc. Natl. Acad. Sci. U.S.,* 48(4), 666 (1962).

Nirenberg, M. W., and P. Leder, "RNA Codewords and Protein Synthesis," *Science,* 145(3639), 1399 (1964).

Risebrough, R. W., A. Tissieres, and J. D. Watson, "Messenger RNA Attachment to Active Ribosomes," *Proc. Natl. Acad. Sci. U.S.,* 48(3), 430 (1962).

Söll, D., and U. L. Rajbhandary, "Studies on Polynucleotides. LXXVI. Specificity of Transfer RNA for Codon Recognition as Studied by Amino Acid Incorporation," *J. Mol. Biol.,* 29(1), 113 (1967).

Tissieres, A., and J. D. Watson, "Breakdown of Messenger RNA During in Vitro Amino Acid Incorporation into Proteins," *Proc. Natl. Acad. Sci. U.S.,* 48(6), 1061 (1962).

Traub, P., K. Hosokawa, G. R. Craven, and M. Nomura, "Structure and Function of *E. coli* Ribosomes. IV. Isolation and Characterization of Functionally Active Ribosomal Proteins," *Proc. Natl. Acad. Sci. U.S.,* 58(6), 2430 (1967).

Wahba, A. J., et al., "Synthetic Polynucleotides and the Amino Acid Code. VIII," *Proc. Natl. Acad. Sci. U.S.,* 49(1), 116 (1963).

Weinstein, I. B., A. N. Schechter, E. R. Burka, and P. A. Marks, "Reticulocyte Protein Synthesis: Response of Ribosome Fractions to Polyuridylic Acid," *Science,* 140(3564), 314 (1963).

Wettstein, F. O., T. Staehelin, and H. Noll, "Ribosomal Aggregate Engaged in Protein Synthesis: Characterization of the Ergosome," *Nature,* 197(4866), 430 (1963).

Regulation

Beckwith, J. R., "Regulation of the Lac Operon," *Science,* 156(3775), 597 (1967).

Bloch, D. P., "On the Derivation of Histone Specificity," *Proc. Natl. Acad. Sci. U.S.*, **48**(3), 324 (1962).

Bonner, J., and R. C. Huang, "Properties of Chromosomal Nucleohistone," *J. Mol. Biol.*, **6**(3), 169 (1963).

Bonner, J., and J. Widholm, "Molecular Complementarity Between Nuclear DNA and Organ-Specific Chromosomal RNA," *Proc. Natl. Acad. Sci. U.S.*, **57** (5), 1379 (1967).

Bonner, J., et al., "The Biology of Isolated Chromatin," *Science*, **159**(3810), 47 (1968).

Busch, H., *Histones and Other Nuclear Proteins*, Academic Press, New York, 1965.

Gutierrez, R. M., and L. S. Hnilica, "Tissue Specificity of Histone Phosphorylation," *Science*, **157**(3794), 1324 (1967).

Hotta, Y., and H. Stern, "Inhibition of Protein Synthesis during Meiosis and Its Bearing on Intracellular Regulation," *J. Cell Biol.*, **16**(2), 259 (1963).

Izawa, M., V. G. Allfrey, and A. E. Mirsky, "The Relationship Between RNA Synthesis and Loop Structure in Lampbrush Chromosomes," *Proc. Natl. Acad. Sci. U.S.*, **49**(4), 544 (1963).

Jacob, F., "Genetics of the Bacterial Cell," *Science*, **152**(3728), 1470 (1966).

Kleinsmith, L. J., V. G. Allfrey, and A. E. Mirsky, "Phosphorylation of Nuclear Protein Early in the Course of Gene Activation in Lymphocytes," *Science*, **154**(3750), 780 (1966).

Liau, M. C., L. S. Hnilica, and R. B. Hurlbert, "Regulation of RNA Synthesis in Isolated Nucleoli by Histones and Nucleolar Proteins," *Proc. Natl. Acad. Sci. U.S.*, **53**(3), 626 (1965).

Littau, V. C., C. J. Burdick, V. G. Allfrey, and A. E. Mirsky, "The Role of Histones in the Maintenance of Chromatin Structure," *Proc. Natl. Acad. Sci. U.S.*, **54**(4), 1204 (1965).

Terner, J. Y., R. M. Goodman, and D. Spiro, "The Effect of Cortisone on Ribonucleic Acid Polymerase and Ribonuclease During Development: Coincidental Evidence for the Identity of Ribonucleic Acid Polymerase with the 'Operator' Gene," *Exptl. Cell. Res.*, **45**(3), 550 (1967).

Tidwell, T., V. G. Allfrey, and A. E. Mirsky, "The Methylation of Histones During Regeneration of the Liver," *J. Biol. Chem.*, **243**(4), 707 (1968).

Index